D1423041

BRITISH OPTICAL
ASSOCIATION LIBRARY
WITHDRAWN

PHOTOSENSITORS

PHOTOSENSITORS

A TREATISE ON PHOTO-ELECTRIC DEVICES AND THEIR APPLICATION TO INDUSTRY

BY

W. SUMMER

Dr.Ing., A.Inst.P., Hon.F.Phys.A.

Past President, The Institution of Electronics.

Hon. Consulting Physicist,
The Physiotherapists Association.

LONDON

CHAPMAN & HALL LTD.

37 ESSEX STREET W.C.2

1957

First published 1957

PRINTED IN GREAT BRITAIN BY PAGE BROS. (NORWICH) LTD., NORWICH

BOUND BY G. & J. KITCAT, LTD., LONDON

CATALOGUE NO. 509/4

ACKNOWLEDGMENTS

IT gives me great satisfaction to express my sincere thanks to the Senior Staff of the Birmingham Public Libraries, Technical Department, for their interest, unfailing patience, and great skill in tracking down for me the publications needed for, and related to, my work.

For assistance given to me by supplying technical information and illustrations, and the permission to publish such data, I would like to extend grateful acknowledgment to the manufacturers of electronic equipment and components as quoted specially in each instance.

The material of Chapter 20 was first published in *The Journal of Scientific Instruments* 1946 ; 23, 7 ; 150 and appeared under the title " Step-Control of a Productive Process ". Permission to reprint this paper has kindly been granted by the Editor of *The Journal of Scientific Instruments*.

W. S.

CONTENTS

PART I

PART II

CONTENTS

PART I

CHAPTER I

INTRODUCTION

THERE is hardly any other device so universally applicable as the photosensitor *. It reacts to the impact of a few quanta of radiant energy of suitable wavelength ; it controls the alinement of the Kincardine Bridge in Scotland ; in plethysmography it records the transparency of blood in man, and it also controls the purity of air in tunnels, ships, transformer tanks, mines, etc. It measures light, matches colour, controls chemical or mechanical processes, maintains temperatures, levels, pressures, etc., to pre-arranged schedules and leads cutter torches according to the shape of a master pattern. The photosensitor counts, and discriminates in counting, according to shape, size, colour, weight, contents, direction of motion ; it inspects and passes or rejects goods and attains insuperable speed of action, accuracy, and constancy. It is many times more sensitive than the keenest human eye and reacts without delay and without fatigue ; neither does it break down easily. Its performance, efficiency, and life are stable characteristics. The photosensitor can " see " where the human visual sense fails, and it still acts under conditions unfit for human beings.

These prefatory remarks and the list of applications (Chap. 2), though by no means exhaustive, will give a fair survey of the enormous field to which photosensitors can be introduced with advantage. It is not only that photosensitors are used for substituting the human sense of vision—at least its physico-physiological component—but that many new methods of production, inspection, and measurement have been made available to the industrial engineer since their advent.

The author has also included a brief historical summary. The history of any particular technical development is not only of theoretical interest but should be known to the engineer who is working in this particular line. Such knowledge will help him to appreciate and recognize the trend of new developments.

* The author has coined this term on the analogy of resistor, capacitor, etc., and puts it forward as a generic term for any type of photo-electric element, i.e. for vacuous or gas-filled photo-cells, photo-e.m.f. cells, photolytic cells, and light-sensitive resistors.

Despite the great amount of theoretical and practical work done in the last twenty years there remain a great many principal factors to be cleared up. In a publication by the Department of Scientific and Industrial Research (DSIR) (*2436*) the report of the working party on photo-emission recommends twenty investigations to be carried out with a view to increased theoretical knowledge and efficiency in practical application.

As much as it was possible under war-time and post-war conditions the author has endeavoured to collect information on advancements from abroad, but the meagre results shown in this book are not altogether due to these conditions.

Scientific publications which have become available since the cessation of hostilities have been scanned carefully to present as complete a picture as possible. English and American literature is well represented ; the most important foreign publications have been brought into the text or mentioned. From France not many publications issued during the Occupation have reached this country and the few that have contain nothing of interest to the reader of this book. Disappointing as this may be, the fact has received corroboration in a statement by an investigator on the Combined Intelligence Objectives Committees, who writes : " No new or improved types of photo-cells were discovered in French firms, and no clues to the probable use of photo-electrically operated camera shutters " (*1454*).

No fundamentally new types of photo-electric (photo-emissive) cells have been produced in the last few years, and of other types of radiation sensitive instruments the lead-sulphide cell (radiation-sensitive resistor) is a very promising development. Emissive-type cells are now available commercially in a variety of different mechanical arrangements, of different degrees and spectral ranges of sensitivity, but omnidirectional cells and those of ring shape are still not available on the British market. A cylindrical model is, however, available as a photo-e.m.f. cell of British manufacture.

Altogether, this book is intended to be no more than an inventory of current practice.

1.1. Historical Data

(Only the more important data have been collated here.)

1725 Du Fay first observes thermionic emission. (*Memoires de l'Académie*, 1733.)

1817 Jöns Jakob Berzelius discovers selenium.

1839 Edmonde Becquerel discovers the photo-voltaic effect. (*Compt. rend.*, 1839, *9*, 561.)

1839 Knox's experiment regarding the electrical conductivity of selenium. (*Royal Irish Acad.*, 1843, *19*, 149.)

1873 On February 12, Willoughby Smith lectures before the Society of Telegraph Engineers (now the I.E.E.), saying he " found that the resistance of selenium bars had altered substantially on being exposed to light, the alteration amounting to some 15 to 30% according to the intensity of illumination ". His lecture was first published in *Nature*, 1873, Feb. 20, and then in the *Journal of the Soc. Tel. Eng.*, 1873, *2*, 31.

1873 M. L. Sale shows that selenium is "colour sensitive" (*Nature* 1873).

1875 Werner Siemens proposes a selenium light-meter.

1876 Werner Siemens finds that the maximum sensitivity of selenium was in the red region of the spectrum (*Sitz. Ber. Koenigl. Preuss. Akad. Berlin*, 1876, pp. 95–116).

1876 W. G. Adams and R. E. Day find that in certain cases a selenium cell upon being illuminated generates a current without the aid of an external battery. This was the first photo-e.m.f. cell (*Proc. Roy. Soc. Lond.*, 1877, *25*, 113).

1878 W. Sabine constructs the first electrolytic selenium cell.

1880 Graham Bell invents the photophone, an instrument that transforms light impulses into sound.

1880 Ayrton and Perry propose electric vision (Precursor of television).

1883 Th. A. Edison discovers unidirectional conductivity in that a faint stream of electrons is emitted from a hot filament and flows across the vacuum (Edison effect).

1883 Hesehus determines the laws governing the actions of light.

1883 Ch. E. Fritts constructs the first selenium front-wall type photo-e.m.f. cell. It consists of a selenium layer deposited on a metal base, the selenium being covered by a gold film (*Am. J. of Science*, 1883, *26*, ser. 3, 465).

1884 A patent is granted to Fritts for his photo-e.m.f. cell (*B.P. 3249*).

1885 Fritts makes selenium cells equivalent to the spectral sensitivity of the human eye by connecting three photo-e.m.f. cells in parallel and providing each of these with a particular colour filter (*La Lumière Electrique*, 1885, *15*, 226).

1885 C. W. WEISS is granted a patent for the first light-sensitive counter using a selenium light resistor (June 10, 1885).

1887 HEINRICH HERTZ discovers the photo-emissive properties of some metals (*Wied. Ann.*, 1887, ***31***, 383 ; *Sitzungsberichte Berl. Akad. Wiss*, 1888, 9 June).

1888 WILHELM HALLWACHS publishes his discovery that negative electricity is emitted from metals when their surface is irradiated by ultra-violet rays. He is also the first to observe the photo-electric fatigue (*Ann. d. Phys.*, 1888, ***33***, 301).

1888 WIEDEMANN and EBERT discuss the ultra-violet sensitivity of photosensitive material (*Ann. d. Phys.* 1888, *33*, 241).

1889 J. ELSTER and H. GEITEL build the first vacuum photo-electric cell using a sodium-potassium amalgam. They show that this cell manifests photo-electric activity when exposed to ordinary daylight (*Ann. d. Phys.*, 1889, ***38***, 40, 497).

1891 The word " electron " is coined by G. JOHNSTONE STONEY. The word itself was already known to, and used by, Homer (ca. 900 B.C.), but it is Stoney who uses it in a modern technical sense. Later on, this word was introduced into all modern languages.

1894 ELSTER and GEITEL find that the photo-electric effect depends upon the orientation of the plane of polarization of the incident light.

1899 P. LENARD measures the ratio e/m for the photo-ions and by this means proves that they are electrons.

1900 Secondary emission is discovered.

1902 P. LENARD builds the first photo-electric vacuum cell which shows signs of increased stability as against the first Elster and Geitel cell (*Ann. d. Phys.*, 1902, *8*, 149).

1904 A patent for a vacuum electronic valve is granted to ROBERT LIEBEN (*D.R.P. 179807*).

1904 J. AMBROSE FLEMING is granted a patent for a rectifying (two-electrode) valve (*B.P. 24850*, dated Nov. 16, 1904).

1904 WEHNELT is the first to study the electron emission from oxides of alkaline earths when illuminated by ultra-violet radiation (*Ann. d. Phys.*, 1904, *14*, 429).

1904 HALLWACHS finds that a plate coated with copper oxide (cuprous oxide) shows photo-electric activity (*Phys. Zschr.*, 1904, *5*, 489).

1905 ALBERT EINSTEIN pronounces the laws of photo-electric emission (The Quantum Law of Emission and Absorption, 1905).

1907 LEE DE FOREST introduces grid control (*U.S. Pat. 841387*, dated Jan 15, 1907).

1920 H. E. IVES makes the earliest specific suggestion for the application of photosensitors for temperature measurements.

1920 T. W. CASE builds the first thallium-sulphide light resistor (*Phys. Rev.*, 1920, *15*, 289).

1920 SLEPIAN is granted U.S. Pat. 1450265 discussing the basic principles of electron multipliers.

1925 A photocell is exhibited at the electrical fair at Grand Central Palace, New York.

1927 L. O. GRONDAHL discovers the back-wall type photo-e.m.f. cell.

1928 L. O. GRONDAHL and P. H. GEIGER are granted *B.P. 277610* for a photo-cell of the cuprous oxide (rectifier) type which upon illumination generates an e.m.f.

1928 Grid-glow valves and thyratrons are produced on a commercial basis.

1928 H. GEIGER and W. MÜLLER describe their tube for counting nuclear particles and radiation (*Phys. Z.* 1928, *29*, 839 ; *Phys. Z.* 1929, *30*, 489, 523 ; *Naturwiss.* 1928 ; *16*, 617).

1930 First production on a commercial scale of cuprous oxide cells as devised by B. LANGE (*Phys. Zschr.*, 1930, *31*, 139, 916, 964).

1931 C. H. BARTLETT develops the dry-disc selenium photo-cell.

1934 P. T. FARNSWORTH describes the image dissector (*J. Franklin Inst.* 1934, *218*, 411).

1936 Secondary multipliers developed by V. K. ZWORYKIN.

1936 V. K. ZWORYKIN et al. give the first detailed description of the photomultiplier (V. K. Zworykin, G. A. Morton and L. Malter, *Proc. I.R.E.* 1936, *24*, 351).

1946 G. K. TEAL, J. R. FISHER and A. W. TREPTOW develop the silicon light-sensitive resistor at the Bell Telephone Laboratories (*J. Appl. Phys.* 1946, *17*, 879).

Chapter 2

APPLICATIONS

2.1 Visual v. Photo-electric Control

Nearly all industrial activities of man are based on and controlled by only one of his five senses : the sense of vision. With the beginning of this century competition and production increased in both speed and volume. A critical condition became obvious when the ordinary means of mechanical production were unable to satisfy the ever-increasing demand ; and new methods of production were put into operation which were based not only on an increase in the hourly output per individual plus machine, but were mostly founded on newly devised machinery and systems of production. This new type of machinery reduced man from a once dominating position to the status of a mere servant of the semi- or fully automatic machine. In the former case the operator was expected to adapt his working capacity to the speed of the machine, which was possible only to a very limited extent. Therefore the fully automatic machine was introduced at an early date. This type of machine was characterized in that it not only did all the heavy mechanical and repetition work, but that it also measured, corrected (or rather, prevented) mistakes and inspected the quality of the product ; in a word it controlled the entire process of production.

The faster and the more detailed the process of production, the faster and the more accurate the control must be. It was mostly by mechanical means that inspection was carried out. This was highly satisfactory in the beginning, because only such controls were mechanized or automatized as were considered to represent the highly refined tactile sense of the human inspector. The automatic control of production methods involving such characteristics as colour, turbidity, optical density ; and of products such as freshly painted or sprayed or red-hot objects, was considered impossible until a means was discovered which might replace, or even surpass, the visual sense of man.

With the advent of the photosensitor an ever-increasing range of production processes, formerly controlled by the visual sense of man, became open to fully-automatic control. Untiring research widened the range of the spectral sensitivity of photo-electric devices and the three types now on the market are sensitive to luminous, ultra-violet, and infra-red radiation, respectively.

Generally, such things as photosensitors, ultra-violet radiators, or infra-red generators are not looked upon favourably by the workshop engineer who, being used to heavy machinery and mechanical controls, does not easily take to the idea of seeing heavy industrial equipment reliably and efficiently controlled by a small object made of glass and a few odd wires.

More than forty years ago the grid-controlled vacuum triode was invented, but it is only during the last ten or fifteen years that the electron valve has been introduced on a wider scale to industrial applications. The rather late utilization of such an important electronic device was not due to failures in design or effectiveness of the valve, but can be traced back simply to the biased opinion or inertia of the industrial worker. This predisposition has long since been superseded by the engineers' trust in the efficiency and dependability of electron valves working under industrial conditions.

The light-sensitive device is now some sixty years old, but the photosensitor has not yet completely convinced the industrial engineer that it has left a long time ago the state of experimental designs and carefully planned applications in the laboratories and has become a practical tool (*1*, *2*).

It is not only in that region of the electromagnetic spectrum, which conventionally is termed the " luminous " range (cf. Chap. 30) and provides the light which stimulates the human sense of vision, that the photo-electric cell offers advantages to the industrial user, but it is especially in the non-luminous (ultra-violet and infra-red) regions that it proves its worth. Industrial processes which necessitated human control and inspection under sometimes exacting and dangerous conditions can now easily be controlled automatically. One such instance, which is characteristic for the whole group of applications, was given when the mounted fuzes of hand-grenades were to be inspected as to the precise fitting of the detonator (*3*, *4*). Visually, this was done by placing the inspector and the test screen in a dark-room. The grenade traversed the beam of an X-ray tube and a silhouette view of the interior arrangement of the grenade appeared on the fluorescent screen.

2.2 Fluoroscopic Method

It is obvious that these unusual viewing conditions have a detrimental effect on the visual and perceptive powers of anyone placed in front of the screen and given the task of repeating the same strenuous job many thousand times a day, namely to notice a dislocation of certain shadows in the silhouette picture. The effects of sensual fatigue due to physical conditions after a short time result in mental fatigue enhanced and accelerated by the hypnotic effects of the slowly flickering picture.

The new testing technique has enormously speeded up the process of inspection; in fact, more than one grenade is reliably tested every second. The X-ray picture on the screen is viewed by a photosensitor: a faulty fuze causes the fluorescence to change which, in turn, effects the equilibrium of the electronic circuit. If a fault is indicated by the relay the faulty fuze is marked and this fact registered on a chart (cf. Chap. 18).

Fluoroscopic inspection can successfully be applied to a wide field of industrial inspection. It is used to trace the presence of foreign bodies in packaged goods; faults in metals; cracks and flaws within any object. Fluoroscopic inspection is advisable where non-destructive methods must be applied.

Infra-red sensitive cells are successfully employed in operations like investigating the presence of carbonaceous matter in lubricating oils (*5*). This is based on the phenomenon that carbon is opaque to infra-red rays, but other impurities are not although both, when inspected in "white" light, show no difference in appearance or transmittance. The textile, dyeing, paint, paper, metal, and other industries open up a wide field to infra-red inspection.

Ultra-violet photosensitors will efficiently measure and control the output of u-v generators, which is of interest not only to the manufacturer but also to the user of industrial ultra-violet equipment, for instance in the irradiation of cosmetic preparations (vitamin D), sterilization of milk, the generation of ozone, etc.

2.3 Photo-electric Control an Economic Factor

The introduction of photo-electric control into industrial processes is not only a highly commendable technical (*6*) but also an economical proposition in that it increases the output, ensures more uniform quality, speeds up industrial operations, reduces cost of production and maintenance costs, minimizes waste, responds to conditions which cannot be observed by human senses, and controls objects which are not fit for mechanical or manual handling. As to being an economical proposition, a few instances may suffice for many.

The first relates to a rotogravure press operating at a web speed of

1000 ft.p.m. Photo-electric cells are used in four-colour printing for maintaining the position of the impressions within the tolerances. This register control reduced waste to less than 45% of the amount previous to the installation (7) and the annual saving was estimated at £3500.

At the *Philadelphia Inquirer* four-colour printing waste expense was cut from 7 to 3% resulting in the saving of £4000 annually (*396*).

At another works (Redson-Rice Corp., Chicago) the Westinghouse register control (*8*) was applied to a lithographic press. An off-register correction of 1/32 inch can be compensated in 0·1 sec., the paper travelling at a speed of 325 ft.p.min. In colour printing the waste of paper due to imperfect colour register was reduced by 75% (*1656*).

A photo-electric maximum-demand controller of electric energy is reported to have resulted in an annual saving of £600 (9).

One of the earliest and most obvious applications of photo-electric devices was to the problem of maintaining illumination at a certain predetermined optimal level. At the Chrisholm Ryder Plant, Niagara Falls, the intensity of illumination was maintained at about 15 ft.-candles by automatically switching on the artificial illumination whenever the level of daylight dropped to 14 ft.-candles and switching off the lamps when the illumination had increased correspondingly. This photo-electric control of factory lighting reduced the lamp replacement by 25% and resulted in the saving of 4000 kWh per month (*10*).

That the automatization of so simple an action as opening a door can result in a monthly saving of £200 in operating costs has been shown by the Brown and Williamson Tobacco Co. All doors of the receiving and shipping departments of this firm are operated by photo-electric devices (*11*, *12*).

Dr. John Johnstone, Director of Research of the U.S. Steel Corporation (*13*) reported savings as high as 50% in the life of a refractory brick lining in open-hearth furnaces when the furnace was accurately controlled and maintained at a given temperature.

The extraordinary usefulness of photo-electric protective gear is demonstrated by an installation which safeguards the die of a six-operation sequence press. This intricate die not only is very expensive but also takes a long time to make. If a part of the pressing should stick on the ram while another is fed into the press the die would be smashed by it. The price of this die was more than the cost of the protective photo-electric equipment (*Bibl. 582*).

2.4 Life Expectancy

A few data on the life expectancy of electronic tubes will overcome the doubts of the maintenance engineer.

Incandescent lamps when operated at rated voltage have a useful life of 1000 hours ; when underrun at a voltage of 5% less than nominal the useful life is doubled. Mercury vapour discharge lamps have a useful life of 1500 hours, and sodium vapour discharge lamps of 2500 hours at rated volts. Thermionic amplifier valves of the indirect heater type may safely be operated over 3500 hours (*1649*), and cold-cathode grid-controlled gas discharge valves perform without a breakdown over 10000 hours (*1637*). D. K. Gannett (*1047*) has shown that the relation between the percentage of a group of valves remaining in service and the time after they have been placed in service follows the exponential law $y = A \,.\, \exp(-at)$ after an initial period of about 3000 hours has passed. Plotted on log-paper this curve is a straight line, Fig. 2.1. On

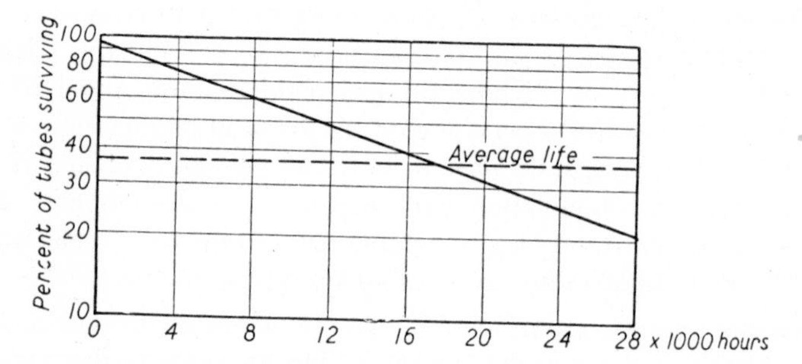

Fig. 2.1. Survival curve of thermionic valves (D. K. Gannett).

the assumption of exact exponentiality the average life of a valve is determined by the time when 36·79% (= 100/e) of the valves remain intact and in service. Gannett reports average lives of valves under normal operating conditions to be in the order of 11,000 to 18,000 hours according to the type of valve used. RCA valves of the 5690 type are designed for 10,000 hours' life (*2444*).

Photosensitors have a useful life which manufacturers sometimes boldly call " unlimited ". In fact as many as 35000 hours may be expected (*14*) at rated volts. A longer life is ensured by reducing the anode voltage of gas-filled cells to as low as 60 volts. The factors influencing the life of composite photo-cathodes have been discussed by Pakswer (*2424*).

The mechanical rigidity of special tubes (RCA) is such that they will withstand accelerations of 2·5g of continuous vibration at a frequency of approximately 20 c/s. for hundreds of hours at maximum rated voltages. They will also withstand impact shocks of 100g for extended periods and 500g for short periods with maximum rated voltages.

2.5 The Human Factor

Another and most important result achieved by photo-electric industrial equipment is the elimination (exclusion is perhaps a better word) of the human factor. Repetition work at high speed and undiminished accuracy throughout the whole day are the backbone of mass production. But repetition work also contributes a large percentage to the causes of fatigue among workmen which is not so much, or sometimes not at all, the result of physiological but of psychological processes.

There is a general reduction in output, showing in varying degrees during the eight working hours of a day and the five workdays of a week. The average percentage decrease in working capacity is illustrating well the influence of long hours on quantity and quality of the output (*16*). That such an influence exists was already pointed out a century ago when reformers (*17*) made an earnest attempt at reducing working hours to twelve, and later to ten a day. In a recent statement by the Chief Inspector of Factories (*18*, *19*) this point was stressed and peculiar results shown.

Factors tending to reduce normal vision are :

Physiological factors—

(1) poor illumination, e.g. insufficient illumination ; glare ; reflexion ;
(2) speed of working resulting in fatigue ;
(3) having food or drink ;
(4) indisposition of other parts of the body, e.g. headache, toothache, etc. ;
(5) irritation by exhalations or fumes which form an essential part of the production process and are unavoidable.

Psychological factors—

(1) lack of concentration ;
(2) nervous strain ; disability ;
(3) irritation by colours (e.g. on walls) ;
(4) irritation by designs (e.g. in textile mills).

Pathological factors—

(1) defects of the eye or optic nerve ;
(2) acute or chronic injury to the nervous system of visual perception ;
(3) colour blindness.

The effect of faulty eyesight in respect to the time required for seeing is shown in Fig. 2.2.

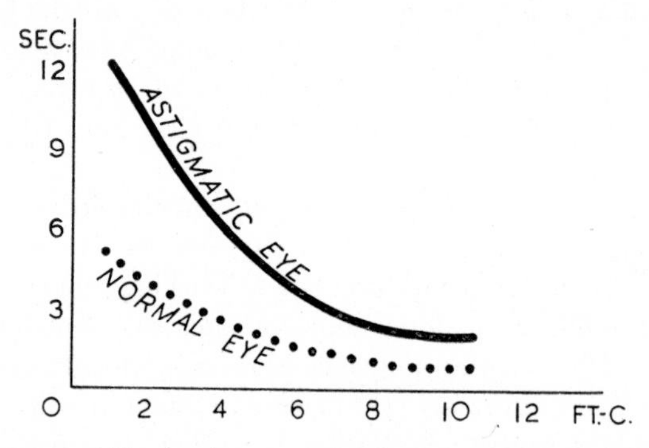

Fig 2.2. Effect of illumination on seeing time—normal and abnormal eyes.

Visual tasks, for instance precision assembly, cause a reduction in the heart rate which, under unfavourable conditions, amounts to 5% and even more. Luckiesh and Moss (*20*) suggest that the very high percentage, viz. 80%, of the mortality cases of workmen involving heart trouble, may have some relation to their particular type of work which is a strenuous visual task.

From the above data and one's own experience it is obvious that the omnipotent factor of fatigue essentially influences the performance of any task requiring concentration, alertness, and speed of perception.

2.6 Reaction Time

The human reaction to a certain stimulus is not instantaneous. There is a time lag between perceiving a sensual stimulus and reacting in logical or pre-arranged response to it. This time lag is called Reaction Time. There are a great many processes in industry where instantaneous reaction of one device to a stimulus given by another device is essential and imperative. Instantaneous, in this relation, may mean anything down to one millisecond or less. From various data it has been established that reaction times smaller than 100 msec. cannot be expected if human beings are involved in relaying (*21*, *22*, *23*, *24*). For visual stimuli the average reaction time is 0·2 sec.

For all industrial applications the time lag in photo-electric cells is considered to be negligible, viz. below 0·01 msec., i.e. smaller than 10^{-5} sec. (static response). The photo-electric cell is superior to the human eye in that its threshold of light flux sensitivity is about 0·02 of the threshold of the eye, and its reaction time (time lag) is practically nil as compared with the respective characteristics of the average man.

Another factor, viz. the spectral sensitivity of the photosensitor, is of greatest importance. In nearly all cases, except for one or two types of photo-e.m.f. cells, this sensitivity is very dissimilar to the colour sensitivity of the average human eye. Some cells are sensitive only to certain parts in a given region of the luminous spectrum. All have a greater sensitivity in one part of the spectrum than in another. For a given wavelength * sometimes the eye, sometimes the photosensitor has the greater sensitivity, and due advantage may be taken of this fact.

2.7 Efficiency of Energy Conversion

The photosensitor is at present used as a :

(1) detector of radiant energy in the ultra-violet, luminous, and infra-red spectrum, respectively ;

(2) measuring instrument of radiant energy in these regions.

On these two fundamental actions all applications are based. There is, however, a third function of a certain type photosensitor which, at the present time, has not yet been fully investigated or at least has not yet resulted in a practical, i.e. technical–commercial application. It is common knowledge that the photo-e.m.f. cell generates electric energy when light strikes its sensitive surface. In other words, this cell transforms radiant into electric energy. There is but one serious setback, viz. the extremely small efficiency at which this transformation takes place. From a power-plant engineer's point of view this " efficiency " is practically nil.

There are some 140 watts of electrical energy available in every square foot of sunshine. But the best photo-e.m.f. cell produces—theoretically

* In the luminous spectrum, " wavelength " may approximately be substituted by " colour ". One must be conscious, however, that the former is a definite and well-defined physical characteristic, whereas the latter is an arbitrary subjective and therefore, variable psycho-physiological perception and conventional term.

—0·1 watt per sq. ft. of sensitive surface. The ideal cell should deliver 66,000 microamp. per lumen but in practice the average cell produces less than five thousandths of this, although cells have been built that give about 1000 to 1200 microamp. per lumen. The average efficiency of energy conversion in a selenium-on-iron type cell is about 0·5%. Zworykin and Wilson (*25*) quote a rather high coefficient of efficiency: this calculation is based on a solar irradiation of the earth's surface at the rate of $3 \cdot 5 \times 10^9$ watts per sq. mile. Since a silver selenide photo-e.m.f. cell produces about $3 \cdot 8 \times 10^8$ watts per sq. mile of sensitive area, if illuminated by the sun, the efficiency is 10% which "compares favourably with the efficiency of generators energized by fuel". B. Lange (*26, p. 187*) arrives at a much lower energy conversion efficiency, viz. about 2%, and Weston Photronic cells have a conversion coefficient of 2·6% (*27*). The Photox cuprous-oxide photo-e.m.f. cell is reported to have a power output of 0·5 microwatt per foot-candle. A stable thallium-sulphide photo-e.m.f. cell having a sensitivity of 10 mA per lumen (10,000 microamp. per lumen) converts the solar radiation into electric energy with an efficiency of 1% (*28*). The statement that "this is a sufficiently high ratio to warrant their possible use as converters of solar energy into electrical energy on an industrial scale" (*1037*) seems to be highly optimistic, at least on the basis of present-day achievements.

2.8 Electronic Engineering and Applications

The immense possibilities of the light-sensitive relay, i.e. the practical utilization of the photo-electric phenomenon as applied to industry, have not yet been fully appreciated. Although the photosensitor has effectively been applied during the last ten or fifteen years to hundreds of widely different industrial problems and, therefore, a certain classification of best solutions has already taken place, there is ample space left for genuine improvement on designing new circuits, and new fields of applications are explored and exploited every day (*29, 1264*).

No list of applications can be regarded as complete. It will become evident to everyone approaching this subject that in nearly every issue of a scientific periodical is at least one article describing a novel or new application. During the time which elapsed from the completion of the manuscript to the publication of the first edition of this book, a substantial number of interesting and valuable contributions to the subject of photo-electric applications in industry have appeared which could not be included in this edition, and the pace of progress increases rapidly.

Industry, for the purpose of this section, may be divided into two major groups :

(a) manufacturers of photo-electric devices ;
(b) users of same.

The list of applications will prove useful to both in that it not only draws the manufacturers' attention to new fields of applications or new groups of industry, but also serves as a guide for potential users, helping them to find out whether a particular process can be improved by the application of photo-electric methods and devices, or whether there are devices already applicable to processes in their own works.

In the latter part of 1944 a survey was undertaken (*29*, *1264*). A very broad cross-section through the American industry was secured by basing the survey on subscribers of 14 different publications, each leading in its particular field of production. Of nineteen thousand questionnaires mailed only slightly more than 4% were returned. A very encouraging fact emerges from this survey. 796 firms were using 16,805 electronic devices, i.e. an average of 21 per firm. Of the 796 replies, 583 came from manufacturers and 213 from non-manufacturers. The metal-working industries top the list with 268 returns, then come the chemical industries with 135 returns. Among the non-manufacturers electric utilities are represented by 92 replies.

In control, measurement and analysis, nearly 12,000 electronic devices are used, and yet the firms under survey considered they had at present 365 problems of control and 240 of measurement and analysis which might be solved by electronic equipment. These firms also suggested another 1303 problems arising out of their daily processes of production, that might be solved by electronic methods. The details of this American report should be an enormous stimulus to both manufacturers and users of electronic equipment in general. The electronic engineer's inventiveness and the user's desire for automatization of output and proper control of production can be directed to constructive use and will be given unlimited scope. The report not only reveals the present and possible future position of the industrial electronics market, but also quotes excerpts from suggestions made by many of the surveyed firms, for instance : " Photo-electric cells could be used to limit travel of furnace doors where high temperatures cause failures in existing limit switches " ; " Temperature control and flame failure alarm in soaking pits and reheating furnaces " ; " In undercutting commutators on small motors, it is impossible to use an indexing arrangement to turn the commutator from mica to mica due to slight variations in the thickness of the mica and the copper, making the bar spacing non-uniform. We are working on an arrangement using the electric eye to position the mica by contrast of colour between the copper and the mica " (*30*).

A survey of photo-cell instruments is made in the *Journal of Scientific Instruments* (*2466*). A photo-electric Fourier analyzer has been built by Furth and Pringle (*2467*, *2468*). A photo-electric sight for solar telescopes has been designed by Roberts (*2469*). A ceilometer, that is an instrument measuring the height of clouds, was developed jointly by the General Electric and the U.S. Weather Bureau (*2470*).

Alphabetical List of Selected Photo-electric Applications

ABSORPTIOMETER
Absorption analyzer
Advertisements, illuminated
Air control in mines
Air conditioning
Alarms against burglary
failure of combustion
fire
overflow of liquids or solids
sabotage
smoke
trespassing
indicating levels of liquids or solids
pressure, changes in
strain and stress
temperature, changes in
Alkalinity or acidity, Measurement of
Alpha-particle counter
Analysis, chemical
Aniseikonic protection
Annealing oven, Opening the doors of, by light from craneman's cabin
Announcing customer arriving at petrol station
Automatic control of rubber, steel, fabric, paper cutting table
Automatic stops for printing machinery, presses, etc., preventing damage to machine or tools
Automatic titration

BANK vaults protected (aniseikonic system)
Barrelling of liquids, Automatic
Beacons for sea and air traffic, Control of
Bessemer steel-making control
Boiler feed-water control
Bottles, sorting, filling, counting, inspecting

APPLICATIONS

- Breakage prevented and production controlled of:
  - fabrics
  - paper web
  - rubber sheets
  - sheet metal
  - wire
  - yarn
- Brewery, control of colour of beer
  - counting of bottles and barrels
- Buoys, Automatic lighting of
- Burglar alarm

- CALENDERS, Protection and control of
- Calibration of watt-hour meters
- Cement, Fineness of, measured
- Checking automobile crank case oil
- Chemical analysis, Automatic
- Chemical process control
- Chlorination of water supply, Control of
- Cigars and cigarettes sorted
- Circular saw, Protection of
- Coal tubs emptied
- Cold-room door, Operation of
- Collapsible tubes, Inspection of
- Colorimetry
- Colour matched or measured
- Colour printing
- Colour temperature measured
- Combustion control of solid, liquid, gaseous fuel
- Compensation for temporary light fluctuations
- Concentration control
- Continuity control of feed of material
- Controlling automatic power or production plant from pre-arranged charts
- Controlling machinery
  - chemical processes
  - feeding mechanisms
  - illumination
  - the thickness of paper
    - wire
    - yarn
- Conveyor control
- Counting of scintillations
- Counting of wet painted objects
  - dyed fabrics
  - dying-away rotations
  - red-hot ingots, tubes, shells, sheets
  - rotations of inaccessible machinery
    - delicate machinery
- Counting at high speed on mass-production lines
- Counting, Differential
  - differentiating
  - integrating
  - non-directional

Counting, predetermined batch
unidirectional
Crack detection
Cutting of printed wrappings for packages
Cutting of predetermined lengths of cloth, paper, rubber, sheet metal, steel

DENSITOMETER, Optical
Descaling sprays controlled by photo-relays
Detection of cracks and flaws
Detection of noxious gases in industrial plant
Detection of missing items (labels, corks)
Dial gauges
Differential counting
Doors shut and opened in cold-storage rooms
garages
hospitals
kitchens
libraries
mines (ventilation doors)
restaurants
warehouses
of furnaces
loading bays
soaking-pits
yards
Draw bench equipment, Control of
Drinking fountain control
Dust, Detection of, in air

EGGS sorted and inspected
Electric hand dryer control
Electric resistors sorted
Electrical machinery protected against flashover
Electrostatic discharge controlled and prevented
Elevators levelled and doors protected
Enamelled wire gauged
Envelope printing controlled
Extinguishing of fires

FACTORY lighting control
Feed of materials controlled
Feed to rubber cutting tables controlled
Filling machine for collapsible tubes controlled
Filling controlled of bottles
boxes
tins
Fire detector, alarm and extinguisher
Flame cutter controlled
Flame failure, Control of
Flashovers, Protection against
Flow of materials controlled
Flue gas analysis
Fluorography

Fluoroscopic inspection
Fly ash density, Control and measurement of
Fog indication and lighting of lamps and signals
Follow-up mechanism
Foreign matter detected in packaged goods
Frequency control in electric power plant
Fruit, Sizing of
Fuel-air ratio controlled
Fuel control (solid, liquid, gaseous)
Fumes, Detection of
Furnace temperature controlled

Garage doors operated
Gas analysis
Gas burner control, Industrial
Gases, Detection of noxious, in Industry
Gauging the thickness of thread
wire
yarn
Gloss control
Grading according to colour
height
size
weight

Hardness of water controlled
Haze, Indication of natural
artificial (scratch)
Hole-in-the-meter indicator
Hopper control
Hot-air towel control

Illumination control
Illuminated advertisements, Control of
Indicating the level of liquids, e.g. of acids
alkalies
boiling liquids
corrosives
polluted liquids
sewage
Infra-red inspection and control of processes
Ingots counted and measured
Intrusion alarm
Ion concentration, Measuring the

Laundry ironers protected
Leaks in air conditioning and refrigerating systems detected
Lens polishing mechanism controlled
coating, Control of
Level control in bins
silos
tanks

Levelling of bridges
cranes
elevators
lifts
Light buoys, Control of
Light, Control of, for photographic purposes
Limit switches for cranes
rail waggons
red hot ingots
Loop control
Luminoscopy
Lustre of textiles measured

Master clock driving slave clock without being loaded itself
Matching of colour in breweries
car industry
dye works
flour mills
oil plant
paint shops
paint works
paper mills
spray shops
textile industry
Measuring the fineness of cement
height of trucks, vans, waggons
objects on conveyor belts
organic matter in sand
pollution of oil or water
turbidity of a liquid
Mercury vapour, Detection of
Metallic sputtering, Control of
Meter testing
Mining industry
Motion control (aniseikonic)
Moulding machines controlled and protected

Nephelometer
Noxious gases detected

Obstruction lights, Control of, on an air field
Oil burners controlled
Oil tester
Opacity measured and matched
Operation of valves, switches, etc.
Optopyrometry
Organic matter in sand, Determination of
Outdoor signs controlled by headlamps of approaching cars
Oxy-acetylene cutters controlled

Packing of cans, tins, Control of
Paint spray control
Particle counter

*p*H, Determination and Control of
Photometry
Pinhole detection in metals
Piston inspection
Piston pin inspection
Power plant control
Precision inspection
Pressure control
Printing machines, Stopping of, in case of web breakage
Process control
Production control
Programming
Protection of moving machinery
objects (aniseikonic)
Pulverized coal, Level and flow control of
Punch press, Protection of
Purification of water
Pyrometric control
Pyrometry

QUALITY control of flour
honey
oil
paper
tiles

RADIATION counter
Reeling and re-reeling of fabric
paper
rubber
wire
yarn
Reflectance, Measurement of
Refrigerators, Leakage of
Register control
Regulation of voltage, frequency and phase
Residual chlorine determination
Retiming of periodic processes
Reversing rolls of calenders in steel mills
Rivet heaters, Control of
Rotation counter
Routeing equipment, Control of
Rubber industry, Feeding mechanisms in

SABOTAGE, Aniseikonic protection against
Safety devices
Sand, Determination of organic matter in
Sandsprayers started
Scales, Automatic
Scanning of continuously produced materials for cracks
flaws
stains
Scintillation counter

Selective counting
Selecting certain colours
heights
sizes
weights
Service station announcer
Sewage disposal plant, Control of sludge level in
Sheen of fabric measured
Shears, Flying, operated
Sintering beds controlled
Sizing of eggs
fruit
Skew control
Slack control
Slave clocks controlled by master clock
Sludge control
Smoke control in combustion plant and chimney stack
alarms in ships
tanks
transformer tanks
Sorting according to colour
height
size
weight
Sorting combined with rejection of faulty parts
Spacing of goods on conveyor
Speed of revolution measured
Spinning mills
Spray shops
Sputtering of metal or paint, Control of
Steam boilers protected
Steel making (Bessemer) controlled
mill operation controlled
Step control
Stopping processing machines working continuous materials
in case of web breakage
Street lighting control
Strong-room alarm and protection (aniseikonic)
Switches operated
Synchronizing A.C. generators
belts
chains
conveyors
production processes

TACHYMETRIC measurements
Telemetering
Temperature, Control of low
high
Template controls multiple cutter
Tension, Control of, in spinning mills
wire draw mills
Testing of dyes

Testing of flour
oil
paint
Textile industry
Thermal processes controlled
Thermography
Thermostatic control
Thickness of enamelled wire controlled and measured
Timber sorted in saw mill according to colour
Timing of periodical processes
Titration, Automatic
Toothpaste filling machine
Torch cutters controlled
Transmissivity (optical) measured or matched
Transport of balls
bottles
boxes
cans
crates
tins
Truck, Measuring height of
Tube filling machine, Control of
Tubes, collapsible, Inspection of
Turbidity measured or matched

ULTRA-VIOLET applications
Unidirectional counting

VACUUM control
Valves operated
Valve stem heater, Control of
Vibration in incandescent bodies, Detection of
Viscosity, Measuring of
Vitamins measured and production controlled
Voltage control

WATER hardness controlled
Water level indicator
Water purification
Web control in textile mills
paper mills
Weighing, Automatic
Wire draw benches, Control of
Wood pulp, Control of
Wrapping machines controlled

X-RAY absorption, Chemical analysis by
X-rays, Control, Evaluation and Inspection by means of

Bibliography References: (*15*, *31*, *32*, *564*, *1119*, *1136*, *1150*, *1151*, *1159*, *1191*, *1240*, *1241*, *1254*, *1307*, *1311*, *1312*, *1315*, *1317*, *1357*, *1716*, *1732*, *1760*, *1792*, *1805*, *1812*, *1861*, *1876*, *1885*, *1886*, *1997*, *2005*, *2364*, *2380*, *2401*, *pp*. *119*, *120*).

2.9. Simplification of Design

The many different applications and types of equipment will perhaps in the near future cause the manufacturer as well as the user to consider a simplification of design which, at least for certain groups of routine applications may even approach standardization.

There are in principle only two different methods of actuating a photo-relay.

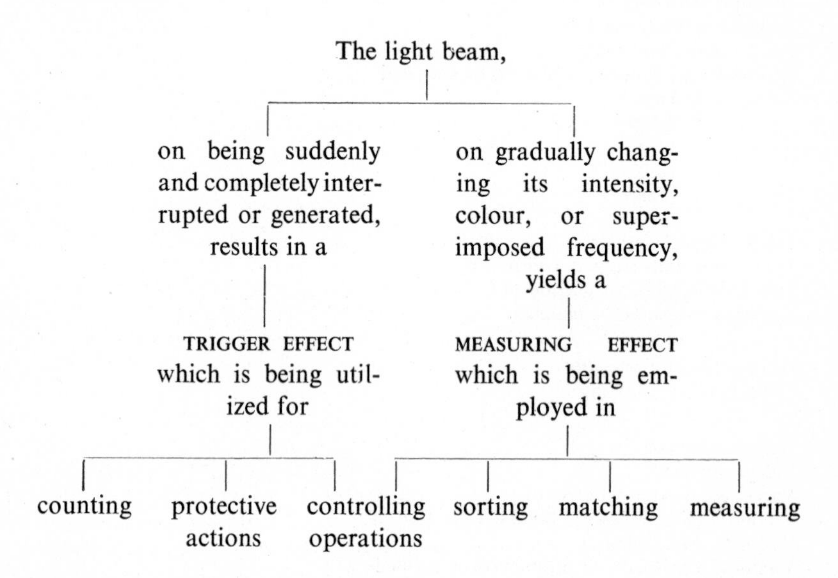

This would lead to suggesting about half a dozen or so different sets to meet nearly all cases arising in general industrial practice. Such a suggestion might include the following :

(1) relay circuit for on–off control ;

(2) balanced two-cell circuit for matching operations and processing control ;

(3) lock-in circuit (D.C. thyratron circuit) for protective devices indicators, etc. ;

(4) Measuring circuit for measuring temperatures, pressures, etc., and for driving a recorder ;

(5) Ratio-meter for measuring the ratio of any two quantities ;

(6) Aniseikonic circuit for protective devices as well as for flaw detectors, etc. ;

(7) limit switches ;

(8) step control circuits.

Optional accessories : time delay relays, recorders, optical or acoustic alarms, stepping relay switches, etc.

CHAPTER 3

THE PHOTOSENSITOR AND THE HUMAN EYE

WHEN photo-electric cells were first produced they were generally compared with the human eye. Scientific workers were impressed by the apparent parallel between the sensitivity to light of the human eye and the sensitivity to radiant energy of various materials ; so much so that Sir Jagadis Chandra Bose, the distinguished Indian scientist, in his American patent specification 755840, gave the enveloping case of his photo-electric cell the shape of a human eye. To call the photo-electric cell an " electric eye " is, however, an inaccurate statement.

3.1. The Structure of the Eye

The principal elements of the human eye are :

(1) the cornea, i.e. the horny transparent portion of the anterior surface of the eyeball ;

(2) the aqueous humour, i.e. the clear transparent fluid which fills the anterior chamber of the eye ;

(3) the iris, i.e. the muscular pigmented tissue which divides the anterior from the posterior chamber of the eye ;

(4) the pupil, i.e. the variable circular aperture in the centre of the iris ;

(5) the lens, i.e. the crystalline transparent body, embedded in the vitreous humour, situated behind the iris. The lens serves as a refractive medium for the incident radiant energy ;

(6) the vitreous humour, i.e. a transparent, jelly-like substance which fills the posterior chamber of the eye ;

(7) the retina, i.e. the innermost coat of the eyeball, lining the posterior chamber ;

(8) the optic nerve, i.e. a bundle of fine nerve fibres leading from the retina to the brain ;

(9) the choroid, i.e. the vascular coat of the eyeball, enveloping the retina ; the choroid continues the iris ;

(10) the sclerotic coat, i.e. the outermost membrane, enveloping the entire eyeball. In front of the iris the sclerotic coat becomes transparent and is called the cornea (cf. no. 1).

These elements are enumerated in the sequence that a light-ray, upon entering the eye, has to traverse one after the other in order to be perceived as a stimulus and to cause a sensation (Fig. 3.1).

The optical characteristics of the average human eye are described below (*33*, *p. 323*) *Bibliography References:* (*551*, *1105*).

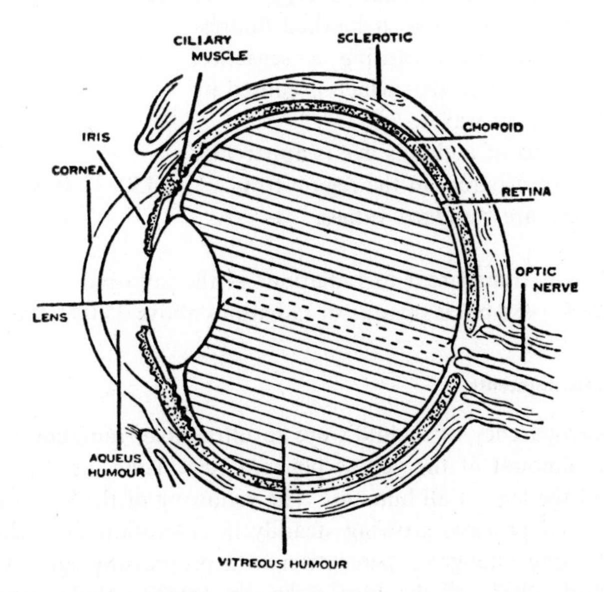

Fig. 3.1 Cross-section of the human eye (from Best & Taylor: *The Living Body*).

3.2. Refractive Indices

Aqueous humour	.. ..	$n = 1{\cdot}3365$
Crystalline lens	.. ..	$n = 1{\cdot}4371$
Vitreous humour	.. ..	$n = 1{\cdot}3365$

According to H. L. Walls (*34*) the retinal refractive index is greater than that of the vitreous humour. For the Standard Eye (Listing eye) the accepted refractive index is 1·332.

3.3. Transmittance (*35*) and Reflectance (*36*, *37*)

The cornea is :

opaque to radiations shorter than	..	2950 A.U.
slightly absorbent to radiation from	..	2950–3150 A.U.
transparent to radiation from	..	3150–7500 A.U.
transparent to radiation from	..	7500–30,000 A.U.

The lens is :

opaque to radiations shorter than	..	3760 A.U.
Upon impact of radiant energy of the lens shows a marked fluorescence thus causing a sensation similar to that which is caused by longer waves.	..	3500–4000 A.U.
The lens of a child's eye is apparently transparent in the region from	..	3150–3300 A.U.
These are standard values.		

The lens is transparent to radiations in the infra-red (*35*, *p. 78*, *36*, *p. 206*, *37 p. 148*), but is opaque to radiations above 25,000 A.U. (*1455*).

3.4. Photo-pigments

The transparency of a child's eye to ultra-violet radiation is due to the small amount of the yellow pigment (lentiflavin, i.e. lens yellow) present in the lens of all humans. The yellowing of the lens nucleus is an ante-natal process, growing steadily in coloration throughout life and restricting blue-green perception with progressing age. A child's lens absorbs 10% of the blue radiation entering the eye while an octogenarian's lens absorbs 85%. This optical characteristic of the lens is represented by the transmission curve of the clear glass 014 of the Corning Glass Works (*38*, *p. 13*) showing the transparency of a child's lens. The young adult's lens is approximately represented by the Corning filter 038, and that of an old man by 338. The human eye contains a set of yellow intra-ocular filters which all seem to play an important role in vision in bright light. The coloration of the yellow spot in the retina was discovered about a hundred years ago (*39*, *40*), but has been disputed as late as forty years ago by a Swedish physiologist (*41*) who maintains that the yellow colour of the macula is due to post-mortem changes, but cannot be discovered *in vivo*. This view has been discarded since and it is now an acknowledged fact that the yellow spot is really yellow.

The combination of the yellow lens with the yellow spot is of great advantage to acute vision in bright light. It is therefore the more astonishing to learn that the coloration of the lens, according to the present state of our knowledge, is of an accidental rather than of an " intended " nature. This is borne out by the statement by one of the foremost physiologists who writes : " The pigment (in the lens) is melamine formed by the interaction of protamine and cysteine liberated by protein-breakdown—the development of the coloration is thus due to an essentially senescent change, and its optical usefulness is the sheerest of accidents " (*42, p. 199*).

The photo-pigments are highly reflecting to infra-red, but they absorb radiation from 3800–7600 A.U.

These pigments are situated in the iris and in the epithelium of the retina.

The eye is, from physiological and physical reasons, unable to evaluate any ultra-violet or infra-red stimuli as no ultra-violet nor long-wave radiant energy can reach the photo-receptors of a normal human eye.

3.5. The Retina

The retina consists of a pigment layer (1) and nine nervous layers which are shown in Fig. 3.2. The layer marked 2 contains the bacillary

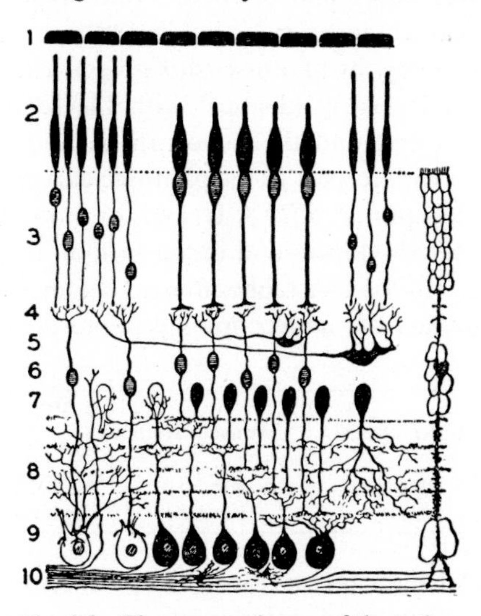

Fig. 3.2 The nervous layers of the retina.

elements often referred to as photo-receptors, light-sensitive elements, sense-cells or, most commonly, rods and cones. In 1866, Schultze (*43*) discovered that the retina possesses two different types of light-sensitive elements, then being classified as rods and cones, respectively. In recent years these photo-receptors are sometimes thought of in terms of a unistic theory, thus refusing to acknowledge any morphological and physiological duality. Mlle. Verrier (*44*) assumes the rods and cones to be extreme variations of an archetype of light-sensitive cells. *Bibliography References:* (*519*, *552*, *1080*, *1365*).

3.6. Photo-sensitive Pigments

In 1875, Boll discovered that the incidence of radiant energy between 4000 and 7600 A.U. wavelength caused a photo-chemical change in the rose-coloured substance which he had found in the rods and which he called visual purple (*45*, *46*, *47*).

In chemical nomenclature this is known as *rhodopsin.* Twenty years later König demonstrated that visual purple is concerned with vision at low intensities. Visual purple, when exposed to light, breaks down into an orange-coloured substance called visual yellow or *retinene* (*48*). In 1930, Gotthelf v. Studnitz reported the discovery of a retinal photo-pigment in the cones which he called " Zapfensubstanz ", i.e. cone-substance, and four years later George Wald hypothesized a cone pigment which he called *iodopsin.* Vision depends on the absorption of radiant (luminous) energy by photo-sensitive pigments. The absorption curve of rhodopsin is nearly identical with the scotopic luminosity curve of the human eye, and the same can be said of the iodopsin absorption diagram with respect to the photopic curve. The absorption maximum for rhodopsin is at 5020 A.U. and for iodopsin at 5750 A.U. A good idea of what rhodopsin and iodopsin look like can be gained from colour charts. In the two representative colour systems the tones most closely resembling the undecomposed photo-pigments are :

	Ostwald System	Munsell System	Dominant Wavelength (*49*, *50*)
rhodopsin	9pa	RP 3/10	5020 A.U. (complem.)
iodopsin	12ni	PB 3/8	4500 A.U.

The absorption of light causes the decomposition of the visual pigments to retinene 1 (from rhodopsin) and to retinene 2 (from iodopsin), these changes being qualitatively proportional to both intensity and frequency of the incident radiation, thereby forming in the retina an achromatic image (optogram) of the viewed object. *Bibliography References:* (*1325*, *1332*, *1388*).

3.7. Photo-receptors

The generally accepted theory about the purpose of the light-sensitive receptors maintains that :

(1) the rods are sensitive at low levels of illumination, viz. below and up to about 0·1 lux, i.e. a brightness between 10^{-3} and 10^{-2} candle per sq. ft., an average value being $3 \cdot 10^{-3}$ c./sq. ft.* This is an average value ; the correct value must be ascertained for each person as it changes individually ; this type of vision is referred to as scotopic or dark-adapted vision ;

(2) the cones are sensitive to illumination higher than the above quoted critical value. This type of vision is called photopic or light-adapted vision.

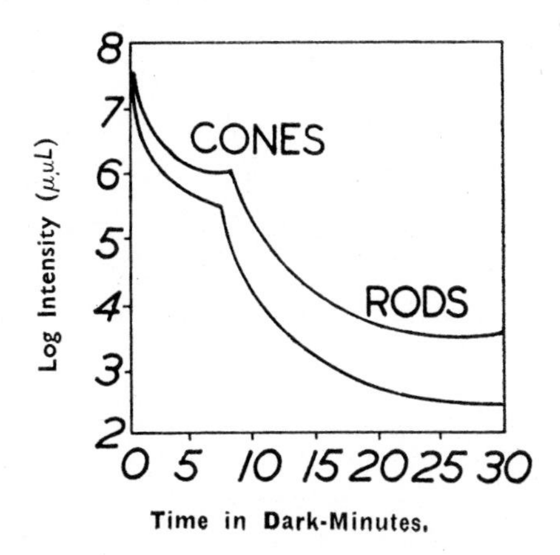

Fig. 3.3 Change in visual function with increasing illumination.

If the relationship between the function and intensity of illumination is shown in a graph, a sharp break indicates the presence of two different types of sense-cells, functioning under, and resulting in, different conditions, Fig. 3.3. To the question as to what happens to the rods

* The equivalents in millilamberts for these three values are: brightness between 0·0034 mL and 0·0338 mL, an average value being 0·01 mL (1 c./sq. ft. = 3·381 mL).

when the illumination increases above the critical level, no definite answer has yet been given (*1447*). Opinions differ rather widely (cf. the work of S. Hecht ; W. J. Crozier ; E. Wolf ; R. Granit ; and others).

The distribution of the photo-receptors is shown in Fig. 3.4, and the variation of the visual acuity, which is a function of the distribution of the light-sensitive cells, in Fig. 3.5. *Bibliography Reference* (*1069*).

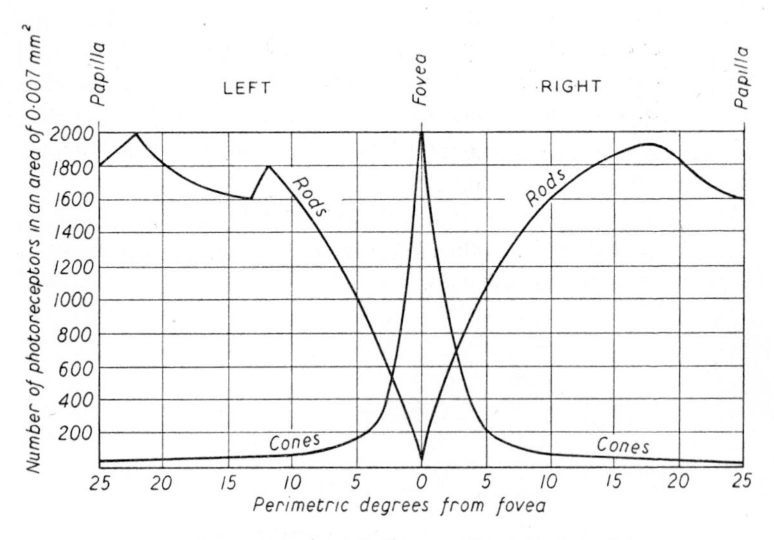

Fig. 3.4. Distribution of photo-receptors in the retina.

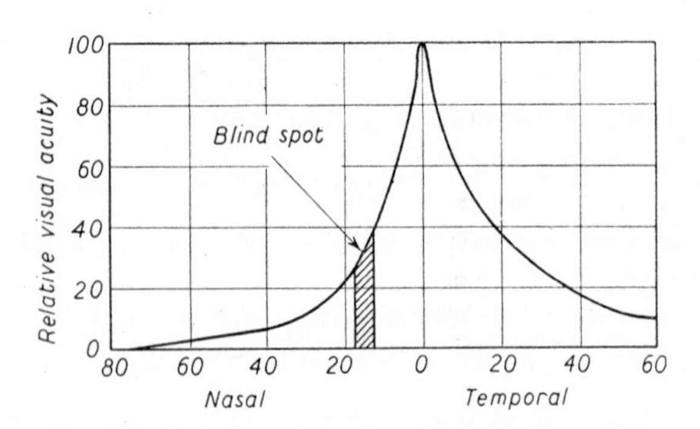

Fig. 3.5. Variation of visual acuity across the retina.

3.8. Threshold

The minimum energy necessary to stimulate a photo-receptor and cause sensation ranges between 2·2 and 5·7 × 10^{-10} ergs at the cornea. These energies represent between 58 and 148 quanta of blue-green light which, as an upper limit, become 5 to 14 quanta absorbed by the visual purple of the retina. S. Hecht states that " . . . it is therefore unlikely that any one rod will take up more than one quantum. . . . In fact, the probability that two quanta will be taken up by a single rod cell is only about 4%. We may therefore conclude that in order to see it is necessary for only one quantum of light to be absorbed by each of 5 to 14 retinal rods " (*53, 364, 1594, 1630, 1631*).

The energy of radiation is expressed by Einstein's law (1905), viz. $E = h\nu$, where E is the energy in erg, ν is the frequency in cycles per sec., and h is Planck's universal constant, viz. $(6{\cdot}624_2 \pm 0{\cdot}002_4) \times 10^{-27}$ erg-sec. (*51*). This constant has been given differently by various observers and methods (*52*) but the above value is the one now generally accepted. In Table 3.1 the energy of a single quantum of light of various wavelengths is tabulated.

TABLE 3.1

Light-Quanta

Wavelength	Colour of light	Wave number per cm.	Frequency $\nu \times 10^{12}$	Energy $E \times 10^{-12}$ erg
4358	violet	22,925	688	4·55
4800	blue	20,850	625	4·14
4916	blue-green	20,350	610	4·03
5461	green	18,300	549	3·63
5550	green-yellow	18,020	540	3·57
5890	yellow	16,990	509	3·36
6031	orange	16,580	498	3·30
6708	red	14,900	447	2·96

Bibliography Reference: (*1594*).

3.9. Luminosity of Vision *

The spectral sensitivity of the average human eye is represented by Fig. 3.6. This diagram is derived from data supplied by Gibson & Tyndall (*54*), and was accepted by the International Commission on

* As to the terminology employed in papers on optical subjects, attention must be drawn to the Report of the Committee on Colorimetry, *J.O.S.A.*, 1944, *51*, 4 and 5, where a number of new terms is introduced (cf. also *R.S.I.*, 1936, *7*, 322). The adoption of the term " Luminosity " for " Visibility " has been agreed upon, the former being defined as the ratio of the photometric quantity to the corresponding radiometric quantity. In the M.K.S. system, the dimension of luminosity is lumens per watt. (Cf. Chap. 30.2.)

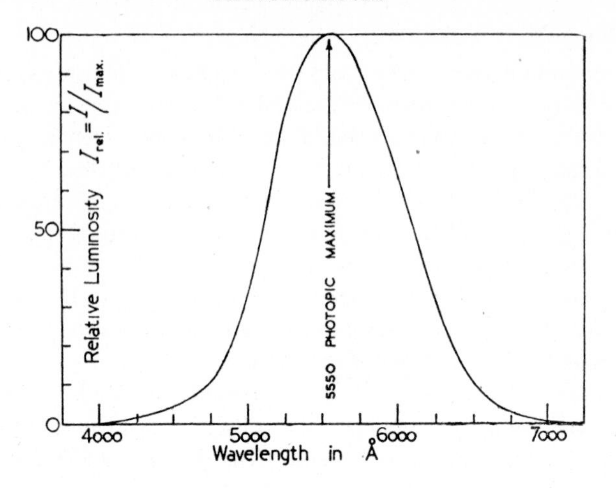

Fig. 3.6. Spectral sensitivity of the average human eye.

Illumination (C.I.E.) (*678*, *679*) in 1924 (*55*), and re-affirmed in the face of suggestions on divergent values in 1936 (*56*). A new determination was made in Russia (*2408*, *2409*). In photopic vision the maximum occurs at 5550 A.U. The luminosity curve is approximated by a Gaussian curve.† The luminosity factors represent the brightness at any wavelength relative to the maximum brightness at 5550 A.U. For photopic vision (*2408*, *2409*) the respective data of Gibson & Tyndall are given in Table 3.2 which also lists the factors for scotopic vision as observed by Stiles & Smith (*1043*). In darkness, when rod vision is exclusive, the luminosity curve shifts towards the short-wave end of the spectrum and a new set of conditions makes its appearance. This shift is called the Purkinje effect.

† Most of the data obtained from mass observation of humans follow the Gaussian frequency law. The two parameters of a Gaussian curve are the arithmetic mean (average) and the standard deviation from this mean value. The general formula of the Gaussian law is

$$y = \frac{h}{\sqrt{\pi}} e^{-h^2 x^2}$$

where h is a constant. For details, see a textbook on Statistics.

TABLE 3.2

Purkinje Phenomenon

Luminosity Factors of Photopic and Scotopic Vision (cf. Table 3.3.)

Wavelength A.U.	Luminosity Factor		Wavelength A.U.	Luminosity Factor	
	Photopic Vision	Scotopic Vision		Photopic Vision	Scotopic Vision
3700		0·0007	5800	0·870	0·1576
3800		0·0026	5900	0·757	0·0934
3900		0·0074	6000	0·631	0·05437
4000	0·0004	0·0177	6100	0·503	0·03121
4100	0·0012	0·0373	6200	0·381	0·01763
4200	0·0040	0·0713	6300	0·265	0·009802
4300	0·0116	0·1253	6400	0·175	0·005362
4400	0·0230	0·2047	6500	0·107	0·002887
4500	0·0380	0·3121	6600	0·061	0·001533
4600	0·060	0·4450	6700	0·032	0·0008023
4700	0·091	0·5948	6800	0·017	0·0004144
4800	0·139	0·7451	6900	0·0082	0·0002115
4900	0·208	0·8757	7000	0·0041	0·0001067
5000	0·323	0·9663	7100	0·0021	0·0000535
5100	0·503	1·0000	7200	0·00105	0·0000267
5200	0·710	0·9668	7300	0·00052	0·0000133
5300	0·862	0·8677	7400	0·00025	0·0000066
5400	0·954	0·7183	7500	0·00012	0·0000033
5500	0·995	0·5487	7600	0·00006	0·0000016
5550	1·000	0·4636	7700		0·0000008
5600	0·995	0·3881	7800		0·0000004
5700	0·952	0·2552	7900		0·0000002

Data on scotopic vision were also compiled by Weaver (*57*) for binocular vision and natural pupils, and by Hecht & Williams (*58*). Other investigators give the respective maxima for monocular vision and artificial pupils as follows (*59*, *60*) :

Observer	Maximum of Photopic Vision	Maximum of Scotopic Vision
Laurens		5070 A.U.
Southall	5700 A.U.	5100 A.U.
Parsons	5800 A.U.	5300 A.U.
Studnitz	5560 A.U.	5040 A.U.

The colour which is equally well perceived under both intense and very weak illumination is generally accepted to be a bluish-green of wavelength 5310 A.U. which means that this wavelength (or rather the group of wavelengths centring at about 5310 A.U.) stimulates rods and cones equally well.

The wavelength of maximum diurnal visibility yields but 46% efficiency in scotopic vision. The average unaided eye is capable of detecting as small a luminous flux as about $0{\cdot}5 \times 10^{-12}$ lumen. *Bibliography References:* (*381, 516*)

3.10. Persistence of Vision and Critical Flicker Frequency

The human eye possesses a peculiar faculty known as the Persistence of Vision.* This is manifested in the inability of the eye to resolve a cycle of more than 12 to 13 repetitions per second into discrete phases, with the result that the sensation experienced is that of uniformity and continuity. At low levels of illumination (intensity up to about 50 lux) 16 pulsations per second are sufficient to eliminate the sensation of flicker. At higher levels of illumination (about 100 lux) at least 45 pulsations are necessary to achieve the same effect, Fig. 3.7. The

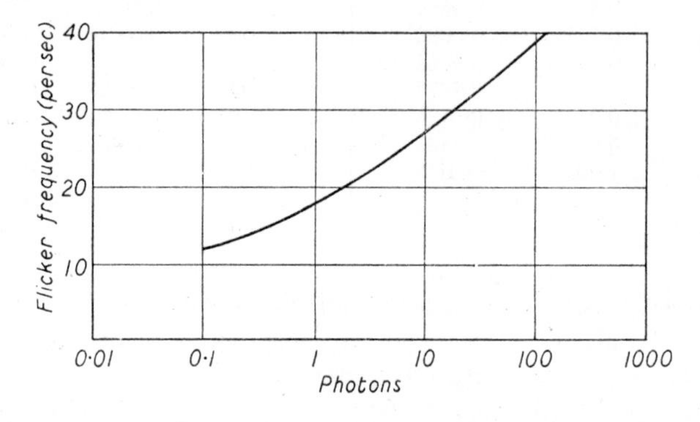

Fig. 3.7. Effect of illumination on flicker frequency.

sensory effect, called flicker, becomes less vigorous as the rate of light flash is increased. The flash rate just producing the impression of steady, i.e. flicker-free illumination is called the Critical Flicker Frequency (c.f.f.) and the point at which this translation occurs is called the Fusion Point.

* In 1890, it was noted that, if one looked first steadily at an electric lamp, and then at an area of relatively low brightness, an after-image was formed on the retina.

T. C. Porter discovered that the relation between the c.f.f. and the logarithm of the illumination is a straight line, and that this line showed a distinct kink at about 0·25 metre-candle (1 metre-candle or lux = 0·0929 foot-candle) (*1446*). This kink occurs at a point where scotopic vision changes to photopic vision (*1447*).

3.11. Visual Perception in the Ultra-violet and Infra-red Region of the Spectrum

Although it is common practice and agreed convention to ascribe vision to a range of electromagnetic wavelengths comprising about one octave from 3800 to 7600 A.U., investigations into the limitations of human visual perception under sub-standard conditions have shown that the photo-chemical basis of vision, i.e. visual purple, functions in exactly the same way when irradiated by ultra-violet or infra-red energy. Visual purple is sensitive to as short a wavelength as 2540 A.U. One of the earliest investigators was F. Schanz (*1448*) who photographed the respective absorption spectra of the human cornea and lens. Ten years later the following facts were known (*1449*) :

(1) The combined tissues of the eye absorb the ultra-violet radiations up to about 3134 A.U. ;

(2) the lens has the largest region of absorption ;

(3) any increase in the salt content in the eye radically changes the absorption.

From recent researches by Goodeve, Lythgoe, and Schneider (*1252*) the following conclusions were arrived at :

(1) Dark adaptation curves are of the same type at 3650 A.U. as at 5461 A.U. ;

(2) the limiting scotopic sensitivity of normal eyes at 3650 A.U. is more than 10,000 times smaller than that to be expected from the photo-sensitivity at this wavelength ;

(3) the limit of vision in the ultra-violet is defined by the threshold of absorption of the normal lens, viz. at 3090 A.U. (*2421*) ;

(4) an aphakic eye, i.e. an eye with no lens, still " sees " at wavelengths >2980 A.U. which is the threshold of absorption of the cornea ;

(5) the colour sensation of ultra-violet vision is variously described as violet, blue, lavender, grey, etc., according to observer and intensity of irradiation ;

(6) the presence of a yellow pigment (phospholipin) in the eye causes the strong absorption of ultra-violet radiation (cf. *supra*) ;

(7) the sensitivity to ultra-violet decreases with age.

For the near infra-red region of the spectrum Goodeve (*1253*) has found the following values for the relative luminosity factor which, for wavelengths >6900 A.U., is determined by :

$$\text{Relative luminosity factor} = -26{\cdot}28 + \frac{170200}{\lambda}$$

when the wavelength is measured in A.U.

TABLE 3.3

Goodeve's Luminosity Factors in the Infra-red Region (cf. Table 3.2)

Wavelength A.U.	Luminosity Factor	Wavelength A.U.	Luminosity Factor
6900	0·0096	8000	0·0000039
7000	0·0042	8100	0·0000022
7100	0·0019	8200	0·0000012
7200	0·00091	8300	0·00000068
7300	0·00043	8400	0·000000375
7400	0·00021	8500	0·00000022
7500	0·000104	8600	0·00000013
7600	0·000051	8700	0·000000075
7700	0·000027	8800	0·000000045
7800	0·000014	8900	0·000000028
7900	0·0000076	9000	0·000000017

These values show various deviations from the international standard. The relative luminosity at 9000 A.U. is about 100,000 times smaller than the luminosity at 7100 A.U. which latter wavelength represents the practical limit of normal human vision. The most recent investigations by Griffin *et al.* (*2420*) arrive at almost identical data.

Bibliography References: (*585, 1083, 2408, 2409*).

3.12. Binocular Depth-Perception

Stereoscopic vision is limited to a range of about 1500 ft. for the unaided eye. The factors governing binocular depth-perception are the interpupillary distance *d* which, according to age and race, varies between 50 and 74 mm., and the threshold angle *a* of depth-perception which is about 30 inches, i.e. 0·000145 radian. The distance *D* of stereoscopic vision is then $D = d/a$ for the unaided eye, and $D' = mkD$ for the instrumentally assisted eye, where *m* is the magnification of the optical device (e.g. field glasses) and *k* a factor by which the distance between the centres of the object glasses has been increased above *d*.

For the reader interested in the physiological and bio-electric aspects of visual perception a short guide to the numerous publications is given here :

Bio-electric potentials : (*61, 62, 63*) ;
Photopic sensitivity : (*73, 74, 2408, 2409*) ;
Colour vision : (*59, 64, 65, 68, 69, 70, 71,72, 553, 1089, 1397, 1398, 1399, 1554*).

3.13. Photosensitors

Photosensitors can be likened to the human eye only in so far as some physico-physiological phenomena are considered. Through negligent phraseology and unmethodical thinking an " equivalence " between photosensitor and the human eye has become a deep-rooted but nonetheless unjustified, concept. It is true that a photosensitor is " sensitive " to colour, but it must be borne in mind that it is a sensitivity which is only comparable to the visual effects in a colour-blind person's system. Suffering from total colour-blindness means that the afflicted person perceives the different colours as different shades of grey or "achromatic colours ". The photosensitor also differentiates colours on this basis. The sensitivity curve of a photosensitor shows graphically the relation between the wavelength of the incident radiant energy and the photo-electric current. It is the equivalent graph for depicting the physiological relation between stimulus and sensation. If not different wavelengths, but different intensities of radiant energy are made to impinge upon the photosensitor, these intensities can so be arranged and graded as to yield an exact duplicate of the first curve and yet the energy may be of a non-selective, i.e. white, colour. If, for instance, the photosensitor is three times as sensitive to green light as it is to red, then the photosensitor will yield treble the amount of photo-electric current if irradiated with green light as when it is with red light, both radiations having the same energy content, though different wavelengths. If, now, the red radiation is made more intensive than the green one, it is quite possible for the photosensitor to produce treble the photo-electric current under red radiation, but only a small current with the green light striking it. This effect demonstrates clearly that the photosensitor " sees " colour in a way different from that in which the human eye " sees " it. If the same experiment is carried out with a normal human observer instead, the result will be different. Light of a wavelength conventionally called green will always appear green however dim or however bright the incident beam of light may be. And red is always seen as red regardless of its intensity within the photopic range. The standard human eye " sees " intensities and " sees " colours as two distinctly different stimuli and transforms them into two distinctly different sensations. The photosensitor does not.

It must be borne in mind that the majority of all those processes and effects which result in colour vision are of a mainly psychological nature. Prof. Polyak writes (*59, p. 408*) " it is legitimate to think that somewhere in the visual system a set of neurons must be present by means of which the numerous cone excitations are reduced to three or four basic processes which, in turn, may be variously combined into compound phenomena. It is plausible to think that a part, at least, of the analyzing and compounding processes already takes place in the retinal membrane ". Stress should be laid on " analyzing and compounding ", which are merely physico-physiological phenomena. It is in the higher brain centres that appraisal of the sensations and " colour vision " takes place. These psychological phenomena, needless to say, are lacking in inanimate matter.

Instruments designed for colour matching are using photo-electric cells which have a purely physical function and faculty. Colour, as explained above, is a purely mental faculty accompanying certain types of brain and retina including the human, and it must therefore be understood that a purely physical means will never be in the position of perceiving or appraising " colour " as long as " colour " is explained in terms of a special psycho-physiological faculty.

The absorption of a light quantum by the light-sensitive cathode of the photo-cell results in the energy $h\nu$ of the photon being imparted to an electron which, now, can move about according to a given set of conditions. The impact of a number greater than unity of photons is necessary to liberate one electron. The passage of a stream of electrons per second past a given point can be measured and is expressed in amperes: the passage of $6{\cdot}25 \times 10^{18}$ electrons/sec. causes a current of 1 amp. As nearly all electrical measuring instruments are based on the measurement of current flowing through their system, but are not concerned with, and can give no information about, the mode of origin of this current, it becomes obvious at once that the " colorimeter " really cannot take into account the frequency of the incident light. Any information given by such an instrument which, fundamentally, is always a current measuring device (with the exception of electrostatic instruments) is, therefore, bound to refer to the quantity—not the quality—of the incident photons.

If the energy of a photon is shown as $h\nu$ erg
and the total number of incident photons be N sec.$^{-1}$
then the total incident power $P = N h\nu$ μW
With a coefficient of efficiency σ $\mu A/\mu W$
the resulting number of electrons, i.e., the
photo-current, $E = \sigma P$ μA

If the photo-cell views two different " colours ", i.e., light of the frequencies ν_1 and ν_2, respectively, and if arrangements are made so that the indicating microammeter shows the same deflexion in both cases, then $E_1 = E_2$. After substitution of the above values for E, the ratio is

$$N_1\nu_1/N_2\nu_2 = \text{const.}$$

The constancy of the ratio must be interpreted so that the photo-current will be the same whether the incident light is of strong intensity N_1 and low frequency ν_1 or of low intensity N_2 and high frequency ν_2. In other words the meter of a colour-matching instrument can indicate the same current whether generated by a strong " red " or by a weak " blue " light. This holds for all values of σ.

This physical relationship between quantity and quality of a radiation is totally different from the psycho-physiological aspect of intensity and frequency which are in no way correlated. Under photopic conditions the mental effect of " red " light is always the same whether its intensity is strong or weak. It can never be perceived as " blue " or any other " colour ".

The other human organ which is sensitive to light, namely the skin, behaves like the photo-cell. The skin also absorbs a range of electromagnetic radiation, ultra-violet, for instance, which produces a specific effect, viz. pigmentation. The degree of pigmentation and of the preceding erythema may well be regarded as a measure of the primary cause. Within the pigmentogenic range the exact frequency of the stimulating energy is of no basic importance as pigmentation can be produced with relative little energy at 3100 A.U. wavelength just as well as with energy at 3650 A.U., except that in the latter instance the intensity must be increased by a factor of 800 to 1000. If this is done the pigmentations produced in either instance will be of the same degree, irrespective of both the quantitative and qualitative differences, and the observer judging from an appraisal of the pigmentation, i.e. from the effect only, will not be in a position to draw any conclusions about the frequency of the causative radiation.

It seems a rather doubtful proposition to find a purely physical means for the determination and matching of " colours " which, as has been shown, is a mental, not a physical, process. Unless a number of conditions are stipulated and rigidly adhered to, it will not be possible to design and operate a physical colour analyzer or matching instrument. These conditions are :

(1) The " spectral " response curve of the photo-cell must be ascertained under illumination produced by a light source at the correct temperature of 2848° K.
(2) The " spectral " response of the photo-cell must be identical with, or coincidental in, the most important parts of the spectrum with the photopic luminosity curve of the average human eye.
(3) The sensitivity must be constant over the entire cathode area. If this cannot be achieved the projection of the light source must at least completely cover the photosensitive cathode.
(4) The photo-cell must be aged, and fatigue, drift, and dark current must be reduced to a minimum.
(5) The electronic circuit should preferably be of the balanced type. In this case the photo-cells must be " spectrally " matched.
(6) Incandescent filaments must be aged and operated at constant rated voltage. If more than one lamp be used with a photo-cell circuit, the spectral emission of both lamps should be well matched.
(7) If colour filters are used they should be of constant density and have a well-defined spectral transmissivity.

" Spectral " response is explained by pointing out that the combination of light source + filter + photo-cell, if the physical characteristics are kept constant, represents a well-defined visual system of such characteristics as might—or might not—approach the system of human vision. In such an artificial system only a certain amount of radiant energy is available within certain ranges of frequencies (wavelengths) : $P_{\text{total}} = h(\nu_1 N_1 + \nu_2 N_2 + \ldots)$ and the total photo-current produced $E = \sigma P$ may, numerically, remain the same in a number of combinations, for instance,

$$L_1 + F_1 + PC_1$$
$$L_2 + F_2 + PC_2$$
$$\ldots\ldots\ldots$$
$$L_n + F_n + PC_n$$

where L . . . light source,
F . . . filter,
PC . . . photo-cell,

although in each individual case, there may be :

$$E_1 = \sigma_1 P_1 = k_1(\nu_1 N_1 + \nu_2 N_2 + \ldots)$$
$$E_2 = \sigma_2 P_2 = k_2(\nu_1{}' N'_1 + \nu_2{}' N'_2 + \ldots)$$
$$E_3 = \sigma_3 P_3 = k_3(\nu_1{}'' N''_1 + \nu_2{}'' N''_2 + \ldots)$$

If the absolute values are $|E| = |E_1| = |E_2| = |E_3| = \ldots$, then no indication can be given by the measuring instrument about any difference in the spectral response of the photo-cells, because, in fact, only the intensity of illumination has been measured and this may well have a constant value for a number of differently " coloured " lights as can be shown by the photograph of a test chart. A photo-cell is no more " colour-sensitive " than a photographic emulsion.

Having the above limitations in mind, the following Table of Agreements can now be compiled : the qualitative values should be identical as far as possible. The total effect of the quantitative values of the instrument should match the qualitative properties of the eye.

TABLE OF AGREEMENTS

	Quality	Quantity
light source	emission spectrum	intensity
filter	transmission spectrum	density
photo-cell	absorption spectrum	sensitivity
eye	hue	saturation (brightness)

The emission spectrum of an incandescent lamp depends on the colour-temperature of the filament. The colour is a mixture of all, or a number of, wavelengths. The number N of photons per sq. cm per sec. per micron emitted in the red end and blue end of the spectrum, respectively, is : $N = B \, . \, 10^{r}$.

TABLE 2

Colour Temperature °K.

A.U.	1000		1500		2000		2500		3000		3500	
	B	r	B	r	B	r	B	r	B	r	B	r
4500	6·4	10	2·6	15	5·4	17	1·3	19	1·1	20	5·0	20
6500	2·7	14	4·2	17	1·7	19	1·5	20	6·7	20	1·9	21
ratio 4500/6500	2·4	−4	0·6	−2	3·2	−2	0·9	−1	0·16	0	2·6	−1

The standard light source is an aged filament lamp of the C.I.E. Standard type A operating at 2848°K. The nearest approximation is a 100-W lamp whose colour temperature is 2860°K. If two lamps are used in a twin circuit they should be aged and spectrally matched, and be operated at rated voltage off a constant-voltage source.

When two photo-cells are used they should be aged and matched and have the same spectral sensitivity which, if possible, should coincide with the luminosity curve of the average human eye. It is of great importance that the cathode be evenly sensitive over its entire area and that the illumination should fall on the whole cathode surface, not only on parts of it.

The filters must be of constant density and spectral transmissivity, and must be stable to the incident radiation. Solarization effects need not be feared, but thermal breakage may occur due to absorption in the red and infra-red region.

Finally, it must always be remembered that photo-electric instruments measure optical quantities whereas visual colour-matching is concerned with the analysis and matching of psychological perceptions.

This knowledge is essential if the problem of selective agreement between the components is to be solved successfully. It is quite conceivable that a colour change which is supposed to trigger the photo-relay is accompanied by such a change in intensity that the photo-electric device is not unbalanced, because the reduction by the one effect is counteracted by an increase in the effect of the other phenomenon, or vice-versa. This peculiarity of " colour sensitivity " of a photosensitor is not stressed enough in the current literature.

There is another potent factor missing in photosensitors when compared with the human eye. The unaided photosensitor is incapable of detecting motion or a moving object as long as the area on the cathode, shaded by the image of this object, does not change its size. Unless equipped with appropriate gratings or réseaux, etc., the photosensitor does not react to the image moving on the light-sensitive surface. It is only with such devices as the aniseikon, iconoscope, and others, that motion can be detected.

3.14. Conclusions

The apparent " similarity " between a photosensitor and the human eye must be restricted to the following items :

(1) The generating of an e.m.f. in the boundary layer of a photo-e.m.f. cell is comparable to the generating of an e.m.f. in the photo-receptor layer of the human retina ;

(2) The electrical behaviour of the retina as a whole is similar to that of a back-wall cell (see p. 49).

(3) In general the range of the spectral sensitivity of the eye is different from that of the cell. Only under certain conditions a close approximation of the two ranges is attainable ;

(4) While the spectral range of the eye depends upon the intensity of illumination (Purkinje phenomenon) the spectral range of the photosensitor is independent of the intensity ;

(5) At the threshold of brightness sensitivity, the eye is about 5 to 6 times less sensitive than a combination of photosensitor plus electronic amplifier ; but with modern equipment this figure may be substantially increased ;

(6) The photosensitor is also sensitive to radiations of wavelengths to which the eye as a whole is insensitive ;

(7) The adaptation range of the eye is about 100,000 times greater than that of the photosensitor, although here also modern development may turn this figure in favour of the photosensitor ;

(8) The retina may be compared to an assembly of many photosensitors arranged in a plane, each cell having its individual connexions to the indicator (iconoscope) ;

(9) Only the individual photo-receptor and its elements, but not the eye as a whole, can be compared to a photosensitor ;

(10) The photosensitor, without auxiliary equipment, is unable to detect motion ;

(11) The photosensitor has no colour sensation which, in fact, is a psychological phenomenon. The photosensitor differentiates between frequencies in the same way as between intensities, viz. by altering its current output ;

(12) The photo-electric concept of the retinal layers leads to the hypothesis that the incident radiant energy causes a series of processes similar to those that occur in a photo-e.m.f. cell, likewise resulting in an electric current.

CHAPTER 4

PHOTOSENSITORS

4.1. The Photosensitor

E. Becquerel discovered that when two electrodes are immersed in an electrolyte a change of potential appears across the two electrodes if one of them is illuminated (*106*). He rightly attributed this electric phenomenon to the presence of radiation on the one electrode. For half a century these liquid cells—now being classified as belonging to the group of photolytic cells—were the only photosensitors.

H. Hertz discovered the photo-emissive properties of metals (*107*), an effect which was fully studied and described by W. Hallwachs (*108*), and since then is known as the Hallwachs effect.

From the standpoint of the works engineer, three different types of photosensitors are of interest, viz. :

(1) The photo-electric cell (photo-emissive ; alkali cell) first described in 1889 (*109*) ;

(2) The photo-e.m.f. (photo-voltaic ; barrier-layer ; rectifier ; dry ; boundary layer ; sperrschicht) cell, first described in 1876 (*884*) and independently again in 1883 (*110*) (selenium cells) and in 1904 (*111*) (cuprous-oxide cells) ;

(3) The light-sensitive resistor (photo-conductive cell), first described in 1873 (*99*).

Bibliography References: (1307, 1888, 1898, 2055, 2101, 2108, 2246, 2248, 2250, 2401, pp. 116, 117, 2407).

4.2. Definition

Fundamentally, a photosensitor is a combination of two electrodes in an electrolyte. When radiant energy of a certain specified range of wavelengths, which is characteristic for different types of photosensitors, strikes one of the electrodes it changes both its physical structure and properties. The electrolyte is either a gas, liquid, or solid, and the photosensitors will be specified as vacuum or gas-filled photo-electric cells ; photolytic cells ; photo-e.m.f. cells ; and light-sensitive resistors (*88*).

4.3. The Photo-electric Effect

Theoretically, every metal exhibits the photo-electric effect if radiant energy of suitable wavelength impinges upon the clean surface of the metal. The characteristics of the photo-electric effect may be varied by varying the operating conditions. This effect is exhibited either as internal or external effect. The former takes place in light-sensitive resistors and photo-e.m.f. cells, the latter in the type of photo-electric cell where the electrodes are separated either by a rare gas or by a vacuum.

Radiant energy is propagated through space in definite quanta, called photons. On impact with matter a certain integral number of photons will be transmitted or reflected, others absorbed, according to the characteristics of the material surface with which they collide. Einstein (*112*) showed that the photo-electric effect obeys the equation

$$h\nu = \tfrac{1}{2}\, mv^2 + \varphi e$$

(Einstein's law), where $h\nu$ is the energy of a photon of incident radiation moving through space with the velocity of light, $mv^2/2$ is the kinetic energy of the electron emitted from the atom by the impact of the photon, and φe is the energy required to release the electron from the metal. The value φ is called the Work Function (cf. section 9) and varies from metal to metal : ν is the frequency of the incident radiation.

The kinetic energy $mv^2/2$ of the ejected electron does not depend upon the intensity of the incident radiation, i.e. number of incident photons, but solely depends upon, and is directly proportional to, the frequency ν of the incident radiation. In other words the kinetic energy of a photo-electron, i.e. an electron released by collision with a photon, depends upon the energy, but not number, of the incident photons. In the photo-electric effect the energy of the incident photon is transmuted into that of the emitted electron. The intensity of the source of radiation varies the total number of electrons released from the surface of the irradiated metal. Photo-electric emission commences immediately a substance is subjected to irradiation with energy of an appropriate frequency (or wavelength). The photo-effect is independent of the intensity of the incident radiation. It is an electronic effect, the time lag being less than 10^{-9} sec.

Bibliography References: (*1096, 1142, 1214, 1236, 1237, 1353, 1501, 1578, 1596, 2322*).

4.4. The Inner Photo-electric Effect

If the energy $h\nu$ of an incident photon is sufficient to raise an electron to a vacant conductivity band level, the electrical conductivity of the substance is increased. The increased photo-electric conductance of a metallic substance is caused by additional electrons in the conductivity band ; these electrons have absorbed the incident quanta of radiation (*113*). The inner photo-electric effect (*2494*) does not lead to the emission of electrons. They move within the semi-conductor. This movement causes the equilibrium in the lattice structure to be disturbed, a fact which results in an appreciable reduction of the resistivity of the material.

In photo-e.m.f. cells no effective time lag is noticeable. In light-sensitive resistors the time lag between receiving the stimulating impulse of radiant energy and producing a change in conductance, amounts to about 0·05 to 0·1 sec.

There are two types of photo-e.m.f. cells differing in the arrangement of their elements (Fig. 4.1a, b). The electrode which is exposed to the incident radiation becomes negative in the front-wall cell, but positive in the back-wall cell. (See next Section).

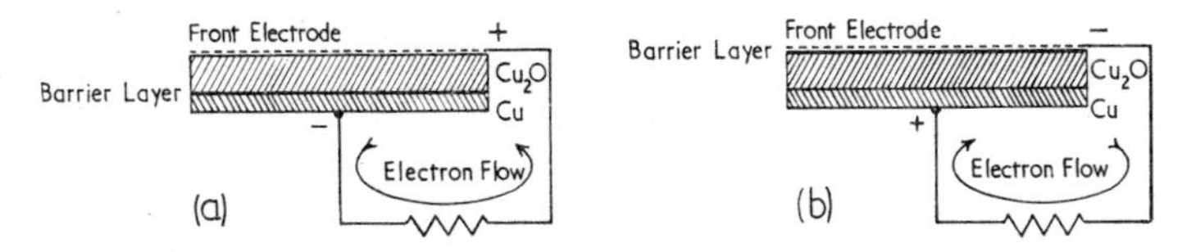

Fig. 4.1 Types of photo-e.m.f. cells: (*a*) back-wall (*b*) front-wall,.

At first, photo-chemical reactions were supposed to generate the electric energy in a photo-e.m.f. cell, and it was not before 1914 that the electronic process was substituted for the chemical theory of interaction (*114*). As far as electrolytic cells were concerned, Goldmann and Brodsky made the definite statement that the generation of electric phenomena by radiant energy is not a reciprocal action between electrode and electrolyte, but that the source of the current is the interface at which absorption of the incident radiation takes place. This interface has been called the barrier-layer, boundary-layer, *sperrschicht*, etc.

This was a great step forward and led to more elaborate theories, one of which, viz. the Electron Diffusion Theory of the Semi-conductor Photo-effect, as proposed by B. Lange (*26*), is based on an insulating layer being of lesser conductivity than the semi-conductor, the electron concentration gradient becoming different in these layers upon irradiation. This theory was hotly contested and since the discovery of Nix and Treptow (*115*) that a photo-e.m.f. cell can be built without it exhibiting the particular rectifier effect, i.e. without having a " boundary ", a new series of hypotheses have come to the fore. A good summary has been given in a paper by Fink and Adler (*92, 116*) containing the following points :

(1) Rectification, photo-e.m.f., and capacitance phenomena in cuprous-oxide metal cells are independent of the nature of the basic metal and are independent also of the presence of a material insulating " barrier " layer. This has been suggested, in a way at least by Jean Roulleau (*117*) who observed that " the photo-electric effect and the rectifying effect are independent of the specific resistivity of the cuprous oxide ".

(2) The seat of the photo-e.m.f. in front-wall and back-wall cells has been located in the upper surface of the semi-conductor (oxide) layer.

(3) In front-wall cells the electrons flow from the semi-conductor into the front-electrode which becomes increasingly negative upon irradiation.

(4) In back-wall cells the electrons flow from the metal into the semi-conductor, the front-electrode becoming positive upon irradiation.

Bibliography Reference: (*1132*).

4.5. The Outer Photo-electric Effect

If the energy $h\nu_1$ of the incident radiation is just sufficient to transfer an electron to a vacant conductivity level, then the electron will settle there, and this effect has been described as the inner photo-electric effect. If, however, the incident photon has an energy $h\nu_2$, where $\nu_2 > \nu_1$, i.e. $\lambda_2 < \lambda_1$, then the electron will not only be raised to a conductivity level, but will be detached and emitted altogether. This phenomenon is known as the outer photo-electric effect which is the basis of the operation of vacuous or gaseous photo-electric cells. When irradiated by a beam of energy, photo-electrons will be released from the cathode and move towards the anode, i.e. opposite from the direction of irradiation, and also opposite from the direction of the photo-current as flowing in the load circuit. The electrons will flow across the inter-electrode space only if their kinetic energy $mv^2/2$ exceeds the gain of potential energy Ve, where m is the mass of the electron, e the charge on the electron, v its velocity, and V the voltage across the inter-electrode space.

Bibliography References: (*1131*, *1132*, *1142*, *1330*, *1349*).

4.6. Characteristics

Special characteristics of the various types of cell will be briefly discussed.

(*1*) *Vacuum Photo-electric Cell*

This is a "hard" type of photo-electric cell usually employing anode voltages up to 250 V. In the States the maximum anode voltage is 500 V but the maximum safe anode voltage is generally not more than 70 to 75% of the above values. For individual working voltages manufacturers' lists should be consulted. Vacuum cells have no time lag even at high frequencies.

(*2*) *Gas-filled Photo-electric Cell*

This type represents the "soft" cell; it is used with a maximum voltage of 90 V (B.S. 586 : 1935). There is an intrinsic amplification due to the ionization of the gas. The amplification factor M, also termed gas factor, is usually 5 to 7, but never greater than 10. The factor M is the ratio N/N_o, where N_o is the number of electrons emitted from the light-sensitive cathode, and N is the number of electrons arriving

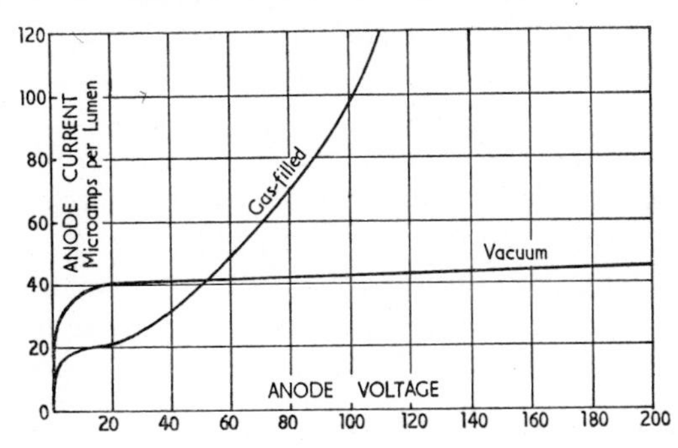

Fig. 4.2 Anode voltage—photo-current curves for vacuum and gas-filled cells.

at the anode after n ionizing collisions with the gas atoms. Fig. 4.2 shows the anode voltage / photo-current curves for gas-filled and vacuum cells, respectively. The latter cells reach saturation at relatively low voltages.

The spectral range of the light-sensitive cathode extends through larger or smaller portions of the ultra-violet, luminous, and infra-red spectrum, respectively. The range depends on the cathode material and its treatment, and in some cases, on the material of the envelope or any other screening materials which are essential in the construction of the cell. The sensitivity in the ultra-violet region has been extended down to about 1850 A.U. by using, for instance, a copper-iodide layer (*89*) distilled in vacuo on to a copper base at 700° C. It is, however, probable that the spectral sensitivity extends further still into the ultra-violet, but is restricted by the transmission limit of the quartz envelope. Quartz becomes quite opaque for wavelengths shorter than 1850 A.U.

(3) *Photo-e.m.f. Cells*

This type of cell (*90*) is built up of a semi-conductor on a metal base. Up to the present only two materials have successfully been used in industrial practice, selenium and cuprous oxide. Thallium cells are also in use for special purposes. The semi-conductor is covered by a translucent or nearly transparent metallic film. There are two different types of photo-e.m.f. cell irrespective of the nature of the materials used in their construction, viz. :

(a) *Front-wall Cells* (*Obverse type*)

These cells are so termed because the active boundary marks the front of the cell. The metal film is the one electrode, the other being formed by the metal base. The translucent film generally is 10 μ or less, and is made of gold, silver, or platinum (*1495*). Cuprous-oxide cells usually have a gold film sputtered on to the semi-conductor, while selenium-on-iron cells are coated with a translucent layer of silver. The thallium-sulphide cell (Bell Laboratories) has a platinum film. The spectral sensitivity of the front-wall cell generally extends over the luminous range of the spectrum, having a maximum in the yellow-green. For all practical purposes the sensitivity curve of a front-wall cell may be said to approach very closely the sensitivity curve of the human eye (p. 34). Front-wall cells are aptly described as *green-sensitive.*

(b) *Back-wall Cells* (*Reverse type*)

This photo-e.m.f. cell consists of a semi-conductor formed on a metal base. The photo-electrons flow in the same direction as the incident light. The back-wall cell is classified as *red-sensitive* because its range extends into the infra-red region with a maximum in the red (*91*) at about 6350 A.U. Not only the range and peak of the spectral sensitivity, but also the shape of the curve representing this sensitivity are characteristic for these two types of photo-e.m.f. cells, Fig. 4.3.

Another interesting type of infra-red sensitive photo-e.m.f. cell has been described by Fink and Mackay (*93*). It is a bismuth-sulphide (Bi_2S_3) cell with 80 % of its activity lying in the infra-red : the sensitivity extends as far as 70,000 A.U. (7 microns). The maximum occurs in the infra-red at a value of about 5 μA/Lm. It has a good stability and small fatigue.

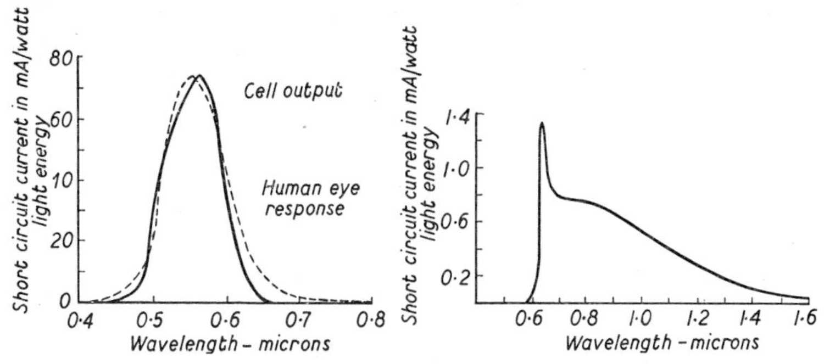

Fig. 4.3 Equal energy spectral sensitivity curves for front-wall cell (left) and back-wall cell (right).

Berraz and Virasoro (*94*) have produced a thallium-sulphide back-wall cell, its spectral sensitivity extending from 8000 to 12,000 A.U. with the maximum at 9300 A.U. The photo-electric yield is about 0·1 μA/μW. The ambient temperature must not exceed 25°C., the safe temperature being from 15 to 25°C. This heat sensitivity is a serious drawback.

All thallium-sulphide cells are destroyed by oxygen. They are therefore encased in an evacuated glass envelope.

Under the United States Patent 2330620 photo-e.m.f. cells are manufactured having a transparent homogeneous front electrode of gold or platinum on a translucent layer of magnesium, cadmium, or zinc which, in turn, is in intimate contact with the surface of the selenium layer. These layers are called inter-cathodic layers.

(c) *Equivalent Circuit*

The photo-e.m.f. cell represents not only a resistance, but also a rectifier, battery, and capacitance, which latter is due to the peculiar structure of the cell. These elements can be so combined in an " equivalent " or " phantom circuit ", Fig. 4.4, to represent the behaviour of the cell as well as show the importance of each of its elements, actual or virtual. In the external circuit having a load resistance R_L, a photo-electric current i_{ph} flows which is given by $i_{ph} = IR_i/(R_L + R_i + R_s + R_f)$. The total photo-electric current I is a function of the active cathode area and the illumination, i.e. it is composed of a constant part and a variable. The capacitance is symbolized by the capacitor C and represents the internal capacitance of the cell. The rectifier R symbolizes the one-way action of the incident light, and the battery E represents

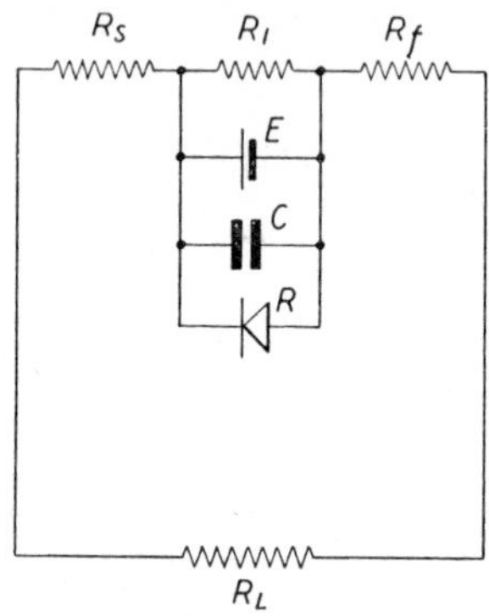

Fig. 4.4 Equivalent circuit of photo-e.m.f. cell.

the generating power of the cell. The output W of a photo-e.m.f. cell is given by $W = i^2_{ph}R_L$ or, after neglecting resistances R_s and R_f which are small in value relative to R_i and R_L,

$$W = 10^6 \, . \, I^2R_L/(1 + R_L/R_i)^2 \quad \mu W.$$

To obtain maximum output a certain relation between R_L and R_i must be attained. If the above equation for W is differentiated according to R_L and $\frac{dW}{dR_L} = 0$ and solved for R_L, the optimal relation is $R_L = R_i$. For cuprous-oxide cells this condition is satisfied because R_i is independent of R_L. Selenium-type cells yield maximum output for $R_L = 0{\cdot}5R_i$ (*95*). In the case of Weston Photronic cells this condition is governed by the relation $R_L = 0{\cdot}625R_i$. The neglected quantities R_f and R_s, respectively, cause the theoretical maximum, as derived for copper oxide cells, to shift. In practice maximum output will be attained with

$$0{\cdot}625 \leqq \frac{R_L}{R_i} \leqq 0{\cdot}750$$

The power output is of the greatest importance when electromagnetic relays are directly operated by photo-e.m.f. cells (*25*, *96*).

(4) Light-sensitive Resistors

These devices change their resistance in proportion to the intensity of illumination. There is neither an e.m.f. generated nor are electrons liberated in this process. The preparation, for instance lead, thallous sulphide or selenium, must be used in the same way as any other resistor would be connected, viz. in series with an external voltage of anything up to 1000 volts. When light falls on the light-sensitive resistor its conductivity is increased sometimes as much as eight to ten times its dark value, or even more. An appreciable current flows through the irradiated resistor depending on the external voltage and on the intensity of the incident energy. Generally, these resistors are more sensitive to long-wave light than to green, blue, and violet. The relation between the light-resistance r_L, the intensity I of illumination, and the dark-resistance r_D of the selenium resistor was found to be

$$r_L = \frac{1}{\dfrac{I^{\frac{1}{x}}}{A} + \dfrac{1}{r_D}}$$

where A and x are constants (*97*).

Light-sensitive resistors are not only of the selenium type as discovered by Willoughby Smith in 1873 (*98, 99*). It was but recently found that germanium, silicon, boron, and others make effective photosensitors in useful spectral regions (cf. sections 4.49 and 4.51).

Bibliography References: (*571, 1529*).

4.7. General Characteristics

In Table 4.1 are listed the typical characteristics of photosensitors, their photo-electric and load circuits.

4.8. Static and Dynamic Responses

The static response Σ_{STAT} can be defined as the quotient of the direct anode current i_a divided by the constant incident light flux Φ, viz.

$$\Sigma_{STAT} = \frac{i_a}{\Phi} \left[\frac{\mu A}{Lm}\right]$$

It can also be defined as the total sensitivity of a photosensitor when a steady (i.e., unmodulated) radiation strikes the sensitive surface. Therefore,

$$\Sigma_{STAT} = \text{const.}$$

TABLE 4.1

Photosensitor Characteristics

Type of Photosensitor	Internal Resistance of Photosensitor	Voltage change	Current change	Electromagnetic Relays	Conditions for Optimal Operation
Vacuum or gas-filled photo-electric cell : When a beam of light strikes the cathode of the cell, electrons are emitted from it.	Very high ; in the order of magnitude of 10^{11} to 10^{12} ohms.	Large	Small	Not directly operated. Electronic amplification necessary.	Maximum sensitivity exists when the load resistance equals the resistance of the electron stream between the cathode and anode. Very high impedance (1 to 25 megohms) in series with the cell which must not be placed more than 15 ft. from its amplifier (20 ft. when D.C.-operated). Low capacitance coaxial cable must be used for connecting cell and amplifier. Increased capacitive reactance in cables longer than 10 ft. reduces the sensitivity of the relay.
Photo-e.m.f. cell : When a beam of light strikes the sensitized surface of the cell, an e.m.f. is generated by the cell.	Low ; in the order of magnitude of 300 to 6000 ohms for the dark cell.	Small	Large	Only high-sensitivity relays are directly operated.	Load resistance as low as possible. Cell can be many feet away from relay. Temperature of cell should not exceed 50° C. (122° F.). No D.C. potential higher than 4 volts, and no A.C. potential at all may be applied.
Light-sensitive resistor : When a beam of light strikes the sensitive preparation, its ohmic resistance decreases.	Medium. Dark-resistance up to 30 megohms. When illuminated the resistance drops down to about 1 megohm or less depending on the material used.	Medium	Medium	Directly operated.	Load resistance should equal the dark-resistance of the light-sensitive resistor. Current capacity from a few milliamps. up to 250 milliamps. and even more, can be attained.

Bibliography Reference: **(1346)**.

The dynamic response Σ_{DYN} is the quotient of the amplitude variation in photo-electric current δi_a divided by the amplitude of variation in incident energy flux $\delta\Phi$, viz.

$$\Sigma_{DYN} = \frac{\delta i_a}{\delta \Phi} \left[\frac{\mu A}{Lm}\right]$$

It is also the total sensitivity of a photosensitor when a modulated beam of radiant energy, having a modulation frequency φ', strikes the photo-sensitive surface. Therefore

$$\Sigma_{DYN} = f\left(\frac{1}{\varphi'}\right)$$

The dynamic response of photo-e.m.f. cells is due to the shunting effect of the capacitance of C in Fig. 4.4. This capacitance is usually of the order of 0·03 to 0·5 μF. (*26,27*), and is the result of the cell being built-up of two parallel elements separated by a third element. The astonishingly high values of Σ_{DYN} of very small-sized cells are due to the small dimensions of these cells.

TABLE 4.2

Type of Photosensitor	Average Absolute Sensitivity $\mu A/Lm$	Relative Sensitivity per cent at Modulation Frequency (c/s)						Reduction due to
		0	100	1000	3000	5000	10000	
Photo-electric								
(a) vacuum	10 to 50	100	100	100	100	100	100	
(b) gas-filled								
Caesium	10 to 150	100	100	97	92	89	80	ionization
Potassium	2	100	100	71	50	18	—	ionization
Photo-e.m.f.								
(a) Cuprous-oxide								
Front-wall	100	100	100	98	94	91	80	capacitance
Back-wall	10	100	100	94	80	67	44	and
(b) Selenium	460	100	97	84	59	45	23	fatigue
Light-sensitive Resistor								
Radiovisor	100	100	100	68	42	35	*36	fatigue
FJ31 (G.E.)		100	100	50	25	15	—	fatigue

The effect of a falling dynamic response can be offset by an amplifier whose frequency characteristic is a rising curve. The resultant should be more or less parallel to the frequency axis (*100*).

4.9. Work Function

In 1905, A. Einstein (*112, 1632*) applied Max Planck's quantum theory to the quantitative calculation of the photo-electric effect and promulgated the basic law that no electrons can be freed by the incidence of photons unless their energy $h\nu$ exceeds that amount W of energy (surface work) which is required to release an electron from the irradiated matter. If $mv^2/2$ is the kinetic energy of the emitted electron, then the Einstein formula reads $mv^2/2 = h\nu - W$. The potential V which is necessary to bring an electron of kinetic energy $mv^2/2$ to rest is called the "stopping", "opposing", or "limiting" potential. Then $mv^2/2 = eV$, where e is the electronic charge $(4{\cdot}8025 \pm 0{\cdot}0004) \times 10^{-10}$ e.s.u. (*51*). The energy which is lost in overcoming the surface attractive forces is $W = e\varphi$ where φ is the work function. This function is a physical constant for a given material and is measured in ergs or

* The dynamic response of Radiovisor Selenium Bridges shows a minimum at a frequency between 5000 and 10,000 c/s, depending on the internal resistance. At higher frequencies the response improves due to the photosensitor's inability to follow and reproduce the fluctuations. This characteristic is reminiscent of the human eye's Persistence of Vision.

electron-volts.* The higher the atomic number of the metal in the periodic system, the smaller is the work function. Amongst the metals the alkali metals have the smaller work functions, and amongst these, caesium has the smallest. Because of their spongy surface (*1701*) which yields much greater an absorption of radiant energy, the alkali oxides have a work function which is smaller still. The alkali metals are electro-positive, i.e., they lose electrons easily and have, therefore, a small W. With the work function decreasing, the "attackability" of the alkali metals by the electro-negative oxygen and the hydroxy-ion (-OH), as contained in the atmosphere, increases. Therefore, alkali cells are always of the enclosed type. Low work functions are attained by the following combinations: sodium, potassium, rubidium, or caesium as a surface layer on silver, beryllium, tantalum, nickel, aluminium, chromium, zirconium, calcium, tungsten, etc. (*155*).

A special photo-electric effect (*1492*) was discovered in 1929. If radiant energy of different frequencies strikes a metal surface the stopping potential V of the material is determined by the high as well as by the low frequency. It is supposed that the electrons of energy $h\nu_{LOW}$ cannot reach the range of the high-energy electrons and, therefore, set up a space charge which it becomes necessary to overcome by allowing for an additional lost energy W_2 which can be considered as part of an "extended" work function, viz., $W = W_1 + W_2$, where W_1 stands now for the energy loss caused by the attractive surface forces. In the case of radiation of a single frequency ν striking the material, V is a function of ν, viz., $eV = h\nu - W$, while V is a function of ν_1 and ν_2 if energy of two different frequencies strikes the material. $V(\nu_1\nu_2) < V(\nu)$. This phenomenon is called "falling-off" effect and results in the potential, to which a material insulated surface charges itself upon irradiation, falling off when radiant energy of a lower frequency is added to the original radiation.

A helpful list of references on the theory of photo-electric emission from metals was compiled by H. Y. Fan (*120*).

Another energy loss in the surface is also incurred when photo-electrons are emitted. This loss is proportional to the change in the temperature of the surface (in the order of magnitude of 10^{-2} to 10^{-3} deg. K.) and the rate of loss of energy per degree above equilibrium

* An electron-volt is a convenient measure of energy, and expresses the work done when an electron moves across an electromagnetic field with a potential drop of one volt. This electron possesses a kinetic energy of $1{,}602 \cdot 10^{-12}$erg or $1{,}602 \cdot 10^{-19}$ watt-sec.

temperature, but is inversely proportional to the photo-electric current. The surface cools off when photo-electrons are emitted. (*118*, *119*, *1042*). *Bibl.* (*1107*, *1133*, *1148*, *1210*, *1231*, *1337*)

TABLE 4.3

Work Functions

Element	Symbol	Atomic weight	Electro-	Work-function electron volt	Long-wave limit A.U.	Reference
Lithium	Li	6·94	positive	2·2	5580	(*122*)
				2·1–2·9	5800–4300	(*125*)
Beryllium	Be	9·02	positive	3·16		(*129*)
Sodium	Na	22·997	positive	1·9	6470	(*122*)
				2·05	6000	(*121*)
				2·46	5830	(*123*)
Magnesium	Mg	24·32	positive	2·42		(*130*)
Aluminium	Al	26·97	positive	2·26		(*130*)
Potassium	K	39·096	positive	1·8	6820	(*122*)
				1·9	6500	(*121*)
				2·24	7000	(*123*)
Calcium	Ca	40·08	positive	2·51		(*127*)
				2·7	4475	(*125*)
Chromium	Cr	52·01	positive		2840	(*131*)
Iron	Fe	55·84	positive	4·7	2620	(*125*)
Nickel	Ni	58·69	negative	5·01	3050	(*123*)
				5·01	2463	(*125*)
Copper	Cu	63·57	positive	4·1–4·4	3010–2750	(*125*)
Zinc	Zn	65·38	positive	4·24	2915	(*128*)
				3·32	3720	(*125*)
Selenium	Se	78·96	negative		8000	(*93*)
Rubidium	Rb	85·48	positive	1·69	7300	(*121*)
				1·8	6820	(*122*)
				2·15	5700	(*124*)
Strontium	Sr	87·63	positive	2·3	6000	(*125*)
Molybdenum	Mo	95·95	negative	4·15	3000	(*124*)
Silver	Ag	107·88	positive	4·61	2680	(*124*)
Cadmium	Cd	112·41	positive	3·94	3130	(*121*)
				4·07	3030	(*122*)
Caesium	Cs	132·91	positive	1·54	8000	(*121*)
				1·90	6500	(*124*)
Barium	Ba	137·36	positive	1·76–2·29	7000–5400	(*125*)
				2·706		(*127*)
Cuprous oxide	Cu_2O*	143·14			14,000	(*93*)
Tantalum	Ta	180·88	negative	3·76	3283	(*126*)
Tungsten	W	183·92	negative	4·54–4·58	2720–2680	(*121*)
				4·52	2300	(*123*)
Platinum	Pt	195·23	negative	6·26	2570	(*123*)
				6·30	1960	(*121*)
Gold	Au	197·2	positive	4·82	2650	(*125*)
				4·90	2520	(*124*)

TABLE 4.3 *Work Functions—contd.*

Element	Symbol	Atomic weight	Electro-	Work-function electron volt	Long-wave limit A.U.	Reference
Mercury	Hg	200·61	positive	4·53	2735	(*124*)
Bismuth	Bi	209·00	negative		2870	(*131*)
Thorium	Th	232·12	negative	3·38	3640	(*122*)
Bismuth sulphide	Bi_2S_3	514·18*		0·0206	70,000	(*93*)
Caesium silver	Ag-Cs_2O-Cs			0·75	10,000	(2576)

* Molecular weight.

4.10. Spectral Threshold

From the Einstein equation $mv^2/2 = h\nu - \varphi e$ it is obvious that for an electron of velocity $v = 0$ (which means that the electron cannot leave the surface of the irradiated material, because the gain $h\nu$ in energy of the electron equals its loss φe, which latter is the result of the electron being emitted), there is a *threshold frequency* $\nu_0 = \varphi e/h$ below which no emission can take place. This minimum represents the frequency at which the photo-electron acquires sufficient energy (minimum energy $h\nu_0$) to emerge from the surface. Since higher frequencies which are necessary for the emission of the photo-electron, are identical with shorter wavelengths, $\lambda_0 = c/\nu_0$ is called the *long-wave limit* or *red limit*, and is defined as the wavelength of the incident light under the impact of which a released photo-electron escapes with zero velocity.

Since alkali metals have a relatively low work function the frequency threshold is equally low, i.e., the long-wave limit lies in the red portion of the spectrum or in the infra-red. On the other hand, electro-negative metals like platinum, tungsten, etc., have high work functions which shift their respective long-wave limit towards shorter wavelengths as far as violet and ultra-violet.

In terms of equivalent volts, the basic equation for the threshold can be written $h\nu = Ve$, where e is the electronic charge and V the voltage through which the electron would have to fall for it to acquire an amount $mv^2/2$ of energy.

An interesting effect is noticeable when doubly evaporated metal films are used as emitting cathodes. R. B. Jones (*132*) has investigated the behaviour of single and double films of platinum, nickel, and tungsten, respectively, and found that the threshold frequency of the doubly evaporated film is approximately that of the component having the lower-frequency threshold. His figures are :

Actual threshold frequencies of single metal films :

W	2338 A.U.
Pt.	2864 A.U.
Ni	3333 A.U.

actual threshold frequencies of double metal films :

Ni-Pt	3318 A.U.
Pt-W	2804 A.U.

A more elaborate list of combinations is given below (*133, pp. 40, 86*).

TABLE 4.4

Long-wave Thresholds of Double Metal Films

Type of Surface	Long-wave Limit A.U.	Work function *eV*
Na–Pt	5900	2·08
K–Pt	7700	1·60
Rb–Pt	7950	1·56
Cs–Pt	8900	1·38
BaO–Pt	9200	1·34
Li–W	6700	1·83
Th–W	4900	2·52
Ba–Ag	7900	1·56
Cs–Cs_2O–Ag	$>$ 10,000	$<$ 1·23

The photo-electric threshold wavelength λ_0 is the measure of the longest wave capable of producing the photo-electric effect in a given material. The values compiled in the two preceding tables show that the photo-electric threshold depends very largely upon surface conditions and methods of measurement. The discrepancies can be traced back to physical and methodological differences.

The photo-electric threshold varies as the chemical constitution of the photo-cathode is changed. If oxygen be admitted into the bulb and allowed to react with the active surface the threshold shifts either towards the long-wave or short-wave region of the spectrum, respectively. If oxygen reacts with thorium, uranium, calcium, barium, caesium, the thresholds shift towards the long-wave end of the spectrum ; if reacting with titanium, iron, nickel, zirconium, silver, the threshold shifts towards the other end of the spectrum ; no such effects can be ascertained in gold (*131*). H. C. Rentschler and D. E. Henry, the observers of the above described phenomenon, stated in a later paper (*134*) that the lowering of the work function of the heavy metals is due to dissolved gases. Similar shifts were observed in solid solutions of nitrogen or hydrogen in zirconium and titanium. The authors attribute the shift to the formation of a monomolecular layer of the active element on another metal or on an oxide. The respective shifts are demonstrated by the following instances :

Solid solution of oxygen in	Threshold of the pure metal	Threshold of the treated metal
Zirconium	3150 A.U.	3400 A.U.
Titanium	2950 A.U.	3350 A.U.
Thorium	3650 A.U.	4350 A.U.

The ultimate sensitivity of photosensitors is discussed by Fellgett (*2430*).

Bibl. (*1146*).

4.11. Spectral Sensitivity

The range of spectral sensitivity of cathode materials as used at present in photosensitors extends over varying portions of the ultra-violet, luminous, and infra-red spectra respectively, according to type and treatment of the photo-electric cathode (*1684*, *1690*). The spectral sensitivity of photosensitors is independent of the number of incident photons, i.e., of the intensity of illumination, but the range of sensitivity as well as the position of the maximum or " peak " sensitivity is a function of the frequency of the incident photons.

Miss E. F. Seiler (*135*) has conclusively shown that, as the atomic weight of the alkali metals increases, the maximum sensitiveness decreases and the peak or wavelength of maximum emission, briefly termed maximum wavelength, shifts towards the long-wave part of the spectrum, (Fig. 4.5).

A further shift in the same direction is attained when the hydrides of the above alkali metals are used, viz. :

Alkali metal hydride	NaH	KH	RbH	CsH
Molecular weight	24·005	40·104	86·488	133·918
λ max. A.U.	4270	4460	4810	5400

The amplitude of the maximum wavelength, i.e., the quantity proportional to the number of electrons released at the maximum wavelength, decreases from lithium over potassium to caesium, and the resonance peak broadens at the same time. Seiler suggested that these changes are probably associated with the increase in the atomic volume.

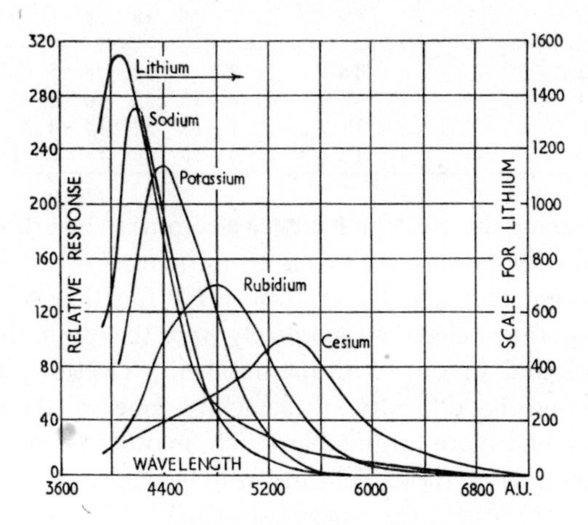

Fig. 4.5. Chart of "Seiler" sensitivities

TABLE 4.5

Constitution and Maximum Wavelength of Alkali Metals

Element	Number of Electron Shells (Quanta)	Number of Planetary Electrons (Atomic Weight)	Arrangement of Planetary Electrons in their Orbits (K.L.M.N. O.P.)	Maximum Wave-length A.U.	Work Function eV	Long-wave limit A.U.
Lithium	2	3	2.1	4050	2·2	5580
Sodium	3	11	2.8.1	4190	2·0	6000
Potassium	4	19	2.8.8.1	4400	1·8	6820
Rubidium	5	37	2.8.18.8.1	4730	1·7	7300
Caesium	6	55	2.8.18.18.8.1	5390	1·6	8000

The phenomenon that the five metals Li, Na, K, Rb, Cs, have low work functions finds its explanation in the simple fact that their common characteristic is the presence of only a single electron in the outermost orbit.

Period	Atomic Number	Valence	Metal	Electron Orbits							Work function
				K	L	M	N	O	P	Q	
Ia	3	1	Li	2	1						2·2
IIa	11	1	Na	2	8	1					1·9
IIIa	19	1	K	2	8	8	1				1·8
IVa	37	1	Rb	2	8	18	8	1			1·7
Va	55	1	Cs	2	8	18	18	8	1		1·5
	73		Ta	2	8	18	32	8	5		3·8
	74		W	2	8	18	32	10	4		4·5
	78		Pt	2	8	18	32	14	4		6·3
	90		Th	2	8	18	32	18	8	4	3·4

The forces keeping this electron (valence electron) in its orbit, are smallest compared with those acting on electrons in other orbits of the atom. It is conceivable that a relatively low work function will suffice to detach the outermost electron completely from the atom, thus creating a free electron and an ion. With the number of electrons in the outer orbit increasing the difficulty of detaching one of these electrons becomes more and more formidable which, in other words, means that the work function of these elements will be higher, the greater the number of electrons is in the outermost orbit.

Incidentally, it becomes obvious from the above data that the work function decreases and the long-wave limit increases, i.e., shifts towards red, as the atomic weight increases. Görlich (*378*) has stated that the " Seiler regularity " cannot be observed with transparent alloy cathodes, for instance of the Cs-Bi and Cs-Sb type. A change in the maxima from Li to Cs does not occur ; the photo-electric current output decreases when one goes from Cs over Rb and K to Na. For Li the current equals that of Rb.

The absolute value of the spectral sensitivity curve represents a certain fraction of the maximum attainable value. This absolute spectral response, expressed as a percentage of the maximum, is called the Quantum Efficiency for that particular wavelength. If the absolute spectral response curve of a photosensitor is graphically represented together with the energy distribution curve of that particular radiation source which is used with the photosensitor, and a new curve be drawn whose ordinates are the product of the ordinates of the above two curves, then the area under this composite graph will be proportional to the output of this particular combination. The ordinates of the new curve are a measure of the spectral sensitivity and are expressed in $\mu A/Lm$. The maximum attainable value is expressed in $\mu A/\mu W$ and equals $10^7 e\lambda/hc$. It is common practice to express the spectral sensitivity σ in microamp. per lumen if the radiation ranges within the luminous part of the spectrum, but to express it in microamp. per microwatt if in any other part.

The Quantum Yield is the same as spectral sensitivity, but is expressed as the number of photo-electrons freed and actually emitted per incident photon (i.e., light quantum) absorbed by the photo-electric surface. The quantum yield is also defined as the ratio of actual emission to theoretical emission at a given wavelength. This definition is in line with the power engineer's conception of " efficiency ".

The spectral sensitivity shows a peculiar effect in that monochromatic light striking the cathode results in voltage/current curves the slope of which is different throughout their whole extent for different wavelengths of the incident light, i.e., for different colours (*136*, *137*).

It is obvious that not only the photo-electric threshold, but also the spectral sensitivity of a photosensitor is a function of the chemical composition and physical structure of the cathode. C. Bosch suggested the sensitizing of cathodes by the use of organic dyes (*1691*). In both the photo-electric vacuum and gas-filled cells the sensitive cathode consists of alkali metals. The range of maximum sensitivity, being of the " peak " type for all cathodes of the single metal group, has successfully been extended by using photo-cathodes consisting of alloys of an alkali metal and a metal of lower conductivity, e.g., bismuth, or antimony (*101*, *1450*, *1451*). The spectral response of alloy cells is fairly constant over the entire range of the luminous spectrum. The cell, described in the above-quoted patent specifications (*1450*, *1451*) yields 60 $\mu A/Lm$ for Light of 2360° K. A typical colour response curve for an alloy cell clearly shows the relative maxima of its component cathode materials. Photosensitors sometimes have cathodes made from non-alkali metal alloys. In such a case the " peak " characteristic is maintained, but the absolute position of the " peak " varies considerably with the metallurgical composition of the alloy. Koller and Taylor (*102*) have demonstrated the behaviour of alloys by using a cathode once made from a 5% cadmium-95% magnesium

NOTE : If investigations into the characteristic properties of photosensitors are carried out regularly, a photo-electric automatic recorder (*138*, *1697*) will prove helpful. The inertia and sensitivity of photosensitors under working conditions can be investigated by, and traced on, cathode-ray tubes (*1479*, *p. 407*). The arrangement for determining the static response of a photosensitor is discussed by R. R. Wright (*1499*, *p. 75*).

alloy, and then from a 95% Cd—5% Mg alloy. In the first case the maximum of sensitivity occurred at 2810 A.U., in the second case at 2735 A.U. A shift of as much as 75 A.U. resulted from a change in the relative composition of the alloy cathode.

In general the curves in manufacturers' lists representing the spectral sensitivity of photosensitors are of a group character and need not necessarily apply to any one photosensitor in particular. Individual deviations from average group characteristics are due to causes at present not likely to be improved upon. In special cases the manufacturers will undertake the task of supplying a photosensitor to exact specifications. Upon request, pairs of photosensitors can be made to specification and can be matched. This is of importance if the pair is to be used in two-cell balanced circuits : cells can be matched for linearity ; output and linearity ; and spectral sensitivity.

W. I. Rutkovsky (*103*, *104*) has developed a method of designing a selenium photo-e.m.f. cell in such a way that its spectral sensitivity curve becomes identical with any given curve in general and the luminosity curve of the standard human eye in particular. The development of this method may lead to the production of photosensitors the spectral sensitivity of which will range over a given restricted region of the spectrum and will, without the use of filters, be insensitive to radiations outside the preferred range.

Another method of achieving the same end was devised by A. Dresler (*105*) who, in a paper read before the *Deutsche Lichttechnische Gesellschaft*, indicated how to approximate the spectral sensitivity curve of any photosensitor to any given curve within its range of total sensitivity. He pointed out that the generally accepted way of using filter combinations was to allow suitably filtered light to reach the entire cathode, which procedure accounted for two serious disadvantages, the great loss of energy and the suppression of certain spectral regions. The latter result is what might be called an " overcompensation ". Dresler suggested to use a compound filter over only part of the cathode area in conjunction with other filters over the remaining area, these latter being designed to compensate for the suppressed regions. Thus he was able to produce a selenium photo-e.m.f. cell the spectral sensitivity curve of which was perfectly identical with the sensitivity of the C.I.E. Standard Observer. The filters used were a green filter VG2 and a yellow filter OG1, both 1 mm. thick (Make : Schott & Gen., Jena). About 14% of the total area was covered by the green filter, about 6% by the yellow filter, and the rest (80%) by a combination of both filters. The total sensitivity to light from an incandescent lamp had been reduced to about 30% of the unarmed cell.

Bibl. (*540*, *1247*).

4.12. Quantum Voltage

The emission of radiation occurs in quanta of energy (particles of radiation): this quantum is called a photon. When its energy is expressed in electron-volts and the wavelength is substituted for the frequency the energy E_λ is

$$E_\lambda = \frac{hc}{e} \times 10^{-7} \frac{1}{\lambda}$$

where c is the velocity of light expressed in A.U. per sec. $= 2{\cdot}99790 \times 10^{18}$ A.U./sec., e the electronic charge $= 1{\cdot}602 \times 10^{-20}$ e.m.u., and λ the wavelength in A.U. for which the energy E_λ is sought. All quantities except λ are constants, and the quantum voltage is, therefore,

$$E_\lambda = \text{const.} \frac{1}{\lambda} \quad \text{or } \lambda . E_\lambda = \text{const.}$$

After substituting the numerical values for the quantities in the constant the equation finally resolves into

$$E_\lambda = 12395 \frac{1}{\lambda} \text{ (electron-volt)} = 1{\cdot}9857 \times 10^{-8} \frac{1}{\lambda} \text{ (erg).}$$

The wavelength of a photon whose energy is one electron-volt, is 12395 A.U., i.e., it is situated in the near infra-red.

The quantum voltage is a measure of the energy of a photo-electron which it has acquired by the impact of a photon. Considering the internal losses φ, called the work function, the maximum kinetic energy E_{MAX} of a photo-electron just after escaping from the surface of the cathode metal is $E_{MAX} = E_\lambda - \varphi$, all quantities expressed in electron-volts. The velocity of an electron leaving the surface at E_{MAX} and travelling in a direction perpendicular to that surface is $V = 5{\cdot}95 \times 10^7 \sqrt{E_{MAX}}$, the velocity being measured in cm/sec. The threshold wavelength can now be defined as the wavelength for which the kinetic energy E_{MAX} is zero. This makes $E_\lambda = \varphi$ for the threshold. In general, the quantum voltage of the radiation must be greater than the work function of the cathode material in order to result in the photo-electric effect.

In Table 4.6 the quantum voltage of typical radiations is set out. If read in conjunction with Table 4.3, it will be seen that no photo-electric effect can be produced if $\varphi > E_{\lambda}$.

TABLE 4.6

Quantum Voltage of Radiation

" Colour " of Radiation	Average Wavelength (A.U.) corresponding to the " Colour " of Radiation	E_{λ}
ultra-violet	2800–3200	4.42678–3.87343
" black light "	3650	3.39589
extreme violet	3800	3.26184
violet	4358	2.84419
blue	4861	2.54988
blue-green	5130	2.41618
green	5461	2.26974
green-yellow	5550	2.23333
yellow	5890	2.10441
orange	6402	1.93611
extreme red	7600	1.63092
infra-red	10,000	1.2395

The saturation current depends on the wavelength of the incident radiation. The energy of one single photon is $h\nu$ (erg) ; thus one watt ($=10^7$erg/sec.) will liberate $10^7/h\nu$ electrons per sec. The charge on each electron being $1{\cdot}60203\times10^{-19}$ coulomb, the theoretical saturation current for a given frequency ν of radiation will be $(10^7/h\nu)\times1{\cdot}60203\times10^{-19}$ amp. In practice, only about 0·2 % of that will be attained (*124*). One ampere* is defined as the flow of $6{\cdot}242\times10^{18}$ electrons per second past a given point of the conductor. In metallic conductors only about one out of 5000 electrons resident in the conductor actually takes part in the phenomenon called " current flow ". The other electrons remain in their respective atoms.

A photo-electric effect also takes place in gases and vapours. Just

* The electric charge on one electron is $e = 1{\cdot}60203\times10^{-19}$ coulomb. Therefore $1/e$ electrons have a total charge of one coulomb. Since one amp. is one coulomb per sec., one ampere is the total of $1/1{\cdot}60203\times10^{-19}$ coulomb per sec. $= 6{\cdot}242\times10^{18}$ electrons. Another definition is based on the fact that there are $6{\cdot}0228\times10^{23}$ electrons per mole (*51*, *139*). The electric charge of all electrons per mole is one Farad = 96,487 coulombs ; the charge per electron is 96487, $6{\cdot}0228\times10^{23}$ coulombs. One ampere is the flow of 1 coulomb per second. One coulomb $= 6{\cdot}0228\times10^{23}/96{,}487 = 6{\cdot}242\times10^{18}$ electrons. Therefore, 1 ampere $= 6{\cdot}242\times10^{18}$ electrons per second (as above).

as radiation, on striking a metal surface, will impart its energy to the electrons in the metal cathode and cause some of them to be emitted if the frequency of the incident photons, and therefore their energy, exceeds a certain limiting value, so will radiation penetrating a gas or vapour cause the formation and emission of photo-electrons under favourable conditions. The thresholds of gases and vapours are higher than those of a metal surface. The minimum energy required to cause emission of photo-electrons from the molecule, a process which results in the gas or vapour becoming ionized, is expressed in electron-volts and is termed ionization potential. This quantity is similar to the work function for solid and liquid surfaces. The energy of each incident photon must be at least equal to the first ionization potential of the atom or molecule of the gas or vapour, respectively.

TABLE 4.7

Critical Potentials of Solid Metals and Metal Vapours
(cf. Table 4.14)

Metal Vapour	Ionization Potential	Work Function
Cs	3.87	1.54
K	4.32	1.8
Ba	5.19	1.85
Na	5.12	1.94
Rb	4.16	2.15
Li	5.37	2.21
Sr	5.67	2.3
Mg	7.61	2.42
Ca	6.09	2.51
Cd	8.96	4.07
Hg	10.38	4.53

4.13. Quantum Yield

The quantum yield is the ratio of the number of electrons emitted by the photo-cathode to the number of incident photons. The number of electrons carried by 1 amp. is $6{\cdot}242 \times 10^{18}$ per sec. The number of electrons constituting the photo-current generated at λ_{MAX} is governed by the " sensitivity " σ, and is $6{\cdot}242 \times 10^{18} \times \sigma$. The number of photons released in the source of radiation and striking the photo-cathode depends on the wavelength of the radiation and is $5{\cdot}036 \times 10^{14}\lambda$. per watt.* The quantum yield q, by definition is

$$q = \frac{\text{electrons}}{\text{photons}} = \frac{6{\cdot}242 \times 10^{18} \times \sigma_{MAX}}{5{\cdot}036 \times 10^{14} \times \lambda_{MAX}} = 12395 \frac{\sigma_{MAX}}{\lambda_{MAX}} = E_\lambda \times \sigma_{MAX}$$

where σ_{MAX} is measured in A/W or μA/μW at λ_{MAX}, the latter being expressed in A.U.

The reciprocal of q is the number of incident photons required to release one electron, viz.

$$\frac{1}{q} = \frac{\text{photons}}{\text{electrons}} = 8{\cdot}0679 \times 10^{-5} \frac{\lambda_{MAX}}{\sigma_{MAX}}$$

The quantum yield, as defined above, is 1 : 2 in cuprous oxide front-wall cells (*26*). In theory it should be 1 : 1 ; in practice, however, the quantum yield is very remote from such ideal conditions and is sometimes as low as 1 : 5000 and even less.

Bibliography References : (511, 1112, 1114)

4.14. Time Lag

The photo-electric current in a gas-filled cell (*14*, *386*) is the sum of

(1) electrons liberated at the photo-cathode by the impact of incident photons ;

(2) ions and electrons liberated in the gas molecules by collision of the photo-electrons (as described under (*1*)) with the gas molecules. Ionization of the gas by collision with photons (cf. previous paragraph) does not contribute to the photo-current.

* To free one photo-electron an energy $E_\lambda = 12395 \frac{1}{\lambda}$ (electron volt) $= 1{\cdot}9857 \times 10^{-8} \frac{1}{\lambda}$ (erg) must be expended in these operations. The total number of electrons which can be detached by the impact of one watt ($= 10^7$erg/sec.) is, therefore,

$$\frac{10^7}{E_{\lambda\,(erg)}} = \frac{10^7 . \lambda}{1{,}9857 . 10^{-8}} = 5{\cdot}036 \times 10^{14} \times \lambda \text{ per sec.}$$

They represent a current of $\frac{5{\cdot}036 \times 10^{14} \times \lambda}{6{\cdot}242 \times 10^{18}} = 8{\cdot}0679 \times 10^{-5} . \lambda$ (amp/watt).

The same result will be achieved when it is considered that the charge on each electron is $1{\cdot}60203 . 10^{-19}$ coulomb and the total charge per second on all electrons detached by the impact of one watt of radiant energy will be $5{\cdot}036 \times 10^{14} . \lambda . 1{\cdot}60203 \times 10^{-19} = 8{\cdot}0679 \times 10^{-5} . \lambda$ (amp).

The direction of travel of the various elements is shown in Fig. 4·6; the velocity of the electrons is much greater than that of the ions due to their large mass and size. Not all ions travel at the same velocity.

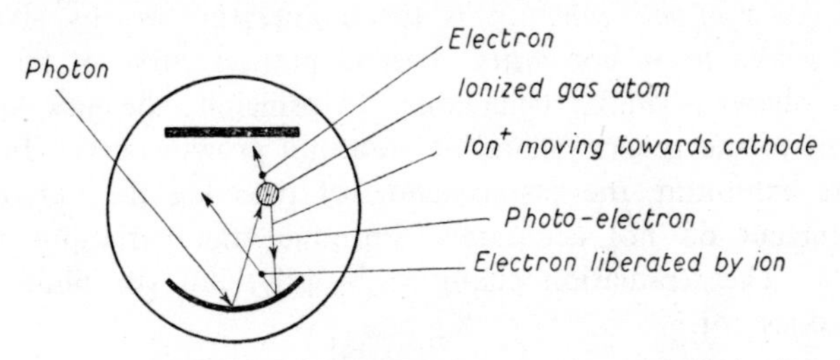

Fig. 4.6. Movement of ions and electrons in a gas-filled cell.

On reaching the cathode, the ions free an electron in the surface of the cathode and this now moves towards the anode, again producing electrons and ions by colliding with gas molecules, just as the primary photo-electron did in the first place. The temporal difference between these subsequent bursts of electrons is proportional to the transit time of the ions. If this transit time equals half a period of the current variations the total output current is reduced to a minimum. (*141*, *142*, *1439*).

Neither vacuous photo-electric cells nor front-wall photo-e.m.f. cells have a time lag, or else it is certainly less than 10^{-8} sec. At irradiation with energy of a modulation frequency of 10,000 c/s. the relative response of such a cell is still very high. Gas-filled photo-electric cells respond similarly to front-wall cells, but back-wall photo-e.m.f. cells show only roughly half the response, and light-sensitive resistors even less. The time lag of gas-filled cells is in the order of about 10^{-5} sec. Light-sensitive resistors have a time lag of about 5×10^{-2} sec. which means that it takes the cell one twentieth of a second to adapt its resistance to the conditions set by the incident energy. If, therefore, irradiation flashes follow one another at intervals less than 5×10^{-2} sec. the light-sensitive resistor will not be able to adapt its resistance accordingly but will maintain it at a lower average. (cf. Note at the end of Table 4.2.)

The graphical representations of time lag characteristics all show the same functional behaviour. The " front " of the curve, corresponding to the impact of energy on the photo-cathode, is very steep, whereas the tail shows a smaller gradient. Time lags of different photosensitors are different in their characteristics (*100*, *p. 314*; *140*, *p. 169*; *143*, *p.* 233), but they all show the same fundamental shape. The photo-electric time lag exhibits the same characteristics as are shown in a curve representing the heating of a non-luminous radiator obeying the general law $y = ae^{-bt}$ where y is the temperature at any given time t while a and b are constants. The adaptation curve of the human eye also shows a similar behaviour. In principle, the time lag curve conforms to the general shape of a natural growth curve. In photosensitors exhibiting the phenomenon of time lag the variations in photo-current do not accurately reproduce the variations in light intensity. The irradiation changes abruptly, but the photo-electric current does not.

Bibliography References : (1071, 1074, 1116)

4.15. Fatigue

This is the phenomenon characterized in that the photo-electric effect cannot in all cases follow the fluctuations of the exciting radiation if this has a modulation frequency above about 100 c/s. This effect is usually called Dynamic Fatigue. (*140, p. 169* ; *144* ; *156, p. 314*). Static Fatigue is the decrease in potential or current of a photosensitor within a certain first period of illumination. A saturation or constant value is reached at the end of that period. Static fatigue is dependent upon the intensity of illumination. In general, selenium photo-e.m.f. cells show a greater static fatigue than cuprous-oxide cells.

Bibliography Reference : (2410)

4.16. Drift

This term describes a phenomenon distinctly different from fatigue in cause and effect. Drift (*145*) or Initial Drift (*146*) denotes the transient change in current in the period immediately subsequent to exposure to radiation. This effect, which is very marked when the cell has been kept in darkness previous to exposure, is completely reversible (*146*). Sandström (*375*) reports that if a selenium photo-e.m.f. cell has been stored in darkness the value of its barrier-layer resistance decreases upon illumination by an amount about ten times the errors of measurement. When again stored in darkness the photocell recovers, i.e., its resistance increases slowly.

The drift of selenium photo-e.m.f. cells has been the subject of a thorough investigation by J. A. Hall (*147*) of the National Physical Laboratory. The following paragraph is quoted from his paper : " The drift, expressed as a percentage, is independent of the current given by the cell, and hence of the brightness to which the cell is exposed. If a cell is allowed to drift by exposure to radiation from a source at a given temperature and the temperature is then increased, the initial response to the higher temperature is almost, but not quite, as great as if the cell had not previously drifted at the lower temperature. Drift is much reduced when deep-red and infra-red radiation is excluded. No drift was observed when the cell was exposed on open circuit. If the illumination of a cell is interrupted for a short period and then resumed, the sensitivity of the cell recovers somewhat during the " rest " period, but rapidly resumes the value it had had just before, irrespective of whether it had previously been allowed to drift for a long or a short period. The speed of recovery depended to some extent on the circuit conditions under which the cell was allowed to recover, and was most rapid when the cell was short-circuited."

The experiments of J. A. Hall and T. Land (*148*) show that an average of one in every two selenium photo-e.m.f. cells of a batch of about twenty gives satisfactory results within a margin of $\pm$ 5° C. when used as radiation sensitive element in high temperature photo-electric pyrometers. A similar percentage was ascertained for cuprous-oxide photo-e.m.f. cells. In a report of the Combined Intelligence Objectives Committee (*1453*), H. J. Eppig of the U.S. Ordnance Department mentions that about 50% of a large total number of such cells possessed spectral responses which were within 5% of each other over the entire spectral region of the cell. If used in photometers, the maximum deviation in measurements of the same lot of light sources, viz. German military flares, by any two instruments did not exceed 10%. This, it was considered by German scientists, was a sound basis for the reproducibility of measurements. The accuracy of photo-e.m.f. cells is discussed in detail by Atkinson, *et al.* (*1084*).

The phenomenon was further studied and a tentative explanation proffered by J. S. Preston (*149*, *150*) summing up the observed irregularities, viz. :

(1) increased departure from linearity of response to wavelengths greater than 6400 A.U. (*151*) ;

(2) drifting depends on the spectral composition of the incident radiation (*152*),

in the following suggestion : " The basic common factor is the existence of a photo-electric, and an associated transparency threshold in the neighbourhood of 6600 to 6400 A.U. . . . (selenium is practically opaque to wavelengths shorter than 6000 A.U.) (*149*) . . . Our suggestion that the comparatively deep penetration of red light into selenium results in a kind of space charge retarding the emission of electrons from the deeper layers is, of course, only tentative ; but such a mechanism would provide for both the non-linearity and the fatigue effects together, provided the space-charge is not built up instantaneously."

A phenomenon which is similar in effect to, but different in cause from, drift is the loss of sensitivity with time. This is called Ageing or Depreciation (*146*) and there is no remedy against its effects other than replacing by a new photosensitor. As a measure of ageing the term Stability may perhaps be introduced which expresses the constancy of the characteristics over a long period of time. Vacuum photo-electric cells also sometimes show an instability which was studied by D. Cavassilas (*153*). The instability occurred in cells with central anodes and was characterized in that with constant illumination and accelerating potential the photo-electric current showed variations during measurement. The explanation proffered attributes this rather anomalous phenomenon to static charges, i.e., to the accumulation of electrons on the inside of the wall of the photosensitor. Loss of sensitivity due to continued irradiation is also discussed by S. Pakswer (*2410*). *Bibliography Reference :* (*592*)

4.17. Flicker

All types of photosensitors, with the exception of vacuous cells, show a definite dependence on the frequency of the incident radiation : in general the output decreases with increasing modulation frequency.

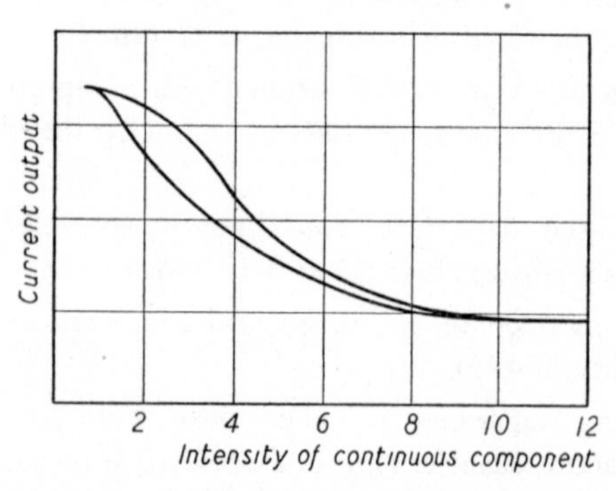

Fig. 4.7. Effect of imposing modulation on continuously irradiated cells.

In gas-filled cells the formation of unstable atoms during irradiation and the ionization effect are responsible for the flicker phenomenon. In photo-e.m.f. cells it is the geometrical arrangement of the electrodes which, giving the cell a small capacitance in the order of magnitude of 0·3 μF (average), results in a reduction of output.

If modulated irradiation is superimposed on a continuous component the current output is reduced, Fig. 4·7, when the continuous irradiation of the photo-e.m.f. cell is increased (*154*).

4.18. Multiplier Photo-electric Cells

The liberation of secondary electrons by photo-electrons (discovered in 1900) was shown to be of an undesirable nature. It must be added, however, that secondary emission can be turned to advantage if the cell has been designed for that purpose. This was done as early as in the 1920's when Slepian laid the foundations to his U.S. Patent 1450265. The principles of photo-electric electron-multipliers are laid down by Zworykin *et al.* (*155, 157, 158, 165, 1284*), Farnsworth *et al.* (*159, 160, 161, 162*), and others (*163, 164, 166*). The modern photo-electric multiplier generally incorporates up to 9 or 11 stages of multiplication with a potential difference between subsequent stages of, at present, 100 to 130 volts, because at and below this impact energy the coefficient K of secondary emission is independent of the angle of incidence. The final current output rises exponentially with the number of stages, viz.

$$I_o = I_{ph} K^n$$

where I_o is the final output current, I_{ph} the initial primary photo-electric current leaving the photo-cathode, K the constant of the cathode material, and n the number of stages. The amplification characteristic of a typical industrial multiplier (RCA.1P21) is given in Fig. 4.8. Amplifications of 10^6 to 10^7 and higher are easily attainable, the amplification being defined as the ratio of anode sensitivity to cathode sensitivity.

The photo-electric multiplier of the type shown in Fig. 4·9, is a vacuum photo-electric cell comprising a photo-cathode, nine secondary emissive electrodes called dynodes,* and an anode. A mica shield which is interposed between the light-sensitive cathode and subsequent multiplier stages or dynodes and the anode prevents ion feedback which would cause the emission of spurious electrons. This undesirable

* DYNODE = dyne (= power) + hodos (= *path*). (Greek)

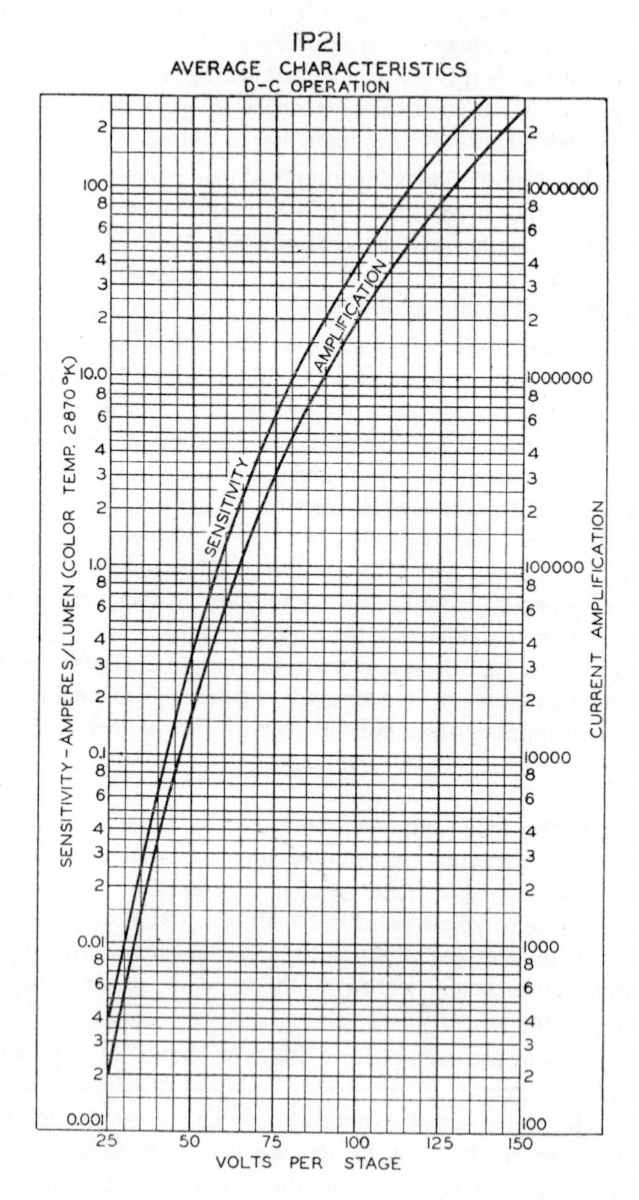

Fig. 4.8. Amplification characteristic of typical photo-multiplier (RCA Type 1P21).

emission would produce uncontrollable regeneration and result in instability. Schaetti (*2487; 2522*) suggests targets made of an Ag-Mg (2%Mg) alloy which is non-photo-electric (*2486*). These targets (dynodes) will emit 9·8 secondary electrons for each primary electron hitting the dynode at a voltage of 500 volts.

The light shield is a grille connected to the photo-cathode, thus closing electrostatically the open end of the electrode assembly. Radiation

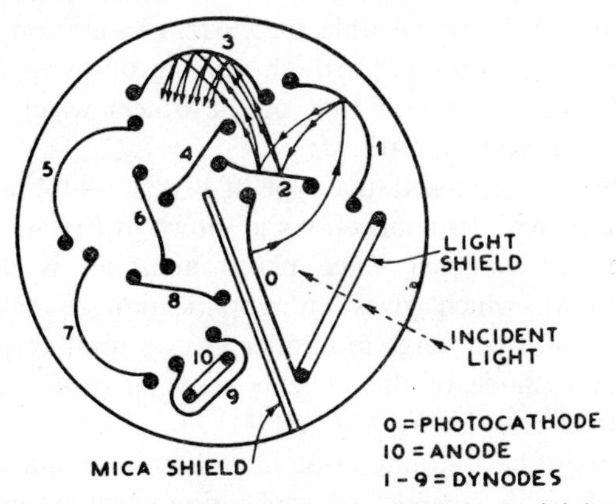

Fig. 4.9. Schematic diagram of 931A photo-multiplier. By joining the successive pairs of dynodes the multiplier can be converted into a 7- or 5-stage tube.

reaches the photo-cathode through this shield. The photo-electrons released from the irradiated cathode *O* are directed by fixed electrostatic fields to the first of a series of nine secondary emitters, i.e., to dynode No. 1. By impact the photo-electron releases a number of secondary electrons, the number being a function of the energy of the photo-electron. Successive impacts occur, then, on dynodes 2, 3, 4, etc., and the exponentially increasing stream of electrons is finally collected by the anode 10 to which the output circuit is connected. The electrical design and mechanical shape and arrangement of the electrode structure is so as to make the output current I_o independent of the instantaneous positive anode voltage over a wide range. The output current is a linear function of the incident radiation. There is no time lag interfering with the flatness of the dynamic response curve unless frequencies higher than 20 to 30 Mc/s are used, at which frequencies transit time becomes a limiting characteristic : the emission time is less than 10^{-11} sec. (*2492*). The lowest value for the time lag between the impact of the primary and the emission of the secondary electron is considered to be 10^{-15} sec. (*2523*). In industrial applications, however, so short a period is not generally required, and the dynamic response of the multiplier cell is, for all practical purposes, identical with the static response.

The electrons are accelerated by a potential difference between successive stages of 100 volts/stage or more. The voltage between the last dynode (No. 9) and the anode should not, in general, exceed a maximum of 250 volts. Although it is not very critical it should be kept as low as will be permissible for current saturation. Control of the multiplication is attained through making one step of the inter-electrode voltages unequal to that of the others which results in a defocusing of the electron path.

Fig. 4.10 shows a representative type of British multiplier photo-cell and another type with its connections is shown in Fig. 4.11.

A 17-stage 120 volt per stage photo-multiplier is described by Lallemand (*2486*), which gives an amplification of 850,000, while an 18-stage 200 volt per stage multiplier gives a total amplification of 10^{10}–10^{12}. The cathode of this tube is made of Sb-Cs, the dynodes being made of an alloy of Ag-Mg. (*2487*).

The reduction of background noise in a photo-multiplier is discussed by Drigo (*2584*), who suggests the application of an external electrode connected to a potential about 200 volts below that of the cathode. This arrangement will reduce the dark current due to static charges on the glass envelope.

The minimum luminous detectivity of a 1P21 RCA photo-multiplier cell is shown to be a function of its operating temperature (Fig. 4.12).

Bibliography References: (*514*, *527*, *580*, *584*, *1238*, *1306*, *1708*, *1787*, *2182*, *2185*, *2338*, *2359*, *2360*, *2365*, *2368*)

4.19. **The Coefficient of Secondary Emission**

The number of secondary electrons liberated by a single photo-electron (*365*), i.e., by a primary electron, is shown in Table 4.8 for a Cs–Cs_2O–Ag surface (*167*). A reduction of the work function results in an increase of secondary emission. In some cases the common logarithm of the secondary emission coefficient is roughly proportional to the change in work function due to contamination (*168*). The secondary electron yield, i.e., the ratio of secondary electrons emitted for each incident primary electron depends on the energy of the primary electron as well as on the kind and condition of the photo-cathode.

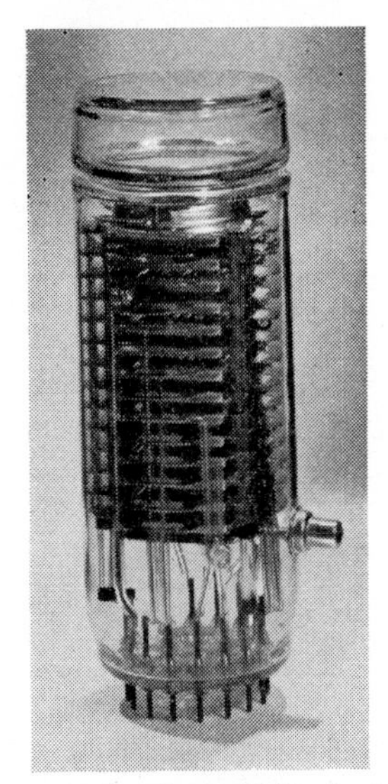

Fig. 4.10. Photo-electric multiplier by Mullard Ltd.

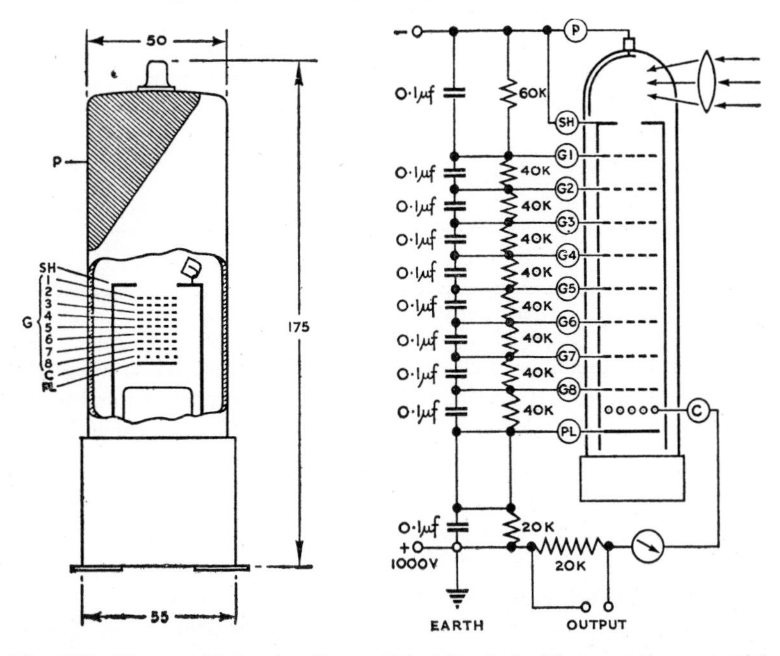

Fig. 4.11. Photo-multiplier by Cinema-Television Ltd. The operating potentials are obtained from a potentiometer across the 1000 V supply.

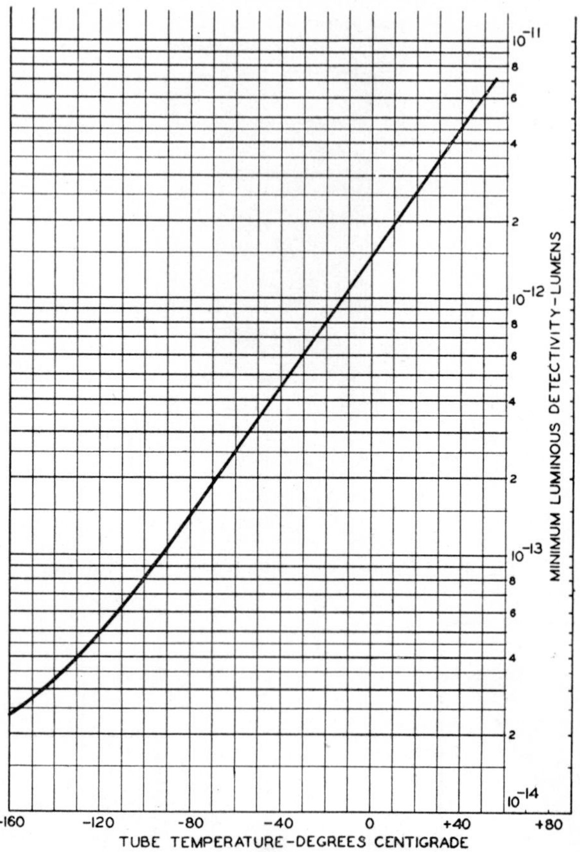

Fig. 4.12. Detectivity-temperature characteristic of the RCA 1P21 photo-multiplier (100 V per stage, 1 c/s band-width).

Degassing the metal is likely to decrease the secondary emission by half or even more. The velocity of an electron is proportional to the square root of the electrostatic potential V through which it has fallen, viz. $v = 5{\cdot}95 \times 10^4 \sqrt{V}$, where v is in cm/sec. and V is in volts.

It is obvious that the kinetic energy $mv^2/2$ of an electron is directly proportional to this electrostatic potential, viz.

$$E = (5{\cdot}95)^2 \times 10^8 . V . m/2.$$

The hypcthetical interpretation of the phenomenon of secondary emission is based on the assumption that the incident electron penetrates to a certain depth into the crystal lattice. The mean depth at which the secondary electrons are dislodged has been calculated by

Jonker to be 33 A.U. below the surface (*2525*). At a depth of about ten atomic diameters secondary emission is originated by 500-volt electrons which impart their energy to the bound electrons of the metal surface. The liberated secondary electron will emerge from the surface unless it has been absorbed or deflected and an increase in the energy of the primary electron need not necessarily result in a proportional increase in the yield of secondary electrons. Due to their greater energy of impact they will penetrate to greater depths of the surface layers, but the paths of the liberated secondary electrons also have increased correspondingly and so have the chances of absorption and deflexion. In all, the yield of secondary electrons will decrease under the above circumstances rather than increase.

Coefficients of secondary emission have been compiled from the papers of various workers and are listed in Table 4.8. It shows that secondary emission from complex and/or contaminated surfaces is essentially higher than from pure metals. A $Cs–Cs_2O–Ag$ layer attains a maximum yield of secondary emission. A. V. Afanas'heva (*169*) states that sputtering of silver or magnesium on to nickel, and oxidation of the silver-magnesium layer in oxygen, increases the coefficient of secondary emission by a factor of at least eight.

TABLE 4.8

Coefficients of Secondary Emission

Surface	Maximum Value of Coefficient of Sec. Emission $K_{max.}$	Volts	Reference
Metals :			
Li	0·56	100	(*168*)
Be	0·90	150	(*168*)
	5·4	600	(*167*)
Mg	0·95	300	(*168*)
Al	0·97	300	(*168*)
	2·4	400	(*167*)
K	0·8		(*169*)
Ca	4·95	520	(*167*)
Fe	1·0	300	(*168*)
	1·27	400	(*167*)
Ni	1·3	600	(*168*)
Cu	1·32	240	(*168*)
	1·27	600	(*167*)
Rb	0·81		(*169*)
Cb	1·17	400	(*167*)
Mo	1·25	375	(*168*)
Pd	1·27	250	(*168*)

TABLE 4.8 *Coefficients of Secondary Emission—contd.*

Surface	Maximum Value of Coefficient of Sec. Emission $K_{max.}$	Volts	Reference
Metals:			
Ag	0·93	250	(*168*)
	1·47	800	(*167*)
Cs	0·72	400	(*168*)
Ba	0·83	400	(*168*)
	2·72	530	(*167*)
Ta	2·2	380	(*168*)
	1·3	625	(*167*)
W	1·33	625	(*167*)
Pt	1·01	250	(*168*)
	1·52	1000	(*167*)
Au	0·14	500	(*168*)
	1·45	780	(*167*)
Th	1·14	800	(*168*)
Non-metals :			
C (lampblack)	0·6–1·0		(*167*)
C (Aquadag)	1·2	200	(*167*)
Si	1·63	380	(*167*)
Complex Surfaces :			
Be (thin) on Mo	2·5	500	(*168*)
Be (thick) on Mo	1·6	600	(*168*)
$Cs–Cs_2O$ on Ag	8·5–11·0	600	(*167, 169*)
on Mg	6·8– 7·5	700	(*167*)
on Ta	4·1– 5·5	600	(*167*)
on Ni	4·6– 5·2	550	(*167*)
on W	3·8– 3·9	600	(*167*)
on Mo	2·5– 3·1	500	(*167*)
on Fe	1·9– 2·7	500	(*167*)
on Au	2·3	600	(*167*)
$Rb-Rb_2O$ on Ag	5·5	800	(*2522*)
$Rb-Rb_2O$ on Ag	5·75	700	(*167*)
$K-K_2O$ on Ag	2·7	600	(*2522*)
$K-K_2O$ on Ag	2·5	600	(*167*)
Cs_3Sb on Ag	8·0	500	(*2522*)
MgO	3·9		(*2522*)
BaO	4·8		(*2522*)
LiF	5·6		(*2522*)
KCl	7·5		(*2522*)
CsCl	6·5		(*2522*)
Alloys:			
Cu-Be (2%)	1·95	400	(*2522*)
Ag-Ca (2%)	4·5	360	(*2522*)
Ag-Al (2%)	2·8	560	(*2522*)

TABLE 4.8 *Coefficients of Secondary Emission—contd.*

Surface	Maximum Value of Coefficient of Sec. Emission $K_{max.}$	Volts	Reference
Alloys (oxidized):			
Ag-Mg (2%)	9·8	500	*(2522)*
Cu-Be (2%)	3·5–5·5	500–700	*(2522)*
Ni-Be (2%)	12·3	700	*(2522)*
Ag-Be (2%)	4·5	500	*(2522)*

The dark current in a photomultiplier is a fundamental limiting characteristic. The dark current arises from thermionic emission at room temperature and the magnitude of the dark current follows Richardson's equation. The number of "dark" electrons emitted at room temperature from a photocathode vary considerably from cathode to cathode and with the material used. A value indicating the average order of magnitude is 10^{10} electrons/sec/cm^2 which is much more than the number of secondary electrons produced by a single incident photon. The detection of individual photons is thus impossible, unless cooling is used to reduce the background or noise electrons to just a few "dark" electrons per minute. Other suggestions than cooling for this purpose have been made by various investigators (*2577*, *2578*, *2579*, *2580*, *2581*, *2582*). (See Section 4.54.)

Bibliography References: *(1161, 1390, 1548, 1552, 1560, 1562, 1563, 1564, 1591, 1592 2576)*

DATA FOR THE DESIGNER

4.20. Electromagnetic Spectrum Chart

In the appendix, Chart II, the electromagnetic spectrum is shown from 1000 to 14500 A.U. The characteristic data of photosensitors, radiators, filters, fluorescent materials, photographic emulsions of different makes ; the dominant wavelengths of a Planckian Radiator at different temperatures, long-wave thresholds, quantum voltages, and equivalent volts are shown together with the Fraunhofer lines for reference. The scale of the spectrum is measured in frequencies, wavenumbers, and wavelengths, respectively ; the main colour regions are

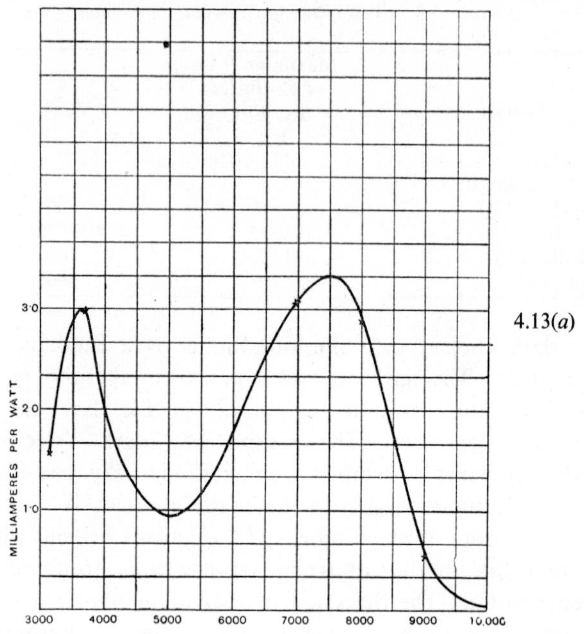

4.13(*a*)

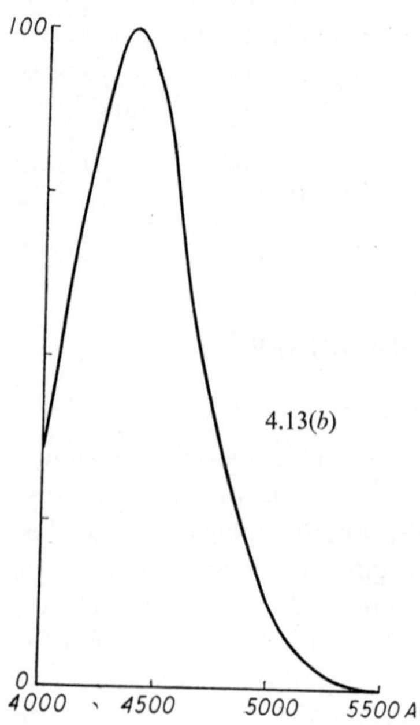

4.13(*b*)

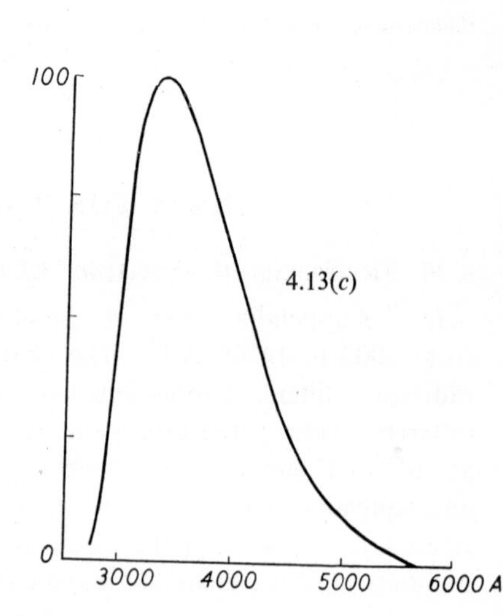

4.13(*c*)

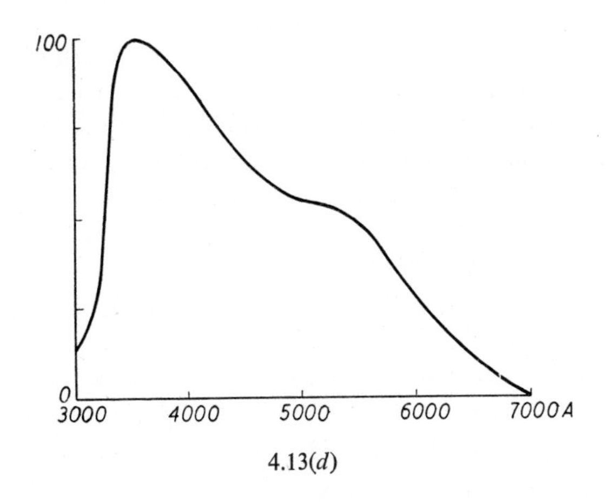

4.13(d)

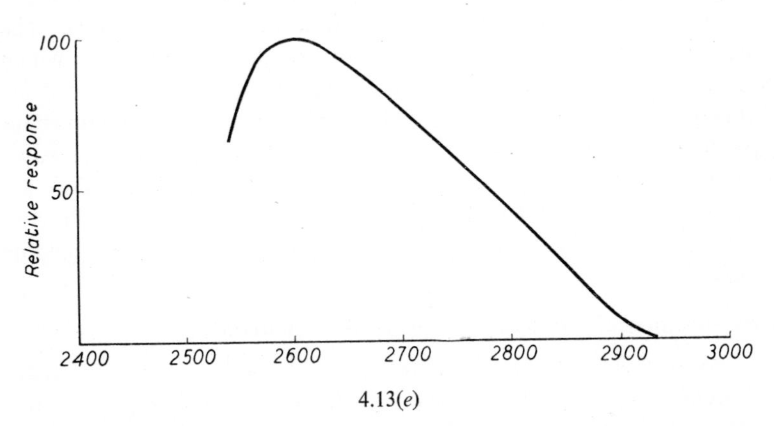

4.13(e)

Fig. 4.13. Spectral sensitivity curves of Osram photo-cells (*General Electric*). (a) Type CMV6; (b) Type KG7; (c) Type UNG7. (d) Type KMV6; (e) Type UDG7.

also given. All these data are tabulated in such a way that the engineer can co-ordinate at a glance all the necessary elements for any desired range of the spectrum within the above limits which, it is suggested, adequately cover the range of industrial applications. The spectral luminosity, i.e., the spectral range within which the human eye perceives " colours ", extends from 3800 to 7600 A.U. (conventional limits). The maximum relative photopic sensitivity is located at 5550 A.U., and the maximum relative scotopic sensitivity at 5130 A.U.

Bibliography Reference : (2192)

4.21. Relative Spectral Sensitivity

The diagrams in Figs. 4.14—4.16 show the relative spectral sensitivity of various types of photosensitors. These diagrams are not a measure of the " absolute " sensitivity and must not be compared with one another without paying heed to the fact that the 100% marks are arbitrary units, each maximum having been made to read 100%.

4.22. Absolute Spectral Sensitivity

The absolute response to incident radiation is expressed in $\mu A/Lm$ for energy between 3800 and 7600 A.U., and in $\mu A/\mu W$ for incident radiation in the other regions of the spectrum. The latter dimension is sometimes used uniformly over the whole range of radiations. The diagrams in Fig. 4.14 show the position of the wavelength at which the maximum occurs and give the absolute sensitivities of various types of photosensitor, thus supplying the answer to the important question as to the maximum response of a cell and its maximum wavelength. The more important characteristics of photosensitors are compiled in Table 4.9 and will be helpful to the engineer who has to decide upon the correct type of photosensitor to serve a definite purpose.

Classification of American Photo-Sensitive materials

The American Radio Manufacturers' Association and Electrical Manufacturers' Association have agreed on standard photo-sensitive surfaces to cover the range of photo-cells used in commercial practice. These surfaces are designated S1, S3, S4, S5, S6, S8 and their response characteristics are shown in Figs. 4.14–4.16.

The absolute sensitivity at any wavelength can be derived from the relative curves by multiplying the relative ordinate at a certain wavelength with the absolute sensitivity as listed in Table 4.9.

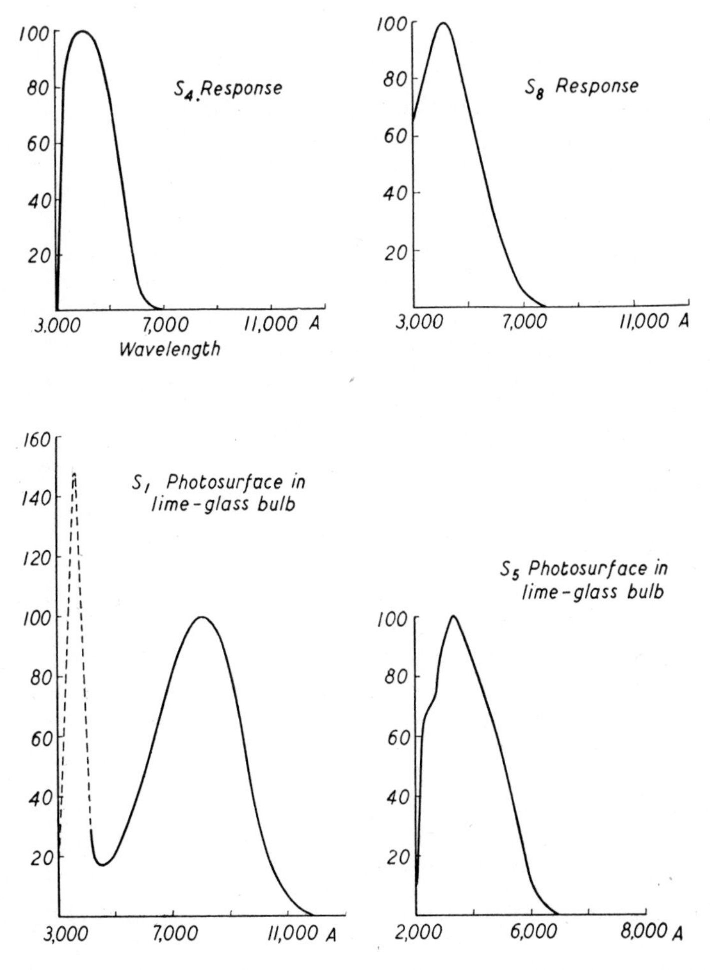

Fig. 4.14. Relative spectral energy curves of four types of photocathode (*RCA*).

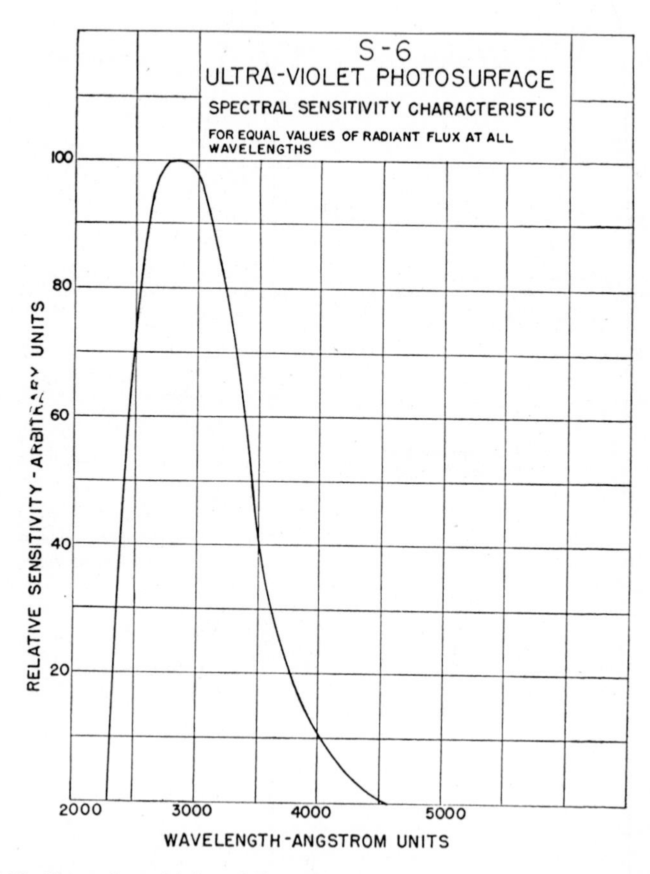

Fig. 4.15. Spectral sensitivity of Type S6 cathode (ultra-violet) (*General Electric*).

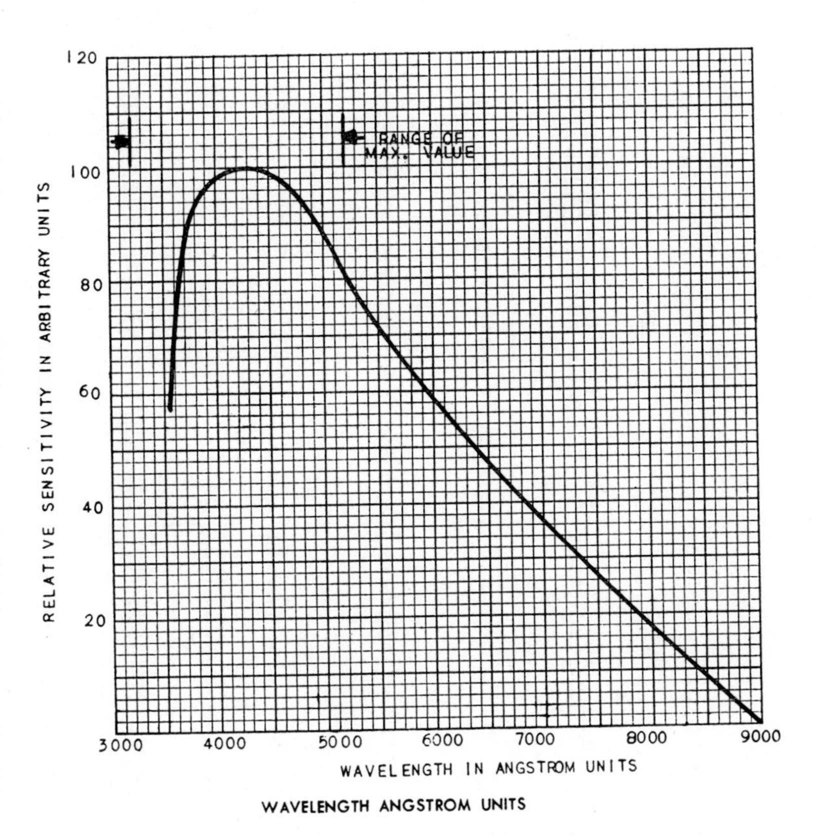

Fig. 4.16. Spectral sensitivity of Type S3 cathode (*General Electric*).

TABLE 4.9

Characteristic Data of Photosensitors

Type	Class	Code	Make	Cathode sensitivity	Cathode projected area cm²	sq. in.	Anode Volts max.	Cathode Current max. μA
Photo-electric	Vacuum	31	1	A, S	1·0	0·16	100	20
,,	,,	32	1	A, B, S	two windows, 20 mm.	diam.	100	20
,,	,,	36	1	A	20·0	3·1	200	20
					twin-	anode		
,,	,,	40	1	A,S	2·0	0·31	100	15
,,	,,	38	1	A	10·0	1·55	100	15
				quartz envelope				
,,	,,	PE–8	2	S_1	6·4	0·98	250	20
,,	,,	CMV6	3	S_1	9·6	1·5	150	15
,,	,,	KMV6	3	K–Ag_2O	9·6	1·5	250	15
,,	,,	PJ22	8	S_1	5·8	0·9	200	20
,,	,,	GL441	8	S_4	5·8	0·9	200	90
,,	,,	WL789	9	Pt	6·5	1·0	500	
,,	,,	WL734	9	S_1	7·1	1·1	500	20
,,	,,	WL767	9	Zr	8·4	1·33	500	
,,	,,	WL773	9	Th	8·4	1·33	500	
,,	,,	WL775	9	Ta	8·4	1·33	500	
,,	,,	1P42	10	S_4	0·18	0·028	180	1·5
,,	,,	917	10	S_1	5·8	0·9	500	30
,,	,,	919	10	S_1	5·8	0·9	500	30
,,	,,	922	10	S_1	2·5	0·4	500	15
,,	,,	925	10	S_1	2·6	0·42	250	15
,,	,,	926	10	S_3	2·6	0·42	500	15
,,	,,	1P39/929	10	S_4	2·6	0·42	250	20
,,	,,	934	10	S_4	2·6	0·42	250	12
,,	,,	935	10	S_5	5·8	0·9	250	30
,,	,,	5652	10	S_4	1·3	0·2	250	12
,,	,,	5653	10	S_4	3·2	0·5	250	20
,,	,,	20AV	11	S_4	11·0	1·7	150	10
,,	,,	20CV	11	S_1	6·7	1·05	250	20
,,	,,	57CV	11	S_1	4·5	0·69	150	10
,,	,,	58CV	11	S_1	1·1	0·17	100	3
,,	,,	90AV	11	S_4	4·0	0·62	100	5
,,	,,	90CV	11	S_1	3·0	0·47	100	10
,,	Gas-filled	13	1	B, S	4·0	0·62	marked	on cell
,,		16	1	S	6·0	0·93	160	20
,,	,,	18	1	S	12·0	1·86	110	20
,,	,,	41	1	S	1·5	0·23	110	20
,,	,,	PE–7B	2	S_1	6·4	0·98	90	20
,,	,,	UDG7	3	Cd	3·2	0·5	90	
,,	,,	UNG7	3	Na	3·2	0·5	90	
,,	,,	CMG8	3	S_1	7·4	1·15	90	
,,	,,	KG7	3	KH	10·0	1·55	250	
,,	,,	PJ23	8	S_1	5·8	0·9	100	90
,,	,,	GL-1P29/FJ401	8	S_3	5·8	0·9	100	135
,,	,,	WL735	9	S_1	7·1	1·1	90	20
,,	,,	1P29	10	S_3	5·8	0·9	100	20
,,	,,	1P37	10	S_4	4·9	0·8	100	20
,,	,,	1P41	10	S_1	1·9	0·3	90	5
,,	,,	868	10	S_1	5·8	0·9	100	20
,,	,,	918	10	S_1	5·8	0·9	90	20
,,	,,	Twin–920	10	S_1	2·0	0·31	90	6
					per	unit		
,,	,,	921	10	S_1	2·5	0·4	90	10
,,	,,	927	10	S_1	2·1	0·35	90	6
,,	,,	928	10	S_1	4·1	0·64	90	10
,,	,,	1P40/930	10	S_1	3·8	0·6	90	20
,,	,,	5581	10	S_4	3·8	0·6	100	10
,,	,,	5582	10	S_4	1·9	0·3	100	10
,,	,,	5583	10	S_4	1·9	0·3	100	10
,,	,,	Twin-5584	10	S_4	2·0	0·32	100	10
					per	unit		
,,	,,	20CG	11	S_1	6·7	1·05	90	5
,,	,,	51CG	11	S_1	8·0	1·25	90	5
,,	,,	52CG	11	S_1	4·6	0·71	90	3
,,	,,	55CG	11	S_1	2·2	0·34	90	2
,,	,,	56CG	11	S_1	8·0	1·25	90	5
,,	,,	58CG	11	S_1	1·1	0·17	90	1·5
,,	,,	90CG	11	S_1	3·0	0·47	90	2
,,	,,	90AG	11	S_4	4·0	0·62	90	2·5

TABLE 4.9

Characteristic Data of Photosensitors—contd.

Internal Dark Resistance: ohms	Average Sensitivity µA/Lm	Light Source at °K	Max. Ambient Temperature °C	Spectral Sensitivity Range A.U.	Spectral Sensitivity Peak A.U.
In the order of magnitude of 10^9 and higher		2600			
		2600			
		2600			
		2600			
		2600			
	23	2700			
	15	2848			
	2	2360		2500–7000	3500
	14	2848	100		
	45	2848	50		
				–2100	< 1700
	15	2870			
	0·02			2000–3150	2350
	0·1			2000–3675	2550
				2000–3000	2400
	25	2870	75		
	150	2870	100		
	20	2870	100		
	20	2870	100		
	20	2870	100		
	6·5	2870	100		
	45	2870	75		
	30	2870	75		
	30	2870	75		
	45	2870	75		
	45	2870	75		
	45	2700	70		
	25	2700	100		
	25	2700	100		
	15	2700	100		
	45	2700	70		
	20	2700	100		
In the order of magnitude of 10^9 and higher		2600			
	150 min.	2600			
	100 min.	2600			
	60 min.	2600			
	20	2700			
	< 0·1			2500–2950	2600
				3000–5000	3230
	130	2848			
	35	2848		3800–5500	4400
	90	2870	100		
		2870	100		
	50	2870			
	40	2870	100		
	135	2870	75		
	90	2870	100		
	90	2870	100		
	150	2870			
	100	2870			
	135	2870			
	125	2870	100		
	65	2870	100		
	135	8270	100		
	135	2870	75		
	120	2870	75		
	135	2870	75		
	120	2870	75		
	150	2700	100		
	150	2700	100		
	125	2700	100		
	125	2700	100		
	150	2700	100		
	85	2700	100		
	125	2700	100		
	200	2700	70		

TABLE 4.9

Characteristic Data of Photosensitors—contd.

Type	Class	Code	Make	Cathode sensitivity	Cathode projected area cm^2	Cathode projected area sq. in.	Anode Volts max.	Cathode Current max. μA
								short circuit current μA/Lm
Photo-e.m.f.	Backwall	PA-1	6	CU_2O–Cu	5·0	0·78	nil	15
,,	Frontwall	PA-2	6	Cu_2O–Cu(Au)*	5·0	0·78	nil	150
,,	,,	1	3	Cu_2O–Cu(Au)*	4·3	0·67	nil	
,,	,,	2	3	Cu_2O–Cu(Au)*	5·4	0·84	nil	
,,	,,	Photronic	7	Se–Fe(Ag)*	13·0	2·0	nil	450
,,	,,	EEL	4	Se–Fe(Ag)*	27·3 max.	4·2	1·5	
,,	,,	EEL–M1	4	Se–Fe(Ag)*				
								Opt. Polarizing current at 20° C.
Light-sensitive Resistor			5	Se	10, max.	1·55	1000	
		C_1	2	PbS	2(10×1)			100–150μA
		C_2	2	PbS	(10×1)			100–150μA
		M_1	2	PbS	10×1			100–150μA
		M_2	2	PbS	5×5			100–150μA
								Cathode Current max. μA
For photometric work the following photo-cells and valves are available :								
photo-cells : vacuum		57CV	11		2×4·5	2×0·7	100	2×5
		39	1	A, B, S in glass A also in quartz	10·0	1·55	100	15
electrometer valves : triode		ET1	3					
		ET3 (sub-miniature)	3					
pentode		ME–1400	11	Va = 45V,	Vh = 4·5V ± 5%,			i_h = 0·16 A.
photometric unit :			3					

*The chemical symbol in brackets, thus (Au), (Ag), gives the chemical composition of the respective translucent film deposited on the photocathode.

List of Makers;

(1) Cinema-Television, Ltd.
(2) British Thomson-Houston Co., Ltd.
(3) General Electric Company, Ltd. (OSRAM).
(4) Evans Electroselenium, Ltd.
(5) Radiovisor Parent, Ltd.
(6) Westinghouse Brake & Signal Co., Ltd.
(7) Weston Electrical Instrument Co., Ltd.
(8) General Electric Co. (U.S.A.).
(9) Westinghouse Electric Corporation.
(10) Radio Corporation of America.
(11) Mullard, Ltd.
(12) Electric & Musical Industries, Ltd.
(13) Edison Swan Electric Co., Ltd. (MAZDA).

NOTE : The Continental Electric Company (U.S.A.) make a type CE-10 with four separate cathodes and one common anode.

Photo-electric cells made by Cinema-Television, Ltd. (CINTEL) are classified as

Sensitivity group S	20–40 μA/Lm	type S_1
,, ,, A	20–50 μA/Lm	3000–7000 A.U
,, ,, B	15–40 μA/Lm	3000–7600 A.U

TABLE 4.9

Characteristic Data of Photosensitors—contd.

Internal Dark Resistance: ohms	Average Sensitivity μA/Lm	Light Source at °K	Max. Ambient Temperature °C	Spectral Sensitivity Range A.U.	Peak A.U.
1800	10	2750		5900–17000	6350
1000	100	2750		4550– 6600	5650
		2848		3500– 7200	5650
		2848		3500– 7200	5650
6000	120	3000		2500– 8500	5800
	550	2848		3000– 8000	5550
	550	2848		3000– 8000	5550
10^7		2848		3500– 8000	5800
				at 20° C. 3000 to 27000	22000

TABLE 4.10

Quantum Theoretical Data of Photosensitors

Code	Actual photo-electric yield Σ_a $\mu A/\mu W \times 10^{-4}$	at $\lambda_{max.}$ A.U.	Quantum yield q electrons per photon	Quantum efficiency 1/q photons per electron	Ideal photo-electric yield Σ_i $\mu A/\mu W \times 10^{-4}$
PA–1	13·6	6350	0·002654615	376·6937	5123·033
PA–2	700	5650	0·1535664	6·511843	4558·29
Photronic	460	5800	0·0983052	10·1724006	4679·3066
CMV6	33	7500	0·0054538	183·3585	6050·828
KG7	55	4400	0·01549375	64·542164	3549·9
KMV6	35	3500	0·012395	80·6777	2823·719
RCA868	50	7500	0·008263334	121·01659	6050·828
917	20	8000	0·00309875	322·71082	6454·2165
918	100	8000	0·01549375	64·542164	6454·2165
919	20	8000	0·00309875	322·71082	6454·2165
920	65	7500	0·010742303	93·089653	6050·828
921	90	8000	0·013944308	71·713502	6454·2165
922	20	8000	0·00309875	322·71082	6454·2165
925	15	7500	0·0024790	403·3886	6050·828
926	20	4400	0·00563409	177·49095	3549·9
927	50	7500	0·008263334	121·01659	6050·828
928	60	7500	0·0099160	100·84715	6050·828
1P39/929	400	3750	0·1322134	7·5635345	3025·414
1P40/930	90	8000	0·013944308	71·713502	6454·2165
934	300	3750	0·099160	10·084715	3025·414
935	200	3750	0·0661067	15·1370790	3025·414
1P29	100	4400	0·02817045	35·49819	3549·9
WL734	15	7500	0·0024790	403·3886	6050·828
WL735	60	7500	0·0099160	100·84715	6050·828
GL-1P29/ FJ401	100	4000	0·0309875	32·27108	3234·547
GL441	400	3750	0·1322134	7·5635345	3025·414
PJ22	20	7500	0·003305333	302·5415	6050·828
PJ23	103	7500	0·01702246	58·7459	6050·828

In Table 4.10 some data of quantum theoretical interest are given for both English and American photosensitors. The photo-electric yield is taken from manufacturers' lists the quantum yield q is calculated according to the formula derived in a previous section of this chapter, viz. $q = 12395\sigma_{max.}/\lambda_{max.}$; the quantum efficiency is the reciprocal of q and gives the number of photons necessary to free one electron. The ideal photo-electric yield is calculated on the assumption that each incident photon liberates one electron. From this definition $\Sigma = \frac{1}{2}.\sigma' = \lambda/12395$. The ideal photo-electric yield is directly proportional to the wavelength of maximum sensitivity and the ratio of the ideal to the actual photo-electric yield is the quantum efficiency.

In Table 4.11 the relevant data of Multiplier Photo-cells are listed. Cells are available for measuring radiation in the far ultra-violet region (*2519*). Maximum sensitivity is at 3400 A.U. At 1800 A.U. the sensitivity of the cathode is reduced to one third of the maximum sensitivity.

4.23. Functional Limitations

There are certain limitations in the use of photo-electric cells. These limitations vary with the type of cell and nearly all are of a functional character. The structural limitations are not mentioned here as they are of little interest to the industrial engineer. The following Table 4.12 is a general comparison of merit.

4.24. Key to Designing a Photo-electric Installation

Table 4.13 is a skeleton guide for the rapid appraisal of the main features of a suggested installation.

TABLE 4.11

Characteristic Data of Photo-multiplier Cells

Code	Make	Cathode sensitivity	Cathode projected area sq. cm.	Cathode projected area sq. in.	Collector max. volts	max. voltage between last dynode and anode	Voltage per stage		Peak anode current μA	Current amplification		Average sensitivity Amp/Lm		Maximum sensitivity A.U.	Number of stages	Maximum ambient temperature °C.
931–A	10	S–4	1·6	0·25	1250	250	75	100	10000	150000	1000000	1·5	10·0	4000	9	75
1P–28	10		1·6	0·25	1250	250	75	100	2500	37500	250000	0·75	5·0	3400	9	75
1P–21	8	S–4	1·6	0·25	1250	250	75	100	1	300000	2000000	13	80	3750	9	75
1P–22	10	S–8	1·6	0·25	1250	250	75	100	10000	30000	200000	0·09	0·6	4200	9	50
CWS–24	3	S–1	13	2·2	800	300			20	6 to 8		200 μA/1m		3750 ;	1	
5311	12	S–1	5	0·8	1700	200	160			10000000				7500		
M20	1	A, B, S	20	3·1	1500	100	100		1000	1000 to 5000				4700	11	50
27M3	13	S–4	2	0·3	950	150	100		100	1000000		10		4000	9	50

TABLE 4.12
Comparative Data

Type and Class of Photosensitor	Advantages	Disadvantages	Typical Applications
Photo-electric Vacuum Cell	large range of various spectral sensitivities ; stability ; static response identical with dynamic response ; linearity of response ; saturation characteristic ; high impedance ;	very small output ; electronic amplification necessary ; relatively high operating potential required ; spectral sensitivity differs greatly from colour response of the standard human eye ; cell must be very close to the amplifier ;	Measurement of optical properties ; Spectrophotometry
Photo-electric Gas-filled Cell	large range of various spectral sensitivities ; stability ; time lag smaller than 10^{-5} sec. good dynamic response ; linearity of response ; high impedance ; relatively low operating potential required ;	very small output ; electronic amplification necessary ; danger of glow discharge ; spectral sensitivity differs from the colour response of the standard human eye ;	Industrial applications ; Counting ; Control of processes ; Safety devices ;
Photo-e.m.f. Cell	no external source of voltage required ; no amplification necessary ; spectral sensitivity sometimes identical with colour response of standard human eye ; relatively stable ; large output ; cells can be connected in parallel or series ; cell may be connected with the relay by a relatively long cable ; linearity of response ;	electronic amplification rather difficult and complicated with the ordinary type cell ; relatively poor dynamic response depending on make and individual cell ; ultra - high sensitive electromagnetic relays must be used for direct operation ; the spectral sensitivity does not extend into the middle ultra-violet; temperature coefficient;	Light meter ; Safety devices ; High temperature measurement ; Control of processes ; Conversion of radiant into electric energy ;
Light-sensitive Resistor	high sensitivity to red and infra-red ; relatively large output ; external voltages up to 1000 volts permissible ; handles rather large currents ; maximum of spectral sensitivity in the red or near infra-red where the human eye is insensitive.	temperature coefficient; not generally very stable ; need for external potential ; dark current ; poor dynamic response.	simple relay switching.

TABLE 4.13

(1) Radiant Energy.	type :	luminous	non-selective, i.e., white ; selective, i.e., coloured ;	
		non-luminous	ultra-violet ; infra-red ; X-rays ;	
	modulation :	none		
		mains frequency		
		artificial	mechanical ; electronic ;	
	reflexion :	none		
		mirrors	total length of rays ; number of reflexions ;	
		spectral distribution	non-selective, i.e., white ; selective, i.e., coloured;	
(2) Source of Radiant Energy	incandescent (tungsten) filament		high thermal inertia ; low thermal inertia ; mains voltage operation ; low voltage operation ;	
	electric discharge		gas discharge	neon helium argon
			vapour discharge	sodium mercury fluorescent types
	stroboscopic effect		desirable	energy source not coated ;
			undesirable	phosphorescent lamps fluorescent lamps 90° phase shift connexion;
(3) Properties of the Object.	optical		achromatic	transparent translucent opaque
			chromatic	transparent translucent opaque
	physical			shape size geometrical dimensions temperature
				condition of surface: hot cold wet sticky
				state of aggregation: solid liquid gas

(4) Critical Changes causing Action.	primary	temperature colour transparency turbidity		
	secondary	measuring indicator	relative absolute	
		indicating device	chemical physical mechanical optical thermal	
(5) General Conditions.	atmosphere	temperature damp dust fumes (corrosive) fog sunshine		
	equipment	indoors outdoors watertight gastight dustproof		
	operation	intermittent		
		continuous	8 hours shift 16 hours shift 24 hours shift	
(6) Photo-electric Cell.	mounting	inside relay housing in separate scanner head		
	type	photo-electric	vacuum	primary emission secondary emission
			gas-filled	
		photo-e.m.f.	cuprous-oxide	
			selenium-iron	single multiple
			others	
		light-resistor	thallous sulphide selenium lead sulphide others	
	spectral sensitivity	range	ultra-violet luminous infra-red	
	amplification	none		
		electromagnetic		
		electronic valve	cold-cathode hot-cathode vacuous gas-filled vapour-filled	

(7) Accessories.	optical	lens filter baffle tube focus diaphragm fluorescent screen fluorescent markers	
	chemical	indicators	
	mechanical	floats levers targets (riders)	
	electrical	relay or contactor	holding current releasing current slug type
		contacts	number make or break load inductive load shockproof in vacuo
(8) Recording.	ink	mechanical electronic	
	photographic	direct cathode-ray tube	
	electrical	metallized paper chemically-treated paper	
(9) Action	of photo-electric circuit	forward reverse	
	of photo-relay	positive negative	
(10) Power Supply	Voltage	alternating current rectified a.c. direct current	
	Frequency	direct current 50 c/s medium frequency high frequency	
	Network	single phase two phase (earthed) three phase (earthed)	

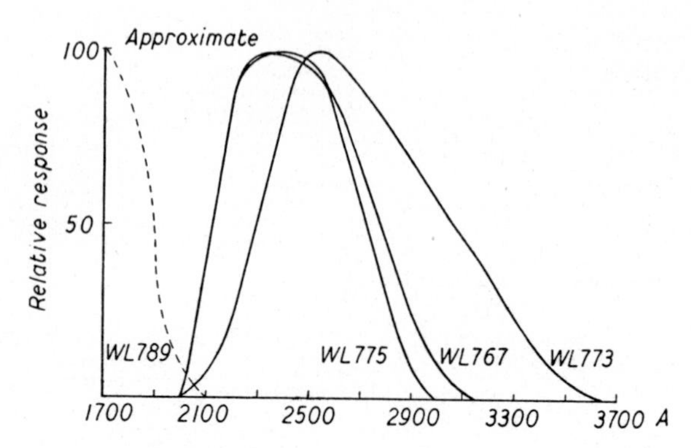

Fig. 4.17. Spectral sensitivity of four ultra-violet photo-cells (*Westinghouse Co., U.S.A.*).

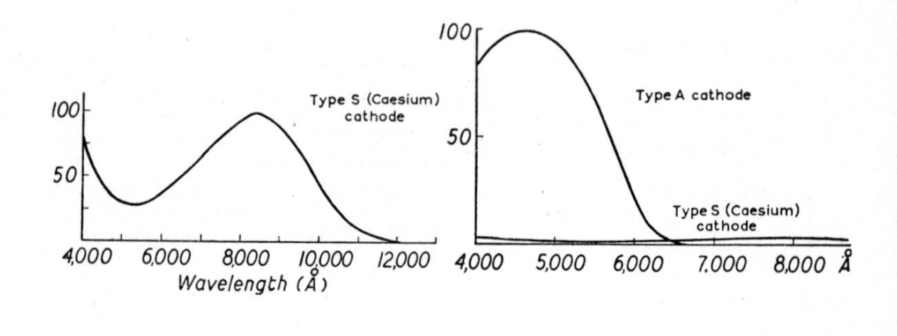

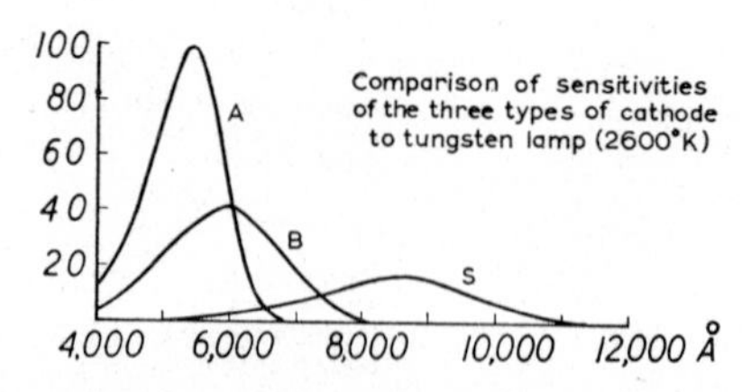

Fig. 4.18. Spectral sensitivity curves of two photo-cathodes made by Cinema-Television Ltd.: A = Antimony-caesium (blue sensitive); B = approximate sensitivity of the eye; S = Infra-red sensitive cathode.

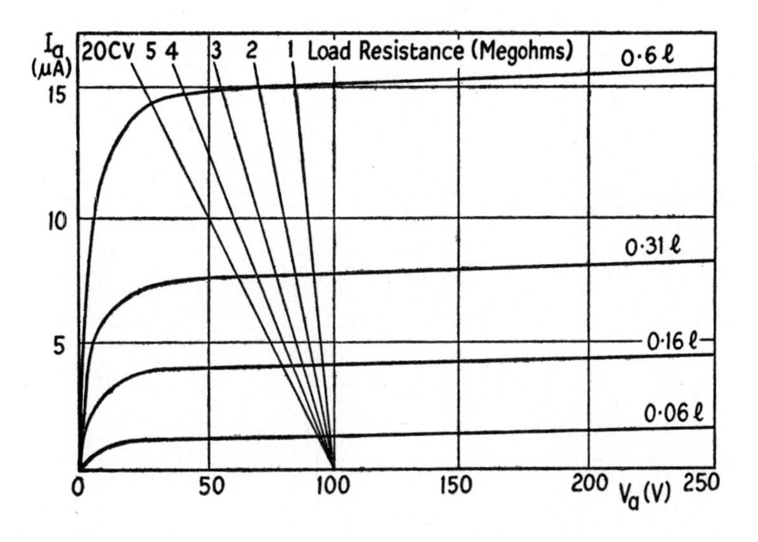

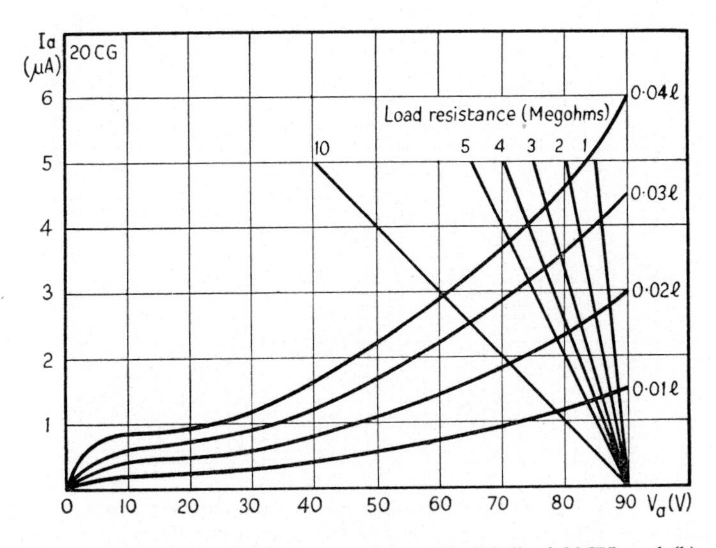

Fig. 4.19. Characteristics of (a) vacuum photo-cells (Mullard 20CV) and (b) gas-filled photo-cells (Mullard 20CG).

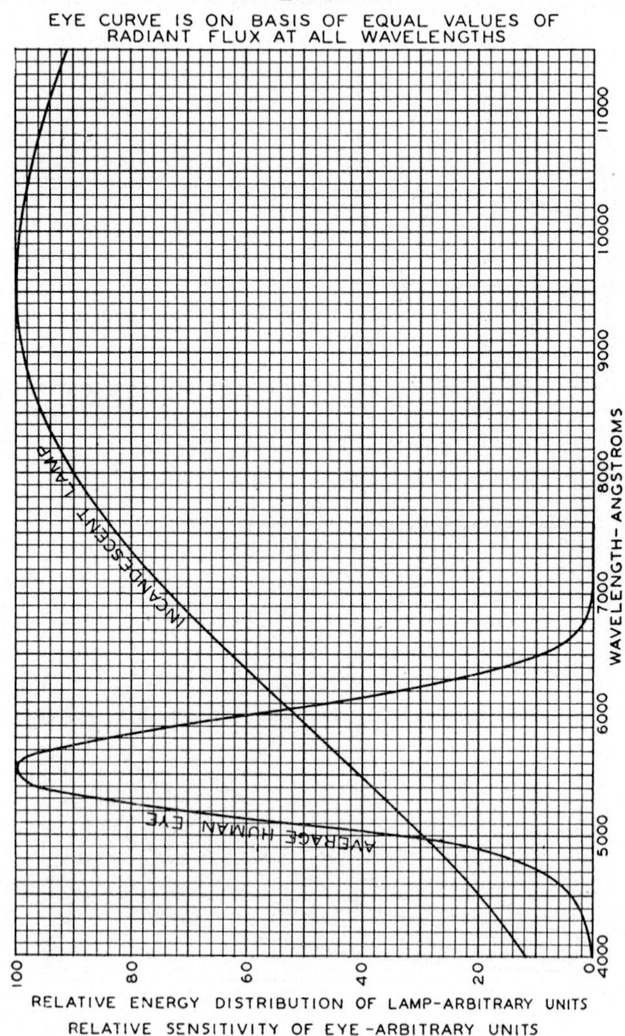

Fig. 4.20. Spectral characteristic of the human eye and of a tungsten lamp at colour temperature 2870° K.—(*RCA*).

4.25. Photo-electric Cells

A marked increase in effective response to a given incident radiation is obtained through the introduction of an inert gas into the vacuous cell. Fig. 4.21 gives a schematic representation of the events taking place in a gas-filled photo-electric cell after a photon *P* of energy $h\nu$ has hit the cathode *C* and an electron, now called photo-electron *PE*, has been released, if the conditions laid down in section 4.9, have been satisfied. The photo-electron of high velocity, in hitting an atom *A*, knocks out an electron *E* from the gas atom which is split into negative free electrons *E* and positive ions *I*. The photo-electrons *PE* as well as the electrons *E* are drawn towards the positive anode *An* while the

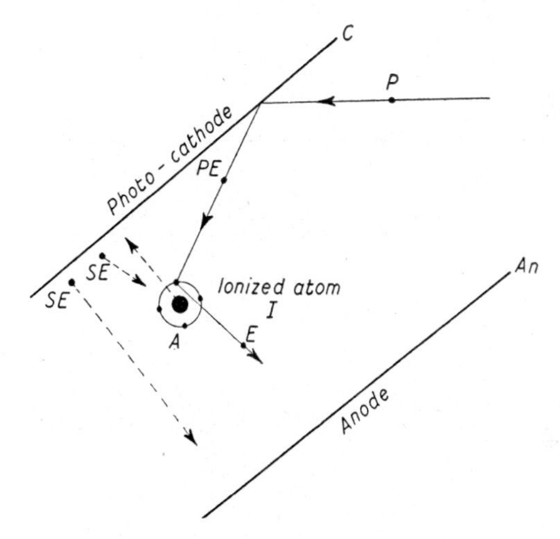

Fig. 4.21. Illustrating action inside a gas-filled photo-cell.

positive ion migrates towards the negative photo-cathode *C*. A cloud of ions collects parallel to the surface of the cathode *C*, exerting such a force that (secondary) electrons *SE* are emitted from the metallic surface, recombination now taking place. The positive ions are neutralized by the negative additional or secondary electrons and the rest of the secondary electrons which managed to avoid recombination are being drawn towards the anode *An*. The total photo-electric current relative to the original or primary photo-electric current *PE*, is increased several times by a factor *G* which is termed the " gas factor " and is never higher than 10. No increase in total current results from the impact of photons on a gas atom since the energy of luminous or long ultra-violet radiation is insufficient to split the gas atom. The first ionization potentials are relatively high, viz. :

TABLE 4.14

First Ionization Potentials of Gases

cf. Table 4.7

Gas	First Ionization Potential Volts
Xenon	12·1
Krypton	13·9
Argon	15·69
Neon	21·47
Helium	24·48

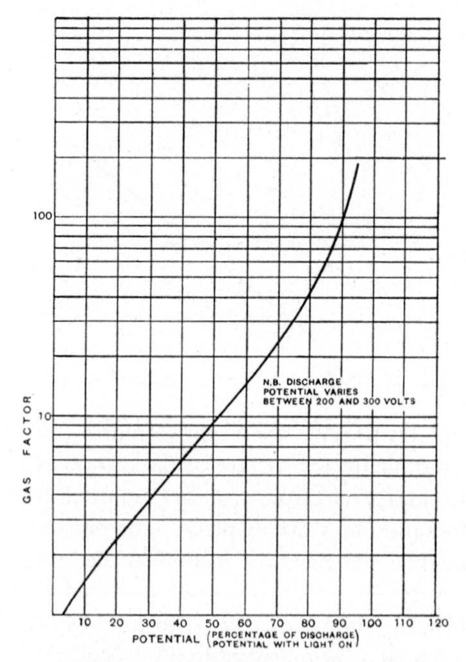

Fig. 4.22. Relation between applied voltage and gas factor.

The interdependence between applied voltage (as a function of the break-down voltage, see above) and gas factor is shown in Fig. 4.22.

In a gas-filled cell the ions, moving at much slower speeds than the electrons, require a time of the order of 10^{-5} sec. to reach the cathode (transit time). In specific cases the exact time is, of course, a function of the geometrical dimensions and the mechanical structure of the electrodes but on an average it will result in setting the limit of dynamic response at about 5000 to 6000 c/s (*181*). The curve approaches a limiting value (sparking potential) at which the cell breaks down by

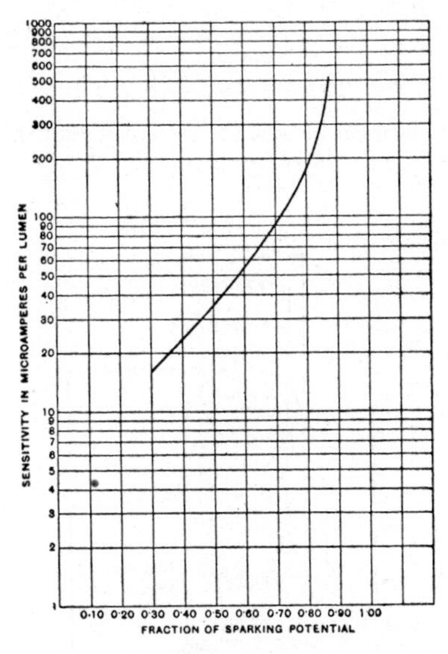

Fig. 4.23. Variation of sensitivity with anode voltage (gas-filled cell).

allowing an electric discharge to start which, once it has set in, cannot be controlled by stopping the initiating irradiation. This behaviour is in effect identical with that exhibited by thyratrons or ionotrons in D.C. networks and here, as with other gaseous discharge valves, the anode voltage must be drastically reduced or even totally removed in order to end the discharge which would destroy the photo-electric cell. If the photosensitors are used at or below the rated value as quoted in the manufacturers' lists there is no risk of causing a glow discharge. Fig. 4.23 gives an instance of how the sensitivity of a photo-electric cell varies with the anode voltage.

Bibliography References: (*471*, *575*, *1061*, *1153*, *1208*, *1212*, *1219*, *1220*, *1221*, *1234*, *1243*, *1588*, *1746*, *2343*, *2350*, *2351*, *2357*, *2361*, *2377*, *2381*)

4.26. Electrodes

Various types of photo-electric cell are marketed to suit either specific circuits or specific conditions of use. The cathode is usually semi-cylindrical or angular, thus making this type of photosensitor

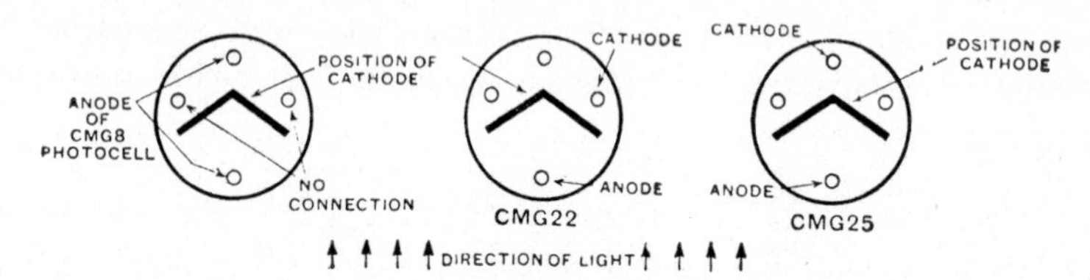

Fig. 4.24. Typical arrangement of unidirectional cathodes showing relation to the base connections.

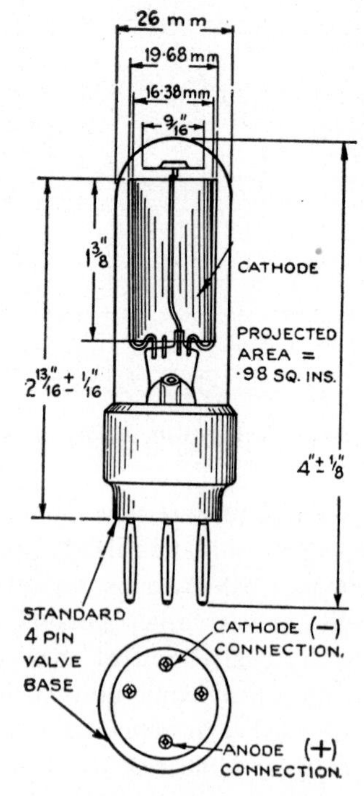

Fig. 4.25. Mazda unidirectional photo-cell PE-7B.

a uni-directional device, Figs. 4.24/4.25. Recently a new type has been developed, the non-directional photo-electric cell, as represented by the RCA type 928, Fig. 4.26, or by the Visitron type R85. These cells have a 360° pick-up and are extremely useful in circuits used in the control of artificial illumination. The end-type photo-cell, Fig. 4.27 is valuable in instruments designed to be operated by indirect irradiation, for instance, by reflexion. Sometimes an arrangement of two

Fig. 4.26. RCA Omnidirectional photo-cell type 928. (*left*)
Fig. 4.27. RCA End-on Photo-cell type 924. (*right*)

electrode systems in a common envelope is necessary to perform certain tasks. This type of tube is called a " twin " photo-cell, Fig. 4.28.

The anode of a photo-electric cell may have any shape which suits the particular purpose of collecting as many electrons as possible

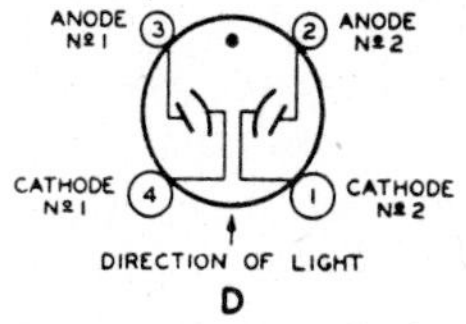

Fig. 4.28. Arrangement of electrodes in twin photo-cell.

without obstructing the incidence of the radiant energy. Common shapes are : rods, rectangular frames, perforated sheet, gauze, rings, spirals or helices. In the CMV6 and KMV6 photo-cell the cathode is a rectangular plate which is surrounded by a guard ring, i.e., a cylinder of wire mesh, Fig. 4.29. The question of an optimum size of the photo-cathode has been discussed by Wlérick (*2482*) who finds no proof of the existence of such a size, but finds that the thickness of the sensitive layer is of importance. The connexions to the anode and cathode are brought out either to the socket, or one to the socket and one to the top of the glass envelope. In two-cell circuits the cathode

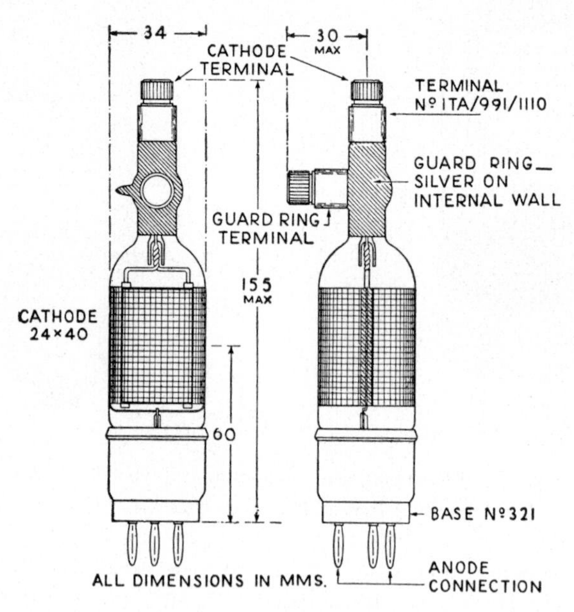

Fig. 4.29. Photo-cell with guard ring. (Type KMV6). (*The General Electric Co. Ltd.*)

of the one cell is connected to the anode of the other cell. In order to reduce leakage losses and to make connexions as short as possible RCA first have produced the electrically identical types 917 and 919, respectively, the only difference being the terminal arrangement. In the 917 type photo-cells the top cap is connected to the anode ; in the 919 types to the cathode. Fig. 4.30 shows a split (quadruple) cathode photo-cell with only one anode. Fig. 4.31 shows in outline some special types of photo-cell—midget, for side-view and end-view operation; a twin-cathode cell, and a twin-anode cell.

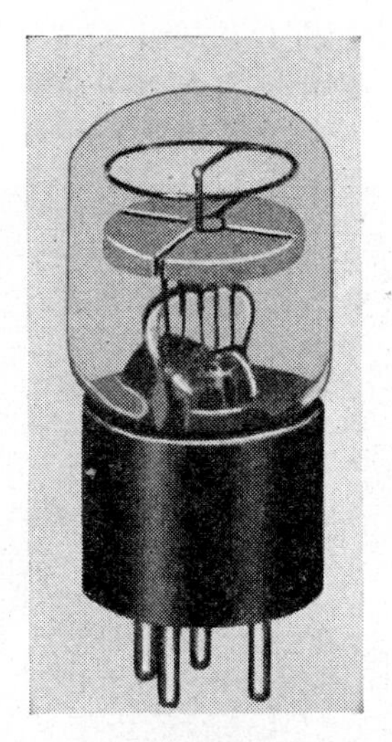

Fig. 4.30. CETRON Split-cathode Photo-cell. (*Continental Electric Corp., Ill.*).

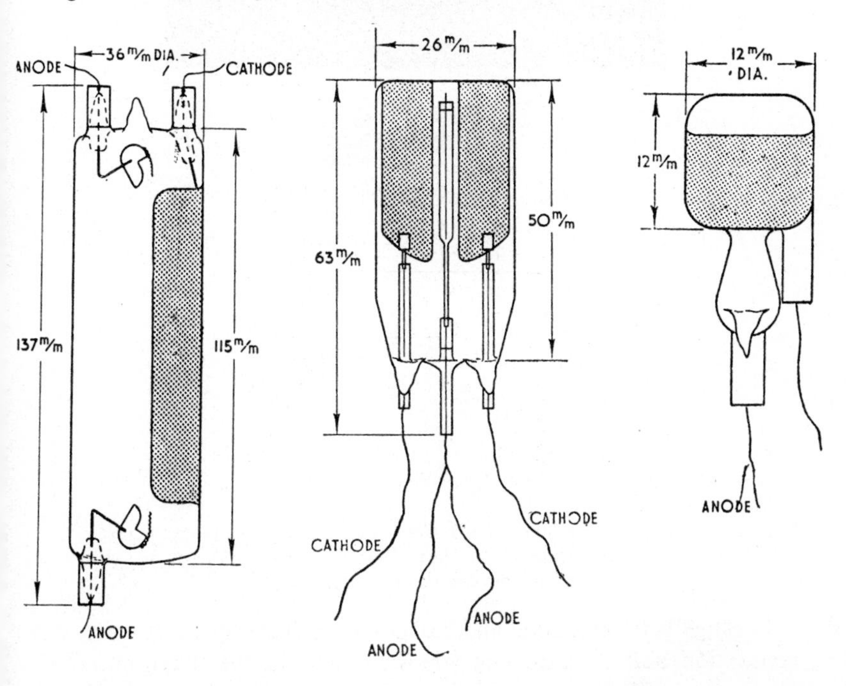

Fig. 4.31. Outline of Cinema-Television (CINTEL) twin-photo-cell: (a) two anodes, one cathode; (b) two cathodes, one anode; (c) midget photo-cell (12 mm × 12 mm).

A special photometric cell (Mullard 57CV) is shown in Fig. 4.32. This is of the vacuum type with a special double-sided cathode and a wire-cage anode.

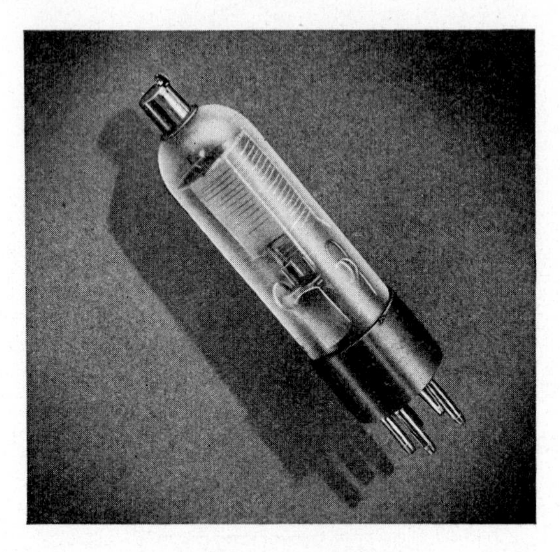

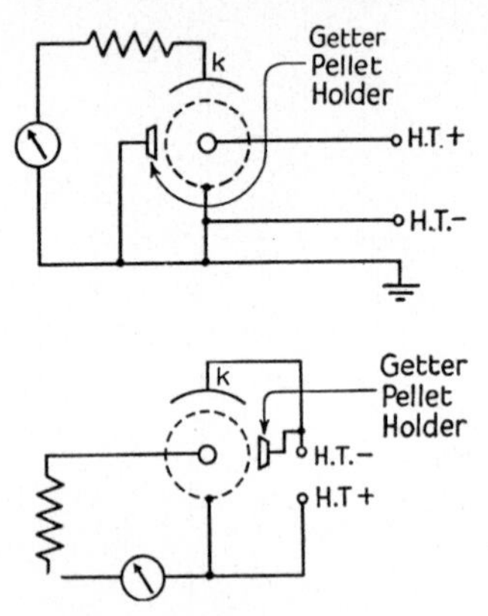

Fig. 4.32. Mullard 57CV Photometer Cell. This cell has maximum sensitivity to red and infra-red radiation and is primarily intended for photometric measurements in this end of the spectrum.

Leakage between anode and cathode is reduced by using a top cap connection and a guard-ring (shown dotted in the diagram). Two alternative methods of connecting the cell are shown, but the preferred connection is for the load to be in the cathode lead. The cell has a maximum sensitivity to red and infra-red radiation. Fig. 4.33 shows the RCA multiplier cell type 931A.

Fig. 4.33. RCA Multiplier Photo-cell type 931-A.

Bibliography References: (*525*, *526*, *1076*, *1113*, *1146*, *1352*, *1359*, *1360*, *1361*, *1553*, *1711*, *1712*, *1713*, *2271*).

4.27. Envelopes

The envelopes are usually of glass but since this material becomes opaque to the shorter ultra-violet radiation (<3100 A.U.), either quartz windows, (Fig. 4.34), are used to admit the shorter waves or, better still, the entire envelope is made from quartz. An interesting feature enabling a glass envelope to be made transparent in the region below 2000 A.U. is incorporated in the Westinghouse WL–789 photo-cell. The glass envelope has been blown into an extremely thin indrawn window of only a few microns in thickness, yet having a diameter of 1·125 inches. The influence of the optical characteristics of the envelope on the overall sensitivity of the cell is shown in Fig. 4.35. Glass is used in the luminous and infra-red, Corex-D and quartz in the ultra-violet range. A special HF-resistant glass has P_2O_5 as its major ingredient and is made by the American Optical Co. (***2455***).

Bibliography References : (*452*, *1985*).

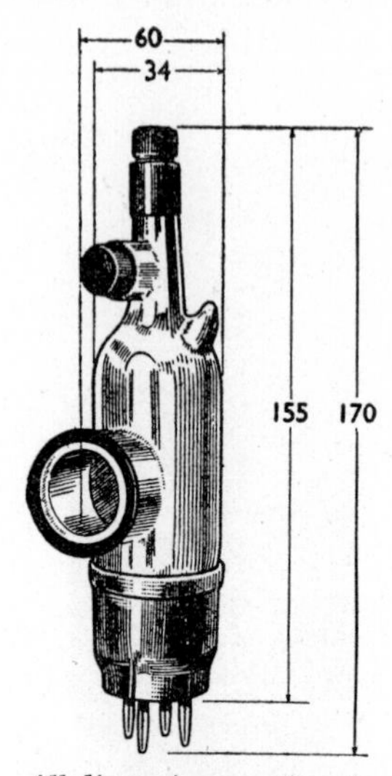

Fig. 4.34. Photo-cell with quartz window for ultra-violet measurement. (*The General Electric Co. Ltd.*)

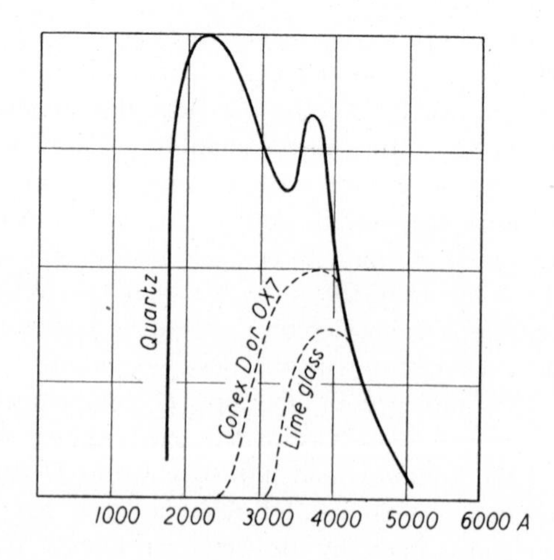

Fig. 4.35. Effect of various types of envelope on spectral characteristics of cell.

4.28 Cathodes

The cathode material is of primary importance as it determines the spectral characteristics of the photosensitor. According to the range of sensitivity in view, the materials may be sub-divided into three groups, viz. :

TABLE 4.15

Cathode Materials

Range of Spectral Sensitivity	Work function	Cathode Materials
ultra-violet	high (3)	Cd, U, Na, Th-Ni, Ce, Ta, Ti*-Ni, Pt, W-Ni, Zr, Ni, Mo, Zn ;
luminous	(3) medium (1. 5)	Cs-Mg, Sr, Ba, Cs-Cs_2O-Ag, Se-Fe, Cu_2O, K, Rb, Li, Na-Pt, K-Pt, Rb, Pt, Li-W ;
infra-red	low (1. 5)	Cs-Pt, BaO-Pt, Ba-Ag, Cs-Cs_2O-Ag.

* Titanium cathodes have a sharply defined long-wave threshold at 3160 A.U. $\pm$ 20 A.U. (*368*)

On rare occasions it becomes imperative to protect the cathode material, whose maximum of sensitivity is centred in one of the three groups as defined in Table 4.15, from the impact of radiant energy which belongs to another group. Such is the case with Tl_2S which is enclosed in a glass bulb not only to protect it from the chemical action of the oxygen in the air but also to be protected against the impact of blue or shorter radiation by making the envelope either of red glass or, when clear, coating it with red transparent lacquer.

A. Dresler (*283*) has shown in the instance of a selenium photosensitor how important it is to know the behaviour of the light-sensitive cell when under selective irradiation (*2410*). The sensitivity of the selenium photosensitor was found to change not only with the intensity but also with the spectral composition of the incident light. Red light from an incandescent light source (with red filter) causes the sensitivity to be reduced with increasing intensity (cf. 4.16). Blue light of an intensity of between 400 and 800 lux produces a straight characteristic or, sometimes, one which shows an increase in sensitivity for an increase in illumination. It has been noted that the spectral composition of the incident light is the more important the more the load resistance increases (*284*).

From among the cathode materials Cs has outstanding merits. A Sb–Cs cathode (*183, 184*) covers the range between 2000 and 6500 A.U., having the maximum sensitivity in the blue at about 4000 to 4600 A.U., Fig. 4.36.

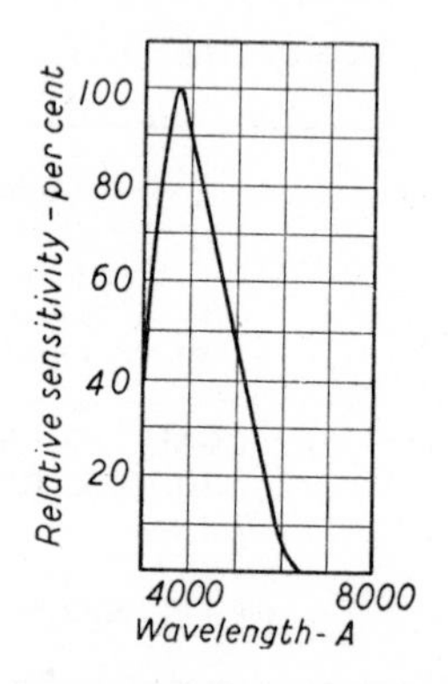

Fig. 4.36. Spectral characteristic of Antimony-Caesium cathode.

Photo-electric cells with transparent cathodes are manufactured by depositing a Cs or Sb–Cs film directly on the envelope without using a metallic support. The caesium film is sensitized by oxygen, not by hydrogen as is usual: the maximum effect is centred at about 4500 A.U. Semi-transparent Cs-Sb cathodes are described in the literature for instance in *Electronics* (*2531*). Li-Sb cathodes follow the general characteristics of the other alkali-antimony photocathodes with the exception that the properties of the Li-Sb cathode in the ultra-violet range differently from what might be expected according to the atomic weight of Li (*2532*). In photomultipliers, the thermionic emission of the cathode is of great importance due to the inherent amplification. In general, photosensitive layers of the S_4 type are more often used than S_1 cathodes. Schaetti and Baumgartner (*2533*) have investigated the case of the Li-Sb and Cs-Sb cathode and have found that the thermionic emission of the former is $4 \cdot 10^{-17}$ A while it is $2 \cdot 10^{-15}$ A for the latter. They have built a photomultiplier with a Li-Sb cathode which is of particular value in scintillation counters (cf. 23.14). With regard to Cs-Sb cathodes Schwetzoff and Robin (*2534*) have shown that if the sensitive layer is formed from pure materials and without the presence of oxygen, the maximum sensitivity occurs at 3550 A with a second smaller peak at 1600 A.U. The number and position of the spectral peaks is assumed to be dependent on possible compounds between the Cs and Sb, and on the presence of impurities in the materials. The same authors have also investigated other metal compounds in an atmosphere completely free from oxygen (*2535*) and find the following values:

layer	spectral sensitivity	maximum A.U.	longwave threshold A.U.
K-Sb	2·3 μA/Lm	3400	5500
Na-Sb	less	3000	4000
Cs-Sb	12 μA/Lm	3550	5500
Li-Sb		2300	

W. Veith (*2536*) has shown that the two metals Cs and Sb must not be considered a chemical compound or alloy, but semi-conductors (*2567; 2568*). This hypothesis is supported by the fact that, in the case of the Cs_3Sb layer each sensitivity maximum occurs at a conductivity minimum. The addition of a little oxygen extends the spectral sensitivity into the red, of more oxygen into the infra-red.

The photo-electric effect of alkali-germanium compounds is discussed by Schaetti and Baumgartner (*2537*).

The same authors have discussed the effects of gadolinium Ga, indium In, and thallium Tl alloyed with Cs (*2567; 2568*). The maximum sensitivity of all these alloys is in the near ultra-violet, while the longwave thresholds are 6000 A.U. for Cs-Ga, 6500 A.U. for Cs-In, and 7000 A.U. for Cs-Tl, which is in accordance with the atomic weight of the substances used. The photo-electric conversion efficiency is 1 μA/L, 1·5 μA/L, and 0·5 μA/L, respectively, as against 30 μA/L for a Cs-Sb cell. If these cells are used at very low temperatures (below —100° C.) the longwave thresholds move towards the blue end of the spectrum. Saturation at low temperatures is reached at lower voltages than at normal temperatures. By alloying Sb with any of the other metals it is possible to shape the spectral sensitivity curve at will and according to a predetermined programme.

The Cs-C_2O-Ag cathode has a very wide range extending from about 3000 A.U. to 12000 A.U., having a first peak at about 3650 to 3750 A.U. and another at 7500 to 8000 A.U. There are, of course, numerous ways of combining various materials in more or less complicated structures and the resulting cathodes correspondingly cover different spectral ranges and are centring about different maximum wavelengths. Relatively simple combinations, for instance, are characterized by a metal base on which an alkali metal layer is deposited. The next step shows a layer of a halide or oxide sandwiched between the metal base and the light-sensitive electron emitter, as instanced in the B.P.547806 using a AgF deposit between a silver base and a caesium layer ; or by the G.P. 710006 where the metal base is first covered with a CaF_2 or CaO layer and then the photosensitive layer is deposited on it. Another combination results in a high maximum sensitivity in the blue and violet region of the spectrum, a rather low response to red and no sensitivity at all to infra-red radiation. E. A. Massa and E. W. Pike (*185*) apply a silver-antimony coating, containing 13 to 17% Sb, to a supporting electrode. The Ag-Sb coating is overlaid (sensitized) by a layer of an alkali metal, preferably caesium. An optical theory of the spectral sensitivity of caesium oxide photo-cathodes has been put forward by Sayama (*2483*, *2484*).

A similar type has been developed by Timofeev and Nalimov (*186*) who prepared a sensitive surface by distilling Cs on to a silver sulphide or silver selenide surface. The most sensitive surfaces have a thickness of about 40 molecular layers of Ag_2S or Ag_2Se, the maximum sensitivity being at 3500 to 4800 A.U. A summarised account of the Ag_2S photosensitor is given by Gleichmann and Soroka (*187*).

A still more elaborate structure is presented in the U.S. Patent 2297467. There, a silver base is overlaid with an alkali metal, e.g., caesium ; over this is placed a thin layer of either Pb, Bi, or Sb, and this is covered by another overlying coat of an alkali metal.

Weber and Friedrich (*113*) have published valuable information about the structure of metallic, in particular bismuth, films. They found bismuth films on Pyrex in high vacuum to exhibit a photoelectric (electron-emissive) effect if the thickness of the bismuth was limited to between 172 and 292 atomic layers and the incident energy had a wavelength of 2537 A.U. The bismuth film was not an uninterrupted entity, but consisted of patches about 500 A.U. long, the gaps between the patches being of the order of 250 A.U. The emission of electrons took place between these individual patches. Investigations into this matter have been greatly assisted by employing electron-microscope techniques (*2503*).

A. Chevallier and P. Dubouhoz (*190*) and others (*2418*) have used sodium salicylate ($NaC_7H_5O_3$) to sensitize photo-cells with potassium cathodes to ultra-violet radiation. This type of cell has been used with advantage in measuring the intensity of fluorescent light as a function of the exciting wavelength. Sodium salicylate shows a constant response to equal amounts of radiant energy which applies over a wide range of wavelengths. Anthracene when irradiated with energy of 1800–2000 A.U. wavelength exhibits a photo-electric effect (*2528*). At the same time there occurs a surface formation of di-anthracene on the crystals. This is regarded as an effect secondary to the internal photo-effect (*2429*). In cells consisting of a photo-conductive anthracene or naphthalene layer the photo-current is proportional to the incident radiation (*2485*, *2514*).

The thickness of the photo-electric layer varies between one and about fifty molecular layers of the sensitive material (*186*). The optical characteristics of the cathode metals vary with the thickness of the layers. The optical constants of rubidium and caesium are discussed by H. E. Ives and H. B. Briggs (*188*), of sodium by the same authors (*189*). A few data on the reflectivity of barium are quoted by N. C. Jamison and R. J. Cashman (*127*) and the absorption of Ag and Au in the region below 2100 A.U. is discussed by Coster *et al.* (*2489*).

Photo-electric cells having a third element, viz., a control grid, have been described in the patent literature (*1281*, *1282*).

Bibliography References: (*493*, *588*, *590*, *598*, *1059*, *1060*, *1077*, *1078*, *1098*, *1111 1130*, *1135*, *1137*, *1138*, *1139*, *1140*, *1141*, *1565*, *1701*, *2000*, *2115*, *2119*, *2121*, *2159*, *2285*).

4.29. Floating Grid

Undesirable photo-electric effects are sometimes experienced in radio valves the grid of which is not connected when it may be sensitive to radiant energy (*285*, *286*, *287*). Even a lighted cigar can cause variations in anode current (*1249*), cf. chap. 7.22.1. Such an effect is readily reduced by applying an aqueous dispersion of graphite to the grid of the valve ; this collodial graphite is resistant to electron bombardment and the generation of secondary electrons is strongly reduced or even eliminated and the protective coating with colloidal graphite renders the metal practically insensitive to the impact of radiation. The chemical affinity of graphite has, however, to be taken into consideration. It cannot be used, for instance, in cells containing caesium because of the high chemical affinity of colloidal graphite to caesium.

Only where excess caesium is to be removed by a process other than baking at high temperatures is the extraordinary capacity of colloidal graphite for adsorbing caesium used. The spectral reflexion of a matt colloidal graphite, (best known under the Trade name of " Dag " or " Aquadag ") varies from 0·15 at 4500 A.U. to 0·18 at 10,000 A.U.

The emission of electrons from irradiated hot or cold oxide-cathodes has been treated by T. W. Case (*191*) and K. Newbury and F. Lemery (*192*). Photo-electric diodes are discussed by Palletz (*2593*, *2594*).

4.30. Spectral Sensitivity

The spectral sensitivities of a number of the best known and generally used photo-electric surfaces are shown in Figs. 4.13—4.18 (p. 86). Of special interest is the caesium-oxide surface which shows a very high sensitivity in the ultra-violet. Since the absorption of short-wave radiation is limited by the envelope rather than by the cathode surface, it is quite feasible that a new material, which is transparent to such short radiations as 1000 A.U. and perhaps even less, will present a new short-ultra-violet detector (*193*). Air heavily absorbs ultra-violet below 1700 A.U.

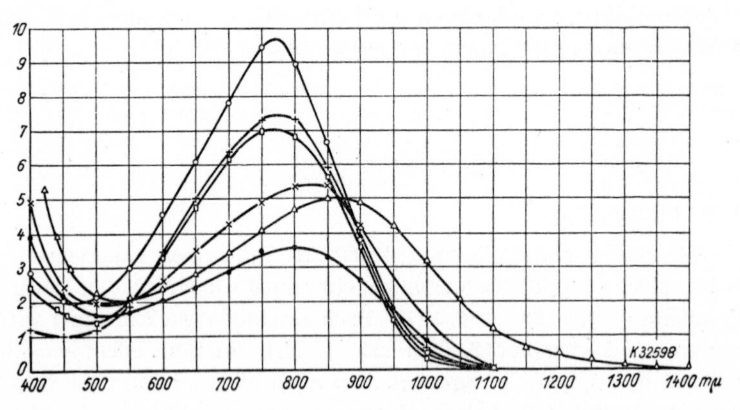

Fig. 4.37. Variation of spectral sensitivity of a number of caesium oxide photosensitors in the luminous and infra-red region.

The reader must keep in mind that the curves representing spectral characteristics are representative of the group or class of photosensitors, but need not necessarily be the spectral characteristic of any one particular cell. In fact they hardly ever are. In Fig. 4.37 a number of different curves are shown for photosensitors of the caesium-oxide type of different makes.

For the quality of a photosensitor, A. Hund (*1460*) gives the formula $Q = g/\Phi$ where g is the conductance of the photosensitor defined by the equation $g = (I_1 - I_2)/(E_1 - E_2)$ and Φ is the flux in lumens. I and E are the (photo-electric) anode currents and anode potentials, respectively.

In Germany, Dr. C. Bosch experimented during the war with the idea of dye-sensitizing a photo-cathode to a certain range in the spectrum, thus extending the technique of dye-sensitizing photographic plates, to the realm of photo-cathodes. He succeeded in one case, using a cyanine dyestuff. The sensitization lasted for four hours and extended to the region of 24000 A.U. (*2430*). (cf. section 4.11.)

Bibliography Reference: (*1130*).

4.31. Interchangeability

Photo-electric cells are interchangeable within certain limits. The following Table 4.16 has been compiled with a view to assisting the designer to choose an alternative type of photosensitor if the originally intended one is not available. A small margin in spectral characteristics has been allowed for, irrespective of mechanical differences. For details the engineer is advised to consult the respective manufacturers' lists.

4.32. Photo-E.M.F. Cells

Principally, the photo-e.m.f. type of photosensitor, Fig. 4.38, consists of a layer of a semi-conductor on a metal disk with a thin translucent or transparent layer of a precious metal sputtered on top. The incident photons passing through the top layer are absorbed near the

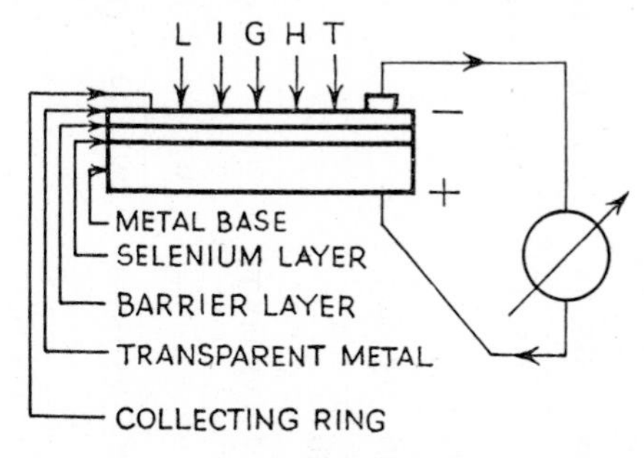

Fig. 4.38. Structure of a selenium photo-e.m.f. photosensitor.

Table 4.16

RCA	CINTEL	WESTING-HOUSE	GE	GEC	BTH	MULLARD	NATIONAL UNION	CETRON	VISITRON	LUMATRON
929	VA.16.SO		GL 929						R.61.BV	
868	GS.118	WL-735	GE-PJ 23				NU-1	CE-1	R.59.A	G-8
918	GS.118	WL-735	GE-PJ 23			56 CG	NU-1	CE-1	R.59.A	G-8
928			GL 918							G-9
919	VS.118.T		GL 919				NU-31 V	CE-31 V	R.82.AV	
920							NU-21 D	CE-21 D		G-18 T G-14
917	VS.118.TA		GL 917				NU-11 V	CE-11 V	R.59.TAV	
		WL-741	GL 923				NU-23	CE-23		
925	VS.16.SO	WL-734	GE-PJ 22				NU-30 V	CE-30 V	R.61.AV R.64.AV	V-9
927	GS.44.X		GL 927			55 CG	NU-5 NU-25	CE-20 CE-25	R.51.A	G-15 F G-16
930	GS.16.SO		GL 930				NU-30	CE-30	R.61.A R.64.A	

Note ;—The " G L " types are equivalents of the corresponding RCA types.

Table 4.16—*contd.*

RCA	CINTEL	WESTING-HOUSE	GE	GEC	BTH	MULLARD	NATIONAL UNION	CETRON	VISITRON	LUMATRON
934	VA.25.X								R.51.BV	
	VS.118	WL-734						CE-1 V	R.59.AV	
	GS.117.A	WL-737					NU-2	CE-2	R.71.A	G-6
	GS.26.T			CMG-8						
	GS.17			CMG-17						
	GS.16			CMG-22						
	GS.18			CMG-25	PE-7B					
	VA.26.T			KG7						
	VS.18.BO				PE-8					
	GS.116.AM							CE-4	R.58.A	G-12
	VS.116.AM							CE-4 V	R.58.AV	
	GS.126.A						NU-7	CE-7		G-7

upper surface of the semi-conductor and under favourable conditions electrons are freed by this action. Depending on the type of photo-e.m.f. cell the direction of electron flow may be away from or towards the incident radiation. Two different classes of photo-e.m.f. cells have been commercially developed, one being the combination of selenium and a metal base, the other cuprous oxide on copper (*2441*). According to whether the cells are constructed as front-wall or back-wall cells, respectively, the flow of the released photo-electrons, is towards or away from the incident energy, thus making the top electrode negative in the former, and positive in the latter type.

Bibliography References: (*468, 568, 571, 573, 576, 593, 1115, 1134, 1146, 1213, 1239, 1245, 1302, 1316, 1318, 1336, 1343, 1344, 1348, 1349, 1350, 1555, 1558, 1559, 1579, 1715, 1716, 2067, 2129, 2175, 2193, 2305*).

4.33. Linearity

The phenomenon of producing a voltage proportional to the incident radiation is based on the " inner photo-effect ". Linearity between the intensity of the incident flux and the photo-electric current in the external load resistance R_L holds good only for the theoretical case of

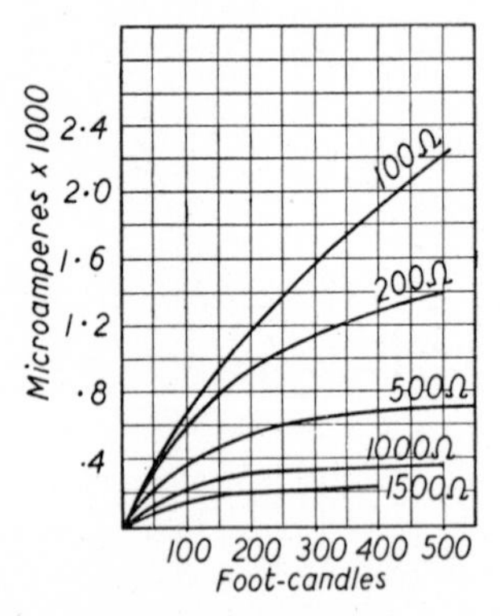

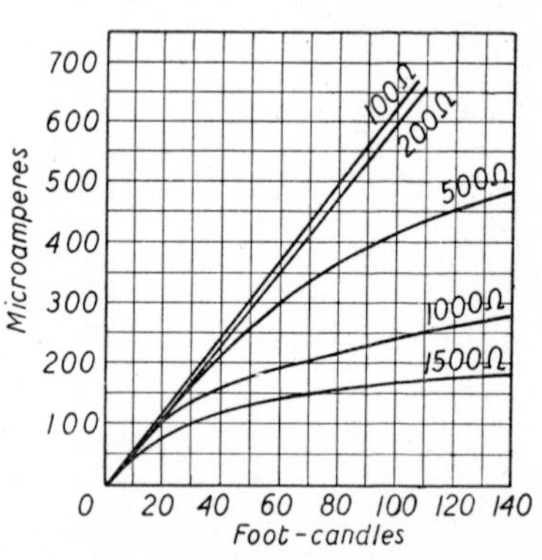

Fig. 4.39. The relation between external resistance, illumination, and photo-current of EEL photo-e.m.f. photosensitors. With 100 ohms, the output of a 45 mm cell is almost linear at both high and low illuminations. Using a smaller cell, the output in microamps for the same range of illumination would be less, but with like resistances, linearity would extend further. (*Evans Electroselenium Ltd.*)

$R_L = O$ and constancy of linearity, Fig. 4.39 is not very difficult to obtain and is based on the condition that the load resistance decreases as the illumination increases. This is shown in Table 4.17 for Weston Photronic cells.

The Table gives the approximate external resistance required to obtain linearity over various ranges of illumination and for cells having various linearity factors. The linearity factor is the ratio of the current output per foot-candle at 200 ft.-c. to that at 20 ft.-c. for a load resistance of 200 ohms.

TABLE 4.17
Constancy of Linearity

Range of Illumination	External Resistance for Linearity Factors of 0·95	0·86	0·80
ft.–c.	ohms	ohms	ohms
1– 10	1370	2500	3250
2– 20	700	1420	1880
5– 50	340	680	860
10–100	170	380	485
20–200	70	200	260
50–500	< 0	70	100

Bibliography Reference: (*1084*, *1106*).

4.34. Fatigue

Varying with make and type, photo-e.m.f. cells exhibit varying degrees of fatigue. The decrease in output after initial illumination is about 1 to 3% and takes place within a short time after the impact of radiant energy.

Bibliography Reference: (*1722*).

4.35. Temperature.

Permanent changes and consequent damage to the cell may be incurred if the temperature of the cell is raised to levels above 45° to 60° C. (113° to 140° F.) either by irradiation with high intensities or by subjecting the cell to high ambient temperatures. Infra-red absorbing filters (cf. Chap. 9) can be used to reduce heating from excessive irradiation, but more complicated measures must be taken if the ambient temperature is too high. Such measures are thermal insulation, cooling by air or water (*849*), etc. The effect of temperature is shown in the curves of Figs. 4.40 and 4.41.

Bibliography Reference: (*1207*).

4.36. Polarized Light

In measuring the intensity of polarized light, errors may amount to as much as 30%. These errors depend upon the spatial relations of the electric vector to the plane of incidence (*194*). (cf. Chaps. 9.25, 11.13).

Bibliography References: (*2319*, *2513*).

4.37. Time Lag

The process being purely electronic, no time delay is experienced with photo-e.m.f. cells.

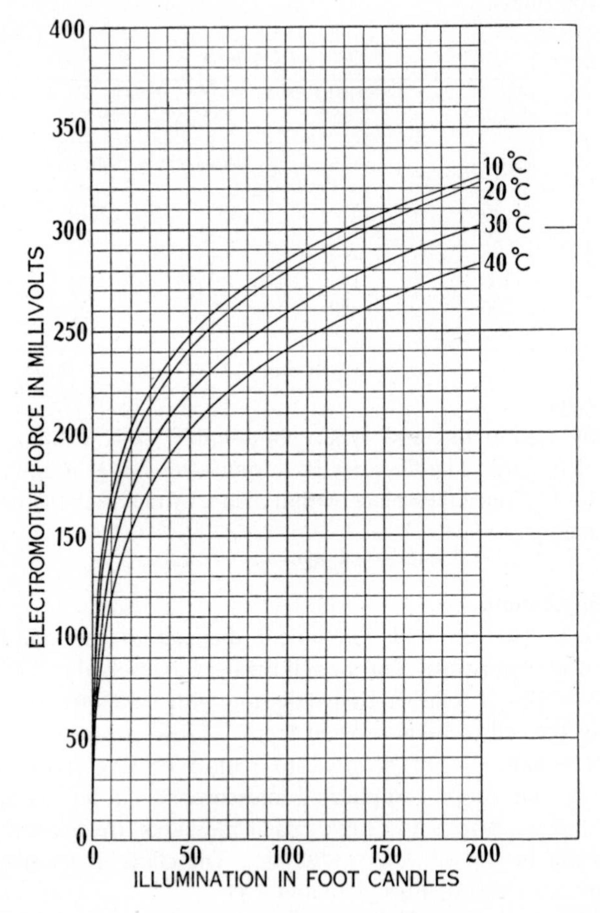

Fig. 4.40. Electromotive Force of Weston type 3GB photo-e.m.f. cell depending on level of illumination and ambient temperature.

4.38. Frequency Response

The smaller the load resistance, the higher the frequencies that can be measured with relatively small loss. This is borne out in Table 4.18 for Photronic cells, model S123.

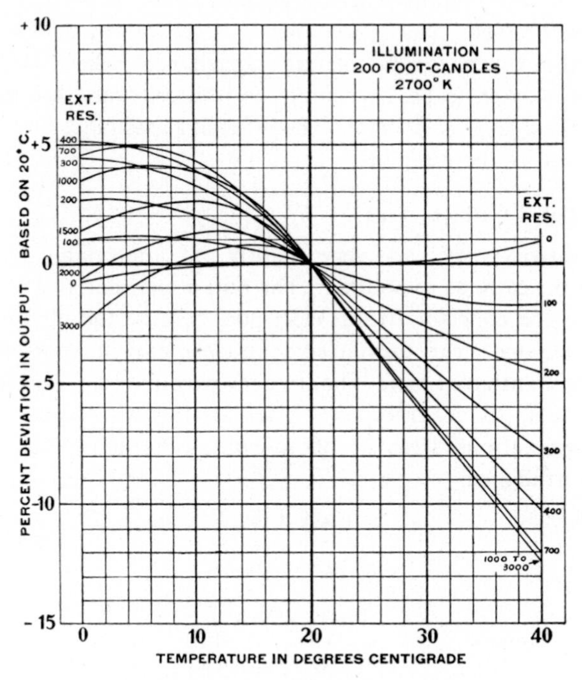

Fig. 4.41. The effect of temperature on photo-current output of Type 3 Photronic Cells (Weston) at 200 ft.c. illumination.

TABLE 4.18

Frequency Response

Frequency c/s	Current Ratio for 100 ohms	Current Ratio for 500 ohms
50	1·00	1·00
100	1·00	0·98
500	0·99	0·79
1000	0·95	0·54

The current ratio is the ratio of the alternating component of current output to the maximum value of the current. The latter is attained when the shunting effect of the capacitance is zero. The various values of reduction in photo-current output, due to the capacitance of the cell, are compiled for two different values of the external resistances, viz., 100 and 500 ohms, respectively.

The smaller the active (i.e., sensitive) area, the better is the dynamic response. For installations where modulated light is applied, only small cells should be used. The capacitance of a cell can be determined by the general formula for calculating capacitances when the relative permitivity is taken to be 7 (selenium-on-iron cells) and the thickness of the blocking layer is 10^{-4}mm. The internal capacitance of a Weston Photronic cell is about 0·5 μF.

4.39. Irradiated Cathode Area

The sensitivity may vary very slightly yet appreciably from one portion of the cathode to another. The output per unit area is slightly higher near the collector (front) electrode, because the photo-electric current generated near the collector travels only a short distance through the translucent metal film, thereby encountering less resistance (cf. Chap. 6.1). B. A. Brice (*195*) gives the following Table of Scale Errors when various areas of photo-e.m.f. cells in two-cell circuits have been irradiated.

TABLE 4.19

Table of Scale Errors

Type of Cell	Sensitive Area of Cell I has been irradiated	Sensitive Area of Cell II has been irradiated	Scale Error
Selenium	wholly	wholly	0·1
	wholly	partly	0·1
	partly	partly	1·0
Cuprous Oxide	wholly	partly	2·1
	partly	wholly	18·3
	partly	partly	18·3
Cuprous Oxide	wholly	partly	1·0
	partly	partly	19·9

If the beam of incident energy has a small diameter it is advantageous to select a cell whose sensitive area has the same geometrical dimensions. This will prevent the cathode from having any parts of it unexposed to the incident radiation since these parts would act as a shunt, thus decreasing the overall efficiency. Very fortunately, indeed, this consideration is not of primary importance since the dark resistance of the cells is rather high : of the order of 20,000 ohms.

Very interesting results have been obtained by Normand and Kay (*2530*) who explored the surface of three cathodes of the same type

(RCA 1P28) with a light spot of approximately 0·35 mm diameter (*2589*) and found "effective sensitivity contours" which differed greatly and individually for each photocathode.

The effects of inter-electrode capacitances are discussed, and a bridge circuit for studying the effects on a selenium type cell is given by A. Hund (*1460, pp. 108, 112*).

4.40. Electromotive Force

The relation between the illumination and the generated e.m.f. is non-linear. (Fig. 4.42). A reduction in incident flux or an increase in temperature cause the e.m.f. of the cell to decrease as shown in Fig. 4.40. The reducing effect of increasing temperature on the value of

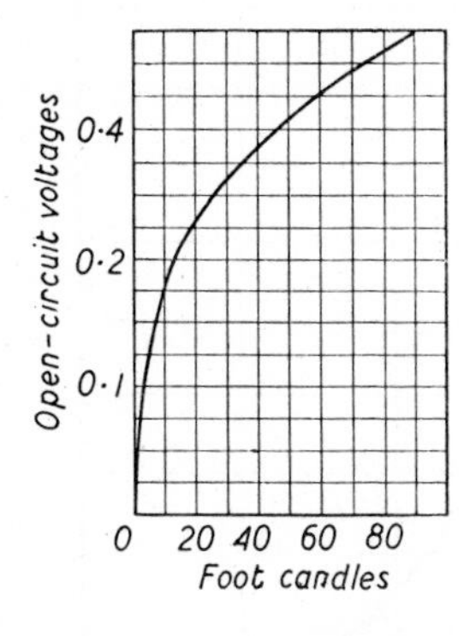

Fig. 4.42. The relation between illumination and the resulting e.m.f. is non-linear.

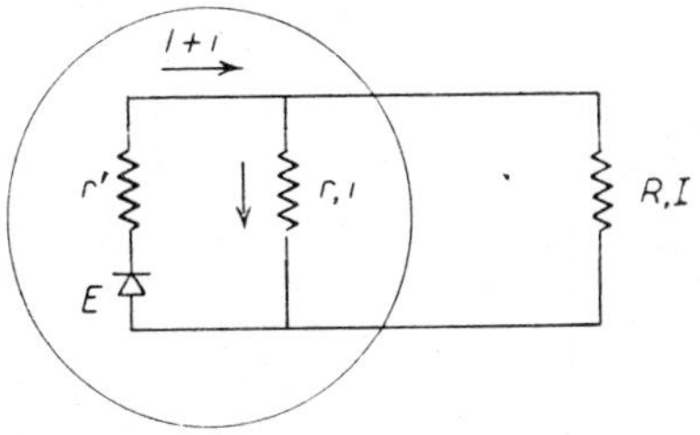

Fig. 4.43. Phantom circuit of a photo-e.m.f. photosensitor.

the e.m.f. is due to the change in internal leakage resistance which is governed by the temperature. According to R. A. Houstoun's view (*366*) the cell has a constant e.m.f. which sends a current through a resistance r'. This latter is inversely proportional to the intensity of illumination L, thus $r' = k/L$. This current returns partly as a current I through the external resistor R and partly as a current i through the internal resistance r, Fig. 4.43. The relation between these quantities is

$$\frac{1}{I} = \frac{k}{E}\left(1 + \frac{R}{r}\right)\frac{1}{L} + \frac{R}{E}$$

Bibliography Reference: (*1117*).

4.41. Spectral Sensitivity

There are two types and ranges of spectral sensitivities available which are determined by the arrangement as well as by the material of the cathode. The spectral curves of front-wall and back-wall cells, respectively, are shown in Fig. 4.43 (Section 4.6). The spread of the front-wall spectral curve is about ± 200 A.U. The shapes of these curves differ from the photopic luminosity curve of the average human eye Fig. 4.44, but it is possible to modify the spectral sensitivity by using optical filters. (Cf. section 4.28). There are some cells available

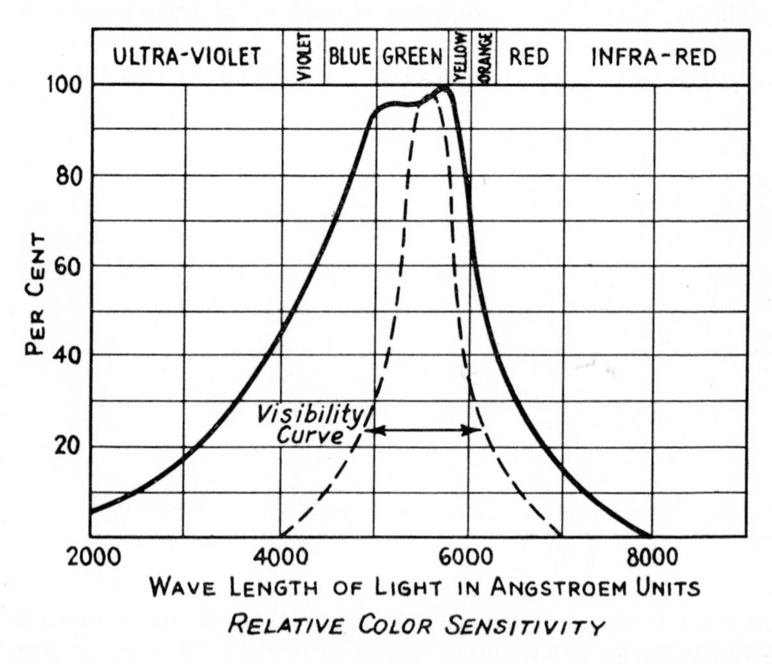

Fig. 4.44. Spectral response curve of an Electrocell (photo-e.m.f. type) compared with the colour sensitivity (Luminosity Curve) of the average human eye.)

the spectral sensitivity of which so closely resembles the photopic curve of the eye that, at least within wide spectral regions and practically admissible limits, a particular cell can be used without filters to match the spectral brightness sensitivity of the eye. If due allowance is made for the spread of data, i.e., for deviations from the agreed standard curve within a certain range, it will be seen that without great error the cell may be said to have a spectral sensitivity nearly identical with that of the standard eye.

Bilbiography Reference: (1085).

4.42. Correction Factors

When photo-e.m.f. lightmeters are employed in measuring radiation from sources other than tungsten at 2700° K., the following factors must be used to account for the varying spectral composition of the radiation from various illuminants. Correction factors must be considered in the above measurements because the luminosity curve of

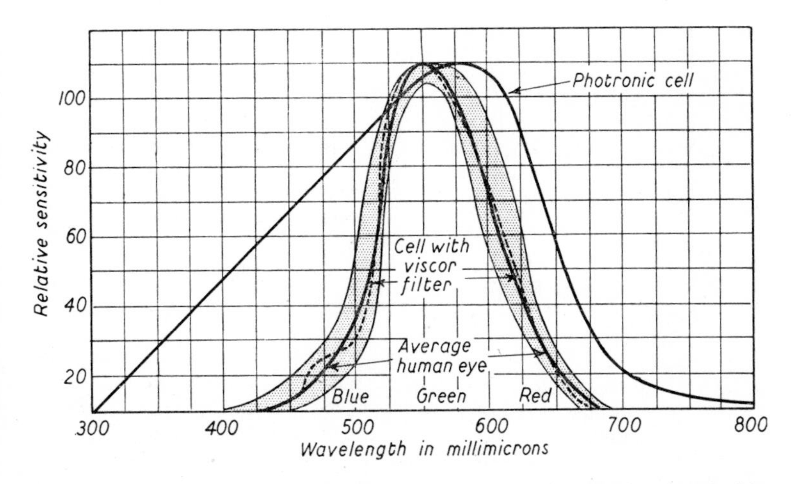

Fig. 4.45. Spectral response curve of a Photronic (Weston) Cell without, and with, a Viscor visual correction filter compared with the colour sensitivity (Luminosity Curve) of the average human eye.

the standard observer and the spectral sensitivity curve of the lightmeter do not coincide. In the following Tables various facts about correction factors are compiled.

The correction factors vary with the type and make of the cell.

Ch. L. Amick (*350, p. 224*) gives another set of correction factors for the use with light meters without, however, stating the type of meter (photo-e.m.f. cell) to which these values refer. These correction factors also differ very appreciably from the values listed above. Further lists are published by E. Melloy *et al.* (*1461*).

TABLE 4.20

Correction Factors of Photronic Cells

Source and Type of Radiation	Correction Factors for Cells without Filters	
	Type 1	Type 3
Daylight	0·97	0·77
Tungsten Filament at		
2000 deg. K.	0·87	0·95
2500	0·98	1·00
2700	1·00	1·00
2848 (C.I.E. Illuminant A)	1·01	1·00
3000	1·02	1·00
4000	1·04	0·94
4800 (C.I.E. Illuminant B)	1·01	0·87
6000	0·99	0·80
Fluorescent Tubes		
Daylight	1·06	0·92
White 2800 deg. K (pinkish)	1·19	1·12
White 3500 deg. K (bluish)	1·22	1·12
Blue	0·67	0·52
Red	0·54	0·60
Green	1·55	1·33
Electric Discharge Lamps		
Neon	0·94	0·97
Sodium	1·43	1·44
Mercury		
High Pressure	1·35	1·20
Intermediate Pressure	1·22	1·04
Low Pressure	1·15	0·99
Various Sources		
Carbon Arc (average)	0·85	0·75
Acetylene	0·95	0·98

For the Ferranti Light Meter the following data are given.

TABLE 4.21

Correction Factors of the Ferranti Light Meter

Source and Type of Radiation	Correction Factor
Tungsten Filament, clear bulb	1·00
, daylight bulb	0·97
Mercury Discharge Lamps	1·14
Sodium Lamps	1·71
Neon-Argon Lamps (blue)	0·90
Fluorescent Tubes	1·00
Gas Burner	1·17

4.43. Cathode Materials

Numerous attempts have been made to find new photo-electric surfaces with characteristics greatly improving upon, or deviating from those already achieved. G. Berraz and E. Virasoro (*196*), by depositing a selenium layer on bronze and providing a frontal electrode of Cd on Au, have produced a photo-e.m.f. cell with a maximum output of 580 μA/Lm at 6000 A.U. F. Eckart and A. Schmidt (*197*) have introduced a second maximum by adding Cd to Se. The first maximum, due to the selenium, is at 5700 A.U. ; the second maximum, due to the additional cadmium, is at 7100 A.U. E. Köber (*198*) produces a very active surface by coating a conducting base plate with a light-sensitive selenium layer to which a cadmium oxide layer is applied ; this being reduced by nascent hydrogen results in a sensitive layer. C. W. Hewlett (*199*, *1406*) coats a metal base with successive layers of selenium, cadmium, and platinum, respectively, C. G. Fink and E. Adler (*200*) improve photo-e.m.f. cells of the copper type by depositing on the cuprous oxide a thin film of about 400 A.U. thickness consisting of a compound of copper and an element of the sulphur group,* for instance Cu_2S.

H. Teichmann (*379*), in a new hypothesis on inter-cathodic layers, has suggested that they act as semi-conductors. Recent investigations by A. F. Ioffé of the Leningrad Physicotechnical Institute (*1435*, *1436*) have opened up a new vista on semi-conductors, a theory which may eventually lead to the manufacture of selenium photo-e.m.f. cells generating an e.m.f. of 1·0 volt as against the present 0·3 volt.

An interesting combination for work in the infra-red is the bismuth sulphide cell by C. G. Fink and J. S. Mackay (*93*). This cell is capable of measuring temperatures as low as 500° C. (930° F.) and is much better than any other cell for radiations up to 800° C. (1470° F.). At and above 1000° C. (1830° F.) the response of the Bi_2S_3 cell becomes about equal with that of other, more standard, cells. As compared to the unipolar conductivity of a selenium cell (2500 : 1) the bismuth sulphide cell has a unipolar conductivity of only 2 : 1 (*2473*).

In special cases the metal base of the photo-e.m.f. cell can be replaced by other neutral materials, for instance by colloidal graphite, when there is no chemical affinity between the graphite and the sensitive layer-forming material. In selenium-tellurium cells which are used for

* The sulphur group comprises oxygen, sulphur, selenium, tellurium, and polonium.

measurements in the infra-red, colloidal graphite is used as an electrode material because it has no affinity with selenium.

For measurements in the near infra-red a number of photo-e.m.f. cells are available commercially. Some of these contain a combination of thallium with an element of the sulphur group. Thallium-sulphide Tl_2S, has an extremely high output of 6000 μA/Lm (*115*, *201*, *1283*)

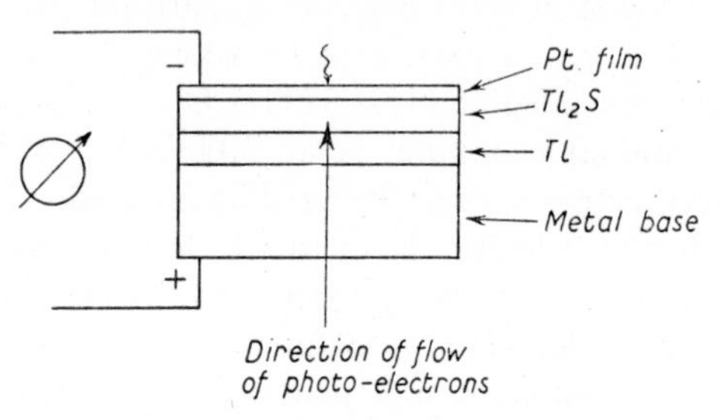

Fig. 4.46. A thallium sulphide photo-e.m.f. cell of the front-wall type.

which is about tenfold the response of other photo-e.m.f. cells at their best: this cell is of the front-wall type, Fig. 4.46. The maximum spectral sensitivity is centred around 9800 ± 200 A.U. for a light source at 2848° K. with the short-wave end of the spectral range at

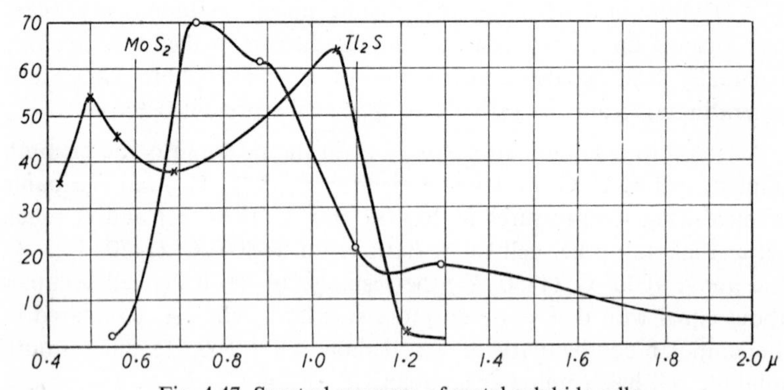

Fig. 4.47. Spectral response of metal sulphide cells.

6500 A.U., and the long-wave end in the near infra-red at about 15,000 A.U., Fig. 4.47. The frequency response is much better than that of other cells as can be seen from Fig. 4.48. It is not before the rather high frequency of 20 kc/s is reached that the photo-electric output shows a decrease of 75%. The short-circuit current is of the order of 3000 μA/Lm. This compares with other short circuit currents as shown :

Cu_2O Front-wall	150 μA/Lm
Cu_2O Back-wall	15 μA/Lm
Se-Fe	450 μA/Lm
Tl_2S photo-e.m.f. type	3000 μA/Lm

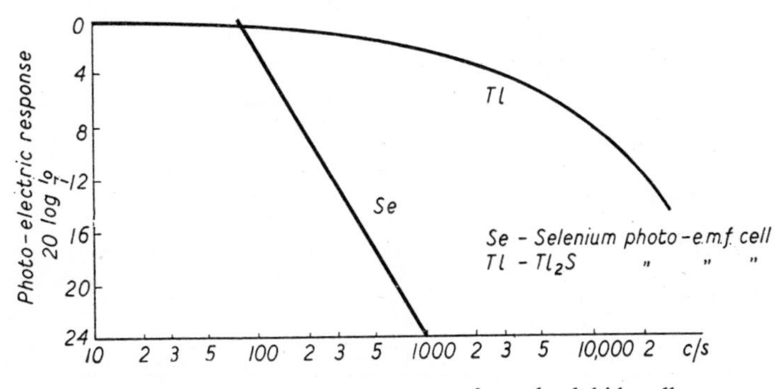

Fig. 4.48. Frequency response of metal sulphide cells.

The internal resistance of thallium-sulphide e.m.f. cells varies individually from 20 to 1,000 ohms, but in a given cell there is no appreciable variation on irradiation.

A thallium-sulphide photo-e.m.f. cell with a still higher average response, viz., 10,000 μA/Lm, having also a high response in the infra-red, consists of Tl_2S with an admixture of metallic thallium (*28*) in the ratio of $Tl : Tl_2S = 2{,}3 : 1$. The energy efficiency of that cell is 1% which means that 1% of the incident energy is converted into electric energy.

The spectral sensitivity is extended farther into the infra-red by photo-e.m.f. cells using molybdenite MoS_2 as sensitive material, Fig. 4.47.

Selenium photo-e.m.f. cells extend their spectral response also into the infra-red region according to observations by Naeser & Krächter (*202*) which statement, as the authors admit, is not corroborated in the general literature on selenium photosensitors.

Several types of photo-electric sensitivity were discovered in germanium-to-metal point contacts (Purdue University). The photoconductive effect approaches unit quantum efficiency at 13,000 A.U. with a white light sensitivity of several thousand microamps/lumen.

There are also photo-e.m.f. effects and another type, called the photo-peak, shows properties which enable the cell to be used as a trigger photosensitor (*1046*).

For the detection of ultra-violet radiation cuprous-oxide cells are unsuitable. The selenium-on-iron type extends its short-wave end of the spectral sensitivity curve into the medium ultra-violet range and cells are available with a good sensitivity at as low as 2500 A.U.

TABLE 4.22

Ultra-Violet Sensitivity of Photo-e.m.f. Cells

Make (Trade Mark)	Relative Response at 3000 A.U.	10% Response at
EMBY	27%	2600 A.U.
EEL	20%	2600 A.U.
ELECTROCELL	18%	2500 A.U.
PHOTRONIC	12%	2870 A.U.

Bibliography References: (*1707, 1717, 1718, 1724, 1737, 1770, 2069*)

4.44. External Voltage

In general the application of an external voltage is not recommended. A small direct voltage is sometimes said to increase the output by as much as 50% and an upper limit of 6 to 8 volts D.C. is agreed upon. A voltage in excess of 8 volts or any alternating voltage will cause irreparable destruction. For values in relation with individual cells and makes the manufacturers' lists should be consulted. Weston cells must carry no external currents in excess of 5mA.

The combined effect of incident radiation and external (applied) voltage is represented by the formula

$$E' - RI = \frac{\frac{k.I}{L} - E}{1 + \frac{k}{L.r}}$$

Houstoun and Howatson's investigations (*366*) have suggested that there is no advantage in using an applied voltage. In the above equation E' is the applied voltage, I and R represent the load. For $R = 0$ the increase in output (in μA) is approximately proportional to E'. Sargrove (*2491*) has invented a method of using photo-e.m.f. cells working under high external voltages.

4.45. Special Shapes

Prior to 1939 the Süddeutsche Apparate Fabrik of Nüremberg in Germany introduced the photo-e.m.f. cell with split cathodes. Split-cathode cells consist of a metal disk on which two semi-circular selenium layers are deposited,* Fig. 4.49. Quadruple split cathodes

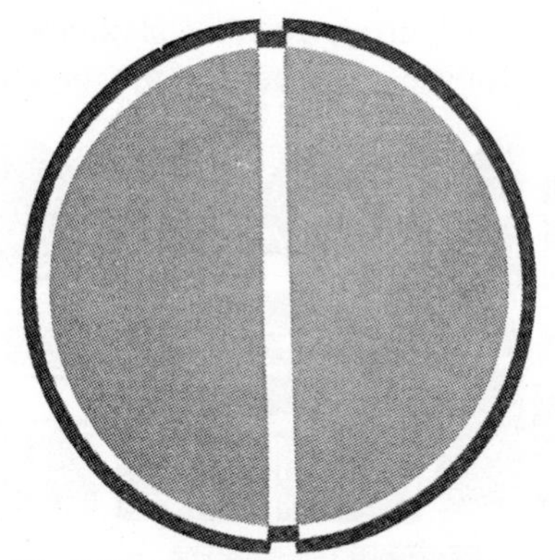

Fig. 4.49. Split cathode photo-e.m.f. cell.

and multiple cells on a common electrode† are special types which are now commercially available, Fig. 4.50. Annular (cylindrical) cells are also available.

Bibliography Reference: (*1706*)

4.46. Protective Coats

Photo-e.m.f. cells are only rarely of the enclosed type. If for some particular reason (corrosive vapours, damp atmosphere, oxygen, etc.), an envelope must be used, care should be taken to ensure that the window of the casing is made of the appropriate material, glass or quartz. Alternatively, organic glasses (cf. Chap. 6) may be used with advantage if the chemical and physical properties of the plastic stand up to the conditions of the surroundings. If no special enclosures are needed, the translucent metal film must be protected against mechanical injuries by abrasive dust, water and condensates, and also against chemical contamination. The protective coat applied to the metal film must be colourless and its characteristic region of high transparency

* Made in Great Britain by Messrs. Evans Electroselenium Ltd., the makers of EEL photo-e.m.f. cells.

† Made in U.SA. by Weston Electrical Instrument Corp.

must coincide with the region of maximum absorptivity of the photoelectric layer. For certain purposes the protective layer may be coloured, thus acting as a filter at the same time. A transparent protective coating has been described by G. W. Hewitt (*203*). The protective layer of a transparent resin, e.g., colophony, ester gum, or abietic acid, containing a plasticiser is applied to the translucent contact film of cathodically-sputtered silver, gold, or platinum and the protective layer is reinforced with glass or asbestos fibre, or cotton.

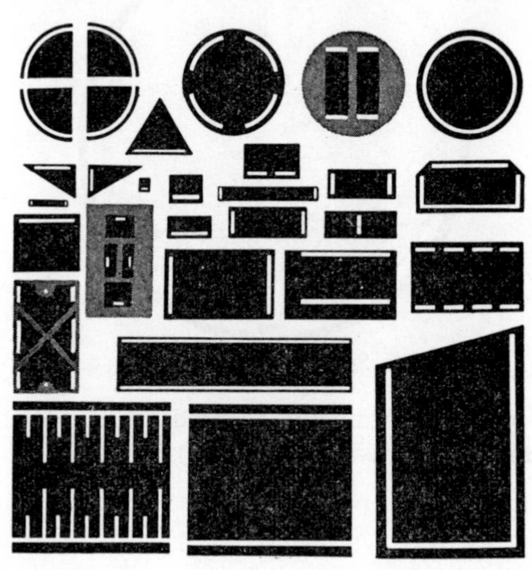

Fig. 4.50. Special shapes of photo-e.m.f. cells (*Weston Electrical Co.*).

4.47. Action of X-Rays

A. E. Sandström (*395*) made investigations into the behaviour of selenium photo-e.m.f. cells when irradiated with soft X-rays (wavelengths ranging from 3·5 to 20 A.U.) and came to the following conclusions :

(1) As regards photo-electric current and photo-voltage the characteristic relationship is the same as when luminous energy strikes the cell ;

(2) In nearly all cases the photo-electric current/X-ray intensity relation is represented by a straight line ;

(3) The photo-electric currents are extremely small quantities.

Cadmium sulphide light-sensitive resistors (cf. 4.51) are also sensitive to X-rays, beta-rays and alpha-particles. One quantum ($h\nu$) of X-rays transports 10^6 electrons, whereas one quantum of alpha or beta radiation transports 10^8 to 10^{10} electrons. (1 microamp. = $6{\cdot}242\ 10^{12} \times$ electrons per second).

Bibliography Reference: (*2362*)

4.48. Multiple Photo-e.m.f. Cells

Multiple photo-e.m.f. cells (*1274*) are composite cells made up of a number of small cells all connected in series. There were one or two types on the market, their common but disagreeable feature being their sensitivity to mechanical shock. Since in a series arrangement the total resistance of the multiple cell is the sum of all individual cell resistances —a figure which, when many small cells are used, may reach a very considerable value—it is evident that, as with all series arrangements, the weakest spot of the entire assembly is the safe and maintained contact of each element in the chain. A disruption or displacement will cause the cell to act as if eclipsed. This disadvantage limited the multiple cell to a laboratory instrument rather than a workshop tool.

Persevering study and methodical work have, however, overcome this difficulty and the new EEL type M1 photo-e.m.f. cell* is so well designed and engineered that even the roughest tests did not succeed in disrupting the mosaic of cells and even severe mechanical shocks do not shift the characteristic of the multiple arrangement.

The EEL selenium multiple photo-e.m.f. cell, Fig. 4.51, consists essentially of a number of small selenium barrier-layer elements connected in series, all being contained in a single unit. In contrast with the more usual type the output current is largely independent of the load resistance of the photo-cell. Consequently, the voltage generated in the load resistance increases fairly linearly with the increasing load resistance value. The voltage generated becomes a maximum with a load resistance of the order of 1 megohm.

Under these conditions the voltage across a load resistance of 1 megohm is as shown in Table 4.23.

TABLE 4.23

Voltage-Illumination Characteristic of the EEL Multiple Photo-e.m.f. Cell

Illumination ft.-c.	5	10	25	50	100	250	500
Volts generated, approx.	1·0	1·8	2·9	4·0	4·8	6·2	7·3

*Manufactured in Gt. Britain by Messrs. Evans Electroselenium, Ltd.

A voltage change in the order of 0·2 volt per ft.-c. over a range of illumination up to 5 ft.-c., may be said to be linear and characteristic for this type cell. The mean rate of change of voltage with illumination is of the order of 0·1 volt per ft.-c. over the illumination range of 0 to 30 ft.-c. With the higher values of illumination of from 100 to 400

Fig. 4.51. EEL Multiple photo-e.m.f. cell type M.1. (*Evans Electroselenium Ltd.*)

ft.-c. voltages from 5 to 8 volts are generated in the load resistance. These voltages and voltage changes are at least ten times as great as the corresponding values obtainable with the more orthodox types of selenium photo-e.m.f. cells. When the voltage response is plotted against logarithmic illumination values the resulting curve is a straight, or nearly straight, line.

Robust thermionic valve amplifiers may readily be operated. Stable trigger circuits can be operated with a voltage change of about 0·1 volt on the grid. The EEL multiple cell may also be used with A.C. amplification by using modulated light. The assembly is protected by a sheet of transparent Perspex.

Bibliography References: (*1316*, *1579*)

4.49. Light-sensitive Resistors

A surprisingly large number of materials (*359*) exhibit a reaction to irradiation in that their electrical resistance changes. L. R. Koller (*140, Table xiv*) gives a list of some twenty compounds all being sensitive to light; most of them, however, show considerable aging effect and are, therefore, of no technical interest.

Generally, the electrical resistance of a metal decreases on illumination (*2456*). Q. Majorana (*360*) thought he had found an effect to the contrary. A. Etzrodt (*361*) investigated this hypothetical effect (known as the Majorana-effect) by separating thermal from optical causes. Single bismuth crystals have a temperature coefficient which ranges from high positive to high negative values. When this coefficient equals zero, the effects of the incident light should become obvious. However, Etzrodt's experiments proved that the effects totally disappeared with the disappearance of the temperature coefficient ; Etzrodt therefore concluded that the Majorana-effect is of a purely thermal nature.

Primarily, a light-sensitive resistor is not a measuring device but only a detector since there is no linear relation between radiant flux and electric current, the principal function being of the type $i_{ph} = k\sqrt{I}$ (*140, p. 168*). The action of a light-sensitive resistor is based on the inner photo-effect. The theory of the light-sensitive resistor is discussed by Stöckmann (*2518*). An appreciable time lag between receiving the energy of the incident radiation and reaching the full change in resistance is a rather discouraging feature in general which in some cases becomes prohibitive. The time lag, on the average about 0·05 sec., can be as great as 0·1 sec. Modern developments tend to greatly reduce the time lag.

The materials mostly in use for light-sensitive resistors of the metallic type are of the selenium, thallium and lead variety.

The resistivity of a tellurium film has been found to decrease on exposure to light. It is slowly restored to normal when kept in complete darkness for about 18 to 20 hours (*2575*). This process can be speeded up somewhat by irradiating the Te film with infra-red radiation.

The pyrolytic formation of a hard smooth pure silicon film of about 5 μ thickness and its deposition on a ceramic or quartz surface was achieved at the Bell Telephone Laboratories (*2626*). Upon illumination a photoconductive effect was found to have a marked maximum at 9000 A.U., the long-wave limit being in the region of 10,500 A.U. The sensitivity of this silicon cell is intermediate between that of the thallium sulphide and the selenium cell. The illumination photocurrent response is near linearity. The outstanding characteristic of the silicon cell is its refractoriness to ambient heat. The cell can be exposed to the direct incidence of midsummer sunshine, even to the heat of an oxygen-gas torch without being destroyed or irreparably damaged.

Bibliography References: (*1079*, *1144*, *1145*, *1147*, *1224*, *1313*, *1326*, *1327*, *1362*)

4.50. Selenium Resistors

There are about half a dozen preferred ways of constructing a selenium light-sensitive resistor, the three original types being the Radiovisor Bridge (*204*), the capacitor-type Selenophone Resistor

Fig. 4.52. The Radiovisor Selenium Bridge (*Radiovisor Parent Ltd.*).

(*143, p. 203, 205*), and the FJ31-Resistor made by the General Electric Co. of America.

The Radiovisor Bridge, Fig. 4.52, is made and used in England, the

FJ31 and the Burgess Radiovisor Bridge, the American cousin of the first mentioned device, in the States. They have extremely thin films of selenium (about 3×10^{-2} mm.) deposited on an insulating base. Since moisture and the oxygen in the air cause an instability and deterioration of the sensitive layer, it is enclosed in an atmosphere of inert gas or in a totally evacuated glass envelope. The thinness of the selenium layer appreciably reduces the time lag which is so characteristic for thicker layers or slabs of selenium. In Fig. 4.53 the spectral sensitivity of typical light-sensitive selenium resistors is shown. They are

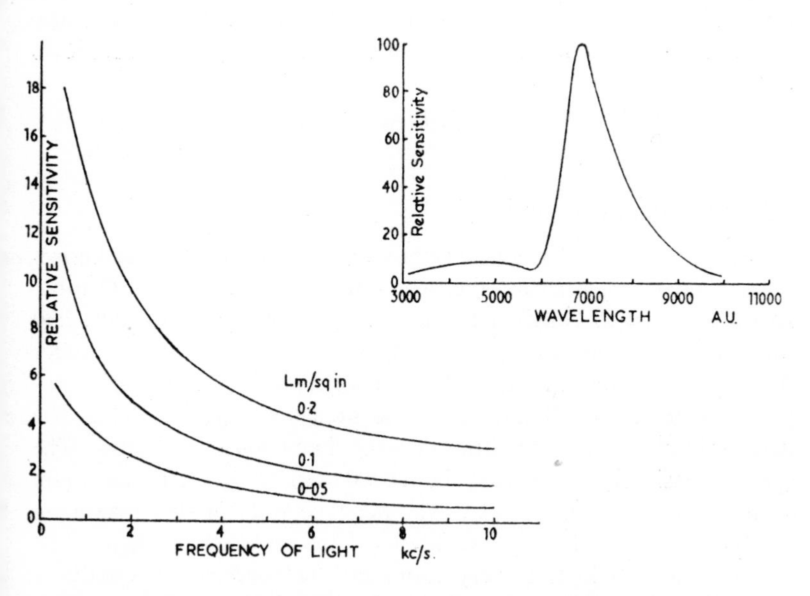

Fig. 4.53. Spectral response of the selenium light-sensitive resistor (high response in red spectrum), type FJ31. (*General Electric Co. Schenectady*).

Fig. 4.54. Frequency response of a selenium light-sensitive resistor.

highly sensitive to orange-red, red, and infra-red radiations, their blue-sensitivity being negligible. The output is seriously reduced by modulated radiation, Fig. 4.54. The internal dark resistance is of the order of 10^6 or 10^7 ohms but is reduced upon irradiation at the ratio of 6 : 1 to 25 : 1. The maximum external voltage across the light-sensitive resistor is, according to the make, anything from 10 up to 1000 volts, and currents up to about 500 mA may be easily controlled (*156, p. 325, 206*). The application of selenium cells to measuring very feeble illuminations is discussed by Terrien and Moreau who conclude that this type of photo-cell is not suitable (*2478*).

The output current i is due to the difference between the conductance C of the dark and irradiated selenium resistor, respectively, viz., $i = C_I - C_D = k\sqrt{I}$. The output current is proportional to the square root of the irradiation and to a characteristic constant k which not only varies with the make, but also shows considerable margin for individual selenium resistors of identical make. Sometimes their constant varies as much as by a factor of ten for two different resistors of the same make.

Bibliography References: (*510, 593*)

4.51. Metal Sulphide Resistors

Besides the change in resistance of selenium (*99*) nothing was known about similar properties of other materials until 1917 when on October 2nd, after a very thorough and long research, T. W. Case (*207, 208, 209*) found that thallium sulphide shows a slight change in resistance under the impact of radiant energy. The Thalofide cell* is an oxygen compound of thallium sulphide on a gold or quartz support (*210*). The dark resistance of the cell varies between 5 and 500 $\times$ 10^6 ohms. The spectral sensitivity ranges from about 6000 to 18,000 A.U., the maximum centring at about 10,000 A.U. Another type with another maximum at about 5100 A.U. has been discussed by Anderson (*143, p. 213*). The response to light is very rapid but the conductivity continues to increase appreciably after the beginning of the irradiation. This time lag sometimes takes up several minutes when large intensities strike the thallium resistor. As a detector of infra-red radiation the Thalofide cell is about 50 times as sensitive in infra-red spectroscopy (8000 to 11,000 A.U.) as a good thermopile (*133, p. 325*). High-sensitivity thermopiles now reach a limit of 10^{-12} or 10^{-13} watt per sq. mm. (*211*). At even lower values of illumination (0·025 ft.-c.) the thallium resistor drops its resistance to about one-half. A selenium

* Thalofide is a compound word made up of the first syllable of thallium and the last syllable of sulphide (or sulfide, in the U.S.A.), the letter - o - having been inserted for euphony.

resistor, for the same change, needs about ten times the illumination (*212, p. 163*). The thallium resistors are sealed into evacuated glass envelopes and protected from incident blue light. A mass-producible type thallium-sulphide resistor sensitive to modulated light was constructed by R. J. Cashman (*1467*) who also produced a lead-sulphide photosensitor. Further details are given by Hewlett (*2428*). German developments are described in the B.I.O.S. Reports (*2432*). The thallium resistor covers part of the luminous and near infra-red spectrum, the long-wave threshold being at about 13,000 to 15,000 A.U.: the maximum is centred around 9500–10,000 A.U. A maximum external potential of about 100V D.C. may be used across the light-sensitive resistor. The lead-sulphide resistor has its long-wave threshold at about 40,000 A.U. and its peak at about 20,000 A.U. It is of interest to note that at peak wavelengths the sensitivity to infra-red radiant energy is about 1000 times that of a thermo-couple (*2388*). Reports from Germany (*1644*) mention that lead-sulphide (*2475*) photoconductive cells (*1659, 1660*) were first manufactured by Gudden (*1658*), Kaspar, Kutzscher, and others during the war and used in high-speed pyrometry. These cells are sensitive to radiation in the luminous range but peak at 27,000 A.U. and have their long-wave threshold at 35,000 A.U. The average cathode area of the German cells is 10 $mm.^2$, the cells having a response time of 100 msec. Lead selenide and lead telluride (*2474*) cells extend their long-wave thresholds even further into the infra-red (*1672, 1678*). The spectral response of lead selenide cells at absolute temperatures of 90° K. and 195° K. respectively has been discussed by Moss and Chasmar (*2429*), and of lead telluride layers by Moss (*2435*). A refrigerator for low temperature operation of photosensitors was described by R. W. Engstrom (*2443*).

Bismuth sulphide and telluride cells (*2473*) were found to respond up to about 40,000 A.U. The maximum centres around 7000 A.U. (Bi_2S_3) and 10,000 A.U. (Bi_2Te_3). In general, bismuth cells are considered inferior to lead photo-conductors.

Various metal tellurides have been prepared and their spectral and other characteristics investigated by Braithwaite (*2571*). The long-wave threshold at liquid oxygen temperature (—183° C.) varies with the metal used and is, for instance, 1·2μ for Cu_2Te and 3·1μ for HgTe.

Observations on the behaviour of cadmium-sulphide crystals as photo-detectors show that the total photo-electric effect is similar in action to that of the grid in a triode at room temperature, but that at very low temperatures a time delay is observable (*2476, 2477*).

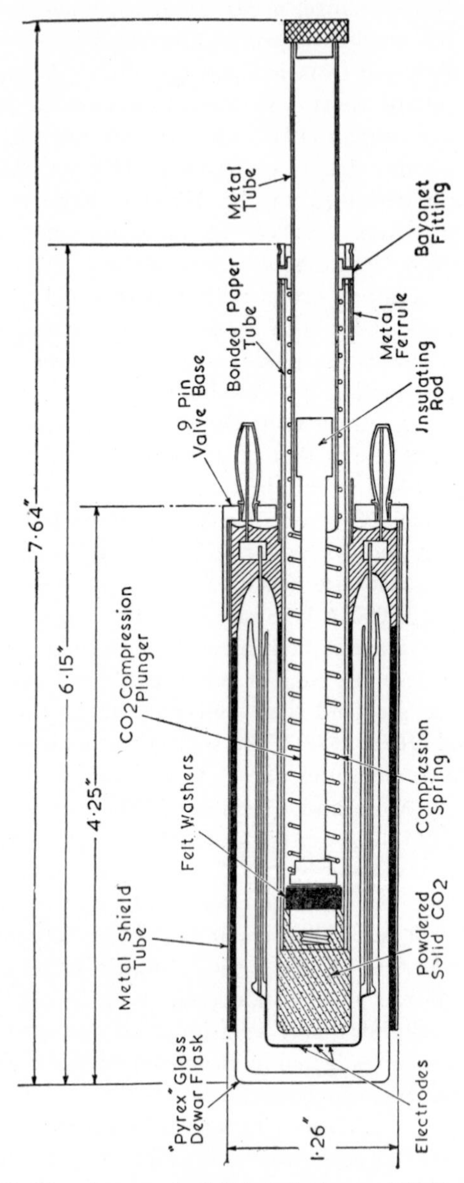

Fig. 4.55. View (approx. half full size) of type C light-sensitive PbS resistor (B.T.H. Co.). Provision is made for using a low-temperature coolant.

The change in the conductance of lead-sulphide cells with a change in temperature has been described by Watts (*2479*).

The infra-red conductivity in tellurium and arsenic is discussed by Moss (*2480*).

In general, lead selenide photo-conductors are considered superior to lead-sulphide cells (*2481*) (see above). Cadmium sulphide and Cd selenide cells are also considered to have a more constant response than Pb cells (*2499*).

Extensive research on lead sulphide PbS has resulted in a reliable photosensitor of the light-sensitive resistor type. It has a high speed of response, is of robust construction, and free from microphony. The lead-sulphide cell is very sensitive to medium infra-red radiations. The characteristics of four types of PbS photosensitors, as manufactured by the British Thompson-Houston Co., Ltd., are listed on the following page.

Type M cells have a film of PbS deposited on a glass button which is protected from chemical and mechanical damage (fumes and dust). The type C cells, Fig. 4.55, are made in the form of a miniature Dewar flask, using powdered solid CO_2 as a coolant. The decrease in cathode temperature extends the spectral sensitivity further into the infra-red, Fig. 4.56. The type C1 lead sulphide cell is of the three-electrode type, and the two sections can be used either in series or independently. The end window in the type C1 cell is made of Pyrex glass while the window in the type C2 cell is made of a glass with specially high transmission in the infra-red. In this model either solid CO_2 (B.P. -78°C. = 195°K.), liquid air (B.P. -195°C = 78°K.) (mole 10% in liquid), or liquid oxygen (B.P. -183°C. = 90°K.) can be used as a coolant.

These cells are useful in low temperature pyrometers (*2511*), extending their range down to 100°C. (= 373°K.). A Black Body at this temperature radiates only about 1% of its energy in the spectral sensitivity range of this PbS cell. The speed of response is very high and enables temperature transients to be shown or the temperature of fast-moving objects to be measured with accuracy and without making physical contact. The heat absorbed by PbS cells in radiation pyrometry has a negligible effect on the accuracy of the pyrometer readings (*2507*). A brief summary on metal sulphide, selenide and

TABLE OF CHARACTERISTICS

YPE	Principal Uses	Number of Electrodes	Dimensions of Sensitive Area	Maximum Diameter	Maximum Overall Length	Base	Cell Operating Temperature	Wavelength Range for 25% of Maximum Sensitivity	Wavelength of Maximum Sensitivity	Element Resistance	Optimum Polarizing Current	Optimum Interruption Frequency	Time Constant	Sensitivity (Optimum conditions): 2·2 microns Radiation	Sensitivity: Tungsten Light	Sensitivity: 200° C Black Body Radiation	Detection Limit (S/N = 1 for 1 c/s Bandwidth): 2·2 microns Radiation	Detection Limit: Tungsten Light	Detection Limit: 200° C. Black Body Radiation
			mm.	in.	in.		°C	microns	microns	ohms	μA	c/s	μ sec.	volts (r.m.s.)/watts (peak to peak)			watts		
C 1	Measurements and Spectroscopy	3	2(10 × 1)	$1\frac{3}{8}$	$6\frac{3}{8}$*	British 9-pin	20	0·3 to 2·7	2·2	50,000 to 200,000 (each)	100 to 150	1000 to 2000	40	5000	200	4	2×10^{-11}	5×10^{-10}	$2{\cdot}5 \times 10^{-8}$
							− 80	0·3 to 2·8	2·4	500,000 to 2·0M (each)	50 to 100	500 to 1000	200	150,000	7000	160	4×10^{-12}	1×10^{-10}	5×10^{-9}
C 2	Measurements and Spectroscopy	2	10 × 1	$1\frac{3}{8}$	$6\frac{3}{8}$*	British 9-pin	20	0·3 to 2·7	2·2	50,000 to 200,000	100 to 150	1000 to 2000	40	5000	200	5	2×10^{-11}	5×10^{-10}	2×10^{-8}
							− 80	0·3 to 3·1	2·4	500,000 to 2·0 M	50 to 100	500 to 1000	200	150,000	7000	200	4×10^{-12}	1×10^{-10}	4×10^{-9}
							−180	0·3 to 3·5	2·5	750,000 to 4·0 M	50 to 100	300 to 700	700	200,000	10,000	300	4×10^{-12}	1×10^{-10}	3×10^{-9}
M 1	Measurements and Pyrometry	2	10 × 1	$\frac{5}{8}$	$\frac{3}{4}$	B3G	20	0·3 to 2·7	2·2	20,000 to 200,000	150	1000 to 2000	40	5000	200	4	2×10^{-11}	5×10^{-10}	$2{\cdot}5 \times 10^{-8}$
M 2	Measurements and Pyrometry	2	5 × 5	$\frac{5}{8}$	$\frac{3}{4}$	B3G	20	0·3 to 2·7	2·2	50,000 to 500,000	100	1000 to 2000	40	5000	200	4	5×10^{-11}	$1{\cdot}25 \times 10^{-9}$	$6{\cdot}25 \times 10^{-8}$

* Without coolant-retaining plunger.

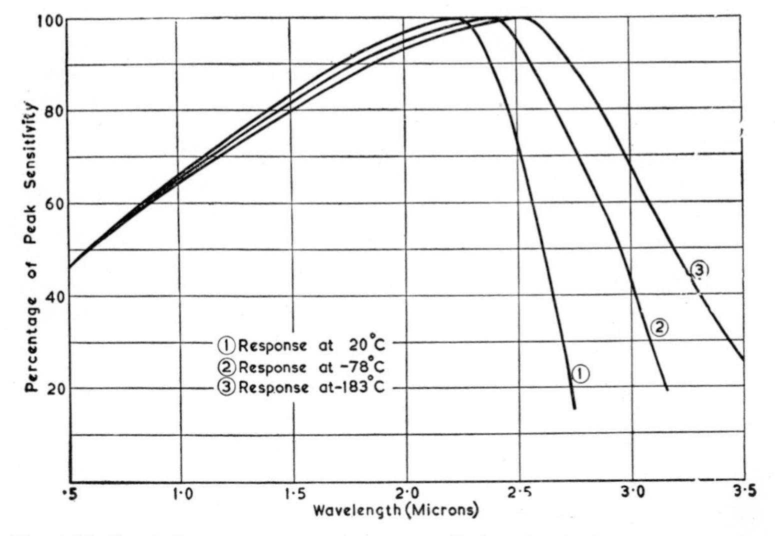

Fig. 4.56. Spectral response to equi-energy radiations impinging at various temperatures on average PbS light-sensitive resistors: curve 1 at room temperature; curve 2 at temperature of solid CO_2; curve 3 at temperature of liquid 0_2.

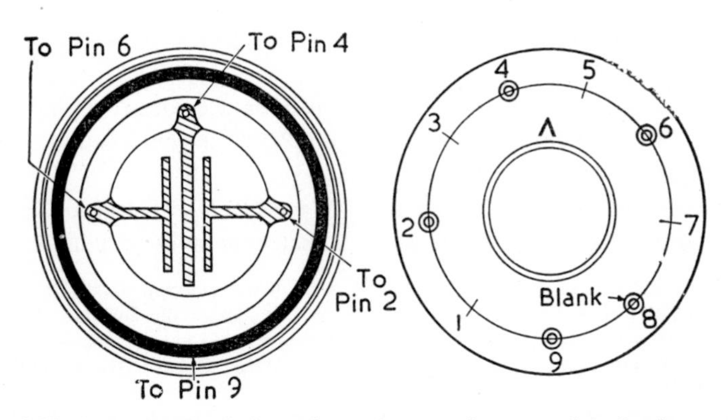

Fig. 4.57. Arrangement of electrodes and connections to valve pins in a type C light-sensitive PbS resistor. (In type C2 the central electrode is omitted. Pin 4 is blank).

telluride cells (*2499,** *2504*) lists some useful data and discusses the applicability of these photosensitive materials in photometric and general purpose circuits.

Other metal sulphides include cadmium sulphide activated with copper (CdS : Cu) (*2492*). The following values relate to a CdS cell with 100V across electrodes 5 cm. long and 0·5 cm. apart. The dark resistance $> 10^{10}$ ohms. The peak sensitivity is at 6000 A.U.

Resistance Values of CdS Light-sensitive Resistors

(Multiplication factor $10^{-8}\ \Omega^{-1}{}_{lux}{}^{-1}$)

Illumination Lx	CdS pure	CdS : Cu	CdS : much Cu at room temp.	CdS : much Cu refrigerated
1	87	9·1	1250	3·85
10	13·3	0·56	33·3	0·37
100	2·5	0·038	0·83	0·04
1000	0·5	0·003	0·038	0·006

The characteristic of CdS light-sensitive resistors is their response between 2500 A.U. and 5200 A.U. which is the maximum spectral sensitivity. In the region mentioned the sensitivity is almost constant, varying between 10 and 25% of the maximum value depending on the strength of the applied electric field which may be anything up to 5000 V/cm.

See the following references for further data on lead sulphide cells (*2493*, *2495*), cadmium-sulphide cells (*2496*), bismuth-sulphide and bismuth-telluride cells (*2473*).

CdS cells are discussed in detail by Weiss (*2509*). Television camera tubes using a metal sulphide or metal selenide layer of a high omhic

* There are one or two technical terms used in the German paper by Görlich which might not be understood by the average student of the German language. These terms are of very recent date and have been formed in an endeavour to keep the German language " clean ", i.e., free from foreign words. The terms in the paper mentioned (*2499*) are :

" Ja-Nein-Vorgänge ", i.e., *yes-no-procedures* = on-off switching;

"Bildfängerröhren ", i.e., *image-catching tubes* = television camera tubes (e.g., emitrons) ;

" Ortungsproblem ", i.e,, *locating problem* = the problem of locating the source or origin of the detected radiation.

" Ortung " is a noun derived from the verb " orten " (to locate) which is derived from " Ort ", a noun meaning a place, a location.

value as the radiation sensitive element will be useful in televising heat processes where the maximum of the emission centres at about 10,000 A.U. The long-wave threshold is 35,000 A.U. (*2150*).

Hexagonal CdS crystals have found useful applications in the high-speed automatic X-ray inspection of homogeneous materials, e.g., in the inspection of packaged goods (rate: 600/min.) or for checking

Cadmium Light-sensitive Resistors

material	longwave peak A.U.	longwave limit A.U.
CdS	5200	9000
CdSe	7400	11000 (*2512*)
CdTe	8500	12000

Lead Light-sensitive Resistors

Temperature °K	Sensitivity peak A.U.	Sensitivity limit A.U.		
	Material PbS	PbS	PbSe	PbTe
290	22000	34000	*	*
195	28000	38000	42000	44000
90	34000	44000	56000	57000
20	37000	47000	*	64000
				(*2505*)

continuity and position of the metal core of electric cables, etc. Individual CdS crystals show variations (up to 1:100) in sensitivity to the incident X-radiation. The dark resistance is proportional to the thickness of the crystal. There is inherent amplification, each electron leaving the crystal causing 10^4 to 10^5 electrons to be carried from the cathode to the anode in a field of 5000 V/cm. This amplification is increased if the exciting radiation is made to strike the crystal near the cathode. Illumination of the crystal with green light (5200 A.U.) will increase the A.C. component of the current while blue and red light have the opposite effect. Green light also reduces stabilization time (*2573; 2574*).

The galena-wire-mesh photo-sensitive arrangement (Bleiglanznetzzellen) using natural PbS crystals (German Pat. Appl. S 116024 VIII c/21 g, inventor F. Michelssen (*2546*)) is also discussed in some detail. A certain inertia in the response of photosensitors in general to the impact of radiation is observed. This inertia or reaction delay (which may be likened to the physiological reaction time) is :

10 μs	for PbS
1 μs	for Bleiglanznetzzellen
< 0·1 μs	for photo-emissive cells (photosensitors showing the external photo-electric effect)

The frequency characteristic of PbS cells has been found by Kolomiets (*2508*) to be 100% at 0 c/s and 70% at 10 kc/s.

Bismuth-sulphide light-sensitive resistors have been built for practical applications (*2519*). Their spectral sensitivity covers the luminous part of the spectrum (*2473*).

Germanium is also a light-sensitive resistor (*2515*, *2516*, *2537*) and cells have been made with the threshold at from 17,000 to 19,000 A.U. The lower limit of spectral sensitivity is at 5600 A.U. The frequency response is flat up to 200 kc/s which will be of paramount importance in a great many applications. The overall quantum efficiency is very good, in fact 3 to 4 photo-electrons for each incident quantum at peak sensitivity (15,000 A.U.).

A very good review for 1949 of the characteristics of infra-red detectors and a large bibliography of recent publications on that subject is given by Sutherland and Lee (*2506*) and by König (*2517*) for the period covering the last ten years. König's bibliography has some 500 entries.

Bibliography Reference: (*2036*)

4.52. Ceramic Resistors

A quite different type of light-sensitive resistor is described by Eugene Wainer (*399*, *1275*). It is a ceramic material, viz., titanium dioxide which, under specified conditions (chemical constitution and manufacturing process) exhibits a marked photo-conductivity. The ceramic body consists in the main of 90 parts by weight of TiO_2 with additions of various titanates or oxides of barium, magnesium, zinc, cadmium, strontium, lead, etc. Best results are produced by a combination of titanium dioxide with oxides or titanates of divalent elements.

Ratios of dark-to-light resistance vary from 10 : 1 to 16 : 1 according to the chemical composition as is borne out in the following Table.

Good photo-conductive properties, including a high ratio of dark-to-light resistance, are attained when the ceramic mass is heated so as to form a non-porous, dense material, the mass being overfired and flashed in a reduced atmosphere while overfiring. Overfired titanium dioxide exists as titanium sesquioxide Ti_2O_3 and, in this state, contains the lower valent oxides of iron, manganese, chromium, or vanadium,

TABLE 4.24

Ceramic Resistors

TiO_2	Admixtures all p.b.w.	Ratio of Dark-to-Light Resistance
90	10 $BaTiO_3$	10:1
	2 $PbTiO_3$; 8 $BaTiO_3$	13·85:1
	8 $PbTiO_3$; 2 $BaTiO_3$	16:1
	5 $PbTiO_3$; 5 $SrTiO_3$	12·5:1
95	1 $PbTiO_3$; 4 $SrTiO_3$	14·3:1

all of which are blue or green, respectively ; this colour is indicative of a strong absorption of red light. The colour of the light resistor, on exposure to light, changes towards blue-brown, blue-black, or lavender. A fired body consisting chiefly of crystalline titanium dioxide having a blue-green tinge will exhibit the highest dark-to-light ratio. It is important to notice that the correctly composed and fired titanium light-sensitive resistor is stable under practically all atmospheric conditions and exhibits but a negligible time lag and fatigue : for nearly all practical purposes the return from light to dark resistance may be termed " instantaneous ". The peak of the spectral sensitivity is in the red. A characteristic absorption has been found in Ti_2O to be located at 4000 A.U. which is the fundamental lattice absorption at 3·06 eV (*2572*). The titanium light-sensitive resistor can be subjected to high temperatures and can be formed into any size or shape as a ceramic. The resistors are rigid and chemically as well as physically stable. The electrodes can be fired on to the surface of the ceramic body and can be given any suitable arrangement. Either side of a disk-shaped body exhibits the photo-conductive effect and the ceramic material is light-sensitive throughout its mass which makes it possible to use it in a powdered state as well. During the second World War the manufacturing process has been covered by secrecy orders which tends to prove that this new photo-electric device will be of considerable importance to all practical applications, and this the more as the ambient temperatures can be in excess of anything known for the usual type of photo-electric devices.

Bibliography Reference: (*1065*)

4.53. Photolytic Cells

Edmond Becquerel (*106*), when experimenting with Voltaic cells (*213*) a modification of the Voltaic Pile, discovered that, if one of the two electrodes immersed in the liquid electrolyte was irradiated with luminous energy, this electrode showed a potential difference against the unilluminated electrode (*214, p. 273*). At first, electrochemical processes in the cell were held responsible for the appearance of an electromotive force and it was not until 1914 that the electronic theory was substituted (*114*). It is for this reason that the photo-e.m.f. cell of to-day has been called " photo-voltaic " since either of these devices generates an e.m.f.

However, recent research has reached back to the original " Voltaic cell " and the Becquerel effect has been produced on a very much improved basis. The liquid electrolyte, sometimes thought to be a handicap in industrial applications of this type of cell has been replaced in some models by a solid porous material holding the electrolyte adsorbed and keeping the metal electrodes moist. Much in this respect had been learned from the manufacture of primary cells and accumulators.

One of the first practical photolytic cells was described by Fink and Alpern (*215*) in 1930 intended for industrial use : it is a cuprous-oxide on copper cell. This material forms the negative electrode, lead is the positive electrode and both are immersed in 35 c.c. of a 1% solution of lead nitrate which is photo-chemically inert, Fig. 4.58. The average sensitivity of this cell is 150 μA/Lm, the maximum sensitivity centring at about 4600 A.U. The photo-electric current *v* illumination curve is linear up to 100 Lm/sq. ft. A dark current of 0·15 μA flows, but in sunshine the cell yields 15,000 μA. The normally expected maximum load of the cathode (8 cm^2) is 25 to 50 μA according to the type of cell. The overload capacity for a short time is 600 times the normal rating. Up to about 10 kc/s distortion is hardly noticeable, but the most serious drawback, is the short life expectancy: 200 to 300 hours.

J. R. Bost and Th. J. Ladshaw, Jr., have described an improved photolytic cell (*216*) as having a cuprous-oxide surface covered with an acid solution of an alkali metal salt such as KOAc, and a co-operating electrode.

The most recent photolytic cell is of the selenium type (*1612*). It consists of a metal electrode which is coated with metallic selenium (cathode), another selenium or platinum electrode (anode), both

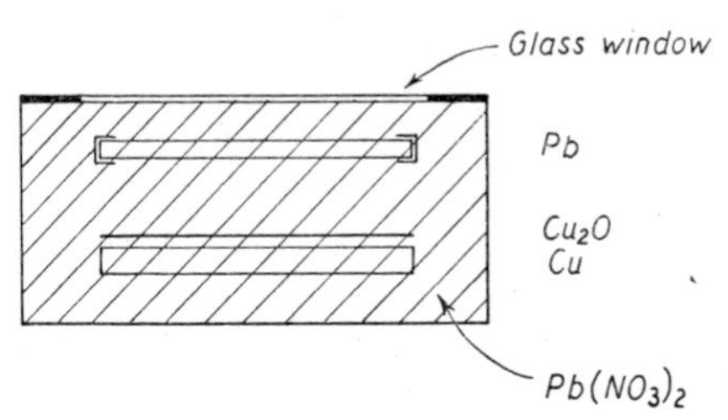

Fig. 4.58. Structure of a photolytic cell.

immersed in an aqueous solution of selenium dioxide. The spectral sensitivity has the long-wave threshold at about 8000 A.U., its maximum at about 5550 A.U. (which also is the maximum response of the human eye) and it is highly sensitive in the blue, violet and ultra-violet region. A second maximum of higher absolute value than in the luminous range seems to be located in the medium ultra-violet. The photo-electric yield is 4 μA/μW.

The cell can also be employed as a light-sensitive resistor with a maximum external voltage of 4V. With only 2V across the short-circuit current is of the order of 1000 μA/Lm.

Bibliography References: (*1230*, *1709*, *1714*, *2319*)

4.54. Germanium Photosensitors

Use is made here of the phenomenon that a germanium p–n junction, upon illumination, produces an increased current which is directly proportional to the illumination. It is essential to bias the crystal in the high impedance (reverse) direction with a suitable d.c. voltage up to a maximum of 50 V. The resulting saturation current is practically independent of the applied external electrical pressure, but is proportional to the incident light.

It is a very useful feature of germanium photosensitors that their geometrical dimensions are very small indeed. The overall size of the

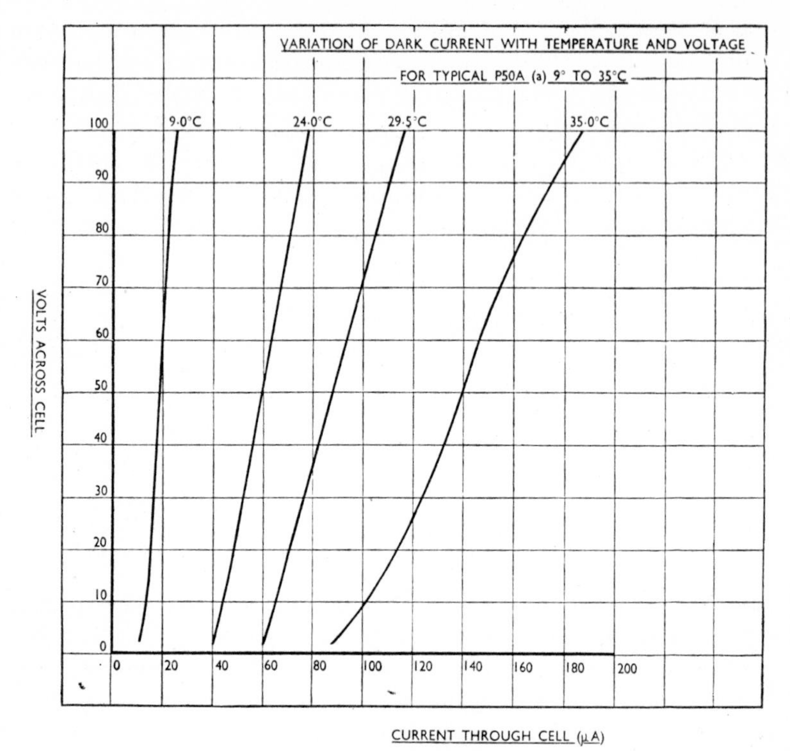

Fig. 4.59 a. Dark current is a function of temperature and voltage across the germanium photosensitor.

crystal is but 0·06″ × 0·03″ × 0·02″, the light-sensitive surface being 0·06″ × 0·02″. The light ray is thus made to strike across the larger of the two exposed p–n junctions. The equivalent active area is 0·06″ × 0·004″ (1·5 mm. × 0·1 mm.).

Mechanically, the germanium photosensitor displays compactness with robustness to a considerable degree. The crystal is built into a metal cup of 7/32″ (5·6 mm.) O.D. and 11/32″ (8·8 mm.) length. This container is hermetically sealed with a glass disc or bulb. The weight is 0·02 oz. (0·6 g).

Electrically, these photosensitors are very stable with time and temperature. The normal operating temperature is 35°C ambient, although it is permissible, though not recommended, to operate the germanium photosensitor in ambient temperatures up to 45° C, and

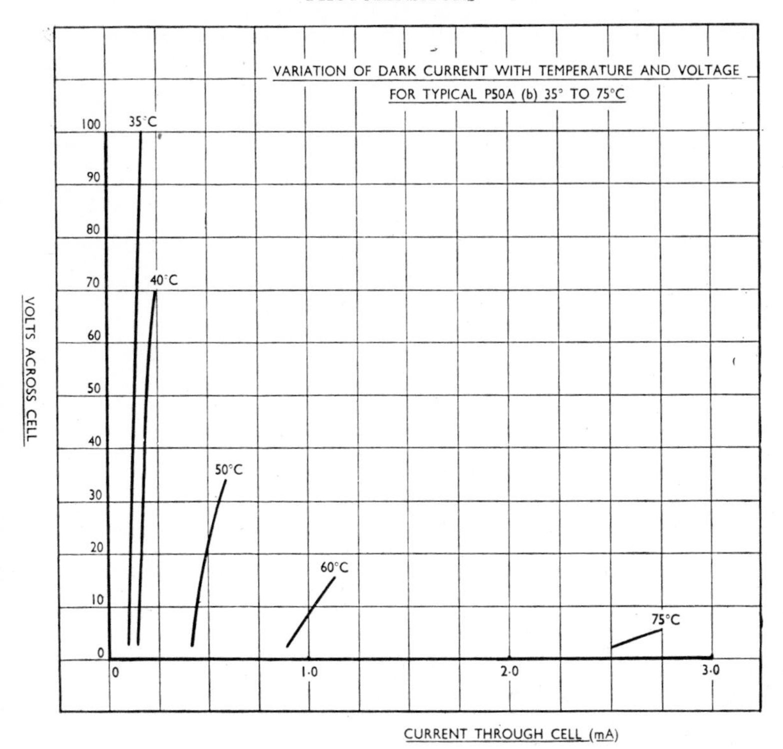

Fig. 45.9 b. Dark current is a function of temperature and voltage across the germanium photosensitor.

even as high as 75° C., if sight is not lost of the fact that under extreme conditions the dark current will rise sharply, thus reducing the stability of the circuit and minimize the reliability of operation. Fig. *4.59 a, b.*

The light-sensitivity of germanium photosensitors is better than that of photo-electric cells of both the vacuous and gasfilled type. The centre electrode of a germanium photosensitor is biased positive against the metal case which forms the negative electrode. The light-sensitivity is 30 mA/Lm (tungsten lamp at colour temperature 2500° K) and reaches its peak in the near infra-red between 1·6 and 1·7 μ. The sensitivity in the maximum region is 1·0 μA/mW/cm². The long-wave cutoff is at 2 μ, the short-wave cutoff at 3000 A.U. which, as the shape of the sensitivity curve in Fig. 46.0 shows, is not due to the filtering action of the glass seal. The maximum ratio between extreme sensitivities of any given germanium photosensitor is not in excess of 3 : 1 for uniform illumination.

Other characteristic data of the type P50A photosensitor, are:

Bias voltage		Current	
recommended	50 V.	max. output	2·5 mA.
maximum	100 V.	max. dark 50V,	0·25 mA.
minimum	1 V.	min. dynamic resistance at 50V,	1 M.Ω
Max. dissipation	50 mW	max. operating frequency	50 kc/s.

Like in all semiconductors, noise is produced in considerable excess of the noise to be expected on theoretical grounds. The actual value of

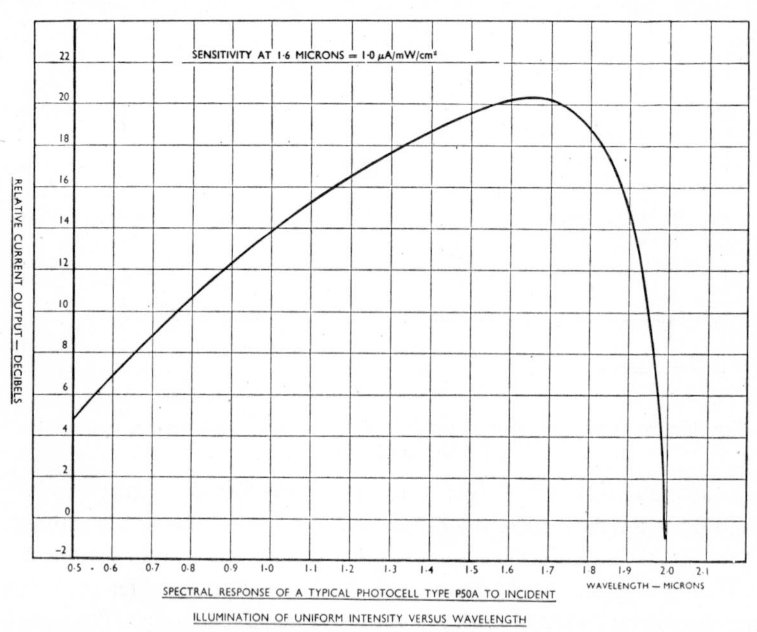

Fig. 4.60. Radiation sensitivity of a germanium photosensitor type P50A.

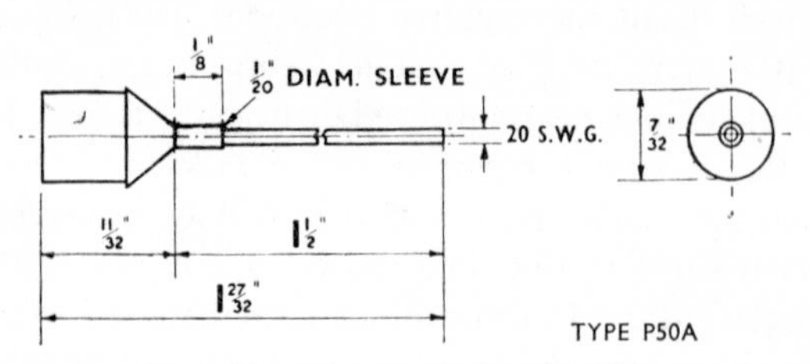

Fig. 4.61. Outline drawing of a germanium photosensitor type P50A.
(*Standard Telephones & Cables Ltd.*)

the excess noise is very small. The excess noise power is inversely proportional to the frequency.

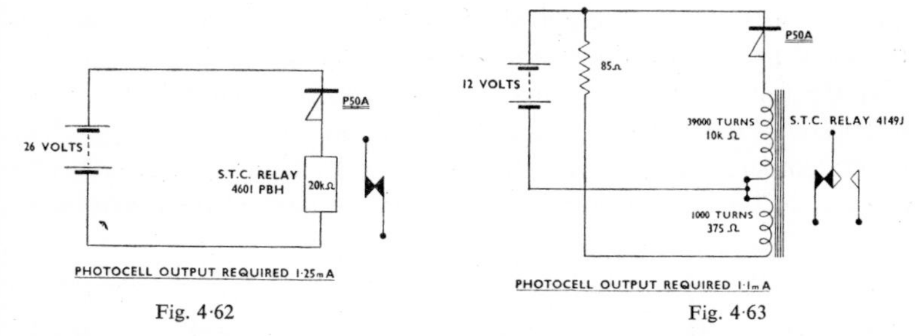

Fig. 4·62 Fig. 4·63

Fig. 4.62. Low speed operation, using a Post Office relay type 3000. Coil resistance 20,000 ohm, operating current 1 mA., releasing current <0·5 mA. Dark current at 20° C. will be 60 μ amp; at 35° C. it will be 200 μ amp.

Fig. 4.63. High speed operation, using a polarized telegraph relay which will operate on d.c. or a.c. of up to 50 c/s. A bi-stable relay is usually fitted, i.e., one where resetting the relay is done by passing current through the secondary winding. For increased sensitivity, the photosensitor is used in a centre-stable wiring diagram and 0·5 mA. is sufficient to operate the relay.

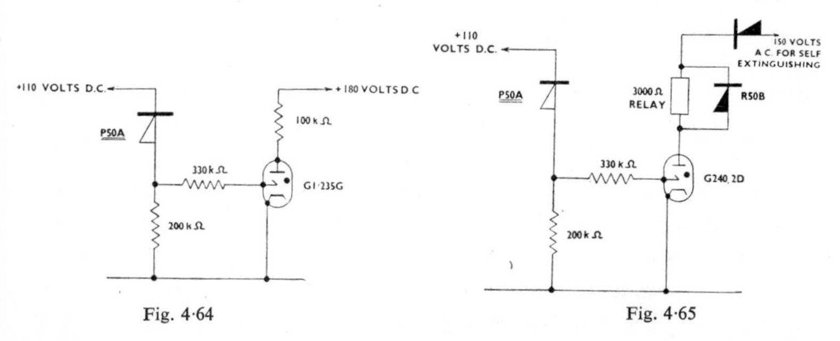

Fig. 4·64 Fig. 4·65

Fig. 4.64. A small cold cathode gasfilled triode can be controlled by the germanium photosensitor.

Fig. 4.65. If the gas triode is wired to operate an electromagnetic power relay, a means must be provided for extinguishing the triode. This is done here by supplying the anode with rectified a.c. Chatter is prevented by shunting the relay with a germanium rectifier R50B.

4.55. Dark Space Radiation

There is present in space infra-red radiant energy of medium wavelengths which, even at ordinary room temperature (290°K.), is the cause of considerable trouble to workers using devices sensitive to infra-red radiation of between 20,000 A.U. and 40,000 A.U. In infra-red photography this dark space radiation heavily fogs the sensitized photographic material while it is exposed to the radiation of the infra-red source to be photographed. In photo-electric work this random radiation produces a disturbing amount of dark current.

In the following Table which is adapted from an early work by M. Czerny (*1470*) the Dark Quanta incident on a surface of 1 cm.² at room temperature are given in column (2). It is not the absolute amount of the dark quanta but the ratio of dark space radiation to

TABLE 4.25

(1) Range of Wavelengths	(2) Dark Quanta	(3) Artificial Quanta	(4) Ratio	(5) Number of Air Mols.	(6) Equivalent Distance
10000 A.U.	$1{\cdot}5 \times 10^{0}$	$0{\cdot}4 \times 10^{16}$	$3{\cdot}75 \times 10^{-16}$	$5{\cdot}5 \times 10^{3}$	3333000 m
15000 ,,	$0{\cdot}95 \times 10^{7}$	$1{\cdot}4 \times 10^{16}$	$6{\cdot}8 \times 10^{-10}$	$5{\cdot}8 \times 10^{10}$	1360 m
20000 ,,	$2{\cdot}0 \times 10^{10}$	$1{\cdot}5 \times 10^{16}$	$1{\cdot}34 \times 10^{-6}$	$1{\cdot}5 \times 10^{14}$	29 m
25000 ,,	$1{\cdot}8 \times 10^{12}$	$1{\cdot}3 \times 10^{16}$	$1{\cdot}4 \times 10^{-4}$	$1{\cdot}6 \times 10^{16}$	3 m
30000 ,,	$3{\cdot}5 \times 10^{13}$	$1{\cdot}0 \times 10^{16}$	$3{\cdot}5 \times 10^{-3}$	$3{\cdot}7 \times 10^{17}$	0·71 m
40000 ,,	$1{\cdot}2 \times 10^{15}$	$1{\cdot}4 \times 10^{16}$	$0{\cdot}86 \times 10^{-1}$	$1{\cdot}7 \times 10^{19}$	0·12 m

artificial radiation which causes disturbances. In column (3) the number of quanta present in various spectral regions (column (1)) of artificially caused radiation is listed. In the next column the ratio of the quanta shows how quickly the critical ratio ONE (unity), is reached. In column (5) the number of air molecules is given which, at 15° C. and 760 mm. Hg, strike a surface of 1 cm.² with such a velocity that the kinetic energy of the impact produces a quantum of corresponding wavelength. For wavelengths > 20,000 A.U. the figures in columns (5) and (2), respectively, differ in general by a factor of 10,000.

Dark space radiation is of no practical significance if photosensitors are used the sensitivity of which ranges up to about 15,000 A.U. With modern thallium-sulphide (long-wave threshold at 14,500 A.U.) and lead-sulphide photosensitors (long-wave threshold at 36,000 A.U.; peak at 25,000 A.U.) (*1467*) the dark current reaches intolerable proportions. The only way of excluding dark space radiation from the immediate neighbourhood of an infra-red sensitive photosensitor is the reduction of the ambient temperature (*1469*). According to the Wien-Paschen law the dominant wavelength of a radiation is inversely proportional to the absolute temperature of the radiant body. Dry ice, liquid air, and others, are convenient refrigerants (*1678*, *2429*, *2435*). E. F. Coleman (*1468*) has been operating light-sensitive resistors of the sulphide type at temperatures as low as – 78°C. (– 110°F.) when using dry ice, and – 183°C. (– 298°F.) when using liquid oxygen. As an immediate result a very marked reduction in dark current due to thermionic emission (and ion feedback) took place which, in turn, made it possible to lower the illumination threshold by about 15 db. (*2505*, *2569*)

The significance of the dark space radiation becomes obvious when column (6) of Table 4.25 is considered. In it, the distances are given at which a Nernst burner* must be placed from the sensitive surface if the number of quanta falling on 1 cm.^{2} per sec. is to be the same as that of the dark quanta in column (2).

* Nernst burners are very effective sources of infra-red radiation. There are electrically-operated types commercially available, for instance one under the trade name of Globar, which uses a rod of silicon carbide as a source of infra-red radiation.

CHAPTER 5

BASIC CIRCUITS

In this chapter a series of arrangements is termed *basic circuits*, because they are typical of whole groups rather than of individual applications and may be altered according to the requirements of specific practice (*217*).

5.1. Basic Circuits for Photo-electric Cells

The direct output of a photo-electric cell of the vacuum or gas-filled variety is too small to energize an electromagnetic relay. There are on the market a very few types of hypersensitive relays (e.g., Sangamo Weston S54, S115) which are operated by a few microamps,

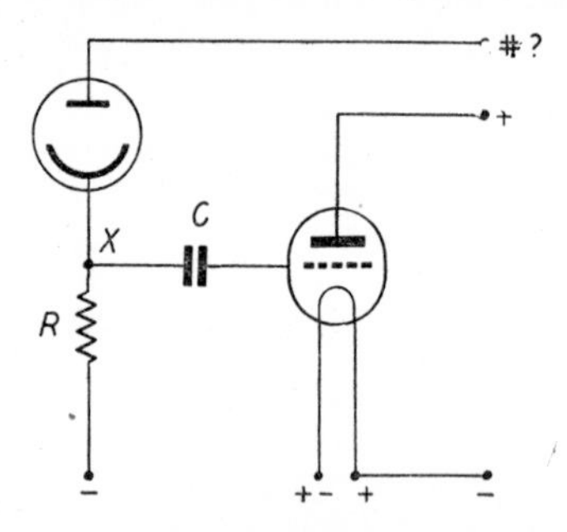

Fig. 5.1. Basic photo-cell amplifier circuit.

but these instruments mostly lack the sturdiness and ruggedness required by industrial gear and are therefore confined to the laboratory. The photo-electric cell will however deliver a relatively large voltage change which can be made to control an electronic amplifier. Essentially, the latter is a voltage amplifying device (the electron-multiplier is a current amplifier) and is well suited to the conditions characteristic of photo-electric practice (*96*, *218*, *219*, *220*). In general the amplifier is based on the simple circuit Fig. 5.1. The voltage changes in X, following the fluctuations in the irradiation of the photo-electric cathode, are transferred to the grid of the amplifier valve and control its anode current. There are many ways of connecting a photo-electric

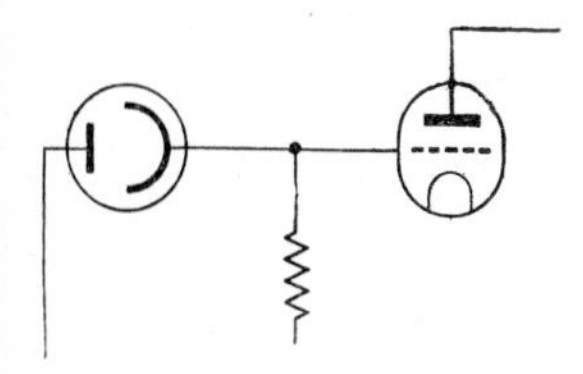

Fig. 5.2. Basic 'forward' circuit, in which an increase in light causes an increase in photo-current.

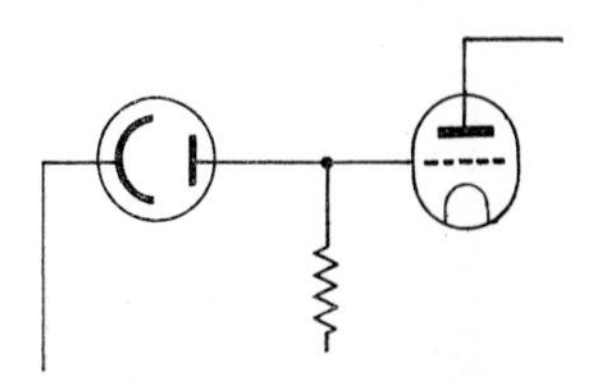

Fig. 5.3. Basic negative, backward, or reverse circuit. An increase in incident radiant energy causes a decrease in photo-current.

cell to an electronic valve but there are only three fundamental results attainable with any of these :

(*a*) an INCREASE in the radiant energy incident on the photo-electric cell causes an INCREASE in photo-current ; this circuit is called *positive*, *forward*, or *obverse* ; (Fig. 5.2)

(*b*) an INCREASE in the radiant energy incident on the photo-electric cell causes the photo-electric current to DECREASE ; this circuit is termed *negative*, *backward*, or *reverse* ; (Fig. 5.3)

(*c*) a simultaneous change in the irradiation of both photosensitors of a balanced two-cell circuit does not affect the existing conditions. The circuit is thrown out of balance if the irradiation of only one cell is changed. (Fig. 5.4.)

The combination of a photosensitor, an electronic amplifier and—if necessary—an electromagnetic relay or contactor, is known as a photo-relay or photo-electric relay. An electromagnetic relay can be operated either by a current which flows continuously, an interruption of this current actuating the relay, or which is operated by a current which flows only during the time the relay is desired to operate. In either case the contacts can be made to open or close a secondary or power circuit.

A balanced two-cell circuit utilizing the high amplification of multiplier cells is shown in Fig. 5.5. This circuit has been designed for quantitative spectro-chemical analysis but it is obvious that it can be used successfully where a highly sensitive high-amplification two-cell circuit is necessary (*221*). The practical combinations of the elements of photo-relays are shown in Table 5.1.

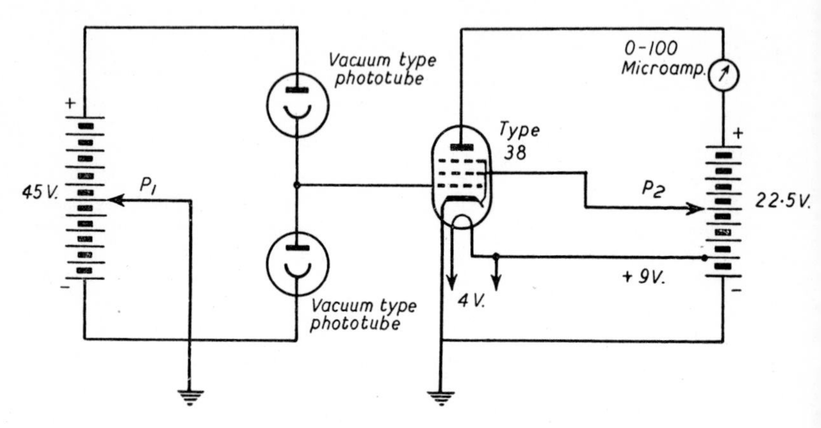

Fig. 5.4. Sensitive balanced circuit for matching measurements.

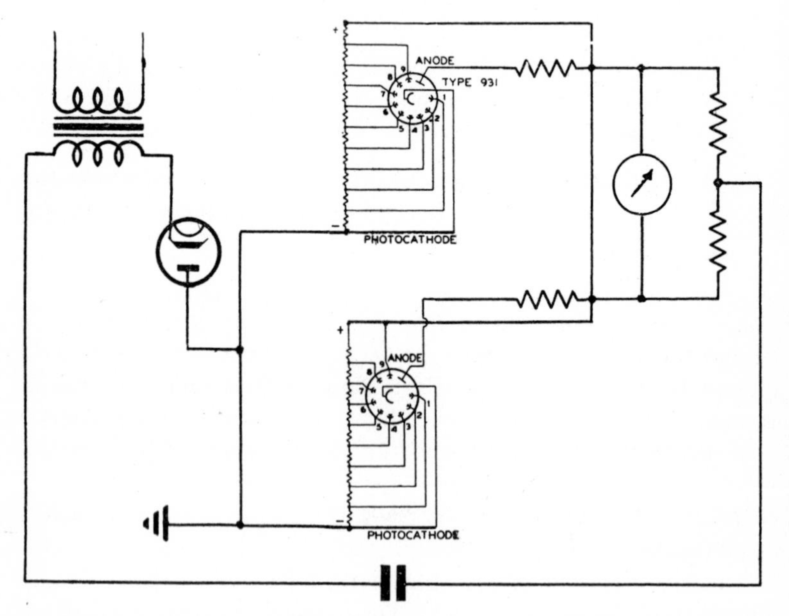

Fig. 5.5. A balanced two-cell circuit utilizing the high amplification of photo-multipliers.

TABLE 5.1

Action of Photo-relays

Photosensitor	photo-current increases		photo-current decreases	
Electromagnetic Relay	energized		de-energized	
Load Circuit	open	closed	open	closed
Action	reverse	forward	reverse	forward

Fig. 5.6 shows a simple control circuit using one stage of triode amplification (RCA), and Fig. 5.7 shows a pentode connected as a

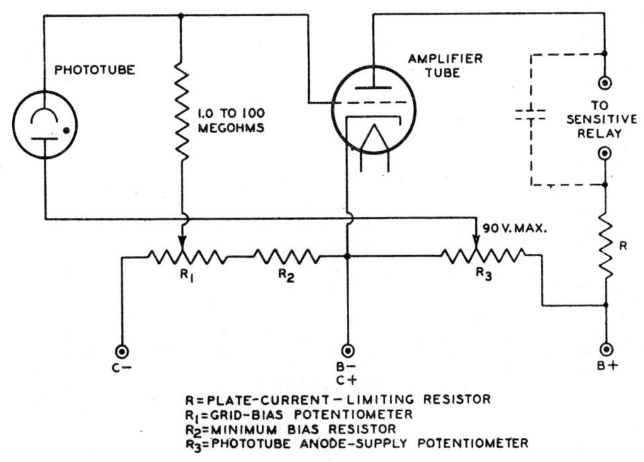

Fig. 5.6. Photo-cell control circuit using a triode. This circuit can be A.C. mains operated if the supply is connected to C − and B +.

triode. In Fig. 5.8 the pentode is followed by a double triode for further amplification, or a thyratron (EN31) can be used to control current through the relay. The output of the cell is directly coupled into the grid circuit of the ME1400, the cathode load resistor acting as the grid resistor of the following valve.

By connecting the two halves of the ECC33 in parallel the cut-off point remains unaltered but the current change at the anodes is doubled. In order to obtain maximum sensitivity with this circuit the bleeder current through the resistors R1 and R2 should be high compared with the current through the valve.

It will be noted that the subsequent amplification of the cell output must be direct—coupled to follow the current changes, and the inclusion of a capacitor will effectively isolate the grid of the following valve. The use of pentodes as amplifiers is discussed in references *288*, *289*.

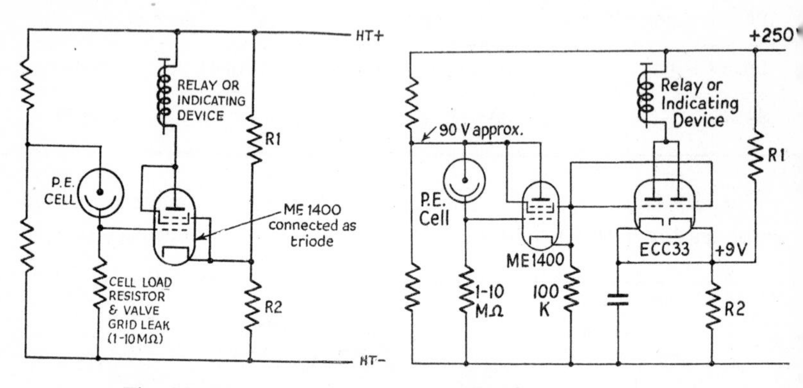

Fig. 5.7. Control circuit using pentode connected as a triode.

Fig. 5.8. Control circuit using additional amplification.

Fig. 5.9 shows a method of changing from positive action to negative action by means of a changeover switch, and circuits involving this principle are given in Figs. 5.10 and 5.11. In the negative action circuits the increasing photo-current causes the grid of the power valve to become more negative and so results in decreasing anode current.

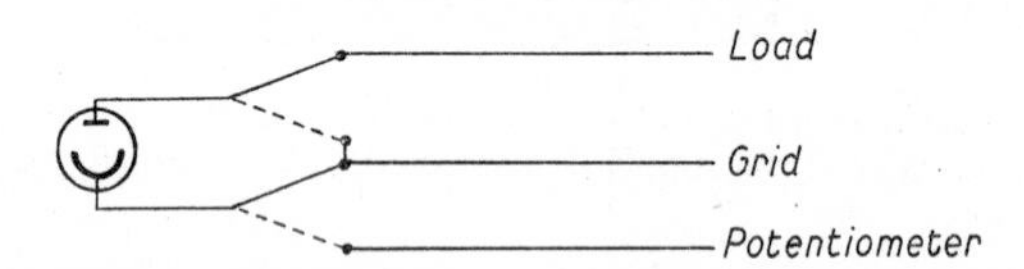

Fig. 5.9. Switching arrangement for alternatively positive or negative circuit.

The balanced two-cell circuit nearly always is based on the principle of two photosensitors being connected in an inverse-parallel circuit in that the anode of the one photo-electric cell is connected to the cathode of the other cell. If an equal amount of light falls upon either cell the electrical equilibrium of the circuit is maintained. A graphical representation of this condition, Fig. 5.12, depicts (a) and (b) as the respective characteristics of the two photosensitors (A) and (B), the

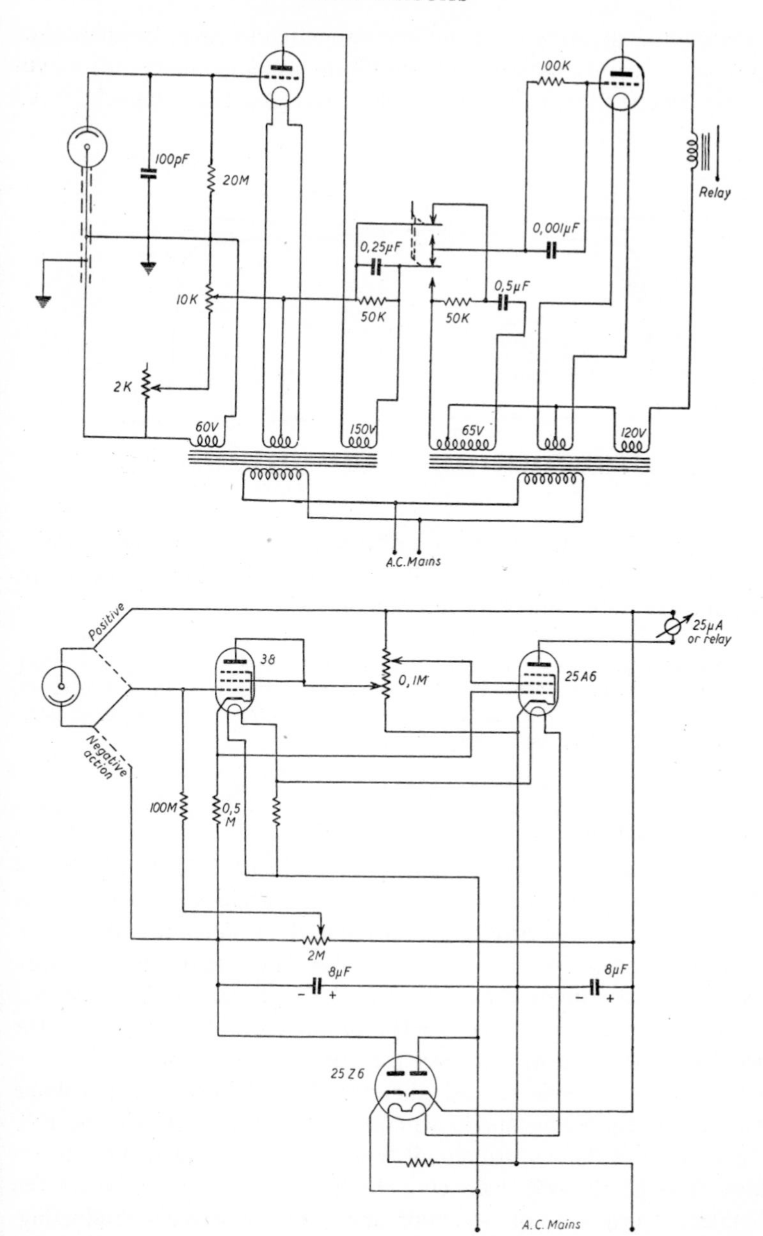

Figs. 5.10 and 5.11. Two circuits showing different arrangements for the operation of the relay either on increasing or decreasing light.

intersection *P* marking the point corresponding to equal irradiation of both cells. If the irradiation of cell (*A*) is decreased, curve (a) moves to (a′), intersection now taking place at (*Q*). The relatively small

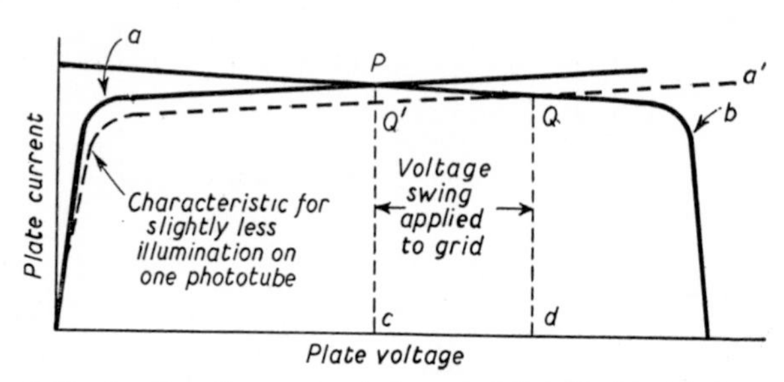

Fig. 5.12. Anode voltage-current characteristic of balanced photo-cells.

difference (PQ') in the irradiation of the respective cells ($PQ' = Pc - dQ$) causes the relatively large voltage swing (QQ'). The current in the output stage is dependent on this voltage swing.

Bibliography References: (*1702, 1710, 1832, 1855, 1860, 1865, 1874, 1879, 1880, 1926, 1957, 1960, 1978, 1979, 2008, 2010, 2061, 2062, 2093, 2102, 2106, 2110, 2127, 2131, 2140, 2142, 2156, 2163, 2172, 2205, 2208, 2215, 2217, 2229, 2236, 2240, 2241, 2242, 2243, 2271, 2349, 2358, 2364, 2369, 2372, 2375*)

5.2. Amplification

With the advent of the grid-controlled rectifier (1928) the number of stages necessary for the amplification of so small a current as that supplied by photo-electric cells was reduced considerably. As a fact, in ordinary relay operations there is rarely more than one thyratron involved in controlling the load circuit. The thyratron characteristics are such that current is conducted through the thyratron, i.e., the thyratron breaks down whenever the grid potential, which is negative relative to the cathode, exceeds the critical breakdown (firing) voltage for the corresponding anode voltage. When the photo-electric cell, which operates the control circuit (grid circuit) is irradiated a current flows through the cell, balancing the negative grid potential on the thyratron. As a result of this action, the thyratron becomes conducting. Thyratrons are made with one grid only or with a control grid and a shield grid. A general comparison of merit is given in Table 5.2 (*222*).

TABLE 5.2

Comparison of Three and Four-Element Tubes

Advantages of 4-Element Thyratron over 3-Element Tube	Grid Emission	Temperature of Grid	Receives very little heat from anode, cathode or arc stream due to shielding effect of shield grid.
		Contamination of Grid	Grid is protected from sputtered or evaporated material from anode, or cathode coating, by shield grid.
		Photo-electric Current	Small Size
			Shielded from internal light.
	Ion Currents	Before Discharge	Small Size
			Low increase in gradient as anode potential increases causes only small increase in residual ionization.
		After Discharge	Small Size
			Grid removed from ion stream causing low density of ionization at the grid.
	Electron Currents	Negative Tubes	Small Size
			Shielded from electrons coming from cathode due to initial velocities.
		Positive Tubes	Small size collects smaller number of electrons.
	Capacity Effects		Small Grid
			Shielded from anode and cathode by shield grid.
	Leakage Currents	External	No base leakage as control grid lead is located on side of bulb.
		Internal	Leakage inside of tube reduced.
	Characteristic		Characteristic can be adjusted by varying voltage on shield grid.
Disadvantages of 4-Element Tube	Cost		Slight increase in cost.
	Mechanical		Extra connexion is required for control grid.
			Slightly greater size.

Note: For a comparison between thyratrons and high vacuum valves see H. J. Reich (*100*, *p. 474*).

Typical relay circuits employing four-element thyratrons are shown in Fig. 5.13.

Grid-controlled discharge valves, i.e., thyratrons (hot cathode valves) and ionotrons (cold-cathode valves), respectively, exhibit the *lock-in* feature if D.C. operated. This means that the control grid, once it has started conduction through the valve, loses control of the discharge which now can be interrupted only by opening the anode circuit or lowering the anode voltage sufficiently. This lock-in feature is particularly desirable if an operation or process is to be started by a given value of an impulse but further changes in intensity are not allowed to interfere with the operation. For resetting a D.C.-operated thyratron the anode voltage is best removed completely for such a period of time as is greater than, or at least equal to, the de-ionization

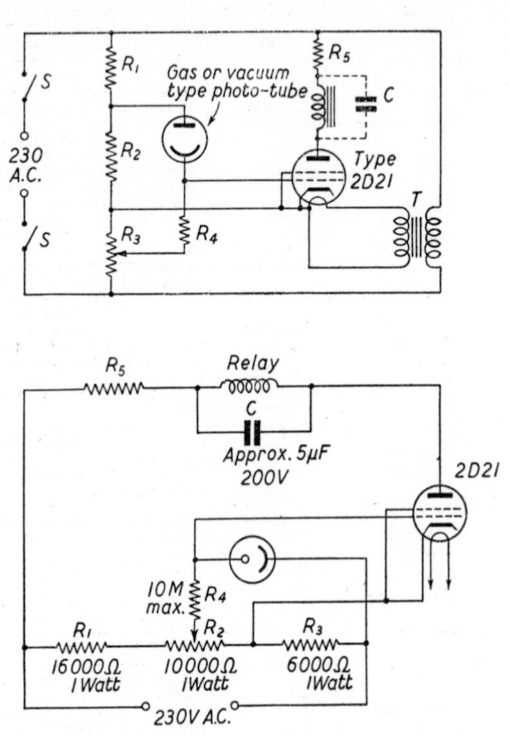

Fig. 5.13. Two A.C. mains operated relay circuits.

time (*1475*) of a particular valve. If automatic resetting is desired a relay of the instantaneous, or delayed-release, type may be used, its load contacts being closed in the rest position and connected in series with the relay coil. For rapid switching rates hydrogen-filled thyratrons are used (*1471, 1606, 1649, 1696*) because of the very short de-ionization time which is characteristic of that gas. Other than mechanical or electromagnetic means must then be adopted.

The Mullard helium-filled triode thyratron type EN 31 has a very low grid current. This enables the valve to be operated directly by a photosensitor.

Principal Characteristics of Thyratrons.

	*EN*31	2*D*21
Type	Triode	Tetrode
Gas	Helium	Xenon
Control ratio	35	250
Min. preheating time	15 sec.	10 sec.
Max. peak anode voltage	1000 V	650 V
Max. peak anode to grid voltage	1500 V	1300 V
Voltage drop	33 V	8 V
Max. peak anode current	750 mA	500 mA
Max. mean anode current	10 mA	100 mA
Heater voltage	6·3 V	6·3 V

There is no lock-in feature if the valves are A.C. operated. The anode current decreases to zero during negative half-cycles of the A.C. anode voltage because the anode becomes negative with respect to the cathode. As long as the grid potential is less negative than the critical value, i.e., the value of the grid potential at which an anode current starts, the valve will fire and conduct during positive half-cycles ; a more negatively biased grid will, however, prevent conduction during positive half-cycles. A change in grid potential therefore controls the anode current. A circuit which may be operated either on A.C. or D.C. is shown in Fig. 5.14a. The values of the bleeder resistances R_1 and R_2 are :

$$R_1 \,.\, i_f = e_{ac} \qquad\qquad R_2 \,.\, i_f = e_{av}$$

$$E = (R_1 + R_2) \,.\, i_f$$

where E . . . mains voltage

e_{ac} . . . rated anode voltage of the photo-cell

e_{av} . . . rated anode voltage of the electron valve

i_f . . . filament current of the valve.

If the circuit is used on A.C. a 500 pF capacitor should be connected between grid and earth. To prevent the relay from rattling, its coil should be shunted by a 2 to 4 μF capacitor or the relay should be of the lag coil or shaded-pole type (copper ring or cylinder).

A suggestion to replace the voltage dropping resistor by a capacitor if the electronic device is A.C. operated was made by G. S. Light (*223*). The capacitance is calculated from $R_c = 1/2\pi fC$ where $R_c = E/I$ and

I is total current consumed by all valves, E is the voltage across the capacitor, and f is the mains frequency. Ultimately, the required capacitance takes the form :

$$C = \frac{10^6 \cdot I}{2\pi f \sqrt{E^2_{mains} - (\Sigma ne)^2}}$$

where n_1 is the number of valves consuming the current I at heater voltage e_1,
n_2 is the number of valves consuming the current I at heater voltage e_2,
etc.

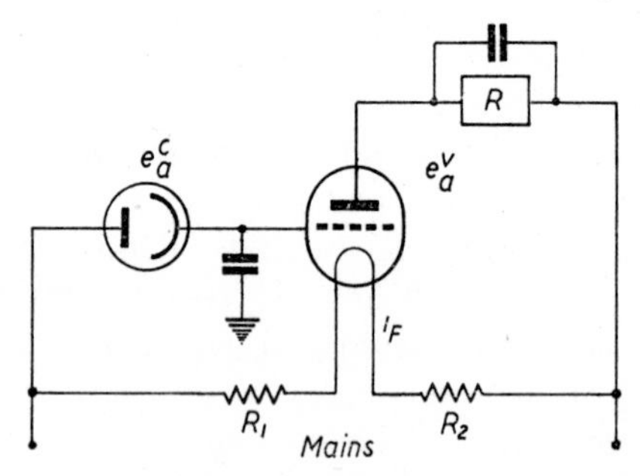

Fig. 5.14 (a). Relay circuit for operation from either A.C. or D.C.

The advantages of the series-capacitor arrangement over the more orthodox series-resistor are enumerated by G. S. Light, as follows :

Advantages :

(1) indefinitely long life ;
(2) less power drawn from the mains ;
(3) practically no heat to dissipate ;
(4) self-compensating for different numbers of valves ;
(5) less damage results if one valve develops a heater-cathode short-circuit.

Disadvantages :

(1) slightly higher initial cost ;
(2) the warming up time is about 3 seconds longer ;
(3) special switching arrangements required for pilot lamps ;
(4) arrangement suitable for A.C. only.

Amplifiers should be of the D.C. type when the light beam rests continuously on the photosensitor, the light source having no or insufficient inherent modulation (*372, 373, 374, 1669*). An A.C. type amplifier will be successfully used if (inherent or superimposed) modulation of the incident beam of radiant energy has been attained. If discrimination must be achieved between a direct current and an

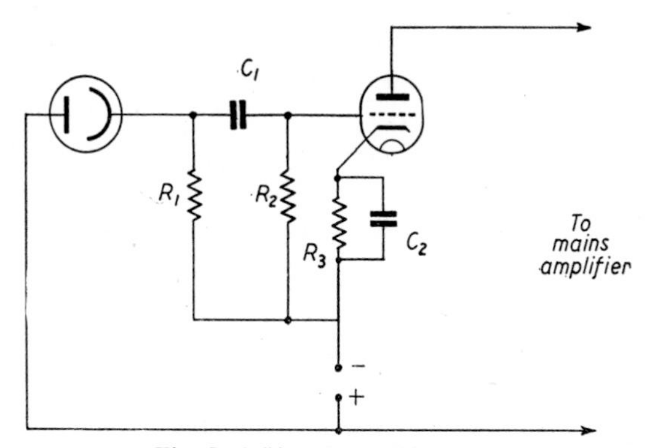

Fig. 5.14 (b). Pre-amplifier stage.

alternating current component of the photo-electric output, a resistance-capacitance coupled amplifier is suitable because only the A.C. component can pass through the network. Such an amplifier can also be used as a pre-amplifier stage, Fig. 5.14b, if modulated radiant energy operates the photosensitor (*121, p. 149* ; *156, p. 320* ; *224, p. 50*). The photosensitor must be coupled to the main amplifier by means of a

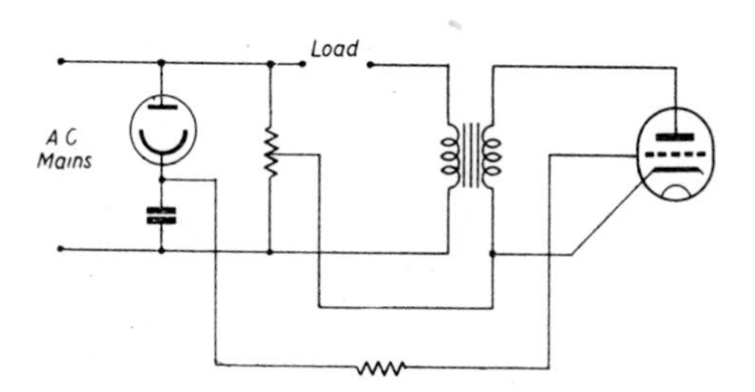

Fig. 5.15. Control circuit in which the load is directly connected to the mains.

resistance-capacitance-coupled valve. Such a circuit converts the modulated impulses of radiant energy into alternating current or voltage impulses.

Amplifiers having a logarithmic response were described by Meagher and Bentley (*382*) and others (*383, 384, 385, 1408*). In a logarithmic amplifier the anode current is linearly proportional to the logarithm of the light intensity for a certain range.

Control by large currents may be achieved by either using high-power thyratrons or, as was shown by H. J. Reich (*100, p. 546*), by means of special circuits which connect the load directly to the mains. This type of circuit responds to modulated impulses as well as to sustained changes of steady radiation, Fig. 5.15.

An amplifier containing no coupling capacitor between the stages was designed by J. F. Scully (*346*). No by-pass capacitor may be used at the input of the double triode, Fig. 5.16, because the high resistance grid resistor, in conjunction with a large capacitance, would introduce an intolerably large time-delay in relay reaction. The inherent inertia

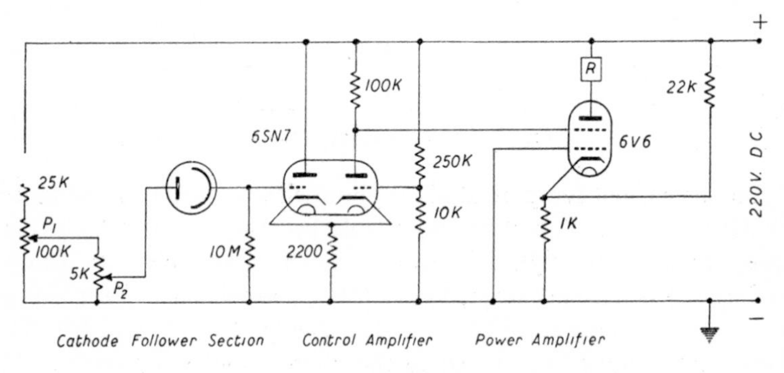

Fig. 5.16. Directly connected amplifier circuit.

of the electromagnetic relay is therefore the only characteristic to limit the speed of the circuit. The circuit is designed for positive action. P_1 is the coarse and P_2 the fine control, respectively. Another arrangement, using only one control, is shown in the inset.

The basic calculations are best shown by the following example. A 50 c.p. lamp is situated 1 m. (= 100 cm.) from a photosensitor whose sensitivity $S = 25\ \mu A/Lm$. The cathode area is 5·0 cm.^{2} The coupling resistor $R = 1$ megohm. The amplification factor μ of the valve is 12, its dynamic anode resistance = 9600 ohms and the mutual conductance 8000 micromhos. The load resistance $R_L = 2000$ ohms.

The light flux on the cathode from the light source will be $\dfrac{50 \times 5}{100^2} =$ $L = 2{\cdot}5 \times 10^{-2}$ lumen. If the anode voltage of the cell is such that the current is saturated, the photo-electric current i_{ph} in the vacuum photosensitor due to the impact of radiant energy, is $L\,.\,S = 0{\cdot}625\ \mu A$. This photo-current i_{ph} flowing through the coupling resistor causes a voltage drop, e.g., $iR = 0{\cdot}625$ V. This change of grid voltage results in a change of voltage across the load resistor $e_L = e_g\mu R_L/$(dyn. anode resist. $+ R_L) = 0{\cdot}625 \times 12 \times 2000/(9600 + 2000) = 2{\cdot}15$ volts. Therefore, the current change in the anode resistor is $i_a = e_L/R_L = 2.15/2000 = 1{\cdot}075\ mA$. The current amplification is $i_a/i_{ph} = 1075/0{\cdot}625 \simeq 1740$. Of the total light output of the lamp, only the fraction given by $\dfrac{\text{cathode area}}{\text{square of distance}}$ is available at the photosensitor. In this instance it is 5×10^{-4} of the lamp's radiation.

Direct current amplification by means of a mirror galvanometer controlling the photosensitor, was described by D. C. Gall (*1679*) and for A.C. by Milatz (*2490*). A photo-electric compensator of very high sensitivity for radiation measurements records D.C. voltages from 1 μV to 1 mV. Spectrum analytical investigations in the region of from 5000 A to 18000 A are made within 10 minutes. A recording instrument is operated directly without further amplification. The paper of the recorder advances 30 mm/min. The zero reference line can be moved to any position, even off the paper. The accuracy is $\pm$ 0·001 μW (*2586*, *2587*). Another system was developed using a high degree of negative feedback. This circuit is especially well suited to receive small voltages from sources having a high internal resistance. A wide frequency region (15 to 100 c/s) is covered. A twin photocell is used in a balanced circuit (*2588*). For a review of present practice and circuits see (*2624*). A control scheme using a tubeless amplifier was described by Fitzgerald (*1695*).

Bibliography References: (*448*, *461*, *481*, *487*, *501*, *513*, *544*, *581*, *1074*, *1170*, *1181*, *1309*, *1314*, *1324*, *1345*, *1347*, *1394*, *1395*, *1396*, *1561*, *1593*, *1903*, *1931*, *1983*, *2043*, *2092*, *2103*, *2128*, *2130*, *2132*, *2136*, *2137*, *2150*, *2154*, *2167*, *2181*, *2196*, *2197*, *2200*, *2206*, *2225*, *2252*, *2253*, *2259*, *2278*, *2286*, *2288*, *2310*, *2323*, *2328*, *2347*, *2378*, *2393*).

5.3. Phase-Shifting Circuits

The property of a resistor and capacitor, or resistor and inductor, when connected across an electron valve, of shifting the phase between the grid and anode voltages, has been used in controlling a power circuit by means of a photosensitor replacing the resistor (*225*, *226*, *227*, *228*). The grid resistor R limits the grid voltage to a safe value,

Fig. 5.17. The grid voltage is the more out of phase with the anode voltage the more the resistance of the photo-electric cell approaches infinite value. With no light striking the photo-cathode the respective voltages will be 180° out of phase (*229*, *230*) and there will be no output current. For speedy calculations of phase-shifting networks,

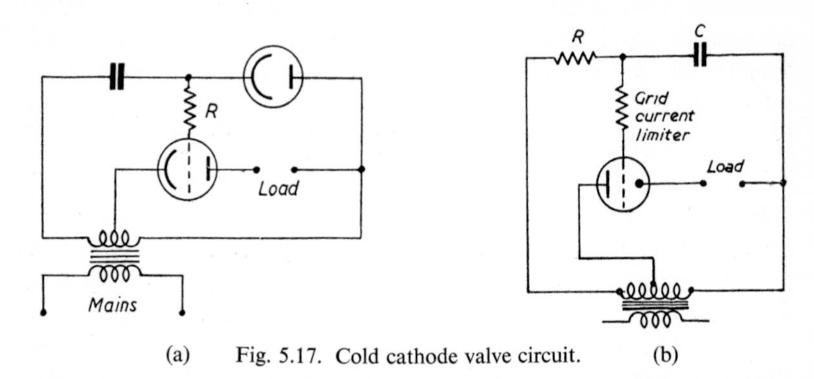

(a) Fig. 5.17. Cold cathode valve circuit. (b)

R. E. Lafferty (*1466*) has devised a very handy nomogram. The photo-electric cell and the valve must be so connected that their anodes have the same instantaneous polarity. The grid voltage will lag behind the anode voltage by an angle α, which is given by

$$\tan\frac{\alpha}{2} = \frac{R_\Omega}{R_c}$$

or, if $1/2\pi fC$ is substituted for R_c,

$$\tan\frac{\alpha}{2} = 2\pi fCR.$$

When the positions of cell and valve are interchanged the phase is reversed, too, and the grid voltage will now be leading the anode voltage.

The anode current of the valve is inversely proportional to the ohmic resistance value and the lag of the circuit. The circuit shown in Fig. 5.17 amplifies the current and the phase is retarded by decreasing resistance. A cold-cathode valve is used instead of the more usual hot-cathode type. In Fig. 5.17b a circuit is shown where the average anode current will increase abruptly when the resistance increases, i.e., when the irradiation of the photosensitor decreases. If the capacitor and photo-cell are interchanged the circuit can be used for measuring, ratio-metering, and other continuously indicating operations.

The principle of phase control is shown in Fig. 5.18a. where the phase of the grid voltage with respect to the anode voltage is controllable. The characteristic voltage below which conduction does not occur is plotted as a function of time underneath the positive anode voltage wave. Whenever the grid voltage is more positive than this critical value conduction will occur. The start of conduction is delayed and anode current thus reduced when the phase of the grid voltage is shifted, as is shown in the two diagrams of Fig. 5.18. High precision of control is insured if impulses (as obtained with an impulse or " peak " transformer) in conjunction with a negative grid bias are used, as is indicated in the diagrams of Fig. 5.18b.

NOTE.—The combined impedance Z of a resistor-capacitor series arrangement is $Z = \sqrt{R^2 + X^2_c}$ where R is the ohmic resistance, and X_c the capacitive reactance of the capacitor $X_c = \frac{1}{2\ \pi fC} = -\frac{159000}{\nu C}$ ohm where f is the frequency in c/s and C the capacitance in μF. The sign of X_c is conventionally considered negative. The current i follows the modified Ohm's law, viz., $i = E/Z$. This current i leads the voltage E by an angle α whose tangent is X_c/R and whose $\cos\ \alpha = R/\sqrt{R^2 + X^2_c}$. The power $W = Ei \cos \alpha$. If R becomes practically negligible, $i = E/X_c$, and $\alpha = \pi/2$.

The combined impedance Z' of a resistor-inductor series arrangement is $Z' = \sqrt{R^2 + X^2_L}$ where $X_L = 2\pi fL$ ohm ; L is the inductance in henrys. The current $i' = E/Z'$ and lags behind the voltage E by an angle α' ; it is $\tan \alpha' = X_L/R$, and $\cos \alpha' = R/\sqrt{R^2 + X^2_L}$. The power $W' = Ei' \cos \alpha'$. If R becomes practically negligible, $i' = E/X_L$ and $\alpha' = \pi/2$.

If two or more impedances are in parallel the total current is the vector sum of the currents through each of the impedances.

In a series arrangement of an ohmic resistor R, a capacitor C, and an inductance L, the following equations must be used :

$$Z'' = \sqrt{R^2 + X^2} \text{ where } X = 2\pi fL - 1/2\pi fC,$$

$$i = \frac{E}{Z''} = \frac{E}{\sqrt{R^2 + [2\pi fL - 1/2\pi fC]^2}} =$$

$$= \frac{E}{\sqrt{R^2 + \left[2\pi fL\left(1 - \frac{f_o^2}{f^2}\right)\right]^2}}$$

$$\text{where } f_o = \frac{1}{2\pi\sqrt{CL}}$$

For $f = f_o$ the circuit is in resonance and the resultant reactance is zero.

In practice, phase-shift is attained by using a capacitor as the reactive element. It would be both difficult to obtain and bulky to use an inductor of such electrical dimensions as would suit the very high resistance of the photo-electric cell which replaces the resistor.

If only small output currents are needed an ionotron, i.e., a cold-cathode valve (glow discharge three-element type) will do the job well (*367*). Up to about 25 mA the designer can make good use of the

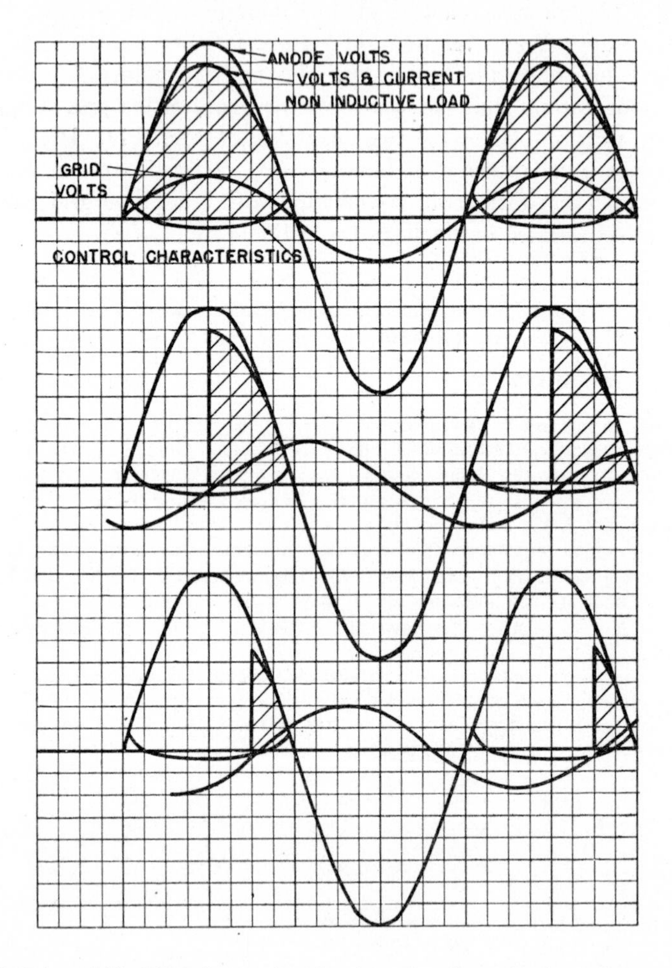

Fig. 5.18 (a and b). Wave forms of grid and anode voltages to show phase control. (a) The diagram at the top shows anode voltage and grid voltage in phase. In the centre diagram the voltages are at a phase angle of 90°. In the bottom diagram the angle is 135°.

characteristics common to all cold-cathode valves, viz., that neither energy nor active cathode material are consumed during the " waiting " periods of the valve. The full line voltage is applied between the cathode and anode, Fig. 5.19, but no current flows through the load circuit unless the control gap has been energized. The grid or starter anode is kept at a potential just below that required for firing. A photo-

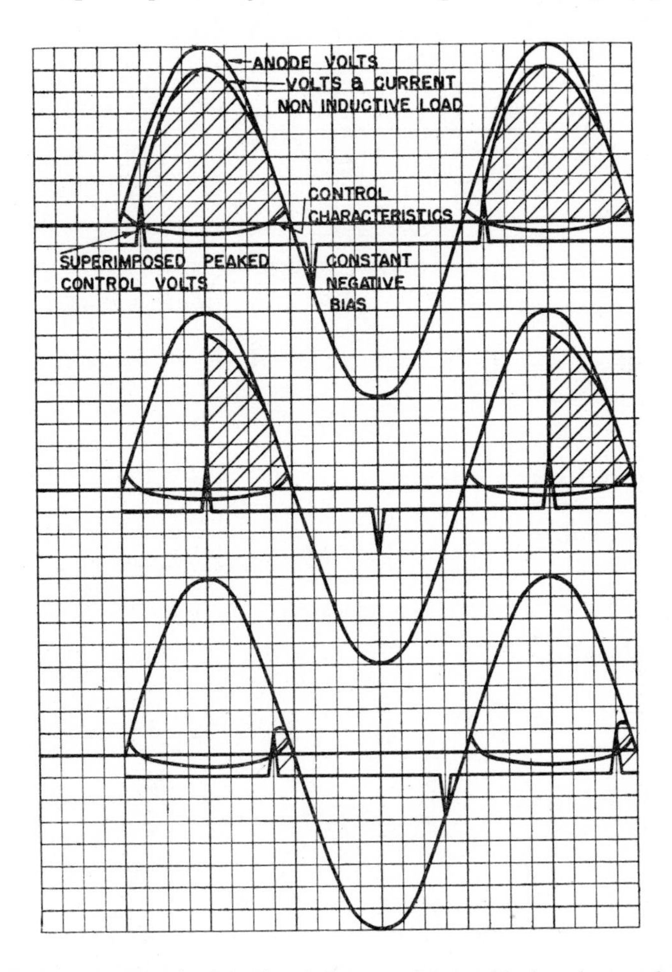

(b) The control voltage is of the " peak " type as generated by impulse transformers. The intersection of the grid voltage and control characteristic is at an angle of 90°. This gives high precision in timing the moment when the anode circuit becomes conductive.

electric cell can be so arranged as to act as energizing agent, Fig. 5.20.

If, for the purpose of experimental arrangements, a three-element cold-cathode valve is not readily available, a two-electrode valve, preferably of the tubular type, will do as an emergency if a metal ring is fitted externally and used as a control element, Fig. 5.21.

In many cases it may be essential for the photo-electric cell to be

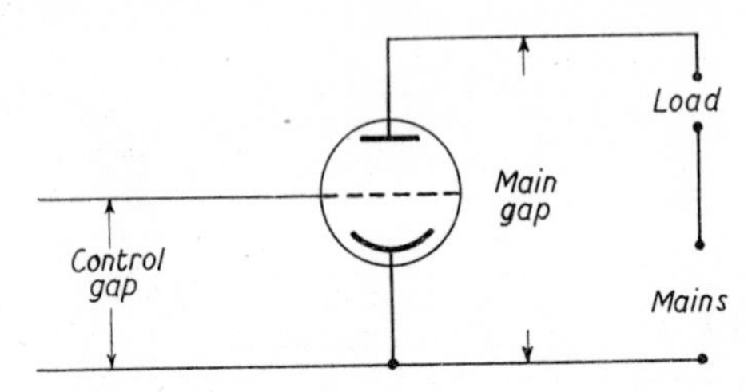

Fig. 5.19. Circuit using an ionotron cold cathode tube.

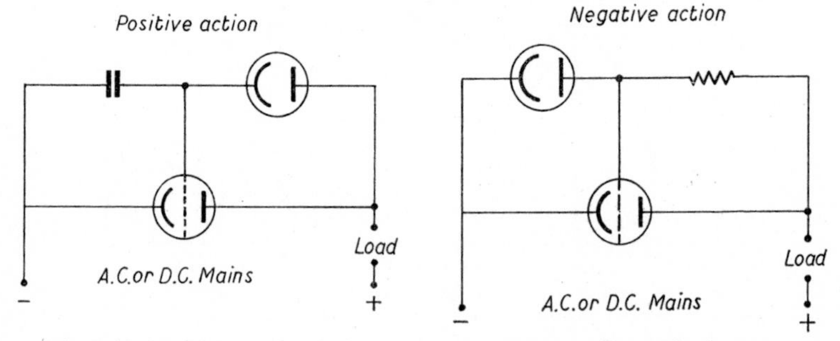

Fig. 5.20 (a and b). Use of photo-cell as an energising agent for ionotron.

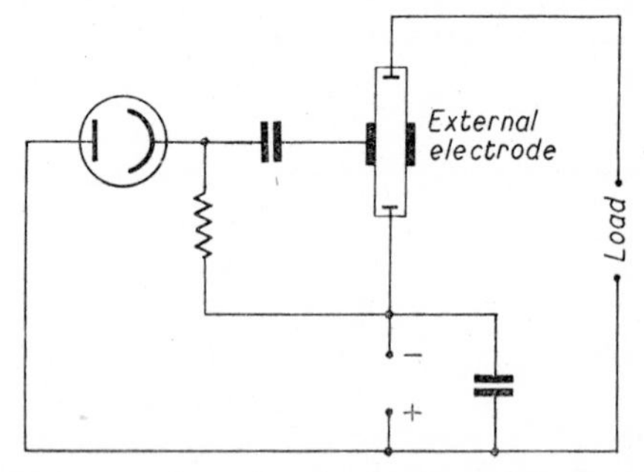

Fig. 5.21. Use of a two-electrode valve in place of the normal 3-electrode type.

mounted separately, i.e., detached from the amplifier, (Fig. 5.22). A matching circuit is shown in Fig. 5.23. An arrangement for measuring phase-shift with a cathode-ray tube is given by R. R. Wright (*1499, p.46*).

Bibliography References: (*1370*, *1371*)

5.4. Shielding

Apparatus and leads are shielded against either mechanical damage or electrical stray fields. The protection against the former nearly always involves metal casing and metal tubing. Electrostatic shielding

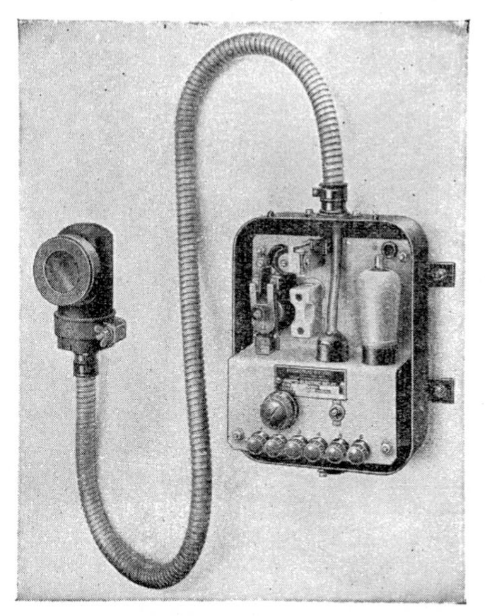

Fig. 5.22. Arrangement of photo-cell detached from the amplifier (*courtesy B.T.H. Co.*).

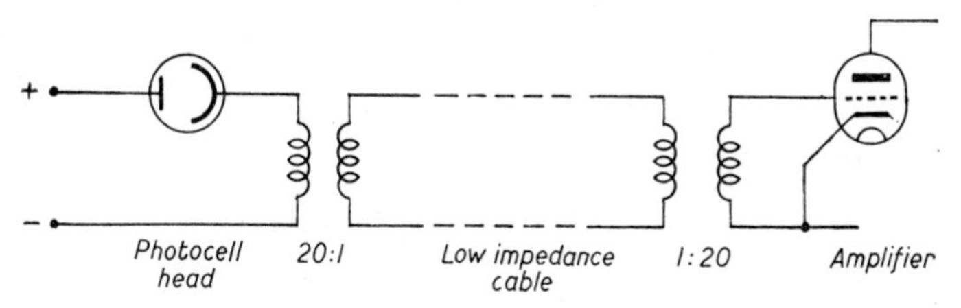

Fig. 5.23. Matching circuit between photo-cell and amplifier.

may be accomplished in a twofold way, either by using a metal chassis and housing or, in case of an insulating material being used, by lining it with sheet metal. With the advent of synthetic plastics, the plastics industry provides the electrical engineer with semi-finished materials in sheets or finished articles which are metallized very effectively. Transparent electrostatic shields have been applied to photo-electric equipment (*1409*) with good results.

Another potential method of shielding instruments, circuits, etc., against electrostatics is to spray the inside of the cabinet with colloidal graphite (*369*, *370*). The earth wire must be safely connected with the metal parts or coatings (metal, or graphite). Electromagnetic shielding utilizes mu-metal.

A recent development in the manufacture of transparent metal films on glass makes it possible to produce a transparent, yet electrically conducting glass. This has been developed at the National Physical Laboratory. The metal oxide film (tin oxide) which is hard and inseparable from the glass surface, and will resist chemical attack, can be earthed and will, thus, avoid electrostatic charges accumulating on the glass. A further advantage is that the metal oxide layer can be electrically heated, if necessary. Ceramic materials can be treated likewise.

Bibliography Reference: (*1854*)

5.5. Basic Circuits for Photo-e.m.f. Cells

The thermionic amplification of the output generated in low-resistance photo-e.m.f. cells is rather difficult, and straightforward methods cannot be applied as in the case of photo-electric cells. The primary rule with most cells of this type is that no external voltage

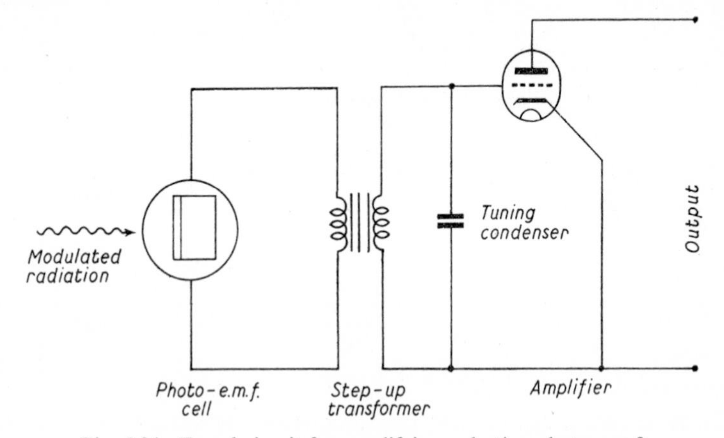

Fig. 5.24. Tuned circuit for amplifying pulsating photo-e.m.f.

must be applied across the photo-e.m.f. cell. Only the high-resistance types (for instance, the EEL multiple cell, Fig. 4.48), are an exception and can be coupled to electronic amplifiers. Generally, a modulated beam of incident energy generates a pulsating photo-e.m.f. which, by means of a tuned circuit, is stepped up and fed into the electronic amplifier, Fig. 5.24. R. W. Gilbert (*231*, *1048*, *1411*) has developed a method by which the D.C. output of a photo-e.m.f. cell is readily amplified 1000 times. The instrument is a photo-electric potentiometer, Fig. 5.25. Essentially, the potentiometer continuously and automatically balances the output circuit against the input circuit. This is accomplished by the use of photosensitors to control the output of an electronic amplifier. Changes in input are instantaneously and

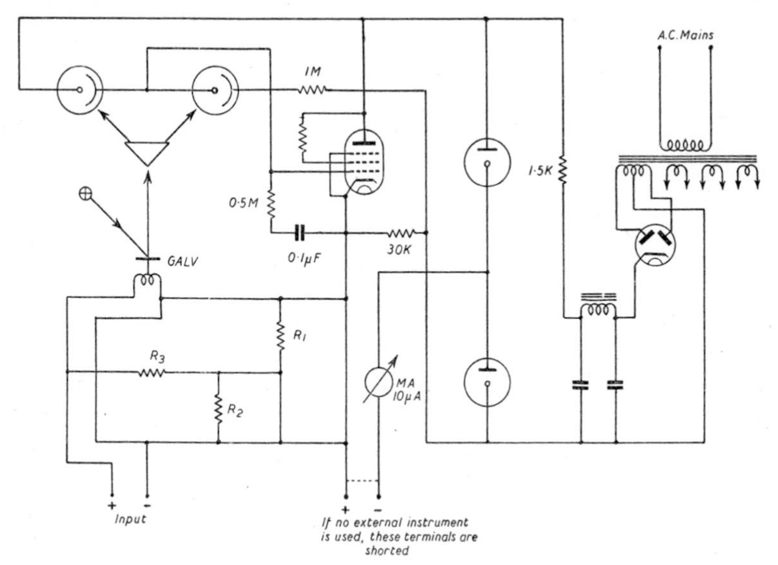

Fig. 5.25. Diagram of Western Photo-electric potentiometer.

automatically reflected in the output circuit. The accuracy of balance depends upon the potential drop across a standard resistor and is not influenced by the electronic equipment. This instrument is known as the Weston Photo-electric Potentiometer Model 721.

Two-cell circuits (*229*, *232*) made up with photo-e.m.f. cells can be connected as shown in Fig. 5.26. The circuit is a series-opposing or differential circuit. The cells are connected in opposition. If the instrument is at zero, the specimen to be tested is of standard quality. The scale of the instrument can be calibrated to indicate relative or absolute quantities. If the pointer moves to the one side of the centre zero it means that the specimen is smaller in the value measured (transparency, for instance) than the standard, and vice-versa. A parallel-type circuit is shown in Fig. 5.27.

More than two cells can be connected in series or in parallel. Series-connected photo-e.m.f. cells are used when a relay or other device is to be operated by obscuring any one of a number of such cells all

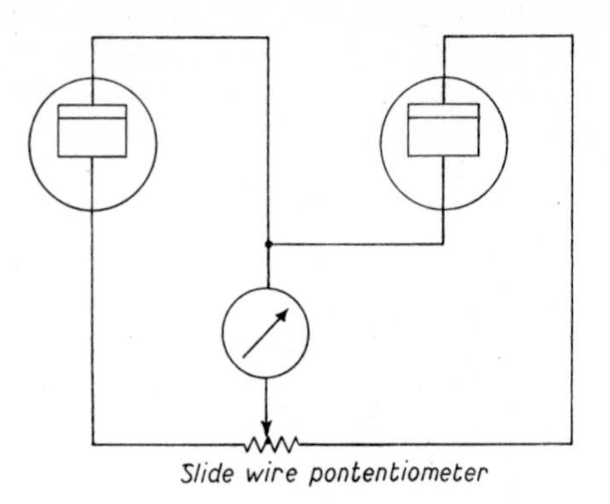

Fig. 5.26. Differential photo-cell circuit.

controlling the same device. Interrupting the irradiation of even only one cell is sufficient to increase the resistance of the cell circuit so much so that a load device, e.g., a relay, is operated. Connecting cells in parallel gives a circuit used in illumination meters.

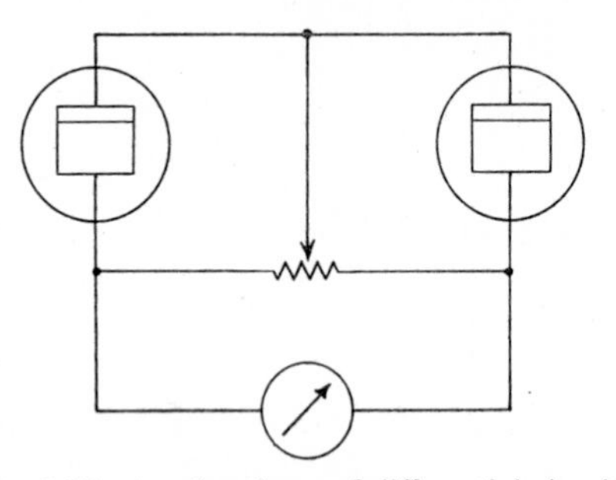

Fig. 5.27. Another form of differential circuit.

A two-cell circuit, mostly used in colorimetric work, is shown in Fig. 5.27, (*195*, *235*, *236*, *237*, *238*, *239*, *1285*, *1286*). These and other circuits are based on the use of a potentiometer to adjust the potential difference across the blocking layer so that there is no current flowing through it. L. A. Wood (*233*) gives the internal leakage resistance of a cell as the reason for the lack of a linear relation between the radiant energy input and the photo-electric current output, and of the variations with temperature of the cell characteristics. If now this internal leakage resistance could increase to infinity there could be no leakage current, which is also true if the potential difference across the blocking layer were to become zero. This can easily be achieved by a " compensating circuit " the principle of which is well known and shown in Fig. 5.28. If the potentiometer is in the correct position, i.e., if the photo-e.m.f. of the cell is fully compensated, viz., reduced to zero,

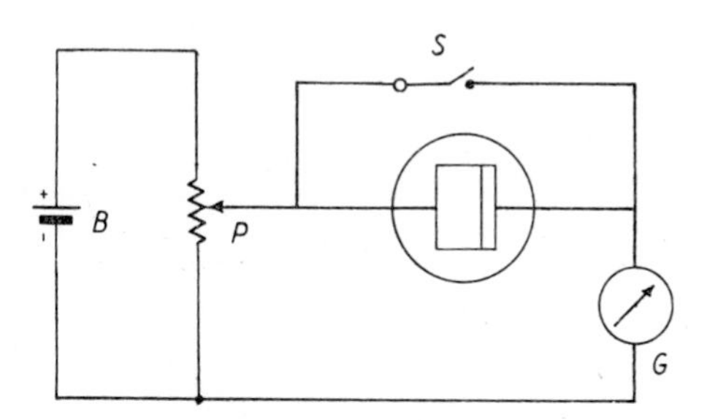

Fig. 5.28. Compensating circuit.

then no current will flow through the instrument G if the key S is closed. If another photo-e.m.f. cell is substituted for the battery B, then a two-cell circuit is the result (*234*). B. A. Brice stated that such compensating circuits " are distinctly superior to other circuits in stability and linearity of response " (*195*). He postulates the following conditions for a successful circuit, viz.,

(1) The resistance of the potentiometer must be small compared with the parallel internal resistance of the cell ;
(2) The photo-e.m.f. cells should have small series internal and high parallel internal resistance ;
(3) Moderately low levels of intensity should be used ;
(4) Photo-e.m.f. cells, as used in two-cell circuits, should be matched for spectral response and have very small, and possibly equal, internal series resistances.

Reasonably monochromatic light should be used with all balanced circuits because the two photosensitors, no matter how carefully they have been matched, will show discrepancies in their respective spectral response. If panchromatic light (tungsten-filament incandescent lamp) were used and either by natural ageing (cf. Chap. 7.8), or by appreciable fluctuations in the mains voltage, the colour temperature of the light source were changed, each cell would react differently according to its individual spectral sensitivity. If, however, monochromatic light of from 250 to 350 A.U. bandwidth is used, possible differences on either side of this range will be of no consequence.

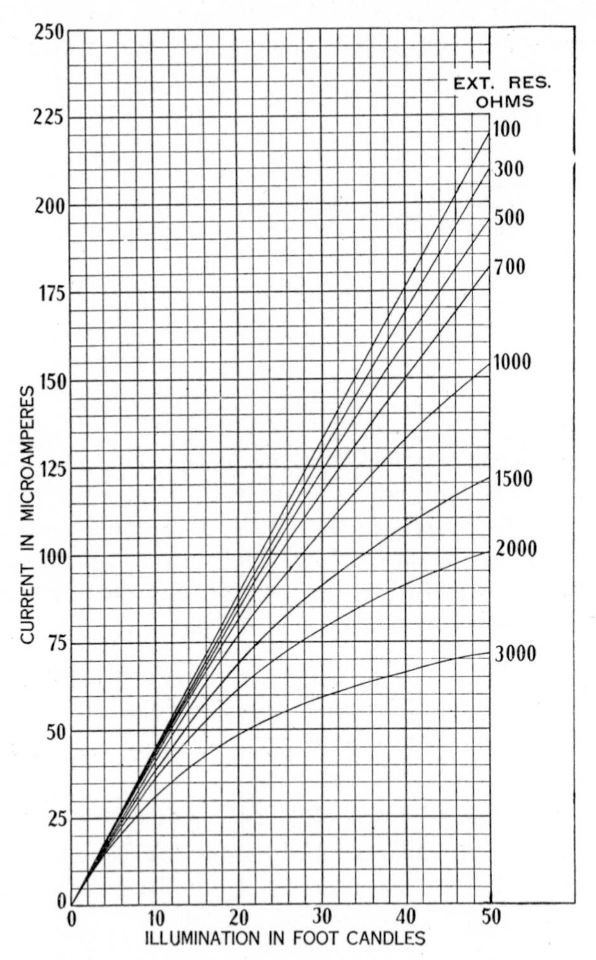

Fig. 5.29. Relation between radiation and current for various values of load resistance.

The circuit in Fig. 5.27 corresponds in principle with the compensating circuit of Fig. 5.28, while Fig. 5.26 represents a circuit in which the potentiometer is so adjusted that under certain conditions the cells operate with practically zero external resistance. This adjustment is indicated by the galvanometer being at zero. Photo-e.m.f. cells show a linear relation between intensity of irradiation and photoelectric current output for a load resistance (theoretically) equal to zero, Fig. 5.29. When only slight voltage changes are available from the photosensitor, the trigger circuit devised by Degelman is useful (*2427*).

Bibliography References: (*1716*, *1722*, *2198*, *2296*)

5.6. Basic Circuits for Light-sensitive Resistors

These photosensitors are connected much the same as an ordinary wire or non-metallic resistor would be circuited. A diagram using a selenium bridge is shown in Fig. 5.30. Light-sensitive resistors of the

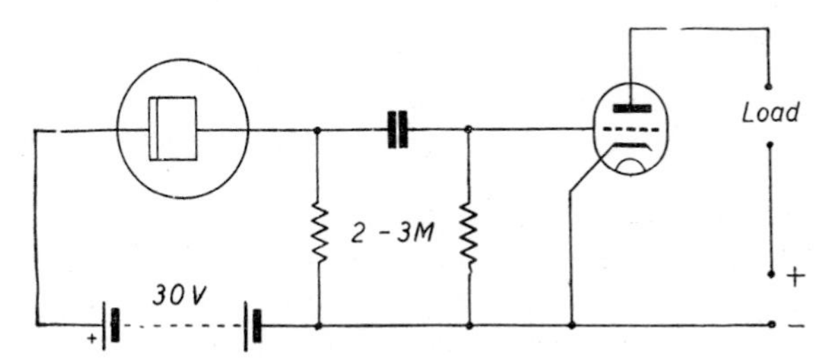

Fig. 5.30. Basic circuit for selenium bridge.

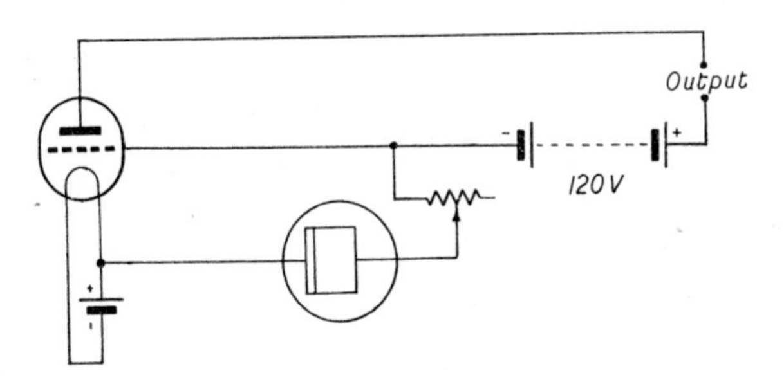

Fig. 5.31. Method of connecting light sensitive resistor to amplifier.

Thirring type are best coupled to thermionic amplifiers by means of resistors, Fig. 5.31. An arrangement for thallium-sulphide resistors, has been used for photo-telephony over a distance of 18 miles. The output can be transformer-coupled or direct-connected to the amplifier (*143*, *p. 213*).

Types of photo-e.m.f. cells which can safely be operated with external voltages across the cell can be circuited like light-sensitive resistors Fig. 5.32. The intensity on the photosensitor should be in excess of 100 ft.-c.

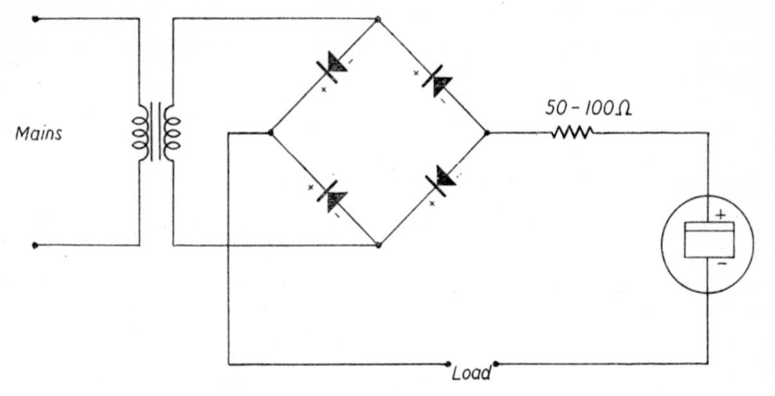

Fig. 5.32. Light sensitive resistor operated from rectifier circuit.

5.7. Basic Circuits for Photolytic Cells

Although of no importance in industrial applications at present, the fundamental diagram of a photolytic cell circuit is given in Fig. 5.33. The photolytic cell, having a low impedance, is coupled by a high-ratio transformer to the electronic amplifier. The cell and transformer are connected with low-impedance cable.

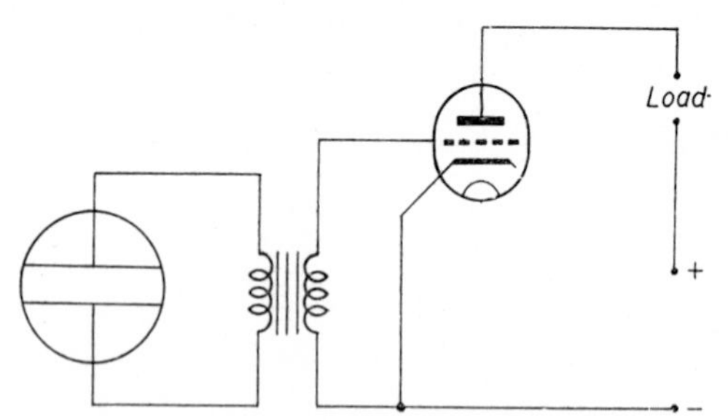

Fig. 5.33. Photolytic cell circuit.

5.8. Pulse Generators

The first type of pulse generator was a circuit now generally known as the relaxation oscillator. Since the gas-filled device used in this circuit is commercially available only within very narrow and small limits of output, this arrangement is not always satisfactory. It consists principally of a series arrangement of a two-element cold-cathode gas-discharge valve, filled with neon, for instance, and a resistor. A capacitor may be connected either across the discharge valve or the resistor, respectively.

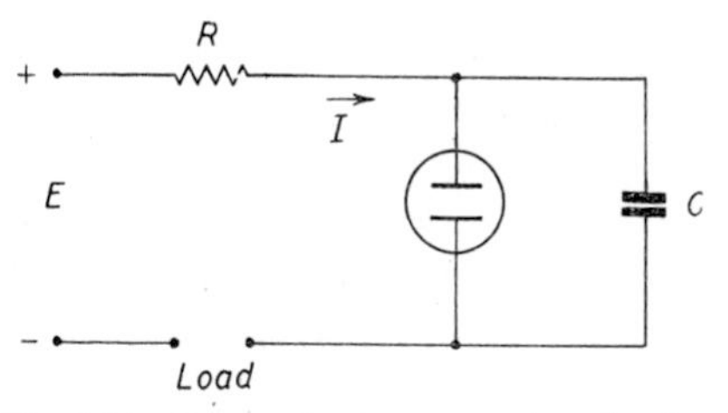

Fig. 5.34. Form of pulse generating circuit.

The basic circuit in Fig. 5.34 (*242*) is the arrangement as suggested by Righi (*240*). The capacitor voltage rises exponentially,

$$V = E_{d.c.}\left(1 - e^{\frac{1}{RC}}\right)$$

The oscillation frequency is approximately given by

$$f \simeq \frac{1}{RC \log \frac{E_{d.c.} - V_e}{E_{d.c.} - V_i}}$$

where V_i is the ignition (breakdown) voltage, and V_e is the extinction voltage ($V_e < V_i$). The upper frequency limit is about 8×10^3 to 10^4 c/s (*241*, *401*).

To insure regular flashing at low frequencies at an extremely constant rate, the light of a flash lamp should irradiate the gas discharge valve (neon lamp) which, as all ionic discharge devices, is somewhat photo-sensitive (*632*). (cf. Chap. 7.22).

With the advent of industrial electronics and television more powerful and more accurately operating circuits have been developed by using the same principle but different circuit elements. Not only the frequency but also the shape of the oscillations is exactly controllable. A number of useful circuits was compiled by J. M. A. Lenihan (*243*) and others (*244*), and a set of new types of gas-filled valve designed for pulse generation was described by van den Bosch before the

Institute of Electronics (*245*). An A.C. operated relaxation oscillator using a type 117L7GT valve was discussed in Electronics (*1472*).

Pulse generators will be of interest to designers of sources of modulated light when electronic means of control are preferred to mechanical " choppers ".

Bibliography References: (*465*, *484*, *2219*, *2231*)

5.9. Rectifiers and Stabilizers

Rectifiers of the discharge valve (two-element thermionic or cold-cathode valve) type or metal rectifiers, supplying half-wave or full-wave rectified A.C. which can be smoothed by electric filters of the

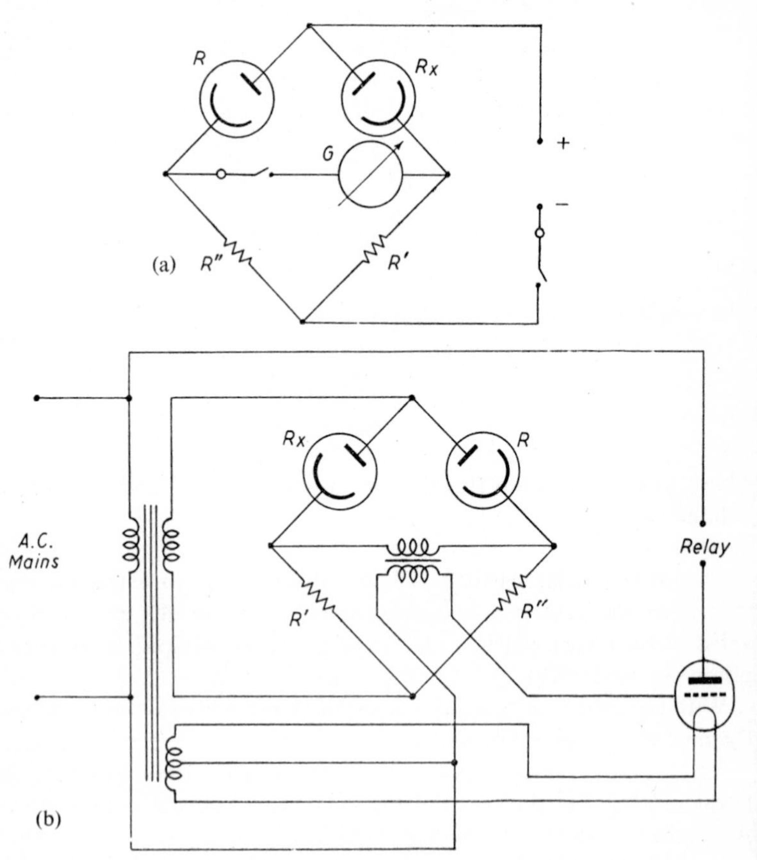

Fig. 5.35. Arrangement of photo-cells in the form of a Wheatstone bridge. (a) for D.C. (b) for A.C. mains.

capacitor or choke input type, are necessary if the photo-electric circuit is to be D.C. supplied from A.C. mains (*1655*).

Fluctuations in external voltages can be suppressed by using, for instance, glow gap dividers, valve voltage stabilizers for D.C. (*79, p. 469* ; *246, 247, 248, 249, 333*) as well as for A.C. (*1279*), silicon carbide resistors (*709*), etc. For heavier currents constant voltage transformers are advisable.

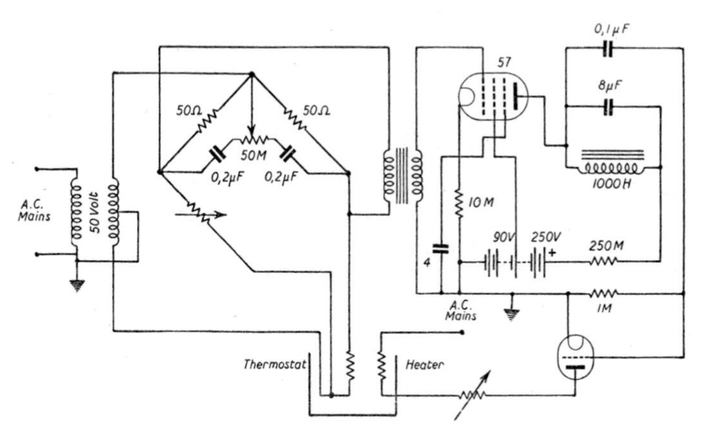

Fig. 5.36. Another form of A.C. bridge.

Fluctuations in current are stabilized by connecting in series with the filaments of the valves to be protected an iron filament in an hydrogen atmosphere, an arrangement known as a " barretter ". These tubes pass a certain constant current for a rather wide range in voltage drop. If the current controlled by the barretter is to be increased up to a maximum of 10% a suitable ordinary resistor may be connected across the barretter. If the rating of the iron-hydrogen resistor is in excess of the controlled current needed by the filaments of the thermionic valves, an ordinary resistor may be connected in parallel with these filaments. A stabilized circuit for use with photo-electric multipliers has been developed by Plymale and Hanson (*2590*).

Two diodes or a double-diode may be used to attain an A.C.-D.C. voltage ratio of up to 1 : 3. Voltage quadrupling circuits are described by Reich (*100, p. 566*).

Power supplies for photo-electric equipment are discussed by Schulman (*1694*).

Bibliography References: (*449, 453, 458, 1157, 1248, 1515, 2212*)

5.10. Wheatstone Bridges

In many circuits the measuring element is a Wheatstone bridge. Fig. 5.35a gives the arrangement for D.C. ,and Fig. 5.35b for A.C. measurements. The general equation is $R_x = RR'/R''$. For optimum conditions the ratio of the two resistors should be unity. The maximum sensitivity is attained for equality of all four resistances. Another A.C. bridge is shown in Fig. 5.36 (*1473*, *1682*).

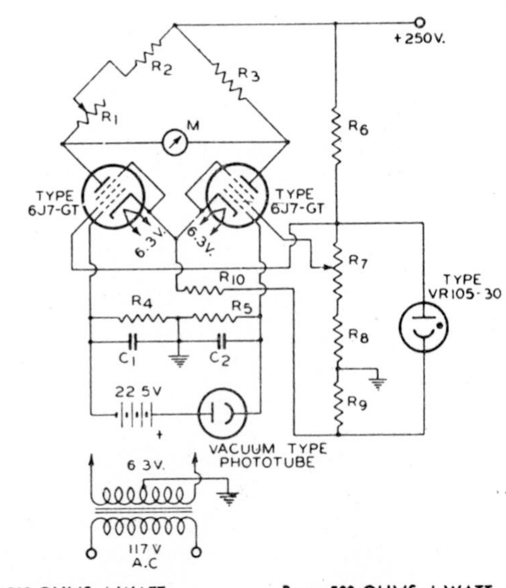

R_1 = 1000 OHMS, 1 WATT
R_2, R_3 = 50,000 OHMS, 1 WATT
R_4, R_5 = 5 MEGOHMS
R_6 = 6,000 OHMS, 4 WATTS
R_7 = 10,000 OHMS, 1 WATT
R_8 = 2500 OHMS, 1 WATT
R_9 = 500 OHMS 1 WATT
R_{10} = 900 OHMS, 1 WATT
C_1, C_2 = 0.01 μf
M = MULTI-RANGE MICROAM METER, 0-10, 0-100 0-1000 MICROAMPERES.

Fig. 5.37. Circuit for the measurement of small values of illumination.

A Wheatstone bridge, using a cathode-ray indicator of the 6E5 type has been described by Cath (*389*).

An arrangement using pentodes in the bridge is shown in Fig. 5.37.

Bibliography Reference: (*457*)

CHAPTER 6

OPTICAL EQUIPMENT

The optical equipment of photo-electric relays is made up of lenses, mirrors, hoods, baffle tubes, etc. Nicol prisms, polarizers, grey wedges, prisms, and others are used only in specialized apparatus.

For the convenience of the reader a few fundamental relations of geometrical optics are given below. For further and more detailed references the reader is advised to consult any of the textbooks on that subject.

6.1. Transmittance and Reflectance

The usually quoted relation :

$$\text{Absorptance} + \text{Reflectance} + \text{Transmittance} = 1$$

will be accepted although it is not quite correct because of the losses by internal reflexion of radiant energy scattered in the medium (cf. Chap. 9.1). Fig. 6.1 shows how an incident beam P_1, after striking the surface of a suitable medium, is split up into its various components, viz. :

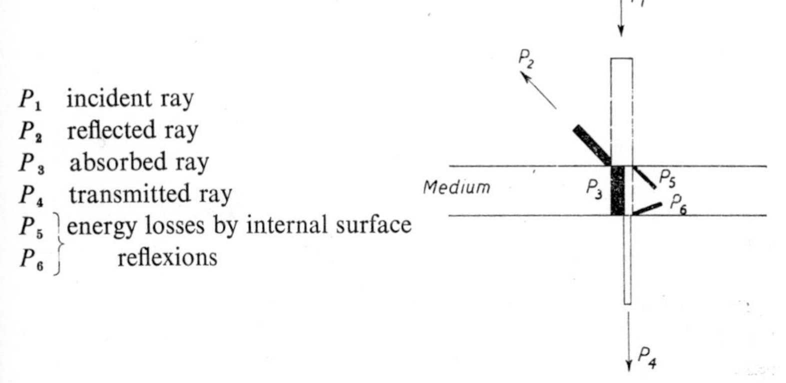

Fig. 6.1. The splitting-up of an incident light beam.

The transmission factor and the reflexion factor are characteristics of a given material ; these coefficients are usually expressed as the percentage of transmitted or reflected radiation, respectively. The reflexion factor is an important item in selecting the best suited material for a reflector within a given range of wavelengths.

In the ultra-violet region aluminium tops the list : anodized aluminium attains a high reflectivity for wavelengths greater than 3000 A.U.

In the luminous region silver is first, aluminium second, anodized aluminium third, the latter showing a decrease in reflectivity between 6000 and 10,000 A.U.

In the infra-red, silver and gold, and (for waves longer than 20,000 A.U.) copper, have about identical characteristics, while aluminium falls a few per cent. short of the above values.

Nickel, steel, cobalt and platinum have too small a reflective power to be used as reflectors. Table 6.1 (*1486*) gives the reflexion factors of various metals.

TABLE 6.1

Ultra-Violet Reflectances of Various Materials

Surface	Per cent. Reflectance at A.U.			
	2652	2967	3663	luminous range (2850° K.)
Aluminium foil		66		86
Aluminium sheet, mill finish		33		53
Aluminium sheet, buffed and polished		56		72
Aluminium sheet, chem. etched	77	80	82	85
Aluminium, rolled, etched, brightened	84	87	92	92
Chrome steel	37–41	41–44	47–50	56
Ni-plated metal		29–34		60–63
Cr-plated metal	53	62	64	65
Stainless steel		30–36		55–65
Rhodium		45		70–78
Tinned metal		10		70

In general the reflectance of aluminium paints increases after exposure to germicidal radiations (2900–2000 A.U.). The respective reflectances are :

before irradiation	56	60	67	70
after irradiation	71	72	73	78

Pringsheim (*614*) gives the reflectances of silver and aluminium, respectively :

Wavelength A.U.	2200	3000	3200	4000	5000	6000
Silver	28	15	5	80	92	94
Aluminium	82	82	82	90	90	89

More data for the ultra-violet region are compiled by Luckiesh (*35, p. 97*; *1622, p. 88*) and by Monk (*1615*) and others ; for the infra-red region by Clark (*36, p. 365*) and others.

The transmissivity of a material must be taken into account when colour filters are used. The catalogues of the manufacturers list the transmissivity of the filters at various wavelengths (*250, 251, 252, 253*). Beer's law (1852) states that the radiant flux P_4, transmitted by a layer of thickness x, is $P_4 = P_1 \exp(-\beta_\lambda cx)$, where β_λ is the specific absorption coefficient, and c is the concentration of the liquid. Bouguer's law (1729) states that equal layers of a material will absorb equal fractions of each kind of energy entering the medium (*254*). Lambert's cosine law relates that the intensity of irradiation of a surface depends upon the angle δ of incidence, viz., $E = E_o \cos \delta$ where E is the irradiation measured on the surface, and E_o is the irradiation in a plane perpendicular to the direction of the incident beam of energy. For different angles of incidence the intensity, in per cent., on the surface is the smaller, the more the angle increases. For $\delta = 60°$ the intensity has been reduced by half, Table 6.2.

TABLE 6.2

δ^0	E%
0	100·00
15	96·59
30	86·60
45	70·71
60	50·00
70	34·20
80	17·36
90	0·00

Photo-e.m.f. cells do not obey the cosine law exactly (*255, p. 373*) because the specific sensitivity of the cathode surface varies from edge to centre, the former being sometimes more sensitive than the latter. (Cf. Chap. 4.39). Therefore, the incident ray should cover the whole of the sensitive area. If only part of the surface is covered by the beam, a stop should be used in a plane perpendicular to the beam. In practice, values greater than the exact cos δ must be considered correct (*145*). The difference between the practical and theoretical value is greatest for nearly parallel incidence (δ nearly 90°).

M. Bouguer first described the Inverse Square law (*257*). If P be the amount of radiation falling from a point source on to an area at a given distance D, and P' the flux falling from the same source of radiant energy on to the same area, now at a distance D', then the relation is expressed by $P/P' = (D'/D)^2$. The inverse square law does not hold for extended radiation sources, for instance, tubular lamps or straight filament (tubular) lamps. In this case the intensity is linear-inversely proportional to the distance from the source (*258*).

Bibliography References: (*526, 1068, 1070, 1537, 2371*)

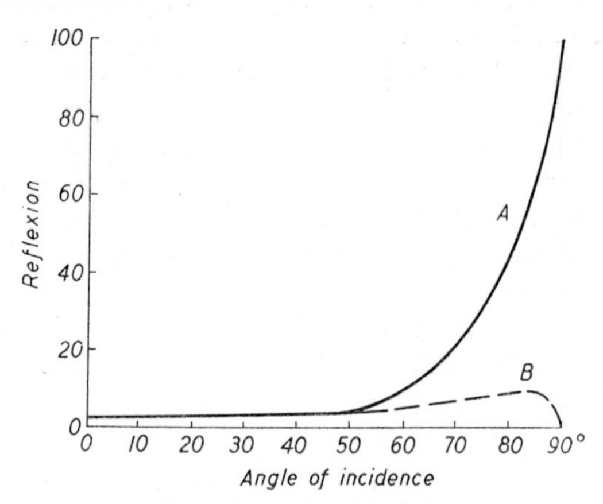

Fig. 6.2. Variation of reflexion with angle of incidence.

6.2. Reflexion Losses

Reflexion is here considered only so far as it is a loss to the transmitted energy. The mathematical expression for the loss by reflexion at one surface of the transparent medium is a rather complicated formula which, for most practical cases, may be reduced to the simple equation—

$$R = \left(\frac{n - 1}{n + 1}\right)^2$$

This formula is valid for perpendicular incidence of light the wavelengths of which are far removed from an absorption band. The variation of R with the angle of incidence is shown in Fig. 6.2. Since the loss occurs at both surfaces the total becomes $2R$.

For practically all applications within the scope of this book the two assumptions, viz., perpendicular incidence and no absorption band, will be satisfied. This makes the total loss $R_{tot} = 2\left(\frac{n-1}{n+1}\right)^2$, a formula which will meet all demands of the designing engineer. The corrected transparency becomes $e^{-a} . l/(1 - R)^2$ where a is the absorption modulus (a function of the wavelength of light), l the thickness of glass, R the reflexion (*259, p. 367*). From this it is evident that the refractive index n is solely responsible for the amount of loss by reflexion. It is also evident that there is no physical, i.e., optical, means to influence the value of R. It is, however, possible to reduce this loss of energy by treating the glass chemically.

(*Bibliography References:* (*525, 559, 1086, 2020*))

6.3. Reduction of Reflexion Losses

In 1892, H. D. Taylor discovered that a tarnished optical surface transmits more light than the untreated surface because the loss by

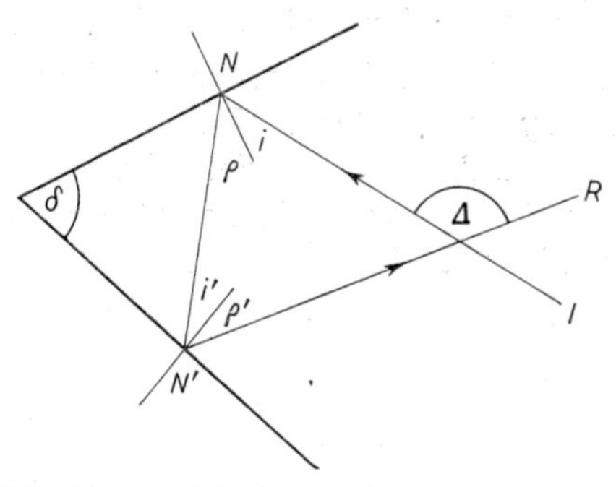

Fig. 6.3. Total deviation of an incident beam.

reflexion is reduced. If for one particular wavelength λ_R the two conditions are satisfied, viz.,

$$n_{Film} = \sqrt{n_{Glass}}$$

$$d_{Film} = \tfrac{1}{4}\lambda_R$$

where d is the thickness of the chemically (or otherwise) produced film on the surface of the glass (*260*), then the loss by reflexion for this particular wavelength λ_R is reduced to zero (*261*, *262*). Lord Rayleigh had already pointed out that a 1 : 200 hydrofluoric acid solution removes a thickness of glass corresponding to a quarter wavelength per hour (*263*, *264*).

For depositing the very thin film on glass various methods are used. The most effective treatment of a light flint glass ($n_D = 1{\cdot}570$) was achieved by exposing the surface of the glass for 18 hours at 80° C. to a 1% solution of acid sodium phosphate. Other recommended solutions with practically or nearly equal effectiveness, are :

1% sol. of phosphoric acid ; or
2% sol. of copper sulphate ; or
2% sol. of nickel sulphate ; or
2% sol. of ferric sulphate plus some free sulphuric acid ; or
2% sol. of potassium dichromate.

The effect of any of these treatments is permanent and results in the reduction of reflectivity which is equivalent to an increase in transmissivity. The relation between time and thickness of film is given by $100\,t = ax + bx^2$ where t is the time in hours, x the thickness of the film produced in t hours, a and b are constants (*259*, *265*, *266*, *290*, *391*, *392*). Optical interference is responsible for this effect.

The Radio Corporation of America reduces the reflexion from the surfaces of lenses by coating them with magnesium fluoride MgF_2 (*267*, *268*). A method for the reduction of the reflectivity of glass surfaces from 6% to 1% by means of evaporation of fluorides in a high vacuum, is described by F. Weidert (*1673*).

Bibliography References: (*521*, *1163*, *1534*, *2404*)

6.4. Deviation

The total deviation Δ, i.e., the angle between the incident and the reflected beam, is double the angle δ of inclination between the two reflecting surfaces, Fig. 6.3. The deviation $\Delta = 2\delta$ does not depend upon the angles of incidence i and reflexion ρ. This formula is essential when the radiation of one source is to be made incident on two objects, for instance, filters, photosensitors, mirrors, lenses, etc. Either a mirror or a prism is used for dividing the beam.

6.5. Refraction

When light passes from a lighter to a denser medium the ratio of the two sines is greater than unity, and vice versa ; $\sin i/\sin \rho = n$. The absolute refractive index n of a medium with respect to the vacuum is

$$n > 1 \quad \text{for material media,}$$
$$n < 1 \quad \text{for gases,}$$
$$n = 1 \quad \text{for reflexion.}$$

Bibliography References: (*1124*, *2334*)

6.6. Total Reflexion and Critical Angle

For light passing from a dense into a light medium, as from water or glass into air or a gas, the limiting angle of incidence giving rise to total reflexion, is called critical angle, viz., $\sin i_{crit} = n'/n$, where $n > n'$. For air $n' = 1$. For any value of i greater than i_{crit} the light beam is totally reflected, i.e., no light from the direction of the incident ray is transmitted into the other medium. For blue light the critical

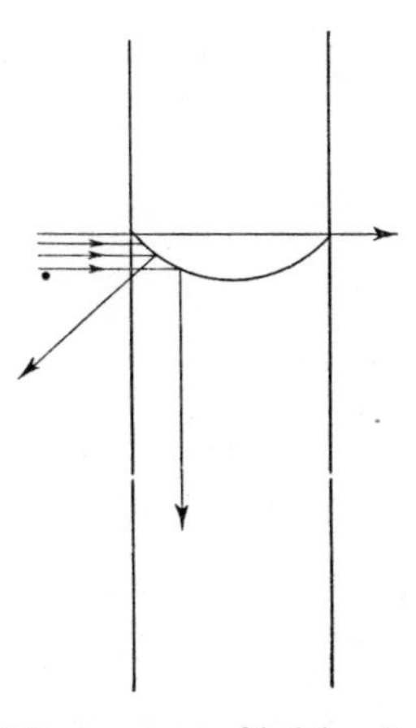

Fig. 6.4. Measurement of height of meniscus.

angle is smaller than for red light. In the case of white light the red rays may be transmitted into the rarer medium (n'), while the shorter ones are totally reflected.

The meniscus of a transparent liquid acts like an opaque disc in a liquid column for a limited distance. This limited distance of opacity is at that point in the curvature of the liquid surface where total reflexion takes place when light strikes at an angle exceeding the critical angle. This phenomenon is utilized in the exact measurement of the height of a meniscus in capillaries (*269*, *270*), Fig. 6.4 (cf. 6.30).

Bibliography References: (*450*, *451*, *1589*, *1590*)

6.7. Refractive Indices

The refractive index for the same material varies with the wavelength of the light used. The refractive index increases in value with decreasing wavelength and with increasing density of the material. For instance,

Change with Wavelength

(values for the same material, viz., Crown glass)

Wavelength A.U.	12560	5893	4047	3034
Refractive Index n	1·5042	1·5170	1·5318	1·5552

Respective data for Perspex and Lucite have been given by A. H. Pfund (*275*).

Change with Density

(values for light of the same wavelength, viz., 5893 A.U.)

	Density	n
Crown glass	light	1·5170
Flint glass	dense	1·6499

In Table 6.3 the refractive indices n_D^{20} of various transparent media are compiled (wavelength of the light is 5893 A.U.).

The ageing of glass surfaces and the consequent changes in the refractive index (April : 1.526 ; August of the same year : 1.483—then constant) are discussed by A. H. Pfund (*1478*).

In general, the higher the refractive index, the greater is the absorption at the shorter wavelengths.

TABLE 6.3

Refractive Indices of Various Transparent Media

Transparent Material	Density	$n_D{}^{20}$	Dispersive Power	Critical Angle in Air for D-Line
Inorganic glasses				
Crown (window) glass	2·4–2·6	1·5170	0·0151–0·0181	41° 14′
Flint glass, light		1·5710	0·0232	39° 22′
Flint glass, medium	2·9–4·5	1·6499	0·0218–0·0340	37° 19′
Flint glass, heavy (Jena)	5·92	1·9044	0·0461	31° 40′
Flint glass, heaviest		1·9626	0·0507	30° 38′
Hysil	2·25	1·4715	0·0151	42° 48′
Pyrex	2·25	1·4754	0·0155	42° 39′
Vitreosil (Fused quartz)	2·21	1·4585	0·0147	43° 17′
Organic glasses (*271*, *272*)				
Lucite	1·19	1·4893	0·0173	42° 11′
Perspex (Plasticized)	1·19	1·4949	0·0186	41° 59′
Perspex (Unplasticized)	1·19	1·4900	0·0172	42° 9′
Transpex I	1·19	1·4900	0·0174	42° 9′
Transpex II	1·05	1·5900	0·0323	38° 58′
The refractive indices of Transpex are maintained to within ±0·0001 of these values.				
Crystals (ordinary ray)				
Fluorite CaF_2	3·18	1·4339	0·0105	44° 13′
Quartz Si	2·66	1·5443	0·0143	40° 21′
Rocksalt NaCl	2·10	1·5443	0·0233	40° 21′
Liquids				
Carbon bisulphide (*393*)	1·25	1·6275	0·0545	37° 55′
Water, 20°C.*	0·998	1·3330	0·0180	48° 44′

* The refractive index of liquid water for radiant energy from the ultra-violet to the infra-red region varies with the temperature (*274*, *1611*).

Refractive indices of metals are quoted by Edser (*273*, *p. 385*). Carbon bisulphide strongly absorbs in the ultra-violet region from 1850 to 2270 A.U. A. H. Pfund gives the refractive index of Carbon Tetrachloride as $n_D{}^{20} = 1{\cdot}4607$. Of the high dispersive power (0·0545) of carbon bisulphide advantage is taken in preparing carbon bisulphide lenses. Hollow bi-convex or plano-convex clear white glass lenses are luted together without frames and can be filled with carbon bisulphide or any other suitable liquid.

The dispersive power is the ratio $(n_F - n_C)/(n_D - 1)$ where

n_C is the refractive index corresponding to the red (C) Fraunhofer line at 6553 A.U.,

n_D is the refractive index corresponding to the yellow (D) Fraunhofer line at 5893 A.U. (sodium line),

n_F is the refractive index corresponding to the blue-green (F) Fraunhofer line at 4861 A.U.

The breaking up of panchromatic, i.e., white, light into its monochromatic components, is called dispersion. The dispersive power is a measure of the angular width of a spectrum. Optical catalogues sometimes also list the Abbé Number (or relative dispersion) which is the reciprocal of the dispersive power; or the mean dispersion $n_F - n_C$; or the dispersion ratio $(n_D - n_C)/(n_F - n_C)$.

Glasses containing boron or fluorine show a small, those containing lead or thallium, a great dispersion.

Organic glasses are synthetic plastics as instanced by Lucite, Perspex, and Transpex. Transparent uncoloured plastics can be classified chemically as:

Cellulose plastics:	cellulose acetate
	ethyl cellulose
	celluloid
Acrylic resins:	Lucite
	Perspex
	Transpex I
Styrene:	Transpex II
Vinyl chloride acetate.	

In particular, Lucite and Perspex are a methyl methacrylate polymer (*275*), Transpex I is an unplasticized polymethyl methacrylate, and Transpex II an unplasticized polystyrene. They all have a high transparency in the ultra-violet. The relatively soft surface of lenses and mirrors made of transparent plastics can be hardened by depositing a film of silica on the optically worked surface. Perspex can be bent to any shape by dipping it for a time in boiling water. As a cementing fluid carbon triethylene or chloroform give good results. Perspex can be hand-polished. Cyclohexanone $C_6H_{10}O$, an excellent solvent for polystyrene, has a specific gravity of 0·948 and a refractive index of 1·4507 (at 20° C.). A non-inflammable thermo-setting material is

Kriston (B. F. Goodrich Chemical Co., Akron, Ohio). It has excellent chemical, optical, and mechanical properties. Its refractive index is higher than that of most optical glasses (*1277*).

6.8. Spectral Transmission of Lenses

Optical lenses or prisms, made of

Calcium fluoride, or Lithium fluoride	transmit in the Schumann region, 1200–2000 A.U.,
Quartz	transmit from 1850 A.U. to 35,000 A.U.
Glass	transmit in the luminous region,
	lower limit of transmission : crown glass 3000 A.U.; flint glass 3150 A.U.
Fluorite	transmit from 7000 A.U. to 10,000 A.U.,
Fluorspar	transmit from 30,000 A.U. to 90,000 A.U.,
Rocksalt	transmit from 80,000 A.U. to 160,000 A.U.,
Sylvine	transmit from 150,000 A.U. to 200,000 A.U.,
Potassium bromide	transmit from 190,000 A.U. to 280,000 A.U.,

Light passing through a material medium ($n > 1$) at an oblique angle is bent and the greater the index of refraction the greater is the

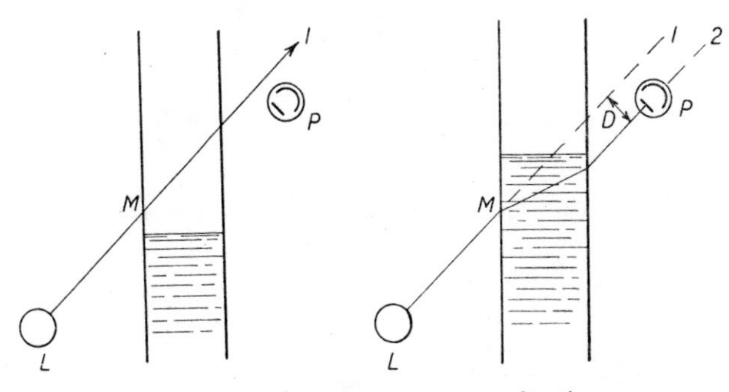

Fig. 6.5. Level gauges based on refraction.

distance D between the two directions. This effect is utilized in instruments like level gauges which operate as indicated in Fig. 6.5. If no liquid has risen to the mark M, the light ray from L will pass through the empty glass tube and emerge in direction 1. When the liquid rises to M the light ray emerges in direction 2 due to refraction by the liquid. If a photosensitor is so mounted that it is in the path of ray 2, but is shielded from ray 1, then the photo-relay will operate when the liquid level reaches M.

If the light passes at right angles through the liquid column the liquid, when reaching the mark M, can be made to act as a cylindrical lens concentrating the beam on the photosensitor.

6.9. Lenses

There are two different types of lenses, viz.,

Positive Lenses	*Negative Lenses*
bi-convex	bi-concave
convergent meniscus (concavo-convex)	divergent meniscus (convexo-concave)

Light, parallel to the optical axis,

converges to the principal focus,	emerges from the lens in divergent beams,

The principal focus is

real	virtual

Of thin lenses, the radii of curvature are

$r_1 < r_2$	r_1	r_2	$r_1 > r_2$	r_1	r_2
double convex	> 0	< 0	double concave	< 0	> 0
plano-convex	> 0	$= \infty$	plano-concave	$= \infty$	$= 0$
concavo-convex	> 0	>0	convexo-concave	> 0	> 0

Bibliography References: (*508*, *509*, *534*)

6.10. Lens Formulae

The relation between the distance p of the object from the lens, the distance q of the image from the lens, and the focal length f of the lens, Fig. 6.6, are expressed by (*273, p. 69*; *276, p. 42*) $1/f = 1/p + 1/q$. In Table 6.4, some particularly noteworthy cases are listed.

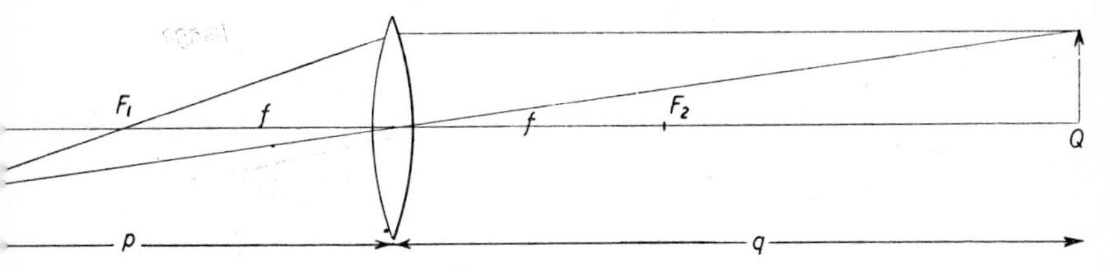

Fig. 6.6. Illustrating the simple lens formula.

TABLE 6.4

Object and Optical Image

p	q	Note
∞	f	Object distant. Image at focal distance from lens.
$2f$	$2f$	Distance between object P and image Q is $4f$. Both are equal in size, $p = q$.
$< f$	neg.	Image is virtual because q is negative.
f	∞	Object is at focal distance from lens. Image is at infinity.

In general the relation $P/Q = p/q$ holds good. The focal length of a thin lens is $1/f = (n - 1)(+ 1/r_1 - 1/r_2)$.

If a set of two lenses is used, the one having a distance d from the other, the lens equation reads $f = (f'f'')/(f' + f'' - d)$, where f' is the focal length of lens L', f'' correspondingly of lens L'', d is the distance between the two lenses L' and L'', and f is the focal length of the combination. If two or more lenses are used, the filament of the lamp (or the emitting surface) may be focused on an aperture in the optical system. The light coming through this aperture is then focused by the second lens to the point where the beam of limited dimension is desired, Fig. 6.7.

The aperture of a lens is the ratio of diameter to focal length of the lens. This is a gauge of the amount of light a lens is collecting and concentrating into the image. The larger the image, i.e., the farther away it is from the lens, the dimmer it will be. An increase in the intensity of the image can be secured by using a larger lens.

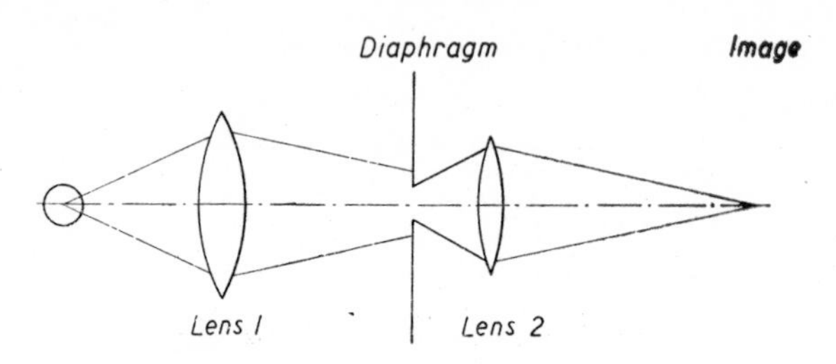

Fig. 6.7. A compound lens and diaphragm.

The power D of a lens is the reciprocal of its focal length in metres or $D = 100/f$, where f is expressed in cm. The factor D is known as the *diopter*, for instance : the power of a lens having a focal length of 4 in. (about 10 cm.), is $D = 100/10 = 10$ diopters.

Bibliography Reference: (*518*)

6.11. Chromatic Aberration

Due to the fact that a single lens acts like a double prism the lens does not focus sharply in one point but shows an extended focus, or rather focal line, caused by the dispersion. This focal line shows all

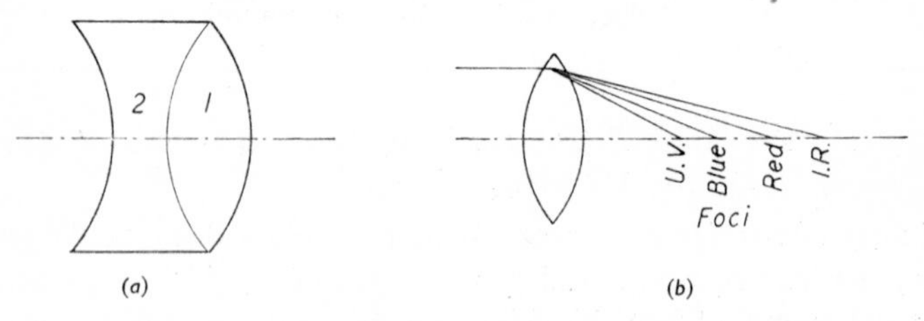

Fig. 6.8. Achromatic lenses: flint glass; crown glass.

the colours of the spectrum, the violet focus being closest to, the red focus farthest from, the lens. The image of an object shows what is known as the " chromatic aberration " of the lens. By choosing the correct components, a compound lens may be constructed having practically no aberration at all. Such a combination of lenses, called an achromatic lens is diagramatically shown in Fig. 6.8a, lens 1 being made of flint glass, and lens 2 of crown glass. The focal length of a lens system for infra-red radiation is greater than that for white light, Fig. 6.8b.

6.12. Plastics for Precision Optical Equipment

In recent years the art of manufacturing high quality optical lenses, prisms, and other optical elementary equipment, from synthetic plastics has attained a very high degree of perfection (*277*). Lenses and prisms can now be cast accurately and on mass production lines by using highly polished glass or quartz dies (*278*) and can be given optical properties which it might not be possible to procure in glass lenses. No grinding or polishing of the cast article is necessary and it can easily be machined without danger of fracture.

The synthetic plastics, used in the production of optical equipment, are cellulose acetate, polyvynyl acetate, stryene, methyl methacrylate, and polycyclohexyl methacrylate (*1276*). According to investigations of the Polaroid Corporation polystrene (similar to flint glass) and polycyclohexyl methacrylate (similar to crown glass) are the two synthetic plastics best suited for the manufacture of high precision optics. To attain low reflexion the finished article is coated with a film 0.000005 in. thick. The ultra-violet stability of polycyclohexyl methacrylate is perfect ; that of polystyrene about 60%.

Other transparent clear synthetic plastics which can readily be dyed and used for filters are iso-buthyl methacrylate, urea-formaldehyde, and allyl esters (thermosetting polymer). The refractive index of the latter is greater than that of most optical glasses ; it is $n_D^{20} = 1{\cdot}57$. The chemical properties of allyl esters (*1277*) make this material also well suited for viewing glasses in chemical processes.

Transparent windows made of synthetic plastics are often used in instruments. A photo-electric instrument is available which measures the optical distortion at the high rate of 24 windows per minute (*279*).

Bibliography References: (*485*, *600*, *1066*, *1099*, *1100*)

6.13. Mirrors

Principally, the same fundamental laws apply to lenses and mirrors alike. In practice only concave mirrors will be used. All rays parallel to the optic axis will pass through the focus of the mirror. If the source of radiant energy is placed in the focus of the mirror all rays will so be directed as to be parallel to the optic axis. Light sources are points only in theory ; in practice they are extended objects. If the area of the source is large relative to the surface of the mirror special methods must be applied. For sources in the shape of a ring, disk, spiral, cone, or *V*, these methods are discussed by Jolley *et al.* (*280, p. 337*), and others (*1629*).

For reflexion from more than one mirror (multiple reflexion) the total reflexion coefficient is the product of all individual reflexion coefficients.

6.14. Forming a Light Beam

With the aid of lenses and/or mirrors light beams of different shapes may be formed. In each case the light source should be as small as reasonably possible.

Bibliography References: (*1719, 2028*)

6.14.1. Nearly Parallel Beam

A nearly parallel beam is formed either by a convex lens or a parabolic mirror, the source of energy being at the focus of the optical device.

6.14.2. Convergent Beam

A convergent beam is formed by a beam of parallel rays falling on a convex lens or a parabolic mirror. The centre of convergence is the focus of the optical device. A convergent beam is also formed by a convex lens if the distance of the source from the lens is greater than the focal length of the latter ; this process may be repeated in that another lens picks up the image produced by the first lens and projects it on to another (final) screen.

6.14.3. Divergent Beam

A divergent beam is formed by either a concave lens, the source of radiation then being in the focus of the lens, or by a parabolic mirror, the source now being between the focus and the apex of the mirror.

6.14.4. Uniform Intensity Beam

If it is necessary to produce a light beam of uniform intensity along a line perpendicular to the axis of a parabolic mirror the method developed by Weinberger (*281*) will be found easily applicable. It is necessary for the reflector to intercept a constant angle of light. Therefore, the horizontal width of the reflector must vary since the reflector is at a varying distance from the source of radiant energy. The chord width c of the mirror can be computed from

$$c = 2\left(\frac{y^2}{4a} + a\right) \tan \theta$$

where a is the distance from the vertex of the parabola to the focus ;
y is the height of a point of the line above the axis of the parabola ;
θ is one-half the angle of light intercepted by the reflector ; Fig. 6.9.

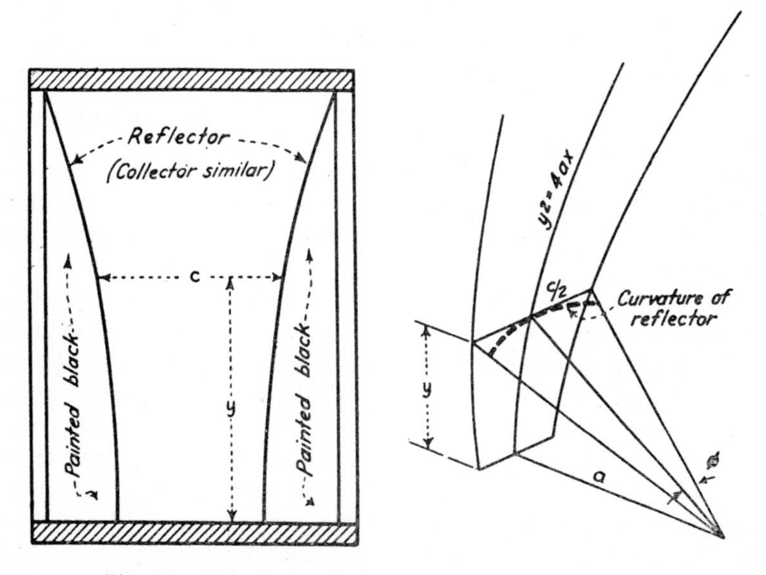

Fig. 6.9. Method of producing a beam of uniform intensity.

6.15. Mirror v. Lens

A polished mirror : will collect more light than a lens and give a large and well concentrated beam. The losses incurred when using a reflector, are between 40% and 50%. Mirror systems are suitable for work with all wavelengths. The material used for the mirror depends on the range of wavelengths.

A lens :	gives a very constant output of light ; produces a beam of very small divergence and small diameter ;
	will collect less light than a mirror. Losses are much smaller with lenses than with mirrors.
	Lenses can be achromatic only over a very narrow range of wavelengths.
	A conventional condenser lens rarely collects more than 1/16 of the light from the lamp (*181*). Of the 4π lumens emitted per c.p., less than 1 lumen is likely to be useful in an optical system.

Bibliography Reference : (*1781*)

6.16. Forming a Light Curtain

One light ray, even after multiple reflexion, will not always provide sufficient protection for the operator of large power presses or other heavy machinery, especially those having a wide work-table or a long stroke.

The effective length of the light beam depends on the number z of reflexions more than on anything else. With an absorption factor y and z mirrors to reflect the beam around the machine, the effective length of the beam will be reduced by a factor $(1 - y)^z$ which, if three mirrors with an absorption factor of 30% are assumed, reduces the effective length by a factor of 0·343. The system of employing three or more equidistantly spaced parallel rays to protect a space of great height or width, might prove unsatisfactory in the case of safeguarding the operator because he will yield to the temptation of putting his hands between two adjacent beams in order to adjust the running machine. If the arrangement of the rays allows an object to interfere with the protected area without operating the emergency relay, the protective device must be regarded as non-effective.

To overcome this difficulty the " light curtain " has been devised. Large lenses are either cut to rectangular shape or screened off by diaphragms with a rectangular aperture, and are mounted in a frame so that there is no space left between the individual beams. Each beam falls upon a photosensitor. The sensitivity of the photo-electric relay is so adjusted as to operate the emergency switch whenever the intensity of the incident light is reduced to 75% or less, depending on the diameter of the lens. Usually this dimension is between three to four times the average diameter of a man's hand, fist, or forearm. This rule of thumb provides for lenses of 10 to 12 inches diameter.*

If photo-e.m.f. cells are employed in a system using a multiplicity of light beams, it is desirable to connect the cells in series and have the

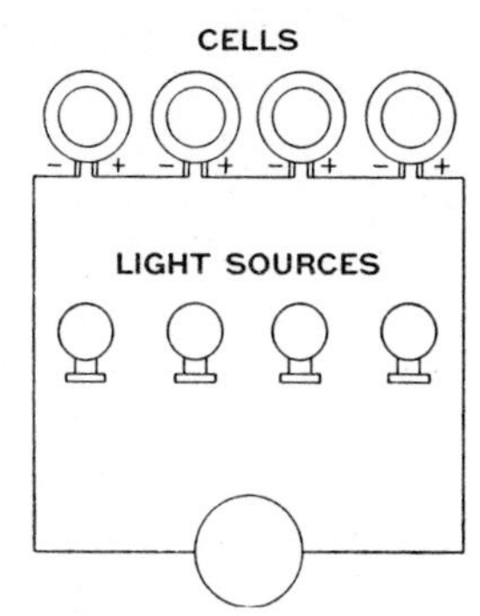

Fig. 6.10. Series arrangement of cells for multiple light sources

whole group work one relay or alarm. The general arrangement, Fig. 6.10, makes use of the current characteristic of the series circuit. Every cell adds resistance to the circuit and the total current output is about identical with the output of one single cell. The obscuration of any one cell in the series-circuit changes the total resistance so much that a substantial current change in the output circuit is available for actuating the relay.

6.17. Prisms

When a ray of white light passes through a prism, the ray is deviated (bent aside) from its original direction and dispersed (spread out) into the spectrum. The violet end of the spectrum is directed towards the base, the red end towards the edge of the prism.

Bibliography Reference: (*2334*)

6.18. Dispersion without Deviation

A spectrum which is not deviated from the direction of the incident ray may be obtained by so combining a crown glass prism and a flint

* For very instructive photographic reproductions of light curtains, cf. Electronics, July 1941.

glass prism as shown in Fig. 6.11. The angles of the prisms must be small and in the ratio of 0·587 to 0·534. The spectrum formed by the flint prism is larger than the spectrum formed by the crown glass prism in the ratio of the respective refractive indices, viz.,

$$\text{Total Dispersion} = S \; \frac{n\text{ (flint glass)}}{n\text{ (crown glass)}}$$

where S is the width of the spectrum formed by the crown glass.

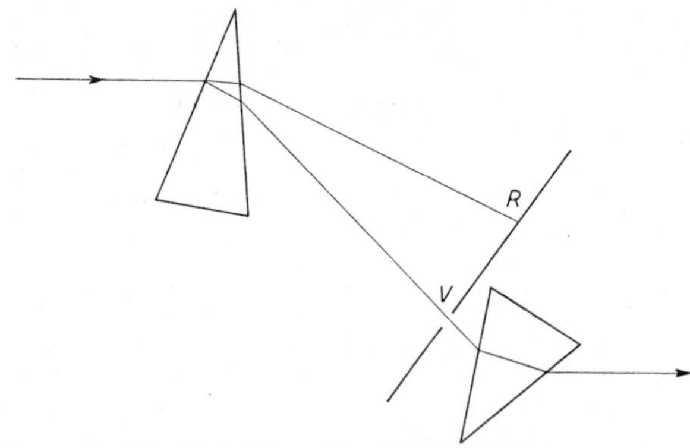

Fig. 6.11. Dispersion without deviation.

6.19. Amici Prism

A very large dispersion without deviation may be produced by combining a set of three crown glass prisms with a set of two flint glass prisms. Such a combination is known as a Direct Vision Prism and has many practical applications, e.g., in direct vision spectroscopes.

6.20. Deviation without Dispersion

By reversing the compound prism in Fig. 6.11 an optical device can be designed which bends a ray from its direction of incidence without producing a spectrum, Fig. 6.12. This compound is termed an Achromatic Prism and is essential in apparatus where it is necessary to bend a light ray without dispersing it.

6.21. Distortion

Images formed by single lenses suffer from distortion. Convex lenses produce what is known as Barrel Distortion ; concave lenses produce Pincushion Distortion. Rectilinear images, i.e., such in which straight lines in the object are reproduced as straight lines, can only be formed by rectilinear, i.e., distortionless lenses.

6.22. **Diaphragms**

A most efficient and generally used means of regulating the width of the light beam is an Iris diaphragm which also is used almost universally in cases where the effective area of the lens is to be varied.

In a recent paper, G. A. Thikov (*282*) suggests another method, viz., that " instead of a change in the effective lens area, recourse should be had to a change in its transparency . . . in such a way that the trans-

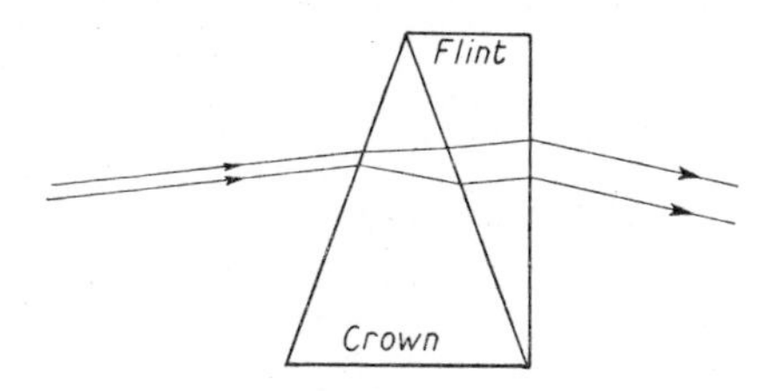

Fig. 6.12. Deviation without dispersion.

parency be equal at any point of the lens. This can be attained with the aid of two photometrical wedges (*334*) as neutral as possible. The optical density of these should vary linearly with the distance from one of the edges." This method makes it possible to work the shutter in front of the lens at full aperture.

A method of preparing strips with uniformly varying blackening has been described by Barr and Scott (*371*). It is based on the illumination of a surface varying directly as the cosine of the angle of incidence of radiation striking it (cf. Lambert's cosine law, this chapter, section 1).

Bibliography References: (*2283*, *2367*)

6.23. **Required Flux**

The " required flux " is the amount of radiant energy required to produce a certain photo-electric current. The " required flux " in lumens of white light is given by

$$\Phi_r = \frac{2{\cdot}83}{\tau\,\sigma}\, i_{ph}$$

where $2{\cdot}83 i_{ph} = 2\sqrt{2}\,.\, i_{ph}$ = the peak photo-electric current,
τ the transmission factor of a filter,
($\tau < 1$ for any filter ; $\tau = 1$ for no filter)
σ the sensitivity ($\mu A/Lm$) of the photosensitor (*1474*).

Bibliography Reference: (*1222*)

6.24. Intensity of Illumination on the Photosensitor, and Photo-electric Current produced

The source of radiation produces on the photo-cathode an illumination which is expressed by

$$E\left[\text{Lumen/sq. cm.}\right] = \frac{\text{Intensity of source}\ [\text{c.p.}]\ .\ \cos i}{\text{square of distance}\ d^2\ [\text{cm.}^2]}$$

The flux F received on the light-sensitive area of the photosensitor is

$$F\left[\text{Lumen}\right] = \frac{IA\cos i}{d^2}$$

where I is the intensity of the source [c.p.],
d is the distance of the source from the photosensitor [cm.],
i is the angle of incidence, i.e., the angle between the incident ray and a normal to the cathode in the point of incidence,
A is the light-sensitive area of the cathode, or window in the bulb of the photosensitor, or the aperture of the diaphragm or lens, whichever is the smallest in the combination [cm.^{2}].

The light must be diffused equally and evenly over the whole cathode area which means that the image of the source must be spread over

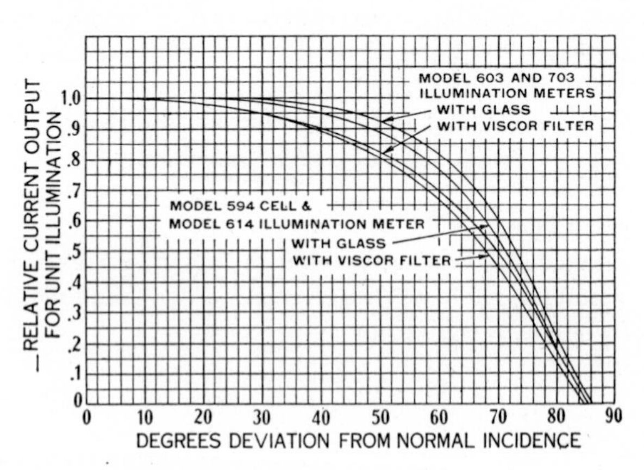

Fig. 6.13. Effect of angle of incidence on current output: Weston Photronic Cell.

the entire cathode. The effect of radiation striking the surface of the cathode under an angle $0° \leqq i \leqq 90°$ is shown in a basic diagram in Fig. 6.13.

The intensity becomes a maximum for $i = 0°$ (perpendicular incidence).

The photo-electric current i, produced by an intensity I (Lumen), is

$$i_{ph} = \sigma I \quad (\mu A)$$

For diffused daylight this formula reads

$$i_{ph} = \sigma FI \quad (\mu A)$$

where the illumination I is measured in ft.-c., falling on the area F, measured in sq. ft.

6.25. Effective Path of Surveillance

The effective length D of the light beam is the maximum distance between photosensitor and light source over which the photo-electric device may effectively be controlled by the source of radiation. The effective length

$$D = \frac{f}{F}(1 - y)^z \sqrt{\frac{A \,.\, I}{\Phi_r}}$$

where D effective maximum path of surveillance,
- f focal length of lens,
- F size of light source (filament, arc, etc.),
- A area of photo-electric cathode,
- I intensity of irradiation on photosensitor,
- Φ_r required flux (Lumen),
- y absorption factor of the mirrors or other optical system used in multiple reflexion,
- $1 - y$ reflexion factor of the mirrors, or transmission factor of the lenses, respectively,
- z number of mirrors, or lenses, respectively.

By substituting for I and Φ_r the above values, the relation between the total flux Φ of the source of radiant energy, the produced photo-electric current i_{ph}, and the maximum path D of surveillance, is given by

$$\Phi = D^4 i_{ph} \frac{35{\cdot}28}{\sigma \tau \left[\frac{f}{F}\left(1 - y\right)^z A\right]^2}$$

The fraction is a constant for a given assembly ; Φ, D, i are variable.

Bibliography Reference: (2383)

6.26. Designing a Baffle Tube.

The design of the baffle tube is governed by the principle that no other light than that from the proper source must reach the far end of the tube.

In Fig. 6.14 the light source *A* controls the photosensitor at the far end of the tube. Generally, the light-source (tungsten-filament; discharge arc, etc.) is not focused on to the cathode, as this method gives rather unsatisfactory results, but the image of the source is

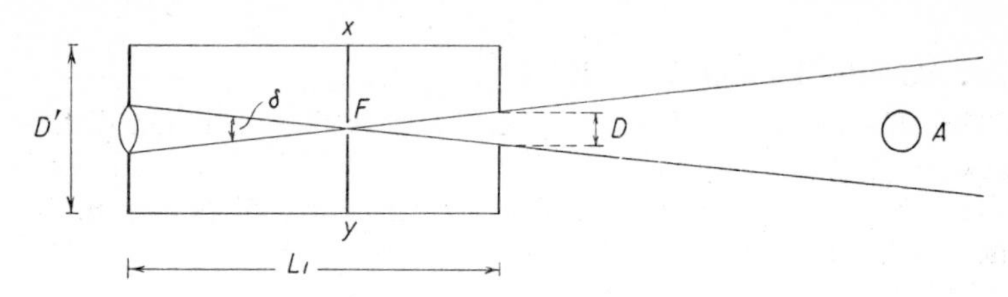

Fig. 6.14. Principle of the baffle tube.

focused on to an imaginary plane, bisecting the tube. The whole area of the far end of the tube should be evenly illuminated. For these conditions, the divergence of the beam is $\tan \delta = D/L_1 = D/nL_2$, where 2δ is the divergence, D the diameter, L_1 the length, n the number of baffles, and L_2 the distance between two adjacent baffles. The extraneous source *B*, Fig. 6.15, is able to throw a beam of radiant

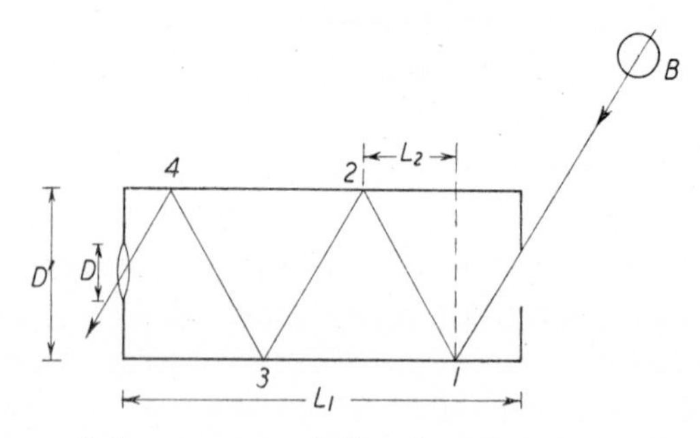

Fig. 6.15. Extraneous light may enter a baffle tube and reach the cell by multiple reflexion.

energy under such an elevation into the "mouth", or near end, of the baffle tube that the several times reflected ray eventually reaches the far end of the tube and emerges through the opening of the last baffle. This means that light from another than the proper source at

A also reaches the photosensitor. As this must not be the case baffles have to be fitted within the tube at the indicated points 1, 2, 3, 4, in order to prevent this ray from being reflected.

A simple method of calculating the dimensions of a baffle tube is is based on the condition that the baffle b next to the mouth of the tube must intercept the entire radiation from an extraneous source B. The angles of incidence of the two outer rays from B are α' and α'', respectively, and the angles of elevation of the source are $\varepsilon' = 90 - \alpha'$ and $\varepsilon'' = 90 - \alpha''$. From Fig. 6.16 the following relations are derived :

$$\tan \varepsilon' = h/L_2 \qquad \tan \varepsilon'' = (D' - D)/2L_2$$

$$L_2 = (D' - D)/2 \tan \varepsilon'' \quad h = L_2 \tan \varepsilon' = (D' - D) \tan \varepsilon'/2 \tan \varepsilon''$$

It is obvious that one baffle will suffice as long as $h > D$. The theoretical limit is $h = D$. In this case the above equation for h is transformed into

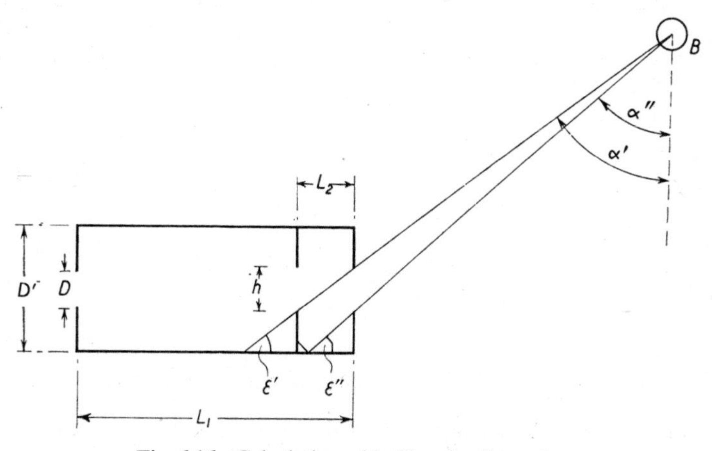

Fig. 6.16. Calculation of baffle tube dimensions.

$$D = (D' - D) \tan \varepsilon'/2 \tan \varepsilon''$$

Because $\varepsilon' < \varepsilon''$, the factor $\tan \varepsilon'/\tan \varepsilon'' = K < 1$.
Introducing K in the above equation, the conditional equation now reads

$$D' = D\,(2 + K)/K.$$

Considering that $K < 1$ the condition is now

$$D'_{min} > 3D$$

If a factor q of safety is introduced, thus making $h = qD$, the outer diameter of the baffle tube will be determined by

$$3D < D' = D\ (2q + K)/K$$

The distance L_2 between two adjacent baffles is

$$L_2 = \tfrac{1}{2}(D' - D)\ K \text{ cotan } \varepsilon'$$

After substituting $D\ (2q + K)/K$ for D', this distance, finally, is

$$L_2 = Dq \text{ cotan } \varepsilon'$$

The factor $q = (100 + p)/100$ when p is expressed in per cent.

A pinhole diaphragm placed at the focus of the lens will effectively shield most of the extraneous radiation and prove satisfactory in many cases. If a pinhole diaphragm is used no baffles need be inserted, and vice-versa.

Bibliography References: (*1799, 2180*)

6.26.1. Extraneous Rays

The exclusion of extraneous rays can easily be attained by using two small parabolic mirrors of 8 to 15 cm. (3 to 6 in.) diameter, the source of radiation and the photosensitor being placed in the respective foci, Fig. 6.17. The formula governing the relation between object

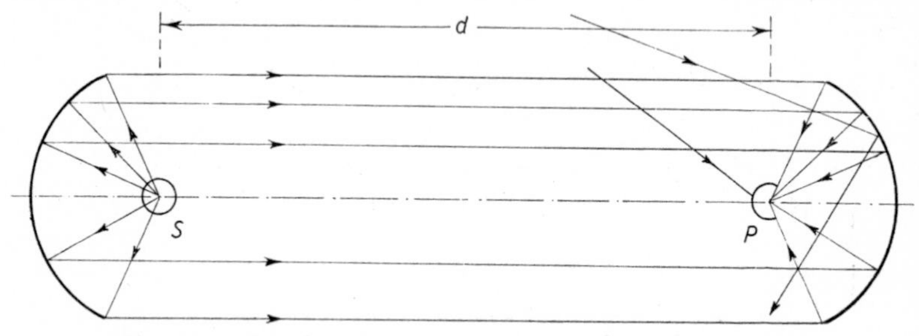

Fig. 6.17. Use of parabolic mirrors to exclude extraneous light.

and image is $s = Sd/f$ where S is the size of the source (filament, arc, etc.), s the size of its image, d the distance between the source and photosensitor, and f the focal length of the mirror.

The photosensitor is put in a housing, blackened inside but having a small aperture in the direction of the collecting mirror. This housing acts as a diaphragm and prevents any extraneous rays, for instance dispersed daylight or directed light from another source, from reaching the photosensitor. Radiation is admitted to the cell only when first striking the mirror parallel to its axis.

Bibliography Reference: (*2733*)

6.27. Basic Optical Circuits

The optical circuits can be reduced to a few fundamental arrangements the most important of which are shown. Fig. 6.18 demonstrates how to split up a beam of radiation, and how a steady beam is modulated by a rotating mirror, thus supplying an alternating current to the grid of the amplifier valve.

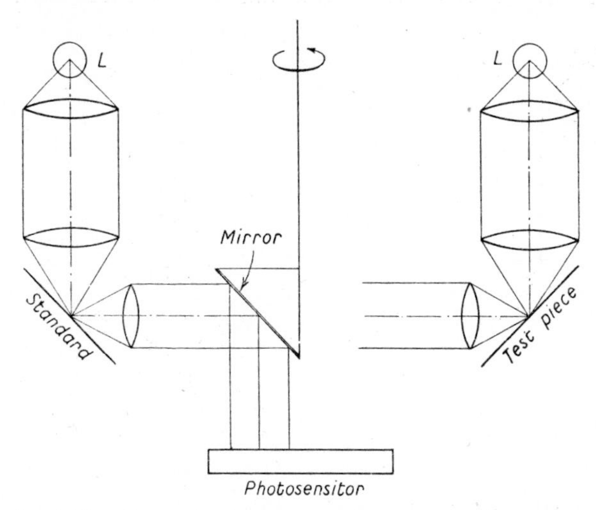

Fig. 6.18a. Form of optical comparator using rotating mirror.

6.27.1. *The Rotating Mirror*

The rotating mirror, or any other device for that purpose, concentrates alternatively the light from the standard and from the test object upon the photosensitor. If the optical properties of these two objects differ from one another the intensity and, therefore the photocurrent, will exhibit a ripple characteristic, Fig. 6.18b. The amplitude

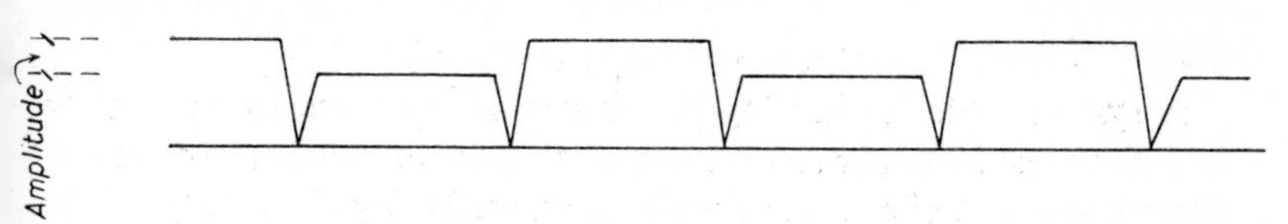

Fig. 6.18b. Waveform of photo-current with unmatched sources.

of the alternating resultant will decrease the more the optical qualities of the two surfaces are alike. An alternative is indicated in Fig. 6.19. These methods are also applicable to photometering. The simple arrangement, Fig. 6.20, shows the shutter so disposed in relation to the two beams that as one beam is in the course of being cut off the other is being allowed to increase gradually. The two intensities can be made to match one another. If the apertures of the shutter are so arranged that each instantaneous sum of the two intensities is constant with time there will be no jumps or ripple in the output circuit and the characteristic will be a straight line parallel to the time axis.

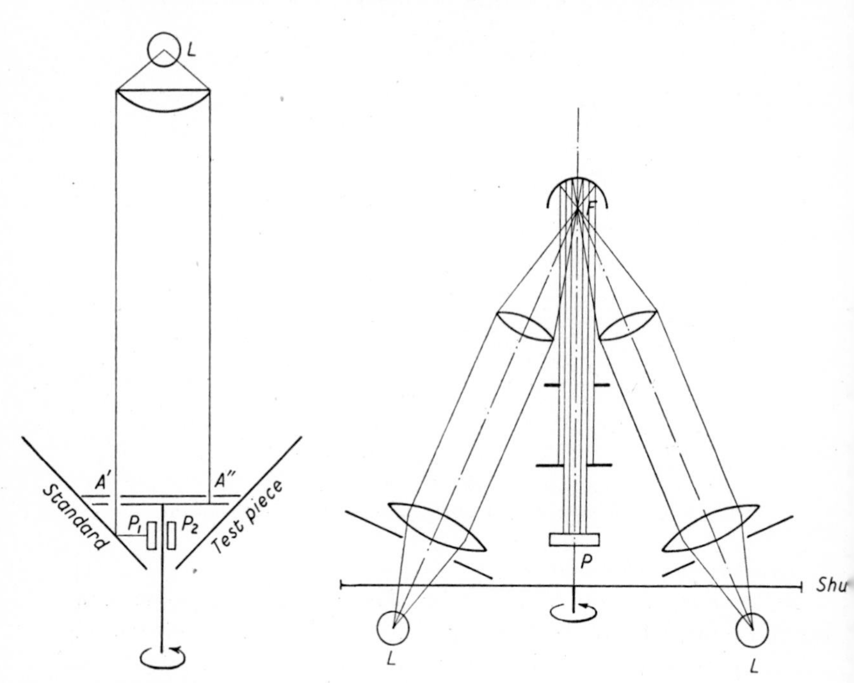

Fig. 6.19. Alternative form of comparator.

Fig. 6.20. Comparator using two light sources.

6.27.2. Opacity-Transparency of Gases or Liquids

A system used in checking the degree of transparency or opacity of a given test length or test volume uses a glass or metal tube closed at either end with a disk of good white glass, preferably of optical quality, and a plano-convex lens, Fig. 6.21. The orifice marked (1) is the inlet and (2) the outlet if a gas or vapour is under observation, the reverse being the case with fluids. The appearance of steam or smoke or any other impurity in the test cell is the cause not so much of an attenuation by selective or non-selective absorption of the transmitted light than of a deviation of the beam by dispersion. If the medium in the test cell becomes turbid (*290*, *291*), the lens *B* cannot focus on to the aperture of a pinhole diaphragm and the photosensitor *A* will be obscured : this provides for negative action. By substituting a parabolic mirror for the diaphragm the deviated ray will be thrown on to another photosensitor *B* which now actuates a photo-relay. This arrangement gives positive action.

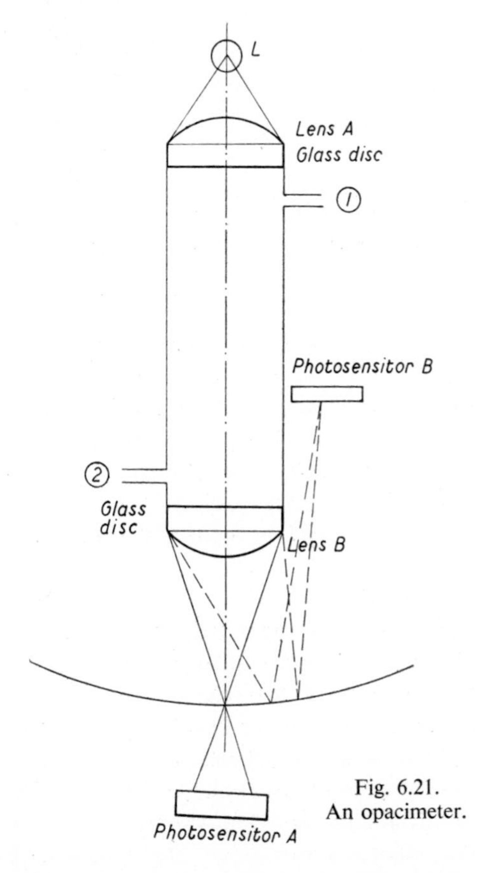

Fig. 6.21.
An opacimeter.

If cell *B* is provided with a graded grey filter having a number of well-defined steps, the densities being in a given ratio, for instance, 1 : 2 : 3 : . . . , a number of relays can be energized separately, each carrying out a given action The electromagnetic relays can be connected in a circuit, as instanced in Fig. 6.20.

6.27.3. Optical Compensator

The principle demonstrated in Figs. 6.19 and 20 can be further developed into optical compensators, Fig. 6.22, showing the application of the principle of compensation to transparent objects (solids, liquids, gases).

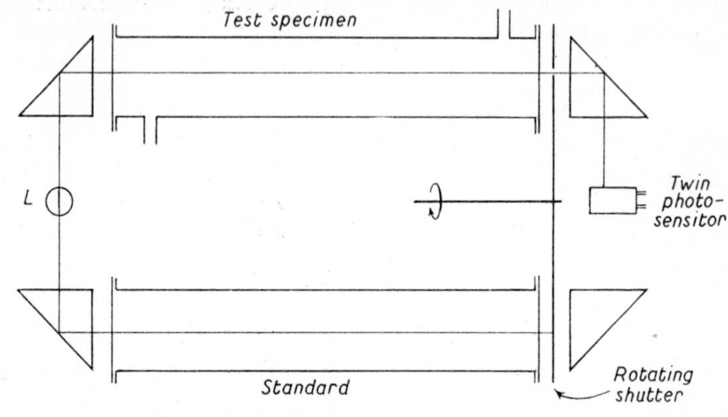

Fig. 6.22. Two-cell arrangement of comparator.

If the photosensitor is connected to a resistor-capacitor-coupled amplifier, the control device in the output circuit of the amplifier will be actuated only when the balance is disturbed. This, however, is indicative of a deviation of the test object from the approved standard. A suitable type of photo-cell is made by Cinema-Television, Ltd.

6.28. Constant Illumination

An interesting circuit was suggested by the Hanovia Chemical & Mfg., Co., and developed as a control for constant illumination for printing motion picture film (*343*). The control circuit keeps the intensity of the lamp constant within one or two per cent. irrespective of any changes in supply voltage, room temperature, or ageing of the lamp. The response of the lamp, a low voltage 250-watt size mercury discharge lamp is instantaneous. The supply voltage is 220 V, D.C., Fig. 6.23. The photosensitor is of the blue-sensitive type. The cell observes the mercury arc whose fluctuations are transferred via the amplifier valve V_1 to the grids of the two 6L6 valves. When the anode potential of V_1 is less than the voltage of the battery, (22·5 volts), the anode current is varied. An increase of light on the photosensitor reduces the current through the lamp, and vice-versa. (cf. Chap. 7.21).

A very simple photoelectric circuit for automatically controlling and maintaining at a constant intensity the emission of a light source (tungsten filament lamp of 12 V, 48 W) has been designed at the National Physical Laboratory, Teddington (*2585*). The percentage regulation is 148 : 1. Normal radio components are used in the circuit.

Bibliography References: (*2244, 2353*)

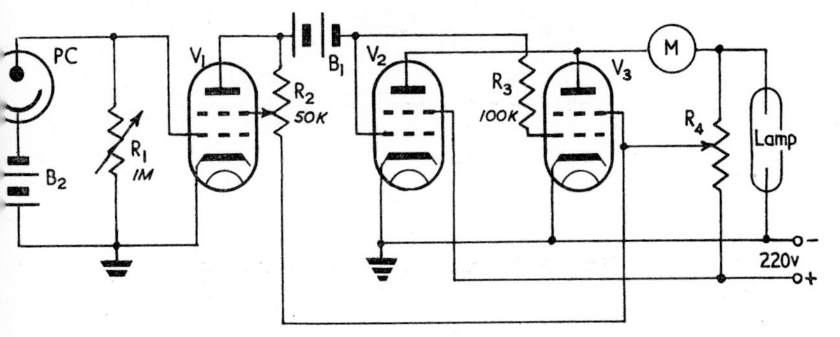

Fig. 6.23. Circuit for constant illumination by electronic control.

6.29. Conduction of Light

The transmission losses in certain spectral regions of transparent materials are so extremely low that they can be used in conducting radiant energy of a particular range of wavelengths. Ordinary glass does not belong to the group of transparent low-loss media. In the luminous range Transpex, Perspex, Lucite (*292, 1045*), in general polymethyl methacrylates and polystyrenes, and other transparent synthetic plastics (*293*), are used in the form of applicator rods to convey luminous energy without heat around corners and so to illuminate the exact spot desired. In the ultra-violet and infra-red regions fused quartz (Vitreosil) is the only material applicable to conveying radiant energy (*294*). The theoretical principles are discussed by H. Pearson (*1627*).

The reduction in intensity of a beam of luminous energy passing through a sheet of Transpex 0·125 in. thick, is 8% for Transpex I, and 10% for Transpex II. These losses are not caused by absorption, but are almost entirely due to internal reflexions.

A high efficiency reflector for use with light conductors has been developed by C. A. Morrison (*380*). The light source is placed at the first focus of an elliptical concave mirror M_1, Fig. 6.24. A spherical concave mirror M_2 is placed in contact with M_1 and the arc of M_2 must not be smaller than the arc whose chord passes through the second focus of M_1. The well polished applicator rod pierces M_2 at the vertex. The diameter of the light conductor should slightly exceed the maximum dimension of the light source. The end of the rod lies at the second focus of M_1 and the rod may be bent to any degree of curvature

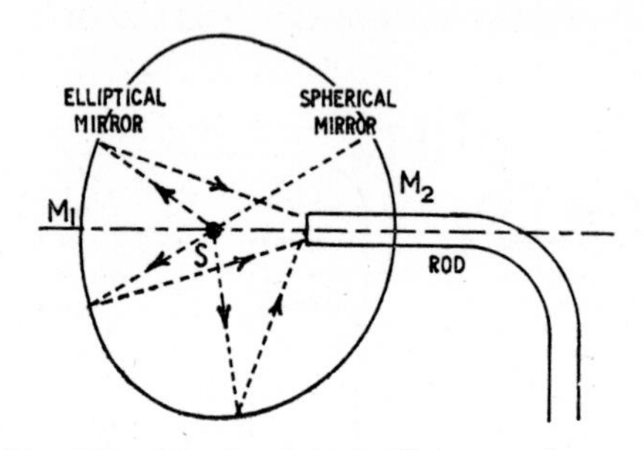

Fig. 6.24. Morrison's high efficiency reflector.

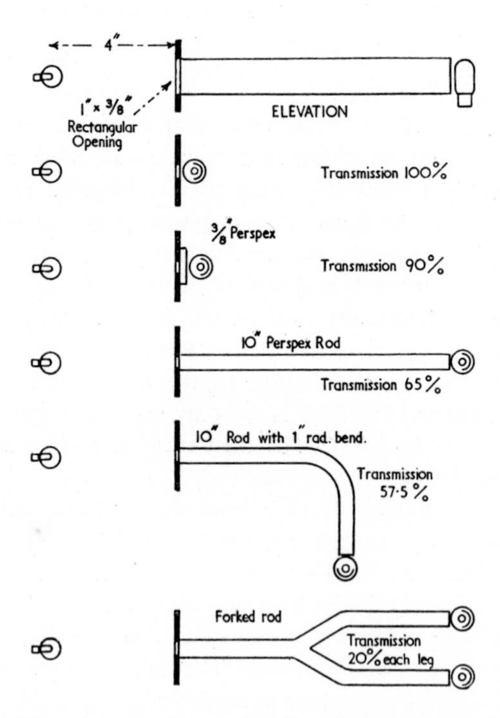

Fig. 6.25. Comparative transmissions through Perspex rods.

provided the angle of the internally reflected rays exceeds the critical angle (cf. 6.7). Transparent plastics, at a safe distance from the heat radiations of the source, may be cemented to the heat-resisting glass or quartz rod.

In Fig. 6.25 the transmission through Perspex rods of various shapes is illustrated (*1050*). It will be noticed that a different light distribution is attainable (1) by varying the distance of the light

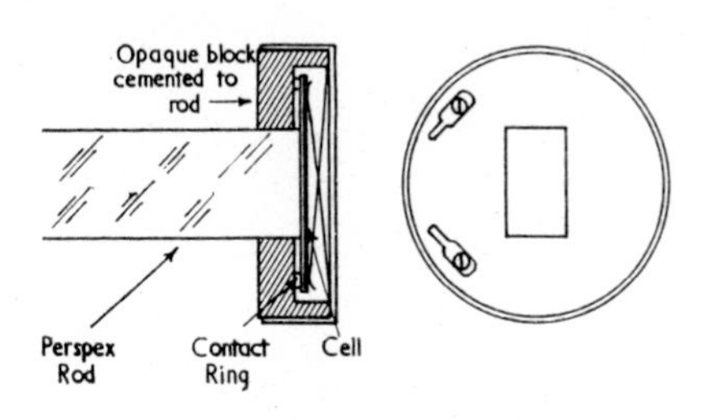

Fig. 6.26. Combination of light conductor and photosensitor.

source from the near or " input " end of the rod, and (2) by treating the " output " end varyingly. A mechanical combination of a light conductor and a photosensitor is suggested in Fig. 6.26. A divided (forked) light guide for use in coincidence scintillation counters has been used with advantage and described by Makiej (*2583*). The Perspex rod is 0·5 inch in diameter and the two halves are cemented together with chloroform.

Bibliography References: (*2220*, *2385*)

6.30. Optical Levers

The sensitivity of optically reflecting instruments, for instance of mirror galvanometers, can be increased by introducing large light beams (*1290*). The usual disadvantages of such a beam can be compensated by utilizing a system suggested by B. H. C. Mathews (*295*), For a magnification ratio of $I_1/I_2 = 10$ the following constants are used :

AB	12 cm.		
BM	3 cm.	*B*	cylindrical lens + 7D
BC	15 cm.	*C*	cylindrical lens + 30D
Cm	8 cm.	*M*	plane mirror
mS	10 cm.		

All optical surfaces must be in perfect condition. An optical lever operating with a single mirror in a very restricted room and achieving a maximum of seven reflexions, has been designed by Hoadley (*2584*). Another arrangement using three reflexions and one (galvanometer) mirror achieves a magnification ratio of 6·4 : 1 (*2586*).

Bibliography Reference: (*447*)

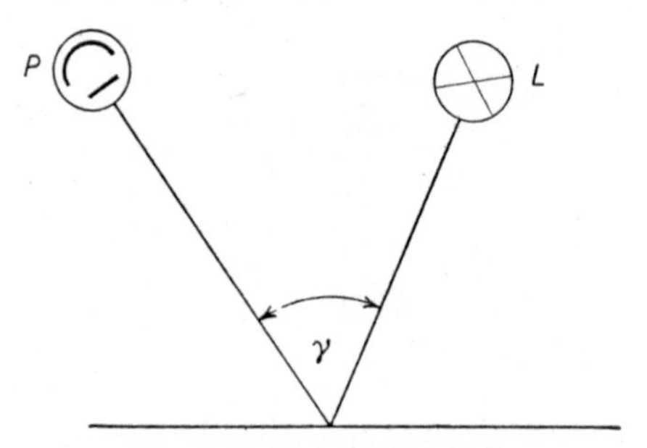

Fig. 6.27. The relative angle.

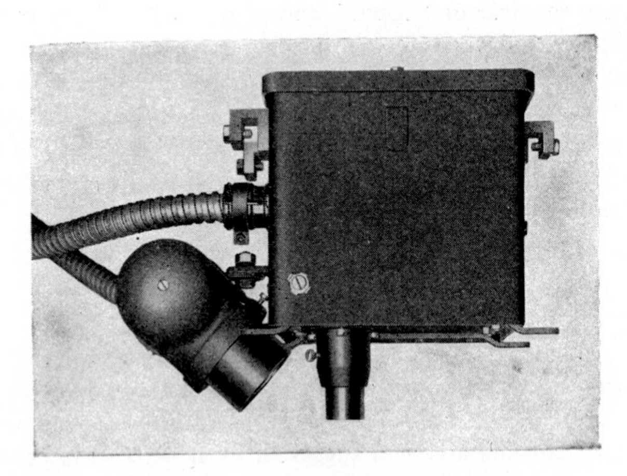

Fig. 6.28. A scanning head with 45° angle.

6.31. Industrial Scanners

Scanner and light source usually form one unit which is called a Scanning Head. The relative position between the scanner (photosensitor with or without amplifier valve) and the light source (with or without filters and other optical accessories) not only can be altered for individual adjustments, but must be variable in accordance with the type of application and surface to be scanned. A glossy surface, resulting in specular reflexion, requires a scanning head with a " relative angle " of 90°. The " relative angle " is the angle between the optical axis of the light source and photosensitor, respectively, Fig. 6.27. Matt or rough surfaces, yielding diffuse reflexion, require a " relative angle " of 45°. The commercially obtainable scanning heads are usually of the 45° type, Fig. 6.28.

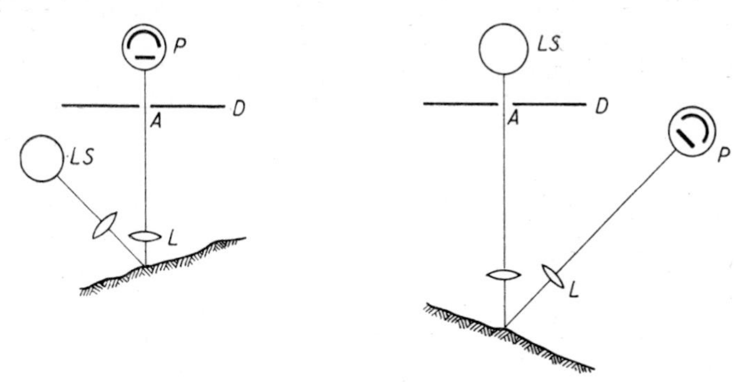

Fig. 6.29a. General illumination of target area.

b. Local illumination of target area.

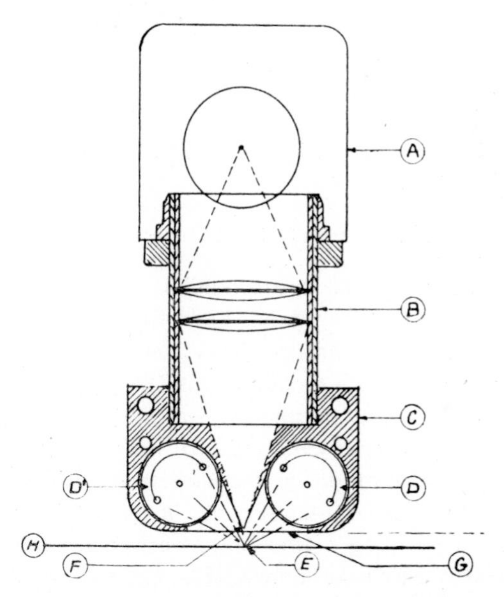

Fig. 6.30. Compact scanning head (Cinephone Corporation).

The collecting lens is so focused as to project on to the aperture *A* of the diaphragm *D* a sharp image of the area to be scanned, Fig. 6.29a. If only a small, but sharply defined, spot is to be scanned the objective lens is so focused that a well-defined image of the aperture (secondary light source) is projected on to the spot, Fig. 6.29b.

Other scanners use compound cells, i.e., a series, or parallel, or series-parallel, combination of small photo-e.m.f. cells, the increase or decrease of illumination on any one of them being the actuating stimulus. A series combination is best suited.

The aniseikon is another type of scanner (see Chap. 10).

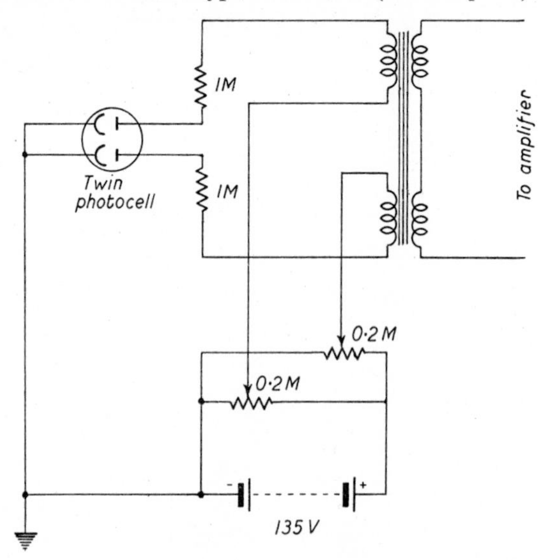

Fig. 6.31. Scanning head using twin photosensitors.

A compact scanning head for all-round use is marketed by the United Cinephone Corporation, Fig. 6.30. Light from the source mounted in the metal housing passes through the system of bi-convex lenses in the tubular collar and through the aperture. The surface to be scanned is highly illuminated without the photosensitors in the annular collar of the scanning head receiving any but reflected light, the intensity of which depends on the condition of the inspected surface. The photo-current is transmitted through a co-axial cable to the remote amplifier.

A scanning head using a twin photosensitor in a push-pull circuit (*402*) was described by Loofbourow, (Fig. 6.31).

Bibliography References: (*1195, 1585, 2002, 2126, 2174, 2202, 2295*)

CHAPTER 7

SOURCES OF RADIANT ENERGY

7.1. Definition

The British Standards Institution defines LIGHT as the " Radiation capable of producing luminous sensation." The wavelengths of such radiation may be considered for practical purposes at between 0·38 and 0·76 micron. (*347*).

The American Committee on Colorimetry is more explicit in saying " Light is the aspect of radiant energy of which a human observer is aware through the visual sensations which arise from the stimulation of the retina of the eye " (*321*).

These are the psycho-physical concepts of Light. Physically, light is a disturbance, electromagnetic in character, travelling in empty space at a finite velocity of $(2{\cdot}9979277 \pm 0{\cdot}25) . 10^{10}$ cm. sec^{-1} (*2521*) which is usually taken as 300,000 km. sec^{-1} or 186,282 miles, sec^{-1}. (Dr. L. Essen, Nat. Phys. Lab., 1947.) (See also *2591*).

In a material medium the disturbance is propagated in wave form. The wavelength of light is the distance from a crest or trough to its adjacent crest or trough, respectively. The number of complete oscillations per second is called the frequency of the disturbance. The wave number is the number of waves per cm. The W.N. $= 10^8/\lambda$, if the wave-length λ is measured in Ångström Units. The amplitude of the wave, which is a sine-wave, to the second power is a measure of the intensity of this disturbance.

Bibliography References: (*1389, 1577*)

7.2. Energy of Radiation

The energy content of a radiation can be subdivided into a number of " parcels " or " quanta " of energy, each quantum being a finite quantity solely depending on the wavelength of the radiation (*112*). Albert Einstein postulated that the energy quantum is expressed by the product of Planck's Constant of Action (*51*) h (erg-sec) times the frequency f of the radiation measured in c/s. The elementary unit of light is the Photon, the energy of which is $E = hf$. The following Table gives the energy quantum of radiations having various wavelengths (*53*).

TABLE 7.1

Wavelength, Frequency, Wave Number and Energy Quantum of Radiation

Radiation (Definition)	Wavelength A.U.	Frequency 10^{12} c/s	Wave Number cm.$^{-1}$	Energy Quantum 10^{-12}erg
u–v	2537	1185	39450	7·84
u–v	3000	1000	33333	6·61
u–v	3650	823	27400	5·45
v	4358	688	22920	4·55
b	4800	625	20850	4·14
b–g	4916	610	20350	4·03
g	5461	549	18300	3·63
g–y	5550	540	18025	3·57
y	5890	509	16990	3·36
o	6031	498	16590	3·30
r	6708	447	14910	2·96
i–r	9000	333	11111	2·20
i–r	10140	296	9860	1·96
i–r	12000	250	8340	1·65
i–r	15000	200	6666	1·32

Bibliography References: (*1210*, *1211*)

7.3. Classification of Light Sources

Different types of light sources can conveniently be characterized according to their emission spectrum, namely as monochromatic, heterochromatic, and panchromatic sources, respectively. The first two emit their energy as a line or band spectrum, while the third type emits a continuous spectrum.

Bibliography Reference: (*2344*)

7.3.1. *Monochromatic Sources*

These are light sources emitting all their luminous energy at one wavelength ; for instance, a sodium vapour lamp ; or the energy is emitted at various wavelengths within a narrow band as, for instance, by a neon lamp.

7.3.2. *Heterochromatic Sources*

Energy is emitted at a few well-defined wavelengths distributed over the spectrum, as for instance, by a mercury discharge lamp.

7.3.3. *Panchromatic Sources*

These are light sources emitting their radiant energy over the whole of the luminous spectrum. This type is represented by filamentous lamps, for instance a tungsten (incandescent) lamp.

7.4. Non-Luminous Radiators

The above classification applies in its principal concepts also to non-luminous (ultra-violet ; infra-red) emitters. In many cases of luminous radiators, non-luminous energy is simultaneously emitted with light. Either luminous and ultra-violet, or luminous and infra-red, or luminous and ultra-violet as well as infra-red radiation is generated and emitted. The undesired regions of the emission spectrum may be eliminated by the use of appropriate filters (cf. Chap. 9).

7.5. Black Body Radiator

This is an idealized, theoretical body which completely absorbs all radiations incident on it or, if used as an ideal emitter, radiates the maximum energy at all wavelengths. Other terms are : Full Radiator ; Planckian Radiator ; Complete Radiator (*1493*).

Bibliography Reference: (*1104*)

7.6. Grey Body Emitter

Any incandescent (panchromatic) body other than a Planckian Radiator. The energy emission E'_{λ} of a Grey Body is related to that of the Planckian Radiator E_{λ} by the factor $e < 1{\cdot}0$, viz., $E'_{\lambda} = e \,.\, E_{\lambda}$. Carbon is a good example of a Grey Body emitter, its spectral emissivity e varying only from 0·8 to 0·5 in the wide spectral region between 4000 and 40,000 A.U. (*254*, *348*). Other terms are : Incomplete Emitter ; Selective Radiator.

7.7. Tungsten Filaments

For tungsten filaments the factor $e = 0{\cdot}3$. Incandescent tungsten filaments have fairly uniform spectral emissivities in the luminous portion of the spectrum. At 2400°K. the variation is from 46·3% at 4670 A.U. to 42·7% at 6650 A.U. If the radiation is the result of thermal excitation only, the emissivity can never exceed unity at any wavelength, since a Planckian Body emits the maximum radiant flux possible at each and every wavelength (*254*).

7.8. Colour Temperature

When a body emits selective radiation which at each wavelength (within the luminous spectrum) is proportional to that of a Planckian Radiator at a different temperature so that its radiation appears to be of the same colour, the temperature of the Planckian Emitter is called the colour temperature of the radiator (*347*).

The colour temperature, although a characteristic of the lamp, is not a constant. It declines during burning, approximately proportional to the twenty-third power of the true temperature of the filament. It also varies with the applied voltage across the filament (*349*). (cf. Chap. 5.5.)

The colour temperature of carbon equals its true temperature. The colour temperature of tungsten and many other metals is higher than their true temperature (*280*).

The colour temperatures of gas-filled tungsten and other lamps are: (after Forsythe *et al.*).

TABLE 7.2

Colour Temperatures of Gas-filled Tungsten and Other Type Electric Lamps.

Type of Lamp	Colour Temperature °K.
Tungsten, Gas-filled	
40 W	2760
100 W	2865
500 W	2960
1000 W	2990
1500 W	3225
Tungsten, Vacuum	
25 W	2493
Point-o-lite	
100 c.p.	2920
S-1 Sunlight Lamp	4000
Car Lamp (aver.)	3000
Fluorescent,	
Daylight	6500
White	3500
Exciter Lamp (*351*)	2870*

* NOTE.—At 7·5 volts filament voltage the colour temperature is 3055°K. and the intensity 560 candles. With only 6 volts across the filament, the figures are 2640° K. and 140 candles, respectively.

Colour temperatures of natural light sources and fluorescent lamps are quoted by Amick (*350, p. 220*), and of various types of electric lamps by Clark (*36, p. 122*).

The colour temperature of photosensitor exciter lamps changes with the characteristics of the lamp (*601*).

TABLE 7.3

Typical Colour Temperatures of Exciter Lamps for Photosensitors

Volts	Amps.	Lm/W	T°K.
8·12	2·0	9·1	2645
8·36	4·0	20·9	3115
8·72	4·0	22·3	3185
9·85	7·5	21·5	3105
10·28	5·0	21·4	3095
4·09	0·75	10·8	2955

The most widely used light source is the panchromatic (incandescent, tungsten filament) lamp, although in some cases electric discharge lamps of both the monochromatic and heterochromatic type are used with advantage.

Different types of lamps are run at different temperatures. The colour temperature of the incandescent filament is one of the most essential data because this temperature controls the quantitative distribution of the radiant energy. The law of Wien and Paschen permits of calculating the wavelength of the dominant radiation of an incandescent body, for instance of the tungsten filament, at a given temperature. The dominant wavelength in A.U. is λ_{dom}=28,970,000/T°K, where T°K is the absolute temperature in degrees Kelvin (cf. Chap. 19.9).

Bibliography References: (*1167, 1168, 1216, 1545*)

7.9. C.I.E. Standard Illuminants

The three C.I.E.* standard illuminants are panchromatic light

* C.I.E. (Comité Internationale de l'Éclairage) is the international abbreviation for the International Commission on Illumination. This was formerly known in English-speaking countries as the I.C.I., but the French style was adopted owing to possible confusion with Imperial Chemical Industries.

sources the incandescent filaments of which operate at the following absolute temperatures, viz.,

Standard Illuminant *A* : 2848°K.

Standard Illuminant *B* : 4800°K.

Standard Illuminant *C* : 6500°K.

Type *A* illuminant represents the light of the sun, 45 min. (time) from the horizon ;

Type *B* illuminant represents the light of the mean noon sun ;

Type *C* illuminant represents the light from an overcast north sky.

The spectral distribution of the three illuminants is given by D. B. Judd (*352*).

The data of photosensitors usually refer to a light source operated at 2848°K. which, on the average, is well represented by a 100-watt tungsten gas-filled lamp. Exact correction filters have been devised for the use with type *A* lamps (*352*). R. Davis and K. S. Gibson (*353*) have produced two pairs of liquid filters for the transformation of type *A* lamps to type *B* and type *C* lamps, respectively (*354*). (cf. Chap. 9.11.) The National Bureau of Standards (*1494*) has developed a special 500-W filament tungsten stereopticon lamp which, when operated at the nominal voltage of 118·0 V has a spectral distribution practically identical with that of a Planckian radiator at 2850° K. The designation of this lamp is B.S.1717.

7.10. Natural Light Sources

Although the sun or the sky hardly ever are reliable sources of light employed in industrial processes, a few data are included for application in those rare cases where the sun or the sky is the only source of radiation. Due to absorption and scattering, the content of ultraviolet radiation may be regarded as negligible. The infra-red energy shows very marked absorption bands due to water vapour and oxygen (*1490*). It must also be borne in mind that the spectral distribution of terrestrially available solar energy is dependent on the altitude (*356*) of the sun and the latitude of the observer, the maximum being in the neighbourhood of 5500 A.U. when the sun is in the zenith, this maximum shifting towards 7500 A.U. for the setting sun. The diurnal variations in the intensity of the luminous radiation by no means is indicative of the variations in the amount of non-luminous energy (*36, p. 130*).

Natural light sources also have a certain colour temperature (*350, 358*).

TABLE 7.4

Colour Temperatures of Natural Light Sources

SUN,	
at horizon	1900°K.
20 min. after rising	2120
30 min. after rising	2380
40 min. after rising	2900
1.00 hour from horizon	3500
1.30 hours from horizon	4000
2.00 hours from horizon	4400
noon	5250
3.30 p.m.	5000
4.30 p.m.	4800
SKY,	
overcast	6000–7000
blue	15000–27000
blue northwest	19000
extremely clear blue NW	25000

Bibliography References: (*1216, 1584, 2033*)

7.11. Spectral Energy Distribution

The average proportion of radiation in the three wavelength-groups corresponding to the classification of the three primary colours Blue-violet, Green, and Red, is listed in Table 7.5.

TABLE 7.5

Group Distribution of Spectral Energy

	Blue-violet %	Green %	Red %
Sun	$33\frac{1}{3}$	$33\frac{1}{3}$	$33\frac{1}{3}$
Carbon filament	5	30	65
Tungsten, vacuum	7	32	61
Tungsten, gas-filled	20	30	50
Hg-arc in glass tube	90	10	0

The spectral energy distribution ($\mu W/cm^2$ at 1 m distance per 100 A.U. band width) for a number of lamps and wavelength-groups is compiled in Table 7.6 (*602*, *603*, *604*).

TABLE 7.6

Spectral Radiant Intensity per 1000 candles

Lamp Watts	40	100	500	1500	*	**	250	***
Colour Temp.	2750	2865	2960	3025	2870	2848	2580	2848
Wavelength A.U.								
3500	0·46	0·54	0·66	0·74	0·54	0·52	0·30	—
4000	1·50	2·07	2·40	2·55	2·08	2·00	1·35	2·03
4500	4·26	4·66	5·02	5·25	4·67	4·55	3·60	4·56
5000	8·20	8·52	8·85	9·08	8·55	8·45	7·85	8·26
5500	13·10	13·16	13·25	10·35	13·17	13·15	12·85	12·82
6000	18·80	18·24	17·80	17·60	18·20	18·36	18·65	17·80
6500	23·35	22·60	21·90	21·40	22·58	22·76	25·30	22·76
7000	27·50	26·60	25·80	24·80	26·60	26·80	31·45	27·35
7500	31·00	29·75	28·20	26·80	29·70	30·00	38·15	31·31
8000	33·70	32·35	29·80	25·15	32·30	32·70	44·00	
8500	35·80	34·25	32·25	30·25	34·15	34·65	48·90	
9000	37·40	35·70	33·50	31·20	35·65	36·20	52·20	
9500	38·60	36·10	*34·00*	*31·50*	36·05	36·60	54·40	
10000	39·30	*36·50*	*34·00*	31·40	*36·40*	*37·15*	56·00	
10500	*39·70*	36·40	33·80	31·20	36·35	*37·15*	56·85	
11000	39·60	35·90	33·00	30·40	35·80	36·70	*57·25*	
12000	38·20	34·30	31·00	28·10	34·20	35·20	56·70	
13000	35·80	32·10	28·50	25·60	32·00	33·00	54·70	
14000	33·10	30·00	25·50	22·80	29·80	30·70	51·20	
15000	29·50	25·90	22·50	20·30	25·70	26·65	46·70	
16000	26·20	22·80	19·80	17·70	22·60	23·40	41·80	
18000	21·00	17·80	15·00	13·20	17·55	18·40	33·10	
20000	15·50	13·50	11·40	10·20	13·40	13·90	25·25	

* as used in calibrating.

** type A illuminant.

*** Planckian Radiator at 2848° K.

In the penultimate column the spectral energy distribution of a 250-W "infra-red" tungsten lamp is listed. This type lamp is used in infra-red drying, paint baking, etc.

The relative energy distribution within the luminous part of the spectrum of a car lamp run at 3100° K. is given in Table 7.7 (*332, 610*).

TABLE 7.7

Relative Spectral Energy Distribution of a Car Lamp at 3100°K.

Wavelength A.U.	Irradiance
3800	0·1188
3900	0·1425
4000	0·1688
4100	0·1979
4200	0·2294
4300	0·2634
4400	0·2998
4500	0·3383
4600	0·3790
4700	0·4215
4800	0·4658
4900	0·5114
5000	0·5582
5100	0·6061
5200	0·6548
5300	0·7040
5400	0·7536
5500	0·8033
5600	0·8531
5700	0·9025
5800	0·9516
5900	1·0000
6000	1·0476
6100	1·0945
6200	1·1403
6300	1·1850
6400	1·2284
6500	1·2704
6600	1·3111
6700	1·3503
6800	1·3880
6900	1·4240
7000	1·4584
7100	1·4912
7200	1·5223
7300	1·5517
7400	1·5793
7500	1·6055

Bibliography References: (*527, 561, 1387, 2344, 2400*)

7.12. Luminous Efficiency

The efficiency of electric energy conversion into luminous energy (light) is very low. The theoretical maximum* to be attained is 621 Lm/W (*605*) but only a small percentage of it is utilized in the electric light sources of to-day. The luminous efficiency in Lm/W and in per cent of the possible maximum are compiled in Table 7.8.

TABLE 7.8

Luminous Efficiencies

Tungsten Filament Lamps 230 V (603)

Wattage	15	40	60	100	300	500	1000	1500
Candle-Power (*1498*)	9	32	55	105	375	674	1520	2410
Lm/W	8·3	10·4	11·7	13·4	15·7	16·9	19·1	20·2
Efficiency %	1·35	1·68	1·88	2·16	2·53	2·72	3·08	3·25

Mercury Discharge Lamps (606, 607)

Wattage	80	125	250	400
Lm/W	38	40	33	41
Efficiency %	6·12	6·44	5·31	6·6

Sodium Discharge Lamps (606, 607)

Wattage	45	60	85	140
Lm/W	55·5	65	71·5	71·5
Efficiency %	8·95	10·5	11·5	11·5

* The mechanical equivalent of light is variously given as 0·0015 W/Lm, i.e. 666·66 Lm/W (*608*) or as 0·001497 W/Lm, i.e., 668 Lm/W (*609*). The value as determined by H. E. Ives (*605*) is 0·0016103 W/Lm, i.e., 621 Lm/W and is now generally acknowledged. The mechanical equivalent is calculated under the assumption that the total energy is radiated at the wavelength of maximum sensitivity of the average human eye, viz., at 5550 A.U. The mechanical equivalent is the ratio of radiant flux to luminous flux at 5550 A.U. Taking into account those wavelengths for which the luminosity factor is greater than 0·02, a light source of one watt produces only 261 lumens of daylight (*613, 614*).

P. S. Millar (*611*) gives the energy balance of a 60-watt tungsten filament lamp as follows :

7·5% rated luminous spectrum ;

13·5% gas loss : heat convection and conduction ;

1·2% end loss : conduction by leads and support wires ;

80·8% filament radiation ; an additional 6% bulb and base heat absorption is involved.

The luminous efficiency of a tungsten lamp declines in proportion to the thirty-first power of the true temperature of that filament (*349*).

Bibliography Reference : (*1595*)

7.13. Thermal Inertia (Flicker)

The thermal inertia of incandescent filaments, especially when of the low voltage type, suffices to suppress ripple effect of an A.C. supply and to ensure a steady beam of light. In cases where modulated light is preferable, the ordinary 50 c/s A.C. mains will supply a modulation frequency of 100 c/s when a gas or vapour type discharge lamp or a special type filament lamp is used, a typical representative of the latter being the Mazda-55-lamp or a 100W 16mm. motion picture projector lamp. For other frequencies a mechanical device, for instance, a synchronous motor-driven slotted disk must be provided. The mathematical treatment of the thermal inertia of a filament was developed by I. Langmuir (*612*).

7.13.1. Time-Constants of Filament Lamps

W. E. Forsythe *et al.* have shown that the time in which a filament reaches a certain brightness is a function of the normal operating current I and has the general form $t = aI^b$, where a and b are constants and both are smaller than unity (*1497*). The total variation in brightness during a cycle is a function of the diameter of the filament. For vacuum and gas-filled lamps, respectively, they give the following data.

TABLE 7.9

Time-Constants of Filament Lamps

	Heating Time t_1 sec.	Cooling Time t_2 sec.	% of Total Variation in Brightness at: 25c/s	60c/s
Vacuum Lamp	$0{\cdot}060 \times I^{0.54}$	$0{\cdot}022 \times I^{0.70}$	$28 \times D^{-1.37}$	$34 \times D^{-1.06}$
Gas-filled Lamp	$0{\cdot}150 \times I^{0.70}$	$0{\cdot}070 \times I^{0.70}$	$63 \times D^{-0.91}$	$75 \times D^{-0.89}$

NOTE: t_1 is the time in which the lamp reaches 90% brightness on heating;
t_2 is the time in which the lamp reaches 10% brightness on cooling;
I is the normal operating current;
D is the diameter of the filament, measured in mils.

TABLE 7.10

Time-Constants of General-Purpose Panchromatic Lamps

Type of Lamp	Watts	Luminous Efficiency Lm/W	Colour Temp. °K.	Time of Heating to 90% of final luminous light output sec.	Time of Cooling to 10% of initial luminous light output sec.	Luminous Output in % of Input	Range of Variation in Light Output in % at: 25c/s	60c/s
Vacuum	40	10·8	2570	0·128	0·058	6·6	40	14
Gas-filled	40	11·1	2710	0·065	0·026	6·8	58	27
	60	12·9	2770	0·102	0·042	7·9	44	18
	100	15·6	2845	0·125	0·059	10·0	33	13
	300	19·0	2915	0·270	0·125	11·0	17	6
	500	20·3	2955	0·380	0·190	12·0	13	4·5
Mazda 55 *	1·45 c.p. 6·5 V		2715	0·071	0·026		50 c/s 25%	

* The data of the Mazda 55 Lamp have been furnished by the Research Laboratories of the British Thomson-Houston Company, Ltd.

From the Table it can be seen that the thermal characteristics of the Mazda-55 lamp are fairly well represented in the mains voltage range by a 40-W gas-filled lamp.

7.14. Data of Monochromatic and Heterochromatic Lamps

These lamps comprise the various gas and metal vapour discharge lamps, respectively. The types commercially available are the mercury and sodium vapour lamps, respectively, and the neon gas (cold cathode) lamp. Other metal vapour lamps are available for laboratory use, for instance, caesium, cadmium, zinc vapour, etc. (*619*, *620*, *621*, *1600*).

TABLE 7.11

Technical Data of Electric Discharge Lamps
partly after S. Dushman (*616*)

Type of Lamp	Watts	Lumens	Luminous Efficiency Ideal *Lm/W*	Luminous Efficiency Actual *Lm/W*	Colour	Life hours	Radiation max. %	Radiation at A.U.	Energy Utilization Ratio
Mercury H.P.	80	3040		38·0				5770 to 5790	0·125
	125	5000	298	40·0	blue-	1500	35		0·133
	250	9000		39·6	green		28	5461	0·132
ME/D	250	(cf. text for details)				500			
Sodium	45	2500		55·6					0·118
	60	3900		65·0				5890 to 5896	0·136
	85	6100	475	72·0	yellow	2500	98		0·152
	140	10000		71·5					0·151
Neon	5	5		1·0	orange-	2500	20	6390 to 6410	
	50 to 200		198	15·0 to 40·0	red		20 (*1496*)	6380 to 6450	0·075 to 0·200

TABLE 7.12

Spectral Characteristics of Mercury-Vapour Lamps (*611*)

Type	Pressure atm.	Watts	Blue Line 4358 A.U. *Lm*	Blue Line 4358 A.U. %	Green Line 5461 A.U. *Lm*	Green Line 5461 A.U. %	Yellow Line 5780 A.U. *Lm*	Yellow Line 5780 A.U. %	Continuous Luminous Radiation *Lm*	Continuous Luminous Radiation %
H–1	1	400	110	0·7	7860	49·1	6800	42·5	1230	7·7
H–2	0·5	250	55	0·7	3770	50·3	3245	43·3	430	5·7
H–4	8	100	25	0·7	1735	49·6	1255	35·9	485	13·8
H–5	0·4	250	70	0·7	4630	46·3	4040	40·4	1260	12·6

TABLE 7.13

Radiation Intensities in μW/cm.² at 1 m. (*617*)
Mercury Lamps

Type	Pressure atm.	Watts	Lumens	Radiation Intensities in the Spectral Regions, A.U.					
				3650	4047	4358	4916	5461	5780
H–3	30	85	3000	25·7	14·5	27·1		33·5	19·2
H–4	8	100	3500	24·5	14·2	26·9	1·6	33·6	30·5
H–5	0·4	250	10000	70·0	38·2	72·0	4·3	90·5	104·0

TABLE 7.14

Relative Radiation Intensities of Sodium Lamps

Wavelengths A.U.	Relative Intensity
4979–83	<0·2
5149–54	<0·1
5683–88	1·2
5890–96	100·0
6154–61	0·3
8183–95	19·0
11382–404	10·0

Other lines are at 11,850 A.U. and 40,500 A.U.

Bibliography References: (*446, 531, 555, 556, 557, 562, 1052, 1055, 1067, 1082, 1223, 1328, 1329, 1331, 1338, 1372, 2216*)

7.15. Compact Mercury Discharge Lamp

A special mercury discharge lamp (*615, 618, 1601*) has been developed by the British Thomson-Houston Co., Ltd., to meet the needs for a mercury type high-intensity light source having as small an arc as possible. The type *ME* is a 250-W lamp, Fig. 7.1. The arc is 3·75 mm. long and 1·5 mm. wide. The initial maximum brightness is 18,000 stilb (i.e., candles per sq. cm.). The control gear consists of a choke and 60 μF capacitor for power factor correction. If the choke is connected in series with a resistor of 35 to 48 ohms (200–250 watts) the lamp can be used on D.C. as well. The spectrum contains the following lines :

2537	2967	3125–32	3650–63	4047
4358	4960	5770–90	10140 A.U.	

other lines are at 11,300, 13,700, 39,400 and 40,200 A.U., Fig. 7.2.

The long-wave ultra-violet, blue, and yellow line, respectively, are the strongest. Table 7.15 shows that the brightness of the type *ME* lamp compares favourably with other light sources used in industry. For sources of high intensity (cf. *1624*).

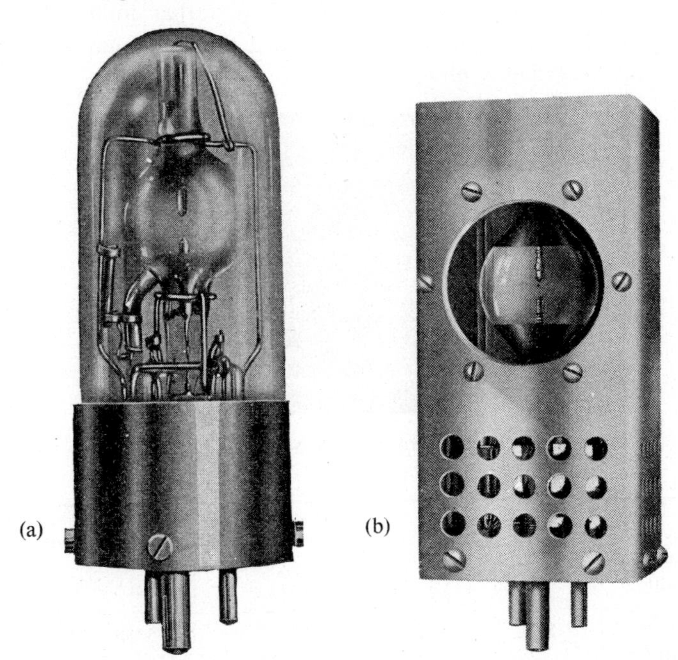

Fig. 7.1. 250 W compact mercury vapour light source in (a) tubular envelope, and (b) in metal box—*B.T.H. Co.*

TABLE 7.15

Brightness of Industrial Light Sources

Type of Lamp	Brightness (Stilb)
Carbon Filament	50
Tungsten Filament, Vac. 10 Lm/w	200
,, ,, Gas. 20 Lm/W	1200
,, Arc, 2 amp.	1500
,, ,, 7·5 ,,	2000
Mercury Discharge, type ME,	18000

7.16. Agreement between Photosensitor and Light Source

If it is desired to operate photosensitors by the light of discharge lamps, maximum efficiency will be attained by mutual agreement between the sensitivity of the photosensitor and the emission of the lamp.

Table 7.16 lists the dominant wavelength, or rather dominant range of wavelengths of the light source as against the maximum sensitivity of the different types of photosensitors.

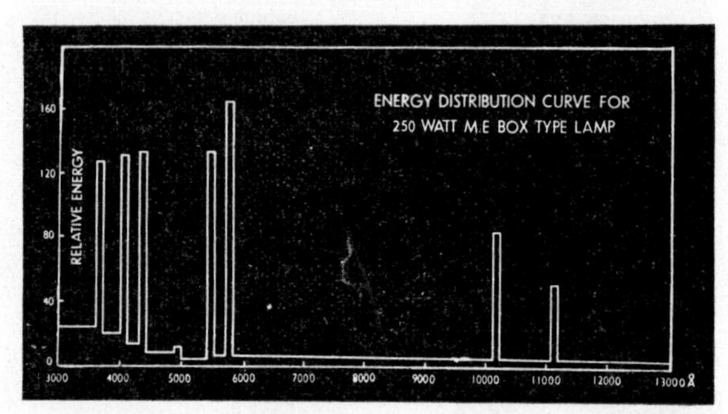

Fig. 7.2. Emission from 250 W M.E. box-type lamp.

TABLE 7.16

Light emitted by (type of lamp)	at max. rad. A.U.	is best used with a Photosensitor type	whose max. sensitivity is at A.U.
Mercury	5780	selenium	5750
	5461	cuprous oxide	5550
Sodium	5893	selenium	5750
Neon	6402	caesium	7500–8000 (at 6400 A.U. the sensitivity is 75 to 80% of the max.)

7.17. Useful Life of Incandescent Filaments

The useful life of a modern tungsten lamp is 1000 hours ; that of discharge lamps 1500 hours for mercury vapour lamps, and 2500 hours for sodium vapour lamps. The life of an incandescent lamp depends mainly on maintaining the correct supply voltage. Fig. 7.3 shows how the life of a tungsten lamp is materially affected by only slight changes in the operation characteristics. A 5% drop in voltage will lower the colour temperature of a lamp by about 75°K., reduce the light output to 83% and the wattage to 93% of the rated values, but the life of the lamp has been doubled. It is therefore possible for the cautious designer to increase the useful life of a lamp by utilizing the effects of a reduced supply voltage. The decrease in wattage and light output may be compensated by the use of the next higher rating of lamp operated at 95% of the supply voltage. An example is given below.

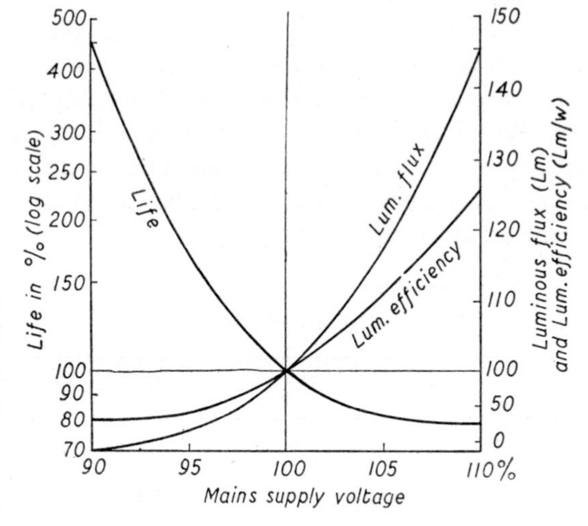

Fig. 7.3. Effect of voltage on the parameters of a tungsten lamp.

TABLE 7.17

Useful Life v. *Supply Voltage*

Voltage rated lamp V	Supply Volts	Wattage W	Light Output Lm	Useful Life Hours
A lamp rated 230 V	is operated at 230 V	at 75 W	yielding 910 Lm	and living 1000 hrs
Using a lamp rated 250 V	on a supply at 230 V	shows a reduction of 19%	of 27%	but its life increases 325%
Therefore, a lamp rated 250 V	and used on 250 V	at 100 W	yields 1320 Lm	and lives 1000 hrs.
The same lamp rated at 250 V	but used on 230 V	consumes 81 W	yields 980 Lm	but lives 3250 hrs.
As against the lamp rated at 230 V	and operated at 230 V	at 75 W	yielding 910 Lm	and lives 1000 hrs.

The lamp characteristics as shown in the penultimate row are very close to those given in the first (and last) row, but the useful life of the lamp, when operated under the conditions as set out in the fourth row, is more than trebled.

7.18. Sources of Ultra-Violet Radiation

Low-pressure mercury discharge lamps (*388*) emit a large proportion of their radiation in the far ultra-violet, mainly at 2537 A.U. (resonance line) (*622*). It is possible to produce lamps which emit practically all their energy at this line. With increasing pressure the number of lines in the mercury spectrum increases and eventually leads to a spectrum of a more continuous nature. Lamps with a pressure up to 80 atm. have been built and operated successfully (*1625*).

TABLE 7.18

Relative Spectral Distribution of Ultra-Violet Radiators

Type	Pressure	Make	below 2537	2537	2537-3000	3000-3341	3650	luminous
T/M5/369	low	2	—	185·0	0·55	1·26	1·00	4·46
UA27A2 350 V ; 4 A	low	3	0·122	0·316	0·75	1·06	1·00	2·39
UA27A2 220 V ; 3·75 A	800 mm.	4	0·475	0·332	0·91	1·08	1·00	2·44
AC Uviarc 600 W ; 183 V ; 3·92 A		3	0·338	0·348	0·92	1·07	1·00	2·61
UV 1 Sun Lamp (*625, 626*)		1	—	—	0·24	0·99	1·00	
A.C. 250 V ; 3·5 A	high	2	0·111	0·281	0·63	1·09	1·00	2·56
D.C. 230 V ; 3·5 A	high	2	0·094	0·348	0·83	1·04	1·00	2·48
A.C. 150 W	low	5	0·123	0·313	0·79	1·10	1·00	2·35
H–3 85 W (*617*)	30 atm.	6	—	—	—	—	1·00	3·69
H–4 125 W	8 atm.	6	—	—	—	—	1·00	4·38
H–5 250 W	0·4 atm.	6	—	—	—	—	1·00	4·41
" Black Lamp " 80 W (*388*)	high	7	—	—	—	0·09	1·00	—

Makers : (1) G.E.C. (England).
(2) Thermal Syndicate, Ltd. (England).
(3) G.E. of America.
(4) Hanovia, Ltd. (England).
(5) cf. Rev. Scient. Instr., 1938 ; 9 ; 325.
(6) Standard American make.
(7) Philips Electrical Ltd.

The relative light emission is calculated from the data of the relative energy distribution diagram by multiplying the relative energy distribution for a given wavelength by the appropriate luminosity factor which may be taken from Table 3.2 or from Fig. 3.6. The relative light emission is the luminosity of an individual spectral line in the spectrum of a radiator (*627*, *628*). The luminosity factors of the mercury spectral lines are given in Table 7.19.

TABLE 7.19

Luminosity of Mercury Spectral Lines

Spectral band	Principal line	Luminosity factor
A.U.	A.U.	
3989–4110	4047	0·0007
4110–4284		0·00140–0·0075
4284–4437	4358	0·0175
4437–4650		0·0325 –0·0750
4650–4838		0·0750 –0·162
4838–5062	4916	0·228
5062–5319		0·423 –0·865
5319–5613	5461	0·98
5613–5951	5780	0·89
5951–6353	6234	0·353

A low-voltage low-wattage battery-driven source of near ultra-violet radiation, constructed with a light-absorbing " black " filter bulb, was described (*629*) as being manufactured in two types, viz., a 2·5W and a 4W lamp, respectively, the voltage being 24 to 28V D.C. The 4W type illuminates an area of nearly 40 in^2. The A.C. is provided by a vibrator. Another development is a 24V battery-driven D.C. radiator which needs no vibrator (*1265*). During the war (1939–1945) British Thomson-Houston, Ltd., developed an excellent low-voltage (12 V) " black glass " lamp of 36W A.C. or D.C. input. It is simply the standard car type lamp with a Wood's filter bulb.

A series of high output ultra-violet sources for the irradiation of luminescent materials is given by Beggs (*622*). The low pressure type (5 μ of mercury vapour pressure) emits most of its radiation at 2537 A.U. The high-pressure type lamp is water-cooled and operates under vapour pressures up to 100 atm.

A useful lamp is the argon-filled glow lamp which has only a very small output but needs no control gear for operation. The maximum output centres around 3300 A.U. with a very low output in the short-wave luminous range, i.e., in the violet and blue. The 0·25W lamp has a useful life of 1000 hours, and the 2·5W type of 2000 hours.

The lamp manufacturers produce two types of ultra-violet lamps, both having a small quartz burner enveloped by a nickel-oxide outer bulb which acts as a filter, the only difference being the wattage, viz., 80 W and 125 W, respectively. The very dark purplish-red, nearly black looking outer envelope is the cause of these radiators being colloquially termed " black " lamps. These lamps emit their energy on the 3650 A.U. line, the other radiations being negligible. In Table 7.20 the emission data of the two sizes are given together with the intensities in absolute units.

TABLE 7.20

Emission Data of the 80W and 125W " Black " Lamps

Wattage W	Make	Wavelength A.U.	Intensity erg/sec/cm²	Transmission through envelope (%)
80	1	4047	13	1·1
		3650	1050	90·9
		3341	60	5·2
		3130	32	2·8
125	2	4047		1·0
		3650		95·5
		3341		2·5
		3130		1·0

NOTE : Makers : 1. Philips Electrical Ltd. (Philora Lamp) ;
2· British Thomson-Houston Ltd. (Mercra Lamp).

In an emergency an ordinary 85W or 125W mercury discharge lamp (street lighting type) can be adapted to be an efficient source of radiation at 3650 A.U. The glass envelope should be opened with a blow-lamp first at the end and then a hole cut by the same method at the side (*631*). The diameter of the hole should be about 10 mm. The lamp should then be totally enclosed in a metal cylinder having an aperture of about 20 to 25 mm. just opposite the aperture at the side. The metal container should be kept dry (use silica gel) as the wire connexions inside the lamp are now laid bare to the corrosive influence of the atmosphere and are liable to rust and break. They can, however, be coated with a protective (high temperature or stove) varnish. The radiation spectrum of a street-lighting mercury-vapour lamp with its envelope removed is detailed in Table 7.21. With suitable filters any particular wavelength can be isolated.

TABLE 7.21

Radiation Spectrum of Street Lighting Hg-vapour Lamp without Envelope

Approx. Percentage of Input Energy radiated at	Wavelength A.U.
0·4	2483
0·5	2537
0·7	2652
0·4	2804
0·5	2967
1·0	3022
1·9	3126
3·0	3650
1·8	4047
3·5	4358
4·5	5461
5·5	5780
74	above 7000

Bibliography References: (*520*, *522*, *538*, *1164*, *1319*, *1504*, *2397*, *2398*, *2399*)

7.19. Sources of Infra-Red Radiation

The best and most reliable source of near infra-red is the completely screened tungsten-filament lamp. The higher the wattage, the bigger is the yield in infra-red radiation (*604*, *611*).

The relation between the various dimensions used in the measurement of energy, is : $1 \mu W/cm^2 = 10$ erg/sec/cm^2.

The appropriate filters are described in Chap. 9. Ventilation is essential in work with screened high-wattage lamps which develop intense heat ; as a fact nearly 96 to 97% of the electric energy fed into a lamp is turned into waste, viz., heat. If not properly cooled the temperature of the lamp will rise until the life of it is seriously reduced. The intensity of natural infra-red radiation is discussed by W. Clark (*36*, *p. 130*).

TABLE 7.22

Spectral Energy Distribution of Infra-Red Radiators

Wavelength A.U.	Peak Radiation at ° K.	Spectral Energy Distribution in μW/cm² at 1 m. Distance from the Lamp per 50 A.U. — Lamp Watts 40	100	500	1000	1500
8000	3300	0·52	1·60	9·2	27·5	48·5
8500		0·56	1·70	9·6	28·8	50·5
9000		0·58	1·75	10·0	29·4*	51·5
9500		0·60	1·80	10·2	29·2	52·0*
10000	2800	0·62	1·81	10·5*	29·0	51·8
10500		0·62*	1·82*	10·1	28·7	51·0
11000	2500	0·61	1·78	9·9	28·3	49·8
12000	2150	0·60	1·69	9·3	26·5	45·7

NOTE.—The asterisk marks the maximum radiation

Most commercially available types of infra-red sensitive photosensitors have their maximum sensitivity in the neighbourhood of 10,000 A.U. The source of infra-red radiation should, therefore, have its maximum emission within the range of about 7,500 to 12,000

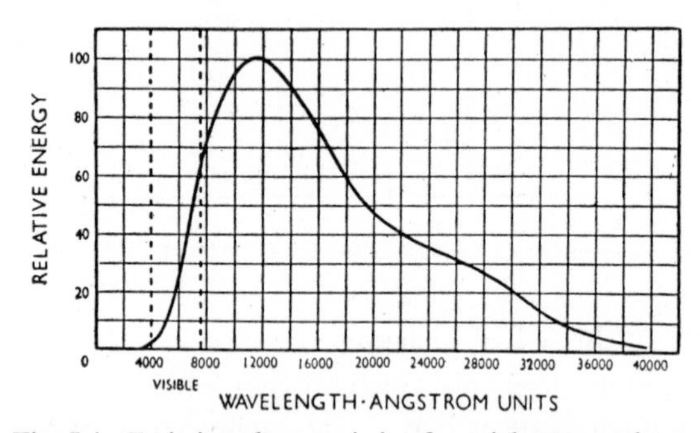

Fig. 7.4. Emission characteristic of special tungsten lamp.

A.U. A tungsten-filament lamp operating at any colour temperature above 2800° K. will suit the purpose. A special type tungsten incandescent lamp (*630*) operating at a colour-temperature of 2530° K. has its maximum emission at about 11,500 A.U., Fig. 7.4, and Table 7.6. The useful life of this lamp, which has been designed for paint drying, is 5000 hours : its luminous intensity is 140 candles. Other infra-red emitters are of the Nernst glower type as, for instance, the Globar, a silicon-carbide rod which is heated electrically.

Bibliography References : (562, 1122, 1123, 1169, 1648, 1878, 2187, 2354, 2395)

7.20. Lamp Houses

The lamp house, Fig. 7.5 and 7.6, must be of sufficient volume to allow for natural ventilation (*1625*). In many cases the lamp housing will be so designed to accomodate any type lamp for a certain range of photo relays. If the lamp is of the low-voltage type the lamp housing should preferably be fixed to the transformer. The housing may have an attachment for the optical equipment (focusing lens, filters, screens, réseaux, etc.) and will provide for the lamp-holder to be adjustable so that it can be alined with the optical axis of the focusing system.

Bibliography References: (*2168, 2392*)

7.21. Constant Illumination

In practice, the only and most disturbing source of fluctuations in the illumination of photosensitors is the inconstancy of the mains voltage supplying the radiator. The illumination from an incandescent lamp varies as the third or fourth power of the voltage (*238*). The temperature of the lamp is a function of the voltage, viz., T°K. $\propto V^{1/2 \cdot 6}$ (*603*) and the colour temperature also varies accordingly (*349*). The result of ageing is that the colour temperature is reduced approximately proportional to the twenty-third power of the true filament temperature. The disturbing effect of fluctuating filament temperature becomes obvious, and is a serious factor, in colorimetric measurements employing two-cell circuits (cf. Chap. 5.5). It is therefore of primary importance to stabilize the voltage in order to have an output of reasonable constancy. Such circuits are rather critical in their demands for high accuracy since it is obvious from the above statement (*238*) that the voltage must be stabilized within millivolts if the output (the illumination) is to be kept within a limit of accuracy of 0·1%. Light regulators have been described in the technical literature (*343*, cf. Chap. 6.29 ; *948, 1187, 1488, 1489*). Fluctuations in intensity, as a result of the time-constant of filament lamps (cf. Table 7.10), are eliminated according to the U.S. Pat. 2348296 (*1432*), by supplying a two-filament lamp with A.C. of different phase relation. Each filament receives a different phase, the angle of which can be measured by a cathode-ray tube (*1499, p. 46*). (cf. Chap. 6.29.)

Bibliography References : (*1315, 1859, 1867, 1987, 2037, 2063, 2070, 2179, 2210, 2224*).

(*Courtesy British Thomson-Houston Co. Ltd.*)

Fig. 7.5. Various types of lamp housing.

7.22. Modulated Light

As shown, tungsten filaments on A.C. supply are liable to exhibit flicker due to lack of thermal inertia, the flicker frequency being twice the supply frequency. The thinner the filament the greater the tendency to A.C. modulation, i.e., flicker. Gas-filling increases this inherent tendency, while coiling reduces it. The conditions for a lamp to have a good inherent modulation, are : (1) a thin filament, (2) a stretched-out filament, (3) a content of gas.

Fig. 7.6. Form of lamp housing, with hood.

7.22.1. Modulation inherent in Gas Discharge Lamps

There are two distinctly different voltages besides the rated voltage which are characteristic of discharge lamps. They are the ignition (or firing, striking, breakdown) voltage and the extinction voltage. A circuit for tracing the characteristics of a neon lamp is discussed by M. von Ardenne (*1479, p. 409*).

A. K. Barker, in a paper on photo-electric effects on neon lamps (*632*) warns the user of the effect that light has on the breakdown voltage. As an instance he quotes the case of a certain type of neon lamp the striking voltage of which, when kept in the dark, was 70 V (*2497*). When the lamp was exposed to moderate daylight, the incident radiant energy ionized the neon gas to such an extent that the electrode gap became conductive at 62 V. When irradiated by a 1000W arc light, which was rich in ultra-violet radiation, a further ionization took place and the lamp ignited at 55 V which equals a reduction of 21·5% from the initial (rated) breakdown voltage. T. W. Case (*634*) had already announced in 1921 that more electrons are emitted when radiant energy falls on a hot oxide cathode than when it strikes a cold cathode (*635*).

The experiments of Barker confirmed a report by A. Stager (*636*) who had observed that the frequency of oscillation in a relaxation oscillator, for instance, of the type shown in Fig. 7.7, is a function of the radiation striking the neon lamp. When placed in the dark and

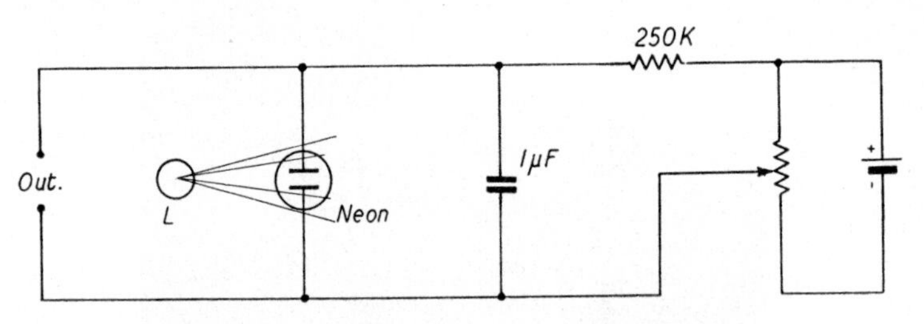

Fig. 7.7. Effect of illumination on neon oscillator.

adjusted to the flashing point (one or two flashes per minute) a match ignited a few yards away from the neon lamp raised the oscillation frequency to 10 or 20 flashes per minute (cf. Chap. 4.29).

It is, therefore, suggested to coat the outside of the glowlamp with an opaque material or to enclose it so that the lamp is not reached by extraneous light. It is possible to transform this disturbance into a beneficial effect by constantly illuminating the discharge lamp with a small light source, for instance, a flash lamp and thus stabilize the discharges. H. J. Reich (*633*) describes how, by utilizing this effect, he succeeded in keeping extremely constant the flashing rate of a relaxation oscillator operating at low frequencies. This effect may also be used to reduce the striking voltage (cf. above).

If the luminous output of the ordinary 5-W neon lamp is insufficient, the crater type will give good results.

Bibliography Reference: (*1156*)

7.22.2. Methods of Modulation

Modulated light is used either when two light beams strike the same photosensitor alternately, the amplifier being expected to discriminate between the two impulses, or when it is desired to avoid the difficulties of D.C. amplification. The following methods are in general use.

TABLE 7.23

Methods of Modulation

Method	Modulation applied to the	Thermal inertia of the Light Generator	Modulating the	Modulated Agent	Type of Modulation	Means producing the Modulation	Supply Mains	Modulation Frequency	Effects of Modulation
Electronic	Light Generator	nil	Generation	Beam Light	Self-modulation	Gas or Vapour Discharge Lamp	A.C.	Same as of Supply Mains	A modulated light beam is emitted by the light source
		small				Filament Lamps of low inertia type			
		nil			Super-imposed modulation	Electronic Switch or Flasher	D.C.	Any. Not below 0·002 or above 10000 c/s if mod. by rel. osc.	
Mechanical		small				Mechan. Control Gear (interruptor, pulsator, high-speed flasher)		low	
Optical	Emitted Radiant Energy	large	Radiation		Pulsation	Chopper disk ; Vibrating Reed ; Stencil and Disk ; other mechanical means	A.C. or D.C.	any ; 100 ; 30000 :	A steady light beam is emitted, but it is modulated before striking the cell
Photo-electric	Photo-current before Amplification	nil or very small*	Current	Photo-Current	Super-imposed modulation	An auxiliary cell, energized by a discharge lamp, produces a carrier		Different from, or same as, that of supply mains	The amplitude of the pulsating current, due to the auxil. cell, varies with the illumin. of the main cell

* This refers to the light source of the auxiliary photocell.

7.22.3. Modulation Superimposed by Electronic Devices

If the supply is either D.C., or if the frequency of an A.C. mains cannot conveniently be taken as the modulation frequency of the light generator, a relaxation oscillator or an electronic switch must be used. Such a device, employing a glow lamp (*1427*) in generating oscillations at a frequency ν, may be locked into step with a control frequency ν' when the ratio $\frac{\nu}{\nu'} \gtreqless 1$, and when ν' is either exactly or very nearly equal to, or is a multiple or submultiple of, ν.

In introducing the control voltage, a transformer is used in series with the one electrode that does not lead to the resistance of the oscillator, Fig. 7.8. The quantities R, C, and N are the three elements of the relaxation oscillator.

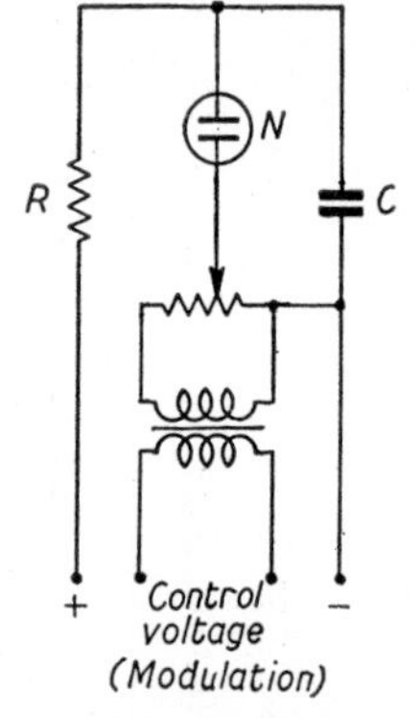

Fig. 7.8. Modulation of a neon oscillator.

Another means of producing modulated light is the electronic switch (*398, p. 44; 623, 637, 639,*) the cold or hot cathode valve being the light source.

If the light intensity of the above lamps should prove insufficient for certain applications, another scheme may be employed which has been developed in the Philips Laboratories (*640*). A gas-filled incandescent lamp can be modulated by a transformer-coupled amplifier. This arrangement was originally designed for optical telephony but it is evident that any source of low audio-frequencies can be used to modulate the lamp. The gas-filled incandescent lamp and the secondary of the output transformer are in series with a D.C. source. Superimposed is the A.C. furnished by the amplifier. The temperature of the filament will vary in accordance with the ripples of the combined supply voltages, i.e., with the frequency fed into the transformer. A maximum frequency of 2000 c/s will be perfectly reproduced by the light source.

Another D.C. mains circuit producing up to 10,000 c/s is shown in the *General Electric Book of Tube Experiments*, and is also discussed by Henney (*79, p. 242*). Also see Henney (*79, p. 296*) and (*1427*), which latter deals with a cold-cathode Pointolite source. The current through the tube is linearly proportional to the signal voltage.

Fig. 7.9 shows a circuit designed to feed audio or radio frequencies into the light source which is here a 6W exciter lamp, operated at

2870° K. The photo-electric amplifier is in resonance with the modulation frequency of the lamp (*641*). This frequency is selected by a band-pass filter in the amplifier and the variable resistor in the anode circuit varies the brilliance of the lamp.

F. V. Hunt has described a circuit with which to measure frequencies up to 7000/sec. The input circuit will be the photosensitor and its

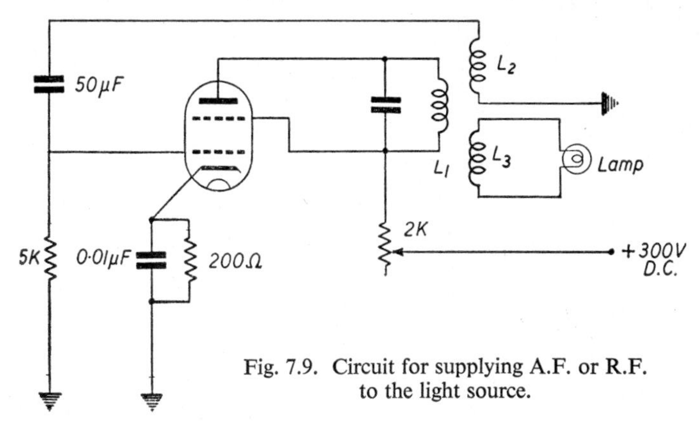

Fig. 7.9. Circuit for supplying A.F. or R.F. to the light source.

amplifier. The output current of the measuring circuit is strictly proportional to the frequency of the modulated light source irradiating the photosensitor (*642*). For higher frequencies the dynamic response of the photosensitor must be taken into account and it will be best to use a vacuum type photo-electric cell.

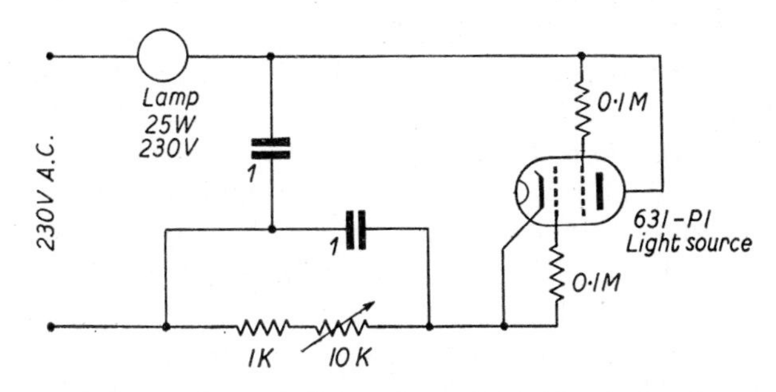

Fig. 7.10. Stroboscopic light source using cold cathode tube.

Another stroboscopic light source, using the 631-P1 cold-cathode strobotron valve, is described by Kline (*643*) who designed the circuit of Fig. 7.10. By adjusting the variable 10,000 ohm resistor the frequency can be varied between a minimum and the mains A.C. frequency.

L. F. Bird of the Hanovia Chemical and Mfg. Co. (*1187*) has developed a modulating arc lamp (overall dimensions 6·5 × 1·5 in.; L.C.L. 3 7/16 in.), the output of which can be modulated with "high fidelity to the control voltage throughout the audio-frequency range and that has stability with long operating life and slow deterioration". The control circuit can be made into a constant intensity circuit (cf. section 22) (*1698*).

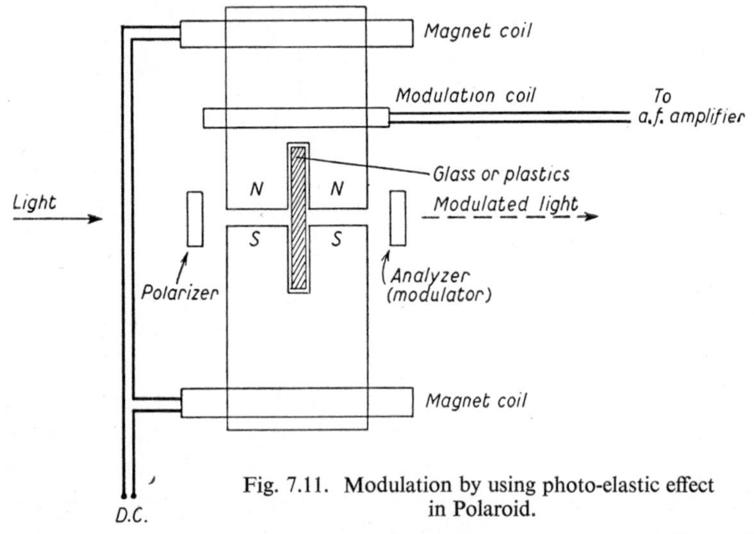

Fig. 7.11. Modulation by using photo-elastic effect in Polaroid.

A crater type modulator glow lamp has been developed by Hilliard (*1608*), and by Messrs. Ferranti, Ltd.

For handling large quantities of light, for which the previously described circuits are not well adapted, a method has been developed by LeClair (*645*). He makes use of the effect that a piece of glass or plastic becomes doubly refracting upon application of pressure. This photo-elastic effect (*1607*) is attained by exerting the pressure electromagnetically and modulating it by means of a modulation coil which is fed from an a.f. amplifier, Fig. 7.11. Practically any given light quantity can be modulated by this method. The light beam, before entering the modulator, passes through a polarizer, conveniently made from a piece of Polaroid (cf. Chap. 9.25) and after double refraction leaves through a Polaroid analyzer.

Other methods of modulating a light source have been described by Zworykin and Wilson (*25, p. 206*).

Bibliography References: (*644, 1218, 2313, 2325, 2333, 2366*)

7.22.4. *Mechanically Controlled Modulation of the Light Generator*

If the modulation frequency is to be at variance with the frequency of the A.C. supply, or if only D.C. is available, a motor-driven interrupter will make and break contact with the light generator at a certain set rate. In most cases a filament-type lamp will be fed by a pulsating D.C. or A.C. supply. Because of the fluctuations due to the A.C. characteristic of the supply current (cf. sect. 13) and the fact that the modulation frequency does not coincide with the mains frequency, it follows that the individual light impulses will be of varying intensity and a D.C. supply or rectified and smoothed A.C. supply will be preferable.

If electric discharge lamps are used on A.C., the supply being mechanically modulated (interrupted), it must be borne in mind that at no time must the instantaneous voltage across the lamp fall below the extinction potential of the lamp, to prevent it from failing. In most cases it will be better to modulate the discharge lamp electronically as is indicated, for instance, by the method developed in the laboratories of the G.E.C. (*1601*).

7.22.5. *Mechanically Controlled Modulation of the Emitted Radiant Energy*

In contrast to the above-mentioned methods which provide for the modulation of the electric supply to the light generator these methods are a means of modulating the radiant energy after its emission from the light source. The most commonly employed device for transforming the steady light flux into pulsating or oscillating light impulses is the chopper disk. The disk is preferably driven by a synchronous motor which will ensure that fluctuations in the rotation of the disk cannot take place, as otherwise the frequency of the light pulses would not be a constant. The light source must be of the high thermal inertia type, i.e., the lamp must have a thick coiled filament, such as a low-voltage, high-current rating.

The means of modulation are many. J. F. Schouten (*646, 647*) has described a simple and efficient method of modulating the radiant energy of a light source with a view of obtaining different waveforms. The waveform is a function of two variables, viz., time and energy. The light beam is made to pass through two controlling elements, the one controlling the time variable, and the other the energy variable. The desired waveform is cut out as a stencil, thus representing the energy which is admitted to the photosensitor. The other element is a disk which, when moving in a periodic motion, represents time. The disk has a number of slits moving across the stencil and thereby scanning it. The central angle between two immediately adjacent slits depends on the angular width of the stencil, arrangements being made for the one slit just to begin when the adjacent slit is just bringing to an end the scanning of the stencil. The stencil must be drawn in a polar system of co-ordinates, the origin of the system being the centre of the slotted disk. The frequency produced by this device is mn, where m is the number of slits, and n the number of rotations per second. A Nipkow disk can also be used for scanning the stencil (*1610*, *1639*).

Another suggestion for the production of low frequencies, viz., one to ten per second, was made by Harris and Scholp (*648*). Another type of chopper was also developed in the Philips laboratories at Eindhoven, making use of the principle embodied in the reed type frequency meter (Frahm's principle). This oscillating or vibrating reed (*649*) may be adapted so as to reflect a beam of radiant energy in its one extreme position and to let it pass unhindered when in its other extreme position, or it can be made to oscillate the intensity between its maximum and any given intermediate value by so arranging the target on the vibrating reed that it cuts off the light beam at any predetermined intensity. The natural frequency of the reed (steel spring) is

$$\nu \propto \frac{1}{2L}\sqrt{\frac{E}{d}}$$

where : ν is the frequency in c/s,
L is the length of the spring in cm,
E is Young's Modulus of Elasticity, in dyne/cm^{-2},
d is the density of the material in gcm^{-3}.

For steel, practically the only metal to be considered by the engineer, $E = 20$ to 22×10^{11} dyne/cm^{-2}. The theoretical length L of the spring will be reduced by the consideration that the natural frequency of the reed must exceed the frequency superimposed on it, as otherwise the spring would oscillate about a node. A length of about 9 in. results in the reed having a natural frequency of between 165 and 170 c/s depending upon the kind of steel used. These figures are not multiples of the superimposed frequency of 50 c/s and a node will not result from this length of the spring. The reed is driven by a suitably shaped magnetic coil.

Bibliography References: (*479*, *2324*)

7.22.6. Amplification of Mechanically-Modulated Radiant Energy

A pre-stage amplifier for photo-electric cells was shown in Fig. 5.14. Resistance-capacitance coupled amplifiers are used with photo-e.m.f. cells.

7.22.7. Constancy of Modulation Frequency

A Wien bridge and a cathode-ray tube form a useful device in measuring the frequency, or the constancy of the modulation, to an accuracy of better than 1 in 1000 (*1614*), Fig. 7.12.

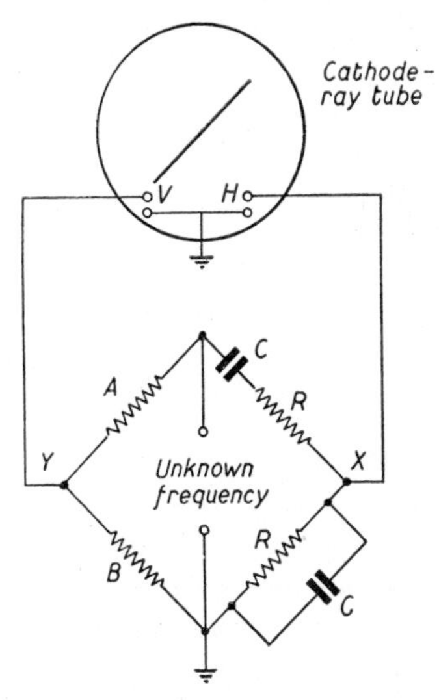

Fig. 7.12. Wien bridge and C.R. tube for checking frequency.

7.22.8. Priming

If for certain reasons it is not desired to cut off the beam of radiant energy totally at the lowest point of the modulation curve the pulsating light flux will have to be superimposed on a continuous and steady light flux (*1428*), thus producing a pulsating current superimposed on a D.C. component. This is easily achieved by increasing the amplitude of the stencil by a certain length L, Fig. 7.13.

7.22.9. Illumination-Photo-current Characteristic of the Gas-filled Cell

All gas-filled photosensitors have a characteristic shown in Fig. 7.14. For any primary current x within the range AC the resultant amplification y would fall within the relatively small and practically negligible range *AD*. If, however, a continuous or " priming " illumination is provided which generates the primary photo-current *AC*, a point *B* will be reached on the characteristic where this curve suddenly attains a much increased gradient, thus yielding high amplification values, all above *D*.

Bibliography References: (*1343, 1360, 1361, 1942, 2003, 2057, 2080, 2137, 2146, 2181, 2213, 2239, 2332, 2340*).

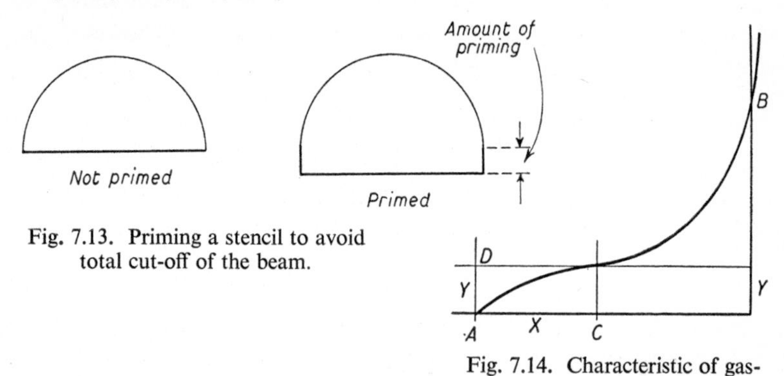

Fig. 7.13. Priming a stencil to avoid total cut-off of the beam.

Fig. 7.14. Characteristic of gas-filled photosensitor.

7.23. Natural Light (Daylight)

Although natural light is only very rarely used as a medium to energize photosensitors, the general characteristics may be briefly listed. The infra-red radiation changes irrespective of the instantaneous condition and intensity of the luminous radiation (*36, p. 130*). Details of the ultra-violet changes in daylight are given by Luckiesh *et al.* (*1292*). The same authors have also published a four-year record of ultra-violet energy in daylight (*1293*).

Bibliography Reference: (*497*)

7.24. Physiological Effects of, and Protection against, Ultra-Violet and Infra-Red Irradiation

This section is intended to remind the engineer who experiments with, or works by, ultra-violet or infra-red radiation that the human tissues are susceptible to this kind of radiation and that severe damage to his health will be the result of neglecting proper precautionary measures.

Highly concentrated infra-red radiation affects the eyes. Bukler (*1616*) and Beaumont (*1617*) describe the effects of irradiation with infra-red rays of a range with which the engineer comes into contact.

The physiological effects of ultra-violet radiation are too well known to need particular warnings. Only a few details are mentioned here. Electromagnetic radiation of a wavelength between 3200 and 2500 A.U. produces a reddening of the skin, called erythema. In particular, the erythemal wavelengths are (*1618, 1619*) :

Erythema Wavelength A.U.	2537	2650	2894	2967	3024	3130
Erythemogenic effect %	80	19	30	100	58	4·5

Wavelengths particularly injurious to the unprotected eye are in the region from 2700 to 2000 A.U., although the naked eye should not be exposed for any length of time to waves below 3200 A.U. When working with mercury discharge lamps in nickel-oxide bulbs (" black " lamps) a sensation of light blue fluorescence in the eye is often observed. This is due to the fluorescence in the anterior part of the eyes, viz., of the lens, since no radiation shorter than 3760 A.U. is transmitted by the lens. It becomes opaque again for radiation above 25,000 A.U. (cf. Chap. 3.3.)

The effect of irradiation, i.e., an erythema, only becomes obvious after the lapse of a certain time period : this phenomenon is called latency. The period of latency is inversely proportional to the wavelength of the radiation. Thus, for infra-red radiation the effect is almost immediate. As for ultra-violet erythema, the latency may be from a few minutes to a few hours, depending on the exposure, i.e., the product of time and energy, and the wavelength of the radiation.

For protection of the eyes, goggles or protective shields must be worn. For protection against the injurious impact of infra-red rays, heat-absorbing glasses of the Aklo, Calorex, or a similar type will be efficient. The shade is a greyish green. Ultra-violet radiation is not transmitted by glasses which, generally speaking, are of an emerald green hue. There are, however, other type glasses which will be more agreeable to the engineer as they distort the natural gamut of colours to a lesser degree. These are, for instance, the glasses made by Chance Bros. and marketed as " Crookes " glasses. They are only faintly coloured. The heavier grades have a very good asborption in the infra-red region also. Some eyeshields are made from synthetic plastics and are of the emerald green type ; they should be impervious to ultra-violet, dark red, and near infra-red radiation (cf. Chap. 9.8).

CHAPTER 8

COLOUR

8.1. Definition

Colour is a property which is concerned with the light as well as the object which is illuminated by it ; colour also depends on the eye as well as the mind of the person who looks at a coloured object.

Colour has a chemical, physical, physiological, and psychological aspect, the first two being of primary importance for the purpose of this book not only with respect to colours of objects or light sources but also as far as reflexions from coloured walls and ceilings, sometimes even from floors, and most certainly from painted machinery, are concerned. During the last few years the knowledge about the rôle which colour plays as a psychological factor has been applied to industrial problems, resulting in the machine operator suffering less under the fatiguing effects of repetition work and carrying out the operations with greater speed and safety.

It is these reflexions of coloured light, in most cases to be treated as extraneous rays, which must be taken into account when coloured objects are to be detected or controlled by means of photo-electric relays. The basic principles of harmonious and disharmonious colours; of the co-operation of coloured objects and coloured light ; of coloured light sources and colour filters, etc., must be understood if the photo-electric relay is to work correctly under conditions which differ from those usually encountered when visual inspection takes place.

Bibliography Reference: (*1550*)

8.2. Colour Theories

From the rather disquieting number of theories which try (or tried) to explain the relations between (1) colour and colour, and (2) colour stimulus and colour perception, two theories have survived so far and are now generally accepted as good working hypotheses. On the Continent of Europe it is the Ostwald Theory (*172*), in America the Munsell Theory (*296*) which are the generally acknowledged and accepted. Lack of space forbids even a brief exposition of the two leading views on Colour, the interested reader being referred to a number of excellent publications on this subject (*297*, *298*, *299*, *300*, *301*, *302*, *303*, *304*).

The general trend of modern colour theory, irrespective of dogmatic differences and discrepancies, is to arrange colour in such a way that equal steps are (1) on a psycho-physical basis and (2) easily measurable, reproducible, and designated by a nomenclature which clearly shows the three characteristics of colour, viz., hue, saturation (i.e., chroma, purity, Munsell), and brightness or lightness (i.e., value, white-black content, Munsell). These terms of colour sensation have their physical counterparts in the dominant wavelength, purity, and luminance, respectively.

TABLE 8.1

Specifications of Colour

Colour	Brightness or Value %	Dominant Wavelength or Hue A.U.	Purity or Chroma or Saturation %
Cardinal	9	6170	55
Old Rose	23	6080	20
Blood Red	17	6000	65
Maroon	7	6000	35
Chocolate	5	5860	30
Russet	12	5850	45
Ivory	55	5750	25
Olive Green	14	5720	45
Apple Green	35	5680	40
Turquoise	32	5000	30
Slate	12	4760	10
Navy Blue	3	4750	20

The addition of black to a pigment reduces the brightness ; the addition of white increases the brightness, but reduces saturation ; the addition of a neutral grey reduces the saturation, but leaves both hue, i.e., the chromatic quality of a surface, and brightness unchanged.

Hue and saturation are determined by the spectral distribution of the stimulus. Brightness (brilliance) is determined by the amount of the stimulus. It is proportional to the logarithm of the stimulus (Fechner's law).

A practical instance is compiled in Table 8.1 (*177, p. 12*).

8.3. Complementary or Opponent Colours

The arrangement of colours in a continuous mode, for instance in a circle, automatically provides for each colour being diametrically opposite to another colour. If correctly arranged, these pairs of Opponent Colours are related by the equation $(\lambda_0 - 5590)(4980 - \lambda_{180}) = 42400$. Helmholtz (*305*) had already suggested a similar mathematical relationship when he postulated the geometrical orbit of the related wavelengths to be an equilateral hyperbola, Fig. 8.1.

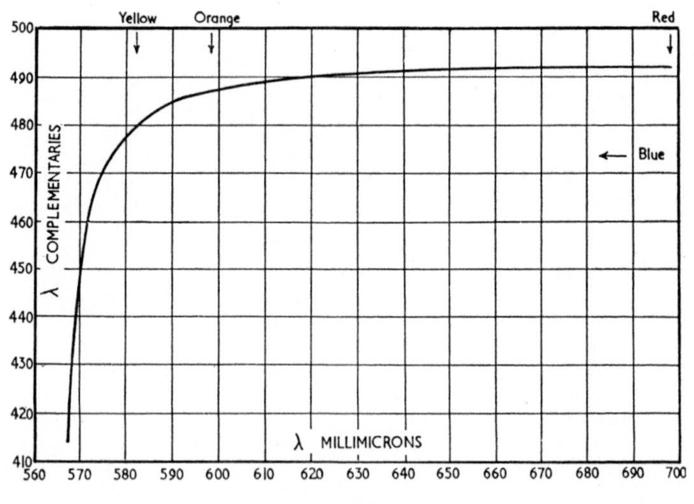

Fig. 8.1.

There are various compilations of complementary colours, the best ones being supplied by Sinden (*306*), and Hardy (*177, p. 31*). Other representative Tables have been computed according to the principles of Munsell's theory (*49*) and Ostwald's theory (*50, 172*) respectively. Other Codes have been issued by the British Standards Institution (*307*), the Colour Council (*308*), and others.

TABLE 8.2

Complementary Colours
(fundamentally after H. Helmholtz and W. Ostwald)

Basic Colour C_0 type	grade	Complementary Colour C_{180} type	grade
	1		13
Yellow	2	Ultramarine Blue	14
	3		15
	4		16
Orange	5	Turquoise Blue	17
	6		18
	7		19
Red	8	Sea green	20
	9		21
	10		22
Purple	11	Leaf green	23
	12		24
type	grade	type	grade
C_{180} Complementary Colour		C_0 Basic Colour	

TABLE 8.3

Complementary Colours
(fundamentally after A. H. Munsell)

Basic Colour C_0	Complementary Colour C_{180}
Red 5/5	Blue-Green 5/5
Yellow-Red 5/5	Blue 5/5
Yellow 5/5	Purple-Blue 5/5
Green-Yellow 5/5	Purple 5/5
Green 5/5	Red-Purple 5/5
C_{180} Complementary Colour	C_0 Basic Colour

There are certain discrepancies in the listed values and two of the best representative compilations of opponent wavelengths are given in Tables 8.4 and 8.5.

TABLE 8.4

Complementary Wavelengths

(After R. H. Sinden)

λ_0	λ_{180}	L_0/L_{180}	λ_0	λ_{180}	L_0/L_{180}
Extr. Red	4965	0·73	5765	4775	7·20
6090	4935	1·10	5755	4745	9·20
5910	4900	2·03	5740	4720	11·60
5860	4875	2·84	5730	4665	16·00
5800	4825	4·80	5720	4590	24·60
5785	4805	5·90	5705	Extr. Viol.	40·00

In the last column the ratio L_0/L_{180} represents the luminosity ratio of each pair of spectral complementaries, L_0 being the luminosity of radiant energy at wavelengths λ_0 and L_{180} (*309*). The indices 0 and 180 are based on the conception that colour designated λ_0 is the basic colour at whose position in the colour circle counting begins. The complementary or opponent colour is diametrically opposite from λ_0 and has, therefore, been marked λ_{180}.

It is a general rule that any two lights, however different in their spectral distribution, exhibit a coincidence of the wavelengths of their respective centres of gravity of the spectral distribution, if these two lights excite colours of the same quality. The quality of a colour is determined by its hue and saturation together (*176*).

8.4. Correct Colour Pairs

In printing, artistic design, advertising, etc., the traditional, but incorrect, colour pairs are still encountered. While no great harm is done in using the wrong colour pairs in artistic designs which, in spite of all attempts of standardizing, are still governed by individual taste more than by individual knowledge about any colour theory, harm is certainly done when physical laws are violated by incorrect applications. In the Table below correct complementary colour pairs are given.

TABLE 8.5

Complementary Wavelengths
(After A. C. Hardy)

λ_0	λ_{180}	λ_0	λ_{180}	λ_0	λ_{180}
3800	5670	4780	5780	4870	5930
4000	5671	4790	5790	4873	5940
4200	5673	4800	5800	4876	5950
4300	5675	4808	5810	4879	5960
4393	5680	4810	5812	4880	5965
4507	5690	4816	5820	4881	5970
4550	5696	4820	5826	4884	5980
4579	5700	4823	5830	4886	5990
4600	5704	4829	5840	4888	6000
4631	5710	4830	5841	4890	6009
4668	5720	4835	5850	4897	6050
4697	5730	4840	5858	4900	6070
4719	5740	4841	5860	4904	6100
4730	5745	4846	5870	4909	6150
4738	5750	4850	5878	4910	6168
4740	5751	4851	5880	4912	6200
4750	5757	4855	5890	4915	6250
4754	5760	4859	5900	4917	6300
4760	5764	4860	5902	4920	6402
4767	5770	4863	5910	4922	6500
4770	5772	4867	5920	4923	{6600 6700
				4924	{6800 6900 7000 7800

Bibliography Reference: (*594*)

8.5. Production of Colour

Colour can be produced by light generators, such as incandescent filaments, electric discharges in gases or vapours, etc., which group as Primary Light Sources. There are other devices which do not generate radiant energy but re-radiate or re-distribute it, such as, for instance, pin-hole diaphragms, filters, etc. These are termed Secondary Light Sources.

A primary light source produces colour by selective emission, a secondary light source by selective absorption. In practice, one speaks rather of the selective transmission of a filter, or selective reflexion of a mirror. An object, which is said to be of red colour, either transmits or reflects radiant energy of a certain wavelength or range of wavelengths, whereas all other wavelengths of the luminous spectrum are absorbed by the object.

8.6. Chemical Constitution and Colour

It is the presence in the molecule of certain unsaturated groups, called radicals, of the chemical elements C, H, O, N, which are responsible for the apparent colouring of matter, Colour is not a characteristic inherent in matter. The above radicals are called colour-bearers or chromophores. The type and number of chromophoric groups present in a molecule influence the wavelengths and amplitude of the absorption band*, in other words, they determine the (apparent) colour and luminosity of it.

TABLE 8.6

Correct Complementary Pairs

C_0	C_{180}
violet	leafgreen
blue	yellow
blue-green	orange
seagreen	red
C_{180}	C_0

It is evident that a phraseology like " The absorption spectrum of a colour is, of course, related to its colour " should be reversed and read correctly " The colour of a substance is, of course, related to its absorption spectrum ". For the practical engineer this might seem a hair-splitting consideration. From the point of view of this book, however, the statement is important, because it fits the aspect that " colour " is an " individual conception " rather than a general quality, and that its cause is just as individualistic as is the perception of its effects. While the generation and spectral distribution of " colour " is governed by chemical and physical laws which permit of exact reproduction, the perception of colour is a subjective event and its interpretation is subject to individual differentiations and deviations.

* The absorption spectrum shows by the absence of certain of its regions the radiations a substance fails to transmit. A " green " substance absorbs all " orange" and " red " rays, but transmits the " yellow," " green " and " blue " rays.

8.7. Physical Properties and Colour

The surfaces of objects are light sources of the second order. They absorb part of the incident luminous energy and transmit or reflect selectively. This concept also explains the " colour " BLACK which is difficult as a colour in psychological terms since the absence of a sensation cannot be called a sensation.

In the following series of schematic diagrams an attempt is made at illustrating the generation of " colour " by means of selective reflexion. The intensity of light depends on the product of the energy $h\nu$ of each incident photon by the number N of these photons striking the surface of the object per second. The energy of each photon is a function of the wavelength of the light. The intensity $I = Nh\nu$. The general layout is shown in Fig. 8.2a.

In Fig. 8.2, W stands for White,
B stands for Black,
C stands for Full Colour,
C_1 etc., for any commercial pigment.

The thickness of the lines (light rays) is indicative of their respective intensities. The absorbing surface is represented by a number of individual " centres " of different absorptive properties. The spacing of the light rays is indicative of the density of flux.

Bibliography References: (*1090, 1093, 1094, 1095, 1216*)

8.8. Apparent Colour Changes

Selective transmission or reflexion are the most commonly used methods of apparently altering the colour of an object or of a light source, transmission being the preferred method. It is based on the absorption of radiant energy the wavelength of which does not suit the structure of the filter or reflector. The transmitted or reflected energy, therefore, is but a fraction of the incident total. The absorbed energy is transformed into heat : under certain conditions more heat may be generated than the object is capable of re-radiating and it becomes hot, or even is destroyed by the heat (chars, burns, cracks).

The fundamentals of physical methods of changing the colour of an object are explained in the following Tables, which show how to alter*

* This is a colloquialism. It should read " how to select the frequency . . ." It is impossible to " alter " the frequency except when resorting to the phenomena of luminescence.

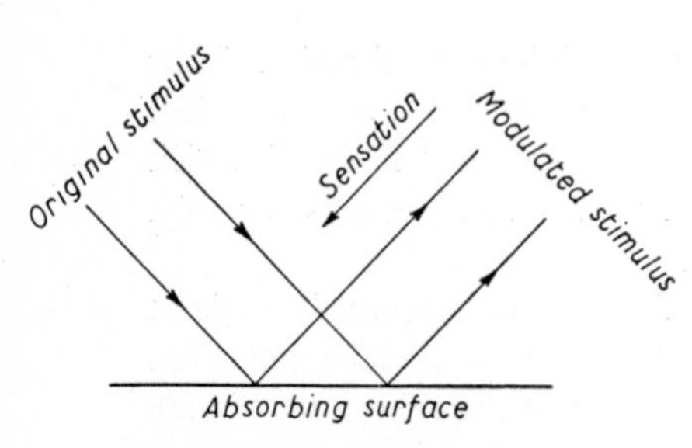

Fig. 8.2a. The original stimulus, i.e., the incident radiation, is reflected from, or absorbed by, the surface, thereby becoming modulated. This physical stimulus will cause a psycho-physiological reaction, called a sensation.

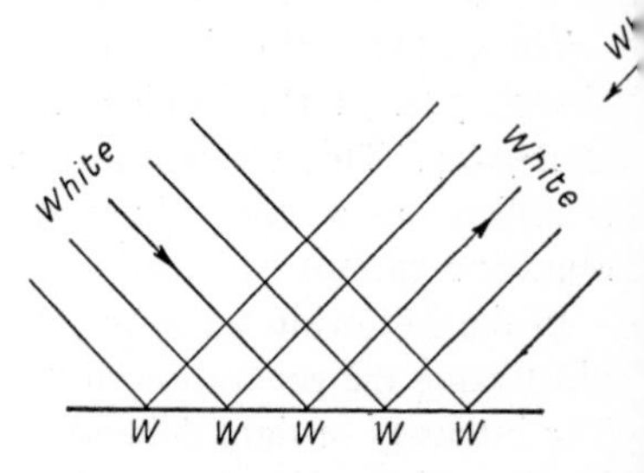

Fig. 8.2b. White light falls on a whit surface and is reflected 100% (ideal case unobtainable in practice). Sensation white light.

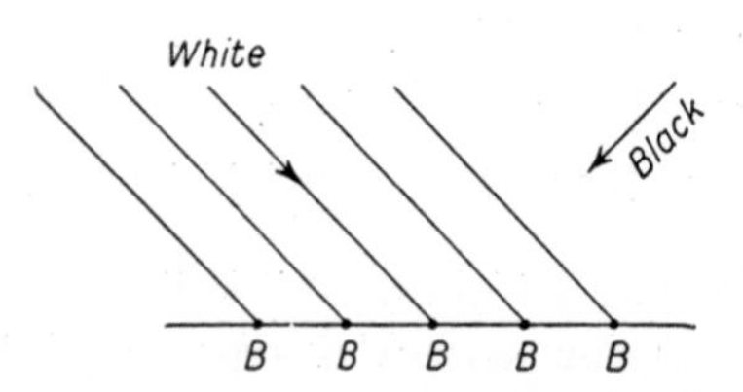

Fig. 8.2c. White light falls on a black surface and is completely absorbed (ideal case, unobtainable in practice). Sensation: black (physical phenomenon: no reflexion, i.e. no energy available at retina).

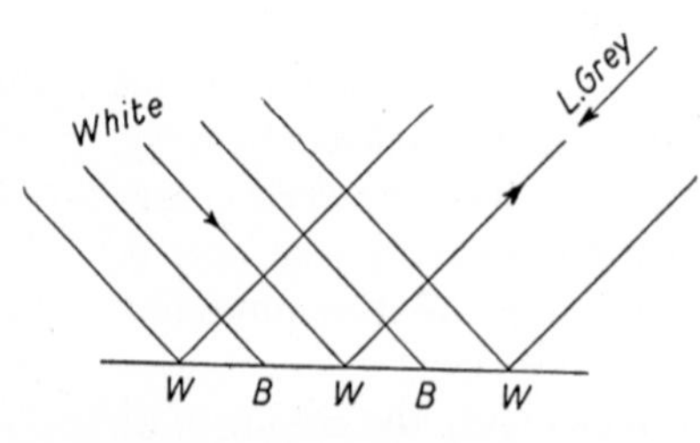

Fig. 8.2d. White light falls on a grey surface and is partly reflected (from white centres) and partly absorbed (from black centres). Sensation: grey (light grey).

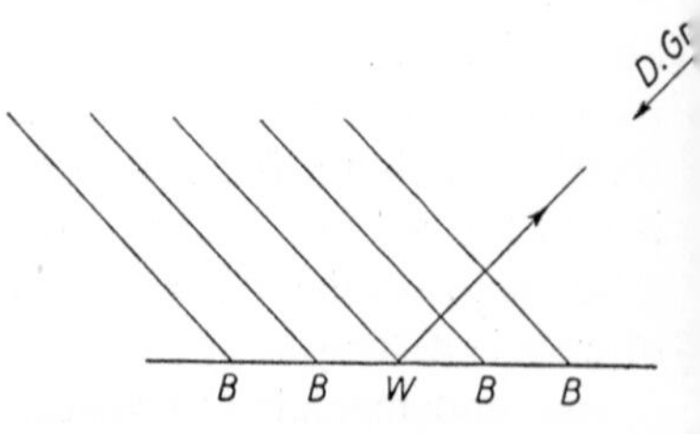

Fig. 8.2e. White light falls on a grey surface and is partly reflected (from white centres) and partly absorbed (from black centres which, in this case, are in the majority). Sensation: grey (dark grey).

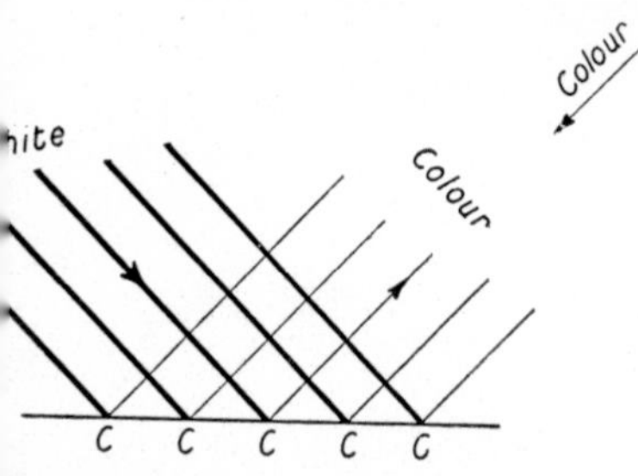

Fig. 8.2f. White light falls on a col-
ıred surface (full or pure colour). The
ıite light is partly (selectively) absorbed,
e remainder is reflected. Sensation:
lour (of the same hue as the surface).

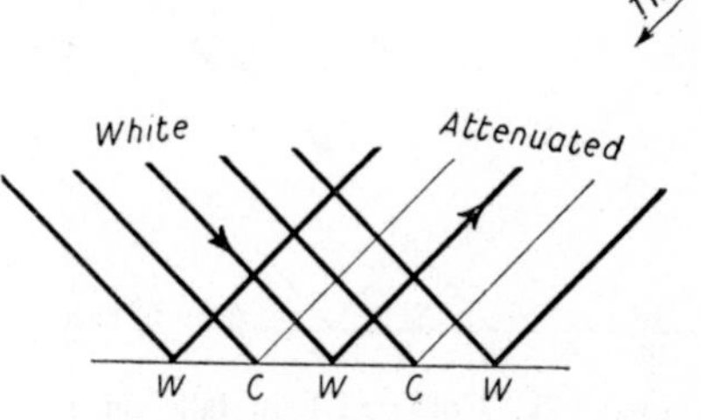

Fig. 8.2g. White light falls on a tinted surface (full colour and white). The white light is fully reflected from the white centres, and selectively reflected from the colour centres. The reflected stimulus is therefore attenuated. Sensation: tint, e.g., if the colour is red, the sensation will be called pink.

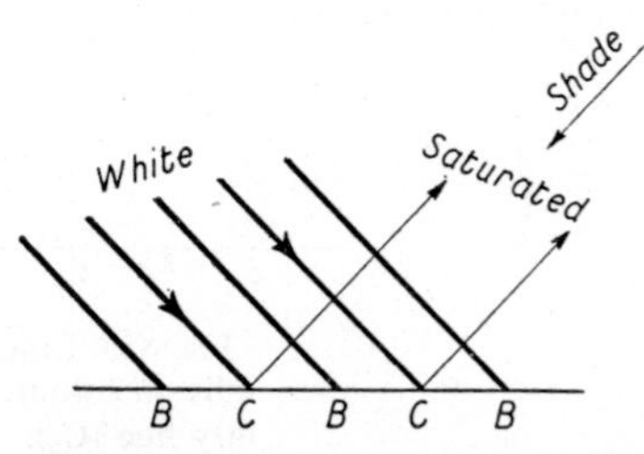

Fig. 8.2h. White light falls on a shaded surface (full colour and black). The white light is selectively reflected from the colour centres and completely absorbed by the black centres. Sensation: shade, e.g., if the colour is red, the sensation will be called maroon (red + black).

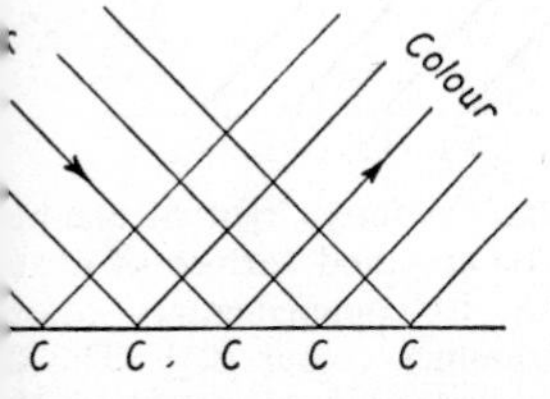

Fig. 8.2i. Coloured light falls on a
ırface of the same hue and is totally
flected Sensation: coloured light of
ıe same hue.

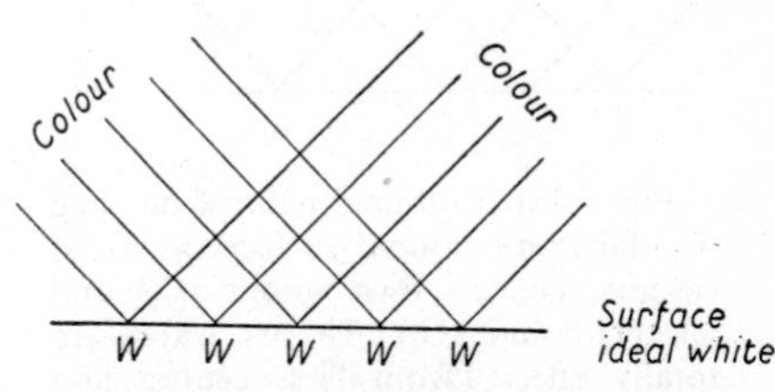

Fig. 8.2j. Coloured light falls on a white surface and is selectively reflected. Sensation. coloured light of the same hue.

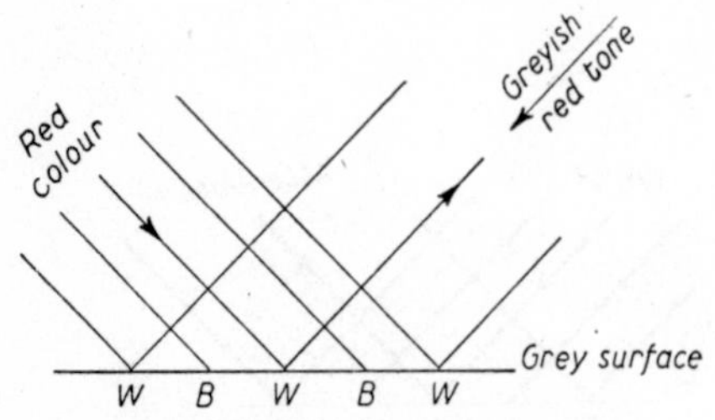

Fig. 8.2k. Coloured light falls on a grey surface and is selectively reflected from the white centres and absorbed by the black centres. Sensation. greyish-red tone (broken maroon).

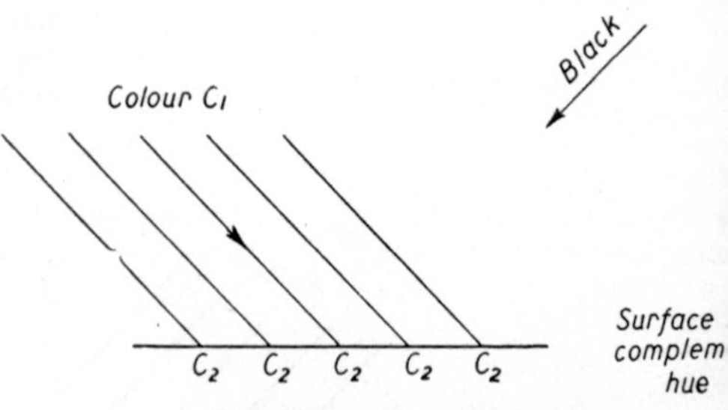

Fig. 8.2l. Coloured light of one hue (C falls on coloured surface of compleme tary hue (C_2). Complete absorption C_1 waves by C_2 pigments. Sensatio black.

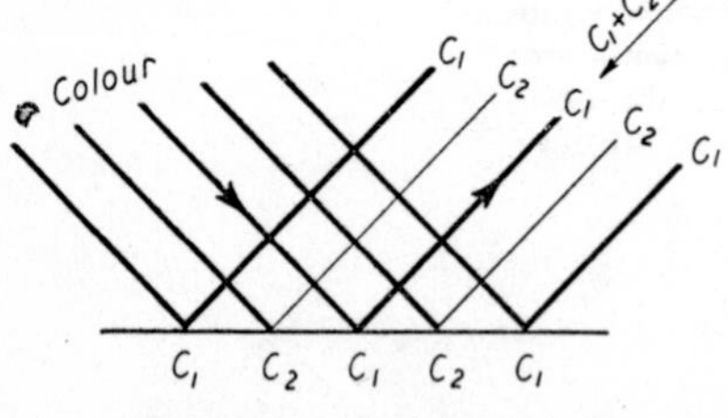

Fig. 8.2m. Coloured light of one hue (C_1) falls on coloured surface of mixed colours, i.e., its own colour (C_1) and another colour (C_2). The C_1 waves are totally reflected from the C_1 centres, and selectively absorbed by the C_2 centres. Sensation: Mixed colour with one colour (C_1) predominating.

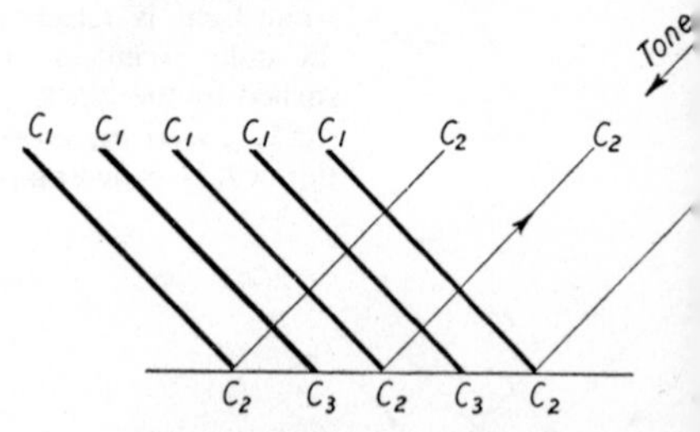

Fig. 8.2n. Coloured light of one hu (C_1) falls on coloured surface of mixe colours i.e., its complementary colou (C_3) and another colour (C_2). The C waves are completely absorbed by th C_3 centres and selectively reflected fror the C_2 centres. Sensation: tone base on C_2 (colour C_2 plus black which is du to C_3).

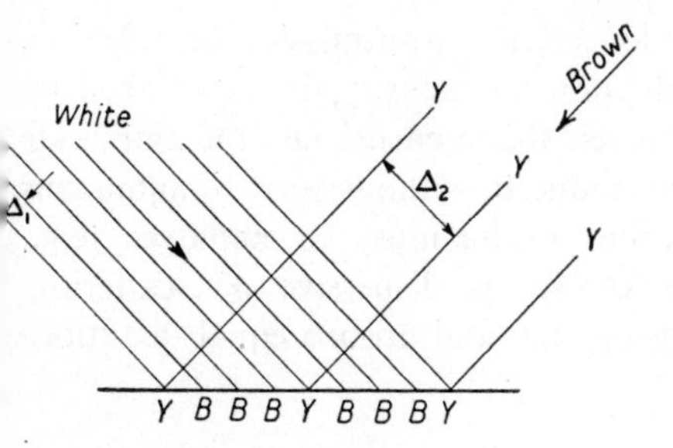

Fig. 8.2o. Brown is a shade of yellow, i.e., it is a mixture of black and yellow. White light falls on a surface painted brown. The yellow centres reflect selectively, whereas the black centres absorb the light. The sensation is, therefore, one of brown (yellow + black).

Fig. 8.2p. White light falls on a black rface on which is located one yellow r any other coloured or white) centre. ne black centres completely absorb the cident light, resulting in a sensation black which, theoretically, should be terrupted by a sensation of yellow as result of selective reflexion from the ne yellow centre. However, if the ergy transported in the yellow beam insufficient to stimulate the sense of sion (i.e., if the energy of the yellow ;ht is below the threshold value of imulation), the visual sense will not act to the subliminal stimulation.

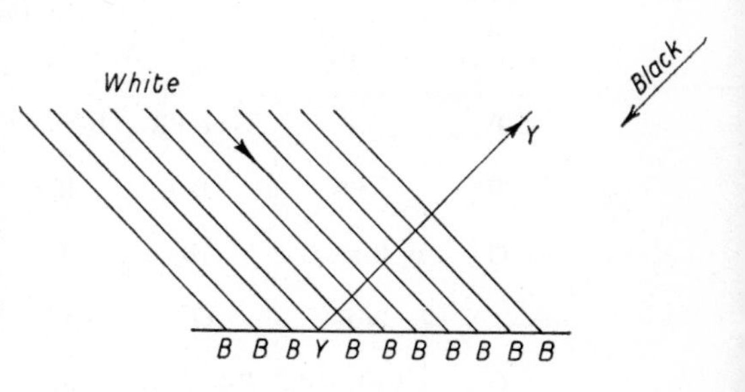

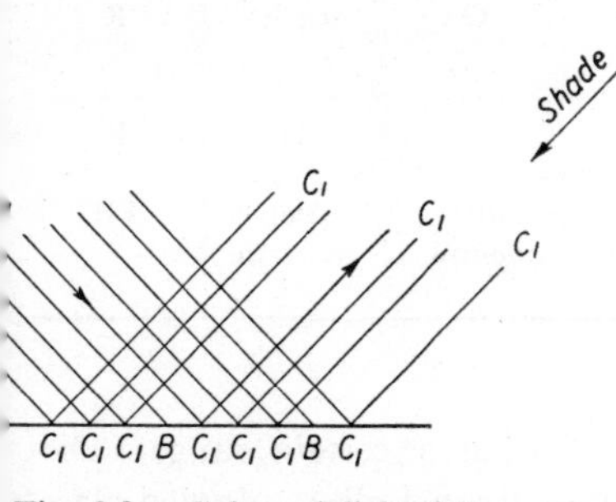

Fig. 8.2q. Coloured light falls on a rface of a shade of the same hue. epending on the number of the black bsorbing) centres per unit area the lepth " of the sensation will vary. The gher the " black "content, the higher ne " saturation " or " depth ". Saturion measures the black content of a nade.

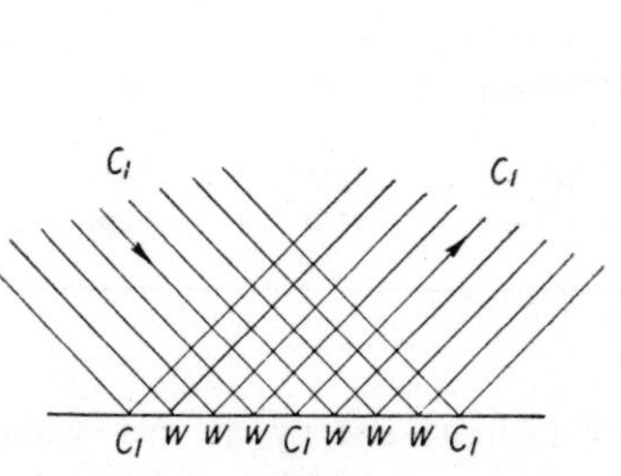

Fig. 8.2r. Coloured light falls on a surface of a tint of the same hue. Depending on the number of white (reflecting) centres per unit area the "brightness" of the sensation will vary. The higher the " white " content, the higher the brightness (luminosity, reflectivity) of the surface. (" Luminosity " is the psycho-physiological equivalent of the physical concept " reflectivity ").

the frequency of radiant energy by selective transmission or reflexion. The loss of energy, i.e., the reduction in intensity, is then linked up with a change in colour. If, however, the intensity, i.e., the amplitude of the radiant energy, is to be reduced without any simultaneous change in colour being permissible, media must be employed (e.g., Polaroid) which are generally known as dispersive or scattering. Such media are uncoloured (achromatic) and absorb equal quantities

TABLE 8.7

Apparent Colour Changes

Colour of Object	Colour of Incident Light					
	P	B	G	Y	O	R
P	P	deep PB	B-brown	Y-maroon	red-maroon	RP
B	PB	B	BG	grey-G	O-grey	P
G	B-grey	GB	G	GY	rusty-green	reddish dark grey
Y	brown	G	YG	Y	YO	O
O	light red	P-brown	faint GY	YO	O	OR
R	RP	P	grey-brown	O	scarlet	R
White	P	B	G	Y	O	R
Black	faint PB	blue-black	green-brown	olive-yellow	deep maroon	PB

of radiant energy at any wavelength within a certain range. Dispersive or scattering media are opal glass, frosted glass, stippled glass, etc., the substance " glass " embracing both inorganic and organic uncoloured materials equally transmissive to waves of any length within the range of the luminous spectrum.

In Table 8.10 the energy distribution in percentage is given for various translucent dispersive or scattering media. Light scattering is defined as " that fraction of the total transmitted light from a normally incident beam which is not transmitted in a straight line" (*312*).

TABLE 8.8

Change of Brightness (constant hue)

Basic Colour of Object	To render Object: Lighter use basic light	To render Object: Darker use complementary light
Pink, Magenta	magenta	green
P	P	G
B	B	OY
BG	BG	RO
G	G	R
YG	YG	P
Y	Y	indigo
O	O	B
R	R	BG

TABLE 8.9

Apparent Colour Changes under Varying Illumination

Colour of Object	Apparent Colour of Object illuminated* by (1) golden-yellow light	(2) blue-green light	(3) mauve light
P	puce	B	B
B	black	B	P
BG	G	pale B	B
G	G	YG	black
Y	white	GY	O
O	O	G-grey	reddish-black
R	R	black	scarlet
Magenta	R	B	pale magenta

* The coloured lights can be obtained by filtering the light of a tungsten filament lamp through
(1) a combination of No. 1 and No. 4 of Strand Electric Co. filters ;
(2) No. 16 filter ;
(3 No. 26 filter.

For more details on glasses and plastics cf. Duntley (*313*) and Herzberger (*314*).

Scattering media are used for envelopes of high-brilliancy light sources in order to reduce their brightness. If all the desired qualities cannot be attained in one material, two- or three-ply glass, e.g., flashed opal, will solve the problem.

Bibliography References: (*1576, 1588*)

TABLE 8.10

Optical Characteristics of Dispersive and Scattering Glasses

Type of Glass	Absorption	Reflexion	Transmission
Satin finish	3– 9	8– 6	89–85
Acid etched	5–17	7–20	88–63
Sand blasted	7–16	11–18	82–66
Opalescent	2–14	13–28	84–58
Frosted	5–10	15–22	80–68
Pebbled	5–10	15–20	80–70
Ribbed	10–15	10–15	80–70
Prism	10–15	10–15	80–70
White	10–30	20–60	70–10
Rippled, Opal flashed	10–15	20–25	70–60
Clear	5	10–15	85–80

8.9. Contrast

If colour in conjunction with photo-electric devices is applied to the many and varied industrial problems of detection or control, it is either equality or contrast of colours which is the actuating phenomenon. In most cases it will be a matter of contrasting two colours, the change in colour being made to result in a change of output of photo-electric current. It will be the aim of the designing engineer to enhance the contrast. Maximum contrast is to be expected from any of the following juxtapositions (*315*).

(1) Complementary colours at their maximum intensities,

i.e., *PB* – *Y*.

(2) High brightness (value) colour *v.* low brightness colour,

e.g., White – Black,
Pink – Maroon,
Orange – Brown.

(3) Colour of extreme purity (chroma, saturation) *v.* weak, greyed purity,

e.g., Emerald green – Olive green.

H. Ketcham quotes two more arrangements but the reader must bear in mind that his article is concerned with psychological effects, while the above quotation is reduced to those arrangements which will effect the physical apparatus, in particular the photosensitor. Due consideration must also be given to the spectral sensitivity of the photosensitor employed (cf. Chap. 9).

8.10. Commercial Pigments

In practice, the coloured surface of an object is never " pure ". Purity (chroma, saturation) of 100% is but a theoretical value. Commercial pigments are a mixture of at least two or three different hues. An approximate qualitative spectral analysis of a few pigments will bear it out.

TABLE 8.11

Qualitative Analysis of Commercial Pigments

Commercial	Usually contains							
	deep V	V	B	G	Y	O	R	deep R
P		*	*				*	
V		*	*	*				*
B		*	*	*				*
G			*	*	*			
Y					*	*	*	
O					*	*	*	
R	*					*	*	*

Table 8.12, giving numerical values of spectral reflexion factors of dry pigments (*316*) provides further information on the composition of commercial pigments.

TABLE 8.12

Spectral Reflexion Factors of Dry Pigment Powders

Pigment	Reflexion Factors in % at						
	4400	4800	5200	5600	6000	6400	6800 A.U.
American Vermilion	8	5	6	9	24	53	66
Venetian Red	5	5	5	7	19	28	32
Indian Red	8	7	7	7	15	20	23
Golden Ochre	22	23	40	63	75	73	73
Chrome Yellow, light	13	18	56	88	90	88	85
Chrome Green, light	10	14	26	20	14	9	7
Cobalt Blue	59	49	23	11	10	11	20
Ultramarine Blue	67	38	10	4	3	5	10

Reflexion factors of other materials (*317*) are given in the following Tables.

TABLE 8.13

Reflexion Factors of Commercial Paints for White Light

Commercial Paints	Reflexion Factor %
White (glossy), Cream, Primrose, Lemon, Golden Yellow, Whitewash	80 – 70
Ivory, Plaster board, Cream matt	70 – 60
Orange, Eau de Nil, Salmon Pink, Sea-green	50 – 40
Grey, Sky blue, Deep buff	40 – 30
Light brown, Golden brown, Dark red	30 – 20
Turquoise, Peacock blue, Brown, Post Office red, Grass-green, Sage-green, Dark blue	20 – 10
Crimson, Blue matt, Ultramarine	10 – 5
Black	5 and less

Table 8.14

Reflexion Factors of Building Materials for White Light

Material	Reflexion Factor %
White glazed brick	80
Concrete, clean	45
Red brick, clean	25
White pine	61
Red oak	32
Stainless steel	60
Iron, galvanized	16
Iron, cast	12
Aluminium paint	72

For reflexion factors of floor materials and others used in rooms, cf. P. Moon (*318*). For coloured papers reflexion factors are compiled below, the colour numbers being the numbers specified by the British Standard Institution (*307, 308*).

TABLE 8.15

Reflexion Factors of Coloured Papers

B.S. Colour	No.	Reflexion Factor %
white paper	—	84
sky blue	1	30
turquoise	2	15
peacock blue	3	11
light brown	10	27
middle brown	11	12
golden brown	14	25
eau de nil	16	47
sea green	17	38
grass green	18	18
sage green	19	19
silver grey	28	37
Quaker grey	29	30
French grey	30	36
lt. battleship gr.	31	31
dk. battleship gr.	32	11
P.O. red	38	17
crimson	40	6
salmon pink	43	44
pale cream	52	76
deep cream	53	70
primrose	54	76
lemon	55	69
golden yellow	56	80
orange	57	42
light buff	58	61
middle buff	59	54
deep buff	60	31
light stone	61	58
middle stone	62	37
dark stone	63	33
Portland stone	64	62

Bibliography References: (*319, 320, 1088, 1628, 1820, 1890*)

8.11. Infra-Red Colours

Although this term is a *contradiction in terms** it will be used in this section by the author, because the evaluation of the reflective power in the infra-red is mostly done by photographic methods yielding visible effects. In recent research work the " infra-red sensitive phosphor " (phosphor means luminophore ; cf. Chap. 13) has been shown to be applicable to this type of work.

The fact must be emphasized that the infra-red reflective capacity of a pigment or dye or printing ink cannot under any circumstances be assessed or anticipated from a knowledge of the reflectivity in the luminous region of the spectrum. In Table 8.16 a few instances are given (*325*) and more will be found in the literature on paints, varnishes, etc. (*322*, *323*).

The acknowledged standard white surface is magnesium oxide freshly deposited by burning pure metallic magnesium. For all practical purposes, this can be substituted by a block or tablet pressed from magnesium oxide of A.R. quality† or by a magnesium carbonate block.‡

An important matter in register control is the application of a small area, about 0·125 × 0·375 in., of such a colour as to exhibit a very distinctive difference in reflectivity from the material or colours used in the design printed on the web under control. Very often the arrangement of such a dot, small as it is, may cause inconvenience either from the designer's point of view or from the engineer's standpoint. It will be the latter's veto which will make the control difficult to be performed if a wide variety from low to high reflective paints or printing inks is used and neither a nearly totally absorbing (black) or reflecting (white) spot is present in the design so as to cause so big a change in the

* As it has been agreed to define COLOUR as a visual sensation (*321*) " infra-red colour " is rightly called a *contradiction in terms* because the human sense of vision is incapable of translating infra-red radiation into luminous, i.e., visual, sensations.

† The maximum limits of impurities of A.R. (Analytical Reagent) magnesium oxide are (*324*) :

Chloride	Cl	0·01 %
Sulphate	SO_4	0·01 %
Nitrate	NO_3	0·002 %
Heavy Metals	Pb	0·002 %
Iron	Fe	0·025 %
Arsenic	As_2O_3	0·0001 %

‡ Magnesium carbonate blocks are supplied by The Tintometer Ltd., Milford, Salisbury, England.

general illumination of the photosensitor that an actuation of the correcting device will result. Such cases can be remedied by using marks of such a pigment having a high infra-red reflectivity.

TABLE 8.16

Infra-red Reflectivities of Various Materials

Material	Infra-red Reflectivity %
Magnesium oxide (B.P. quality)	100
white canvas	93
sisal	80
alpha-cellulose	100
celotex, unprimed	70
celotex, primed	100
brick, yellow, fireproof	88
brick, red	38
white pine wood, fresh	100
white pine wood, weathered	32
grey sand	61
grey asphalt	25
new cement road	40
black road asphalt	15
glass mirror	27
iron, bright	35
iron, rusty	20
tin, new, pure	82
copper, new	50
leaded sheet iron	35 – 45
galvanized iron	25 – 35
steel	28
aluminium paint	53
chrome yellow	80

The paint industry has developed a paint which, strange as it may sound, is termed a " white " black. The absorptivity in the luminous range of the spectrum is very high, about 95·5%. To the normal human eye it therefore looks a matt black. In the infra-red, however, it has a very high reflective power, nearly 50% at and from 9100 A.U. upwards. An infra-red photographic plate or a photosensitor sensitive to infra-red radiation, will represent this paint as nearly white when observed under infra-red irradiation (*323*).

Not many data are available on the reflectivity in the infra-red of printing inks. Methods of obtaining such values are relatively simple ; either the photo-electric method described by F. Scofield (*326*), or a substituting photographic method (*323, 327*) can be used.

The general layout is shown in Fig. 8.3. The circuit may be any high-sensitivity two-cell circuit. If one lamp is used with two mirrors little care need be taken to prevent the lamp from operating at a colour temperature slightly different from the one for which it was designed.

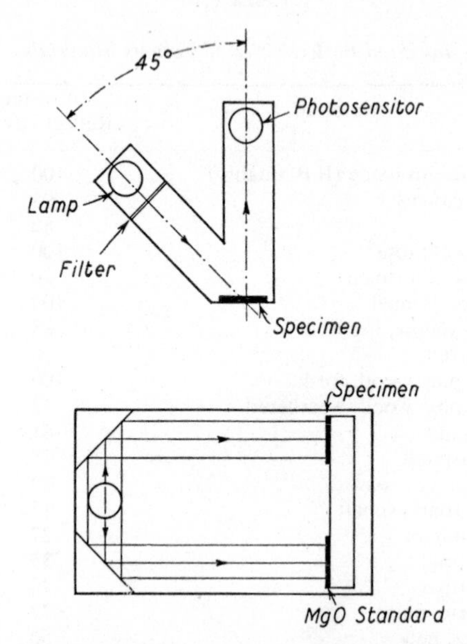

Fig. 8.3 (top). A simple comparator. The reflectivity of the specimen is measured by the photosensitor and expressed in terms of photocurrent.

(bottom). A comparator in which a surface of a block of magnesium oxide or magnesium carbonate is used as the white standard (maximum reflectivity) against which the specimen is measured. The photosensitors viewing the standard and the specimen can usefully be connected in a balanced twin circuit.

If two separate lamps are used it is advisable to have a pair of matched and aged lamps working at the correct colour temperature of 2848° K, a feature easily attainable by running the lamps at rated volts*. It is of far greater importance that the photosensitors should be identical in their spectrometric qualities as far as this can be attained. If their respective spectral sensitivities differ quantitatively or qualitatively no correct measure of the infra-red reflectivity can be obtained.

Bibliography Reference: (*1123*)

* Pairs of lamps are obtainable from The Tintometer Co., Ltd.

CHAPTER 9

OPTICAL FILTERS

9.1. Transmissivity, Absorptivity, and Reflectivity

The energy of a ray falling on a medium is considered to split up into three parts, the sum of which equals the incident energy (see Chap. 6.1). One part τ is transmitted through, another part α is absorbed in, and the rest ρ is reflected from, the surface of the medium, viz. :

$$\alpha\% + \rho\% + \tau\% = 100\%$$

A material is called transparent if τ is large compared with the two other coefficients. A material is a good reflector if ρ is large compared with α and τ. If, for a certain material, τ and ρ are negligible quantities, the material absorbs the radiation and appears to be of black colour. The above formula may also be written $P_1 = P_2 + P_3 + P_4$ or, using relative values, thus

$$P_2/P_1 + P_3/P_1 + P_4/P_1 = \text{Unity}$$

where

ρ .. coefficient of reflexion (%),
α .. coefficient of absorption (%),
τ .. coefficient of transmission (%),
P_1 .. intensity of the incident beam of energy,
P_2 .. intensity of the reflected beam,
P_3 .. intensity of the absorbed beam,
P_4 .. intensity of the transmitted beam.

Referring to the last equation the following terms are generally used :

$P_2/P_1 = R$ .. Reflectivity,
Reflective capacity,
Capacity of reflexion,

$P_3/P_1 = A$ .. Absorptivity,
Absorptive capacity,
Capacity of absorption,

$P_4/P_1 = T$ .. Transparency or Transmissivity,
Transmissive capacity,
Capacity of transmission.

Bibliography References: (*2367, 2374*)

9.2. Transmission, Density, Opacity, Translucency

Optical filters are coloured media which are transparent only to a certain range of wavelengths. The other part of the radiation emitted by the source is, by absorption, reduced in intensity to such an extent that it has no effect on the photosensitor. The relation between the transmission τ of a filter and its density δ is governed by the formula (Hurter & Driffield) $\delta = \log 1/\tau$, the density of the filter also being a measure of its opacity $OP = 1/\tau$ and its translucency $Tr = 1 - OP$. Opacity is sometimes also defined as the ratio of two reflexion coefficients, viz., $OP = \rho_B/\rho_W$, where ρ_B is the reflexion factor of a given material backed by a non-selective black background, and ρ_W the same for a non-selective white background.

If two or more filters are used simultaneously the total transmission τ is the product of the partial transmission factors, viz., $\tau = \tau_1 . \tau_2 . \tau_3 \ldots . \tau_n$. The resultant density δ may be found by summarizing the partial densities, viz., $\delta = \delta_1 + \delta_2 + \delta_3 + \ldots + \delta_n$. If there are, for instance, three filters, having partial transmission coefficients of 80%, 65% and 75%, respectively, the total transmission will be $\tau = 0{\cdot}80 \times 0{\cdot}65 \times 0{\cdot}75 = 0{\cdot}39$ or 39%.

9.3. Extinction Coefficient

Bunsen has introduced the coefficient of extinction, viz., $\varepsilon = \log T/d$, where P_1 is unity, and the coefficient, therefore, reads $\varepsilon = \log P_4/d$. This factor is defined as the reciprocal value of that thickness d (measured in cm.) which a layer must have in order to reduce the transmitted intensity to a tenth of the incident energy ; thus $P_4 = 0{\cdot}1P_1$. If a beam of radiant energy is transmitted through several layers, the specific (or partial) coefficients of extinction being ε_1, ε_2, etc., the total extinction will be $\varepsilon = \varepsilon_1 + \varepsilon_3 + \ldots + \varepsilon_n$. A beam of radiant energy is considered extinguished when it has been reduced to one tenth of its initial intensity.

9.4. Standard Thickness

For most filters the manufacturers issue computations of the transmissivities either tabulated or in graphical form, quoting a so-called " Standard thickness " to which the given factors relate. It is evident that a curve representing the transmissivity of a filter of certain thickness, 0·25 in. for instance, will be shifted parallel to itself to lower values if thickness increases, and to higher transmissivities if the thickness is reduced. To find out just how much this change is, a simple formula may be used or Table 9.1 consulted. If τ represents the fraction of the incident energy of any wavelength which is transmitted through unit thickness, then τ_1 is the fraction transmitted through a thickness d: it is $\tau_1 = \tau^d$. If the values are not related to unit thickness but to any standard thickness, the equation reads $\tau_1{}^D = \tau^d$, or expressed logarithmically $D \, . \log \tau_1 = d \, . \log \tau$ when τ now stands for the transmissivity at standard thickness D which is different from unit thickness.

If the density formula is brought into the picture in order to eliminate logarithmic calculations the formula based on unit thickness reads $\delta_d = d \, . \, \delta$ and for any standard thickness $\delta_d = (d/D) \, . \, \delta$ where δ is the density for unit thickness, δ_d the density for any thickness d, and D the standard thickness. Unit thickness is 1 mm.

TABLE 9.1

Corresponding Values of Density and Transmissivity

T%	δ	T%	δ	T%	δ
100	0·0000	70	0·1549	40	0·3979
95	0·0213	65	0·1871	30	0·5229
90	0·0458	60	0·2218	20	0·6990
85	0·0706	55	0·2596	10	1·0000
80	0·0969	50	0·3010	1	2·0000
75	0·1249	45	0·3466	0·1	3·0000

Examples: Given: the transmission of a filter at a certain wavelength is $\tau = 94\%$ for a thickness $D = 0{\cdot}2$ mm. To find: the transmission τ_1 through a thickness $d = 1{\cdot}4$ mm. It is $\log \tau_1 = (d/D) \log \tau$. After substituting the above values, $\tau_1 = 0{\cdot}647$. If the calculation is made with the respective densities, as interpolated from Table 9.1, the result is the same.

More tables and methods are given by H. P. Gage (*650*)., W. S. Plymale (*2592*) and others.

9.5. Compound Filters

If a narrow band of the continuous spectrum is to be obtained from the radiation of a tungsten filament lamp, one filter alone might not be satisfactory within the selected limits. Two or more filters may then be combined to yield the correct band. A basic rule is to select filters whose maximum transparency coincides with or very closely approaches the maximum of the band. The position of the maximum wavelength of a filter is a function of the qualitative composition. The percentage transmission and the width of the band transmitted by a compound filter is a function of the quantitative composition of the different filters. Diagram *a* of Fig. 9.1 shows the desired band of wavelengths

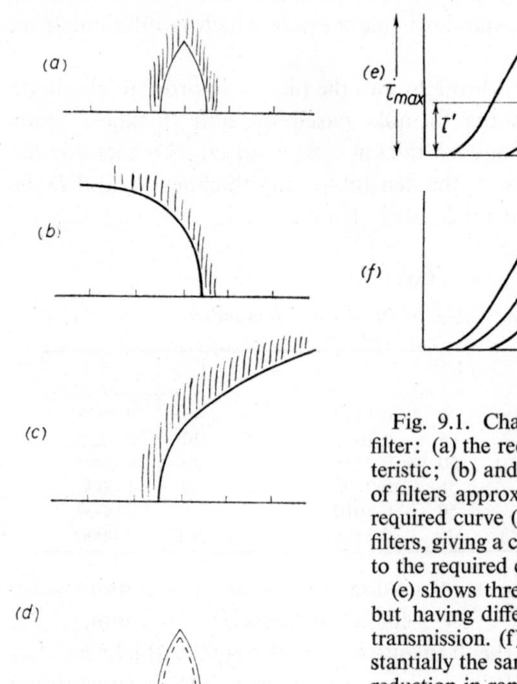

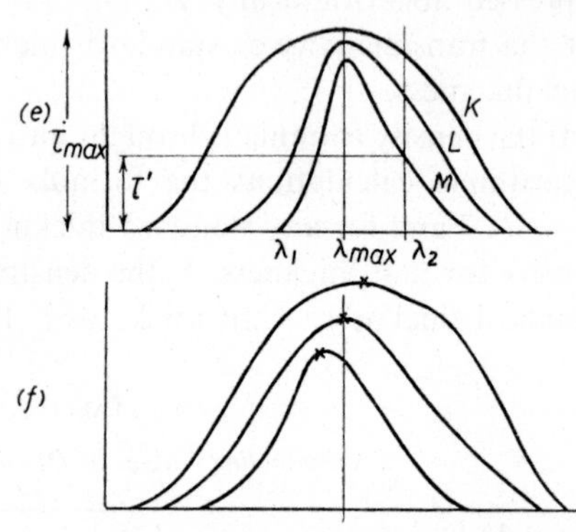

Fig. 9.1. Characteristics of a compound filter: (a) the required transmission characteristic; (b) and (c) the transmission curves of filters approximating to each side of the required curve (d) superposition of the two filters, giving a characteristic approximating to the required curve.

(e) shows three filters of the same colour but having differing degrees of cut-off and transmission. (f) shows three filters of substantially the same colour, showing the even reduction in range and transparency.

which, it may be supposed, cannot be transmitted by a single filter. A compound filter consists of two (or more) filters having transmission curves as shown in *b* and *c*, respectively. By causing the light to pass first through the one and then the other filter, only the wavelengths corresponding to the width of the narrow band, as indicated in diagram *d*, will have passed through the compound filter. Diagrams *e* and *f* show each three filters of equal type, for instance all green or all yellow, but of different transparency. It will be seen that the transparency of the filters decreases at a much slower pace where the individual curves are tightly packed as compared to the other half of the diagram. In *e*, three filters *K*, *L*, *M*, have maximum transparency τ_{max} at the same wavelength λ_{max}. For the light filter K the transmission at the limits λ_1 and λ_2 of the band is practically equal to τ_{max}. The other extreme is represented by the very heavy, i.e., dark, filter M. The transparency at λ_1 is practically nil, and at λ_2 only about 40% of $\tau_{\lambda 2}^{(K)}$. The maximum transparency $\tau_{max}^{(M)}$ is still at λ_{max} but $\tau_{max}^{(M)} = 0{\cdot}90\ \tau_{max}^{(K)}$. Both the type and the density (transparency) of a filter are of importance when used as a component of a compound filter.

9.6. Materials for Filters

Optical filters may be solid, liquid, or gaseous. Only solid or solidifiable filters will be dealt with here. The material most commonly used for filters is glass and polished plate glass quality will suffice in practically all industrial applications. The glass may be either stained in the mass, or clear glass can be used having one or both sides flashed with a layer of suitably coloured glass.

Gelatine and celluloid, either natural or hardened, make very good filters if the dyes are stable which, however, is not always the case. These filters are not suitable for the ultra-violet range. Some of the dyes fade when used continuously, or with strong light sources. Ultra-violet radiation causes discoloration of all organic materials, gelatine, etc., and also attacks many inorganic glasses. The thin sheets of gelatine or celluloid are cemented between two plates of clear inorganic glass for protection against mechanical injuries. If gelatine is used the edges of the cemented filter must be damp-proof to prevent the gelatine from absorbing moisture.

In recent years good progress has been made in the use of organic glasses of various chemical composition (Chap. 6). The optical qualities of these transparent plastics are often superior to those of inorganic glasses. This is shown, for instance, by the data for Perspex, Lucite, and others. The most outstanding physical property of these products. is the high transparency in both the colourless and coloured types. The transparency in the ultra-violet and infra-red regions, respectively, is much higher than that of glass ; a further advantage is the easy workability and machinability of these plastics and the fact that highly accurate lenses can be moulded for optical instruments. A disadvantage is the relative softness of the surface which can easily be scratched and marred.

Transparent colourless plastics can successfully be coloured by means of a water soluble dye developed by Morton Schwartzman (*652*) of the Great American Colour Company, Los Angeles. This type of dye is fast to sunlight and does not affect the surface of the plastic. Fourteen standard colours are marketed: sky blue, green, turquoise, yellow, orange, scarlet, magenta, purple, royal blue, amber, brown, red, ruby, and violet.

To dye methyl methacrylates and urea-formaldehydes it is only necessary to immerse or dip the plastics for a time not exceeding two minutes into a hot bath consisting of 1 part by weight in 10 of concentrated dye in distilled water. 250 g. dye solution (i.e., 25 g. conc. dye in 225 g. water at 190° F.) will give maximum strength for 128 sq. in. of plastic material.

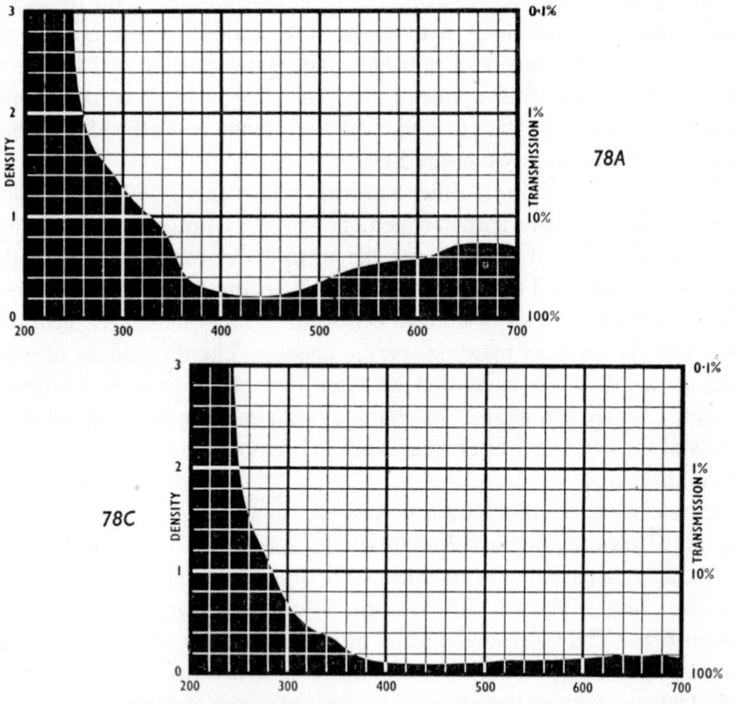

Fig. 9.2. Density and transmission characteristics of four filters for photometric work (see section 9.10) (*by courtesy of Kodak Ltd.*).

These dyes are a step forward in providing the engineer with a means of producing filter combinations or dyed plastic lenses to precise specifications. It should be noted that after dyeing moulded methyl methacrylate it is necessary to place the plastic over an open vessel containing acetone or amyl acetate: the vapours will clarify the plastic to its original transparency.

For cementing acrylic plastics a mixture of equal parts of monomeric methyl methacrylate (inhibited with 0·006% hydroquinone) and methylene dichloride will prove satisfactory. Before using the mixture one small capsule of benzoyl peroxide per pint of solvent mixture must be added. For small areas as will generally be encountered with in filter work, methylene dichloride alone will also do. Other solvents, for instance, acetic acid, or acetone, should not be used as they tend to matt the surface.

For polystyrene plastic filters the best cementing solvent is benzol or xylenol (*1636*).

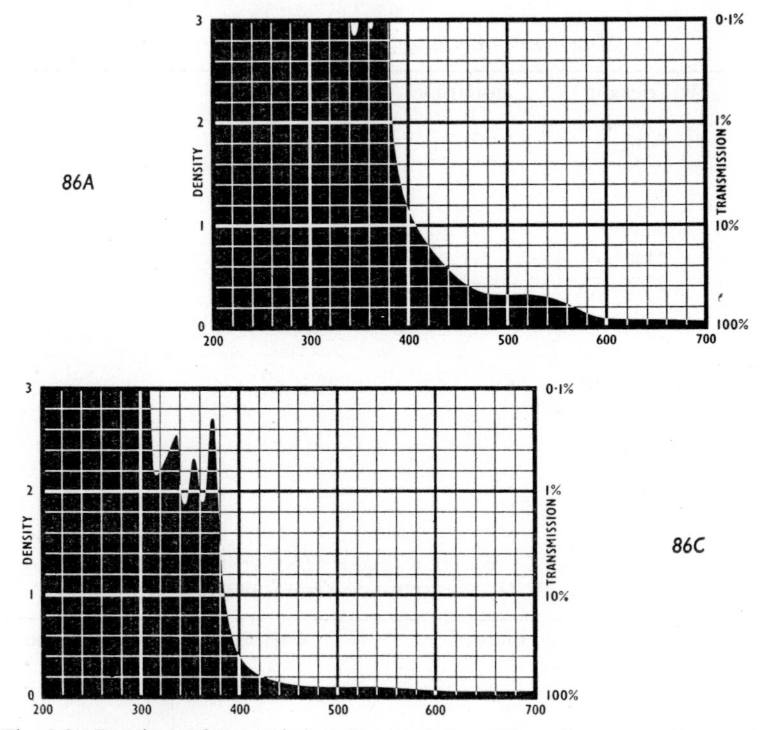

Fig. 9.2. Density and transmission characteristics of four filters for photometric work (see section 9.10) (*by courtesy of Kodak Ltd.*).

9.7. Transmission Curves

Fig. 9.2 shows the absorption and transmission curves for a set of typical filters, the density being plotted against wavelength in millimicrons. The right-hand scale gives the transmission corresponding to the density, expressed as a percentage in a logarithmic scale. It should be noted that these values are not absolute, and manufacturers' data should be consulted for accurate work. The filters to which the curves of Fig. 9.2 refer are the 78 and 86 Wratten series (see Section 9.10).

9.8. Colourless Filters

Colourless materials are often used for protecting dyed gelatine and other materials which, when uncemented, would be unstable due to atmospheric reactions. Other materials, for instance, quartz, Vitreosil, and other ultra-violet transmitting glasses, are ideal envelopes for ultra-violet sensitive photosensitors.

TABLE 9.2

Transmission Coefficients of Transparent Vitreosil

Wavelength A.U.	Transmission %	Thickness of specimen mm.	Reference *(655)*
1863	80		
1936	90		
1990	93		
2144	93	11	*(653)*
2288	94		
2537	95		
2749	95		
luminous range	aver. 100	up to 10	
10000	93		
20000	93	1·5	*(654)*
40000	72		

TABLE 9.3

Transmission Coefficients of Ordinary Plate or Window Glass
(*259, p. 434*) (Specimen thickness 2 mm.)

Wavelength A.U.	Transmission %	Wavelength A.U.	Transmission %
3100	0		
3200	18	luminous range	aver. 90
3300	41·5	8000	90
3400	65	10000	90
3500	76	15000	90
3600	82	18000	90
3700	85	20500	92
3800	87	30000	20
3900	87·5	40000	0
4000	88		

There will be slight differences in the above values for glasses of different chemical composition. The values of Table 9.3 are, however, good averages. Glass which is absolutely free of iron oxides transmits well into the 2500 A.U. range (*2439*).

The transmission of Perspex, Lucite, and Transpex, respectively, is shown in Fig. 9.3.

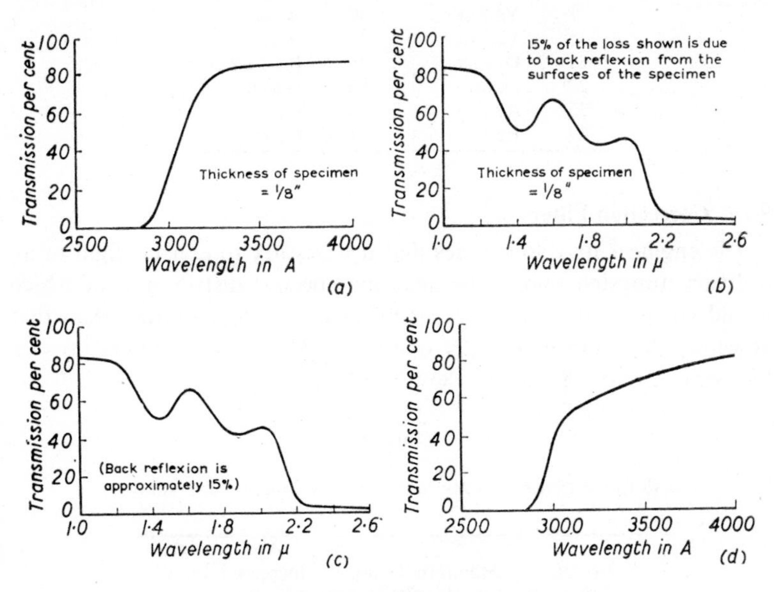

Fig. 9.3. Transmission curves of:
(a) Perspex in the *u-u* range
(b) Transpex in the *i-p* range
(c) Perspex in the *i-r* range
(d) Lucite in the *u-v* range

Most of the glasses which are transparent to ultra-violet radiation are more or less intensely coloured. The series WG of the Schott & Gen. (Jena) Glassworks are colourless glasses with a transmissitivy in the ultra-violet as high as 25% at 2810 A.U. (cf. Chap. 7.25). Glasses coloured with the oxides of Fe, Cu, Cr heavily absorb the short-wave end of the luminous spectrum.

9.9. Complementary Filter Sets

Exact complementary colours are represented by the following sets of filters (cf. Chap. 8.3).

TABLE 9.4

Complementary Filter Sets (Wratten)

C_0		C_{180}	
No.	Colour	No.	Colour
8	Yellow	50	Blue
15	Yellow	49	Blue
21	Orange	45	Blue-green
22	Orange	60	Green
25	Red	58	Green
29	Red	44	Green

9.10. Correction Filters

The engineer may sometimes find it necessary to convert light of an ordinary tungsten lamp into light the spectral distribution of which would correspond to a higher or lower colour temperature than that at which the lamp is actually operated. The Wratten filters provide two series : No. 78 and No. 86 (*657*, *658*).

TABLE 9.5

Bluish Correction Filters for Increasing the Colour Temperature

No. of Filter	Standard Temp. deg. K.	Apparently Increased Temp. deg. K.
78	2360	5500
78AA	2360	4400
78A	2360	3200
78B	2360	2800
78C	2360	2500

The specification of a spectral corrective filter is discussed by J. S. Preston (*1645*).

Bibliography Reference: (*495*)

9.11. Liquid Standard C.I.E. Correction Filters

Exact correction filters have been devised (*352*, *353*, *354*, *357*) for the use with Standard Illuminant *A* (2848° K.). R. Davis and K. S. Gibson have produced two pairs of liquid filters for transforming the spectral distribution of Illuminant *A* (2848° K.) into the spectral distribution of Illuminant *B* (4800° K.) and Illuminant *C* (6500° K.), respectively. The liquids together with the proper two-compartment cell are marketed by The Tintometer Co., Ltd. (cf. Chap. 7.9).

TABLE 9.6

Yellowish Correction Filters for Decreasing the Colour Temperature

No. of Filter	Standard Temp. deg. K.	Apparently Decreased Temp. deg. K.
86	5500	2360
86A	3200	2360
86B	2800	2360
86C	2500	2360

TABLE 9.7

Liquid Standard Illuminant Correction Filters

Filter for the conversion of type A to type B light :

Solution B–1		*Solution B–2*	
Copper sulphate	2·452 g.	Cobalt ammonium sulphate	21·71 g.
Mannite	2·452 g.	Copper sulphate	16·11 g.
Pyridine	30·0 cc.	Sulphuric acid ($d = 1{\cdot}835$)	10·0 cc.
Dist. water to make	1000·0 cc.	Dist. water to make	1000·0 cc.

Filter for the conversion of type A to type C light :

Solution C–1		*Solution C–2*	
Copper sulphate	3·412 g.	Cobalt ammonium sulphate	30·58 g.
Mannite	3·412 g.	Copper sulphate	22·52 g.
Pyridine	30·0 cc.	Sulphuric acid ($d = 1{\cdot}835$)	10·0 cc.
Dist. water to make	1000·0 cc.	Dist. water to make	1000·0 cc.

Filter for the conversion of a lamp run at 2360° K. to a type B lamp :

Solution X–1		*Solution X–2*	
Copper sulphate	3·707 g.	Cobalt ammonium sulphate	26·827 g.
Mannite	3·707 g.	Copper sulphate	27·18 g.
Pyridine	30·0 cc.	Sulphuric acid ($d = 1{\cdot}835$)	10·0 cc.
Dist. water to make	1000·0 cc.	Dist. water to make	1000·0 cc.

(*656, p. 67*)

9.12. Conversion of Tungsten Light to Sunlight Quality

Ilford filter No. 810 and Corning filter 590 are practically equivalent to Wratten 78 filter in that they all apparently raise the colour temperature of a tungsten incandescent lamp to the colour temperature of sunlight. The Corning 590-filter is remarkable in that its standard temperature is 2848° K. A list of filters for the reproduction of sunlight and daylight was published by Davis and Gibson (*353*).

Bibliography References: (*1167, 1168*)

9.13. Liquid Filters

These are used only in laboratory work as they are not very stable and must be replaced frequently. A list of such filters for singling out mercury lines is given by Pringsheim and Vogel (*614, p. 41*).

Bibliography References: (*530, 1537*)

9.14. Contrast Filters

To brighten any particular colour a filter of that same colour should be selected. To darken a given colour a filter should be used which approaches its complementary colour. cf. Chap. 8, Table 8.8.

9.15. Monochromatic Filters

These filters have a very low total transmission but are capable, either singly or in combination, of separating the lines of a mercury vapour lamp, or any other spectral line. The following filters give the desired results (*659*).

TABLE 9.8

Filters for the Isolation of Mercury Lines

A Mercury Vapour Lamp emits Luminous Radiation at the Wavelengths		Per cent of Emission	Isolation achieved with				
			Wratten Filter		Ilford Filter		Corning Filter†
A.U.	Colour	%	No.	τ*	No.	τ*	No.
4047	violet	11·8	—	—	—	—	306+428+597
4078	violet	2·4	50	—	—	—	—
4358	blue	21·9	50	7·0	805+806	5·26	038, 511
4916	blue-green	0·6	—	—	—	—	—
5461	green‡	28·3	62	8·0	807	10·0	350 512§
			77A	68·0‖	—	—	—
5780	yellow	35·0	22	70·0	—	—	348+430

* Specific transmission in per cent stands here for the transmission of the specific wavelength through the filter irrespective of the energy of the light source. The total transmission of the combination Filter + Lamp is calculated by multiplying the emission factor of the lamp by the transmission factor of the filter, for instance, emission at 5461 A.U. is 28.3% of the total emission of the mercury vapour lamp; from this only 8% is transmitted by a Wratten No. 62 filter. Therefore, the total output of Filter + Lamp at 5461 A.U. is $28{\cdot}3 \times 0{\cdot}08 = 2{\cdot}27\%$.

† In all the above cases the transmission of the Corning filters is less than 15%.

‡ The 5461 A.U. line is the most powerful source of monochromatic radiation so far known.

§ For complete isolation of the 5461 A.U. line add filter 430 which totally absorbs the red and infra-red lines of the mercury vapour lamp.

‖ The combination of No. 58 with either No. 77 (28%) or No. 77A (27%) will prevent the long-wave energy from reaching the photosensitor. This red and infra-red energy is emitted by the hot quartz or glass enclosure of the lamp.

Monochromatic filters should have a range (band width) of about 300 A.U. on the average. When used in colorimeters a combination of twelve to fifteen monochromatic filters will cover the entire range of the luminous spectrum and will enable spectral transmission or reflexion curves to be plotted without having to resort to a spectrophotometer. The total transmission of reasonably monochromatic filters is low and high intensity sources must be used. Most of the filters listed in Table 9.9 transmit a small percentage in the red (>7000 A.U.) and infra-red.

TABLE 9.9
Wratten Monochromatic Filters

Name	No.	Total Transmission *	Maximum Transmission at A.U.
α	70	0·6	7000
β	71A	0·9	6400
γ	72	1·3	6100
δ	73	1·6	5700
ε	74	2·0	5300
η	75	1·5	4900
θ	76	0·1	4400

* The total transmission is calculated for light of approx. 5500° K.

The colorimetric specifications of Wratten filters are given in a paper by MacAdam (*1476*).

TABLE 9.10
Ilford Monochromatic Filters

Name	No.	Maximum Transmission at A.U.	Limits of Transmission A.U.
Violet	601	4300	3800–4800
Blue	602	4700	4400–5000
Blue-green	603	4900	4750–5300
Green	604	5200	4900–5500
Yellow-green	605	5500	5300–5800
Yellow	606	5800	5500–6300
Orange	607	6000	5700–7200
Red	608	>6800	6100–infra-red

TABLE 9.11

Corning Monochromatic Filters

Combination	Maximum Transmission at A.U.	Limits of Transmission A.U.
738+586	3650	3500–3900
306+428+597	3950	3700–4100
038+511*	4350	4100–4700
368+511†	4650	4420–5000
338+554	4920	4700–5300
352+430+502	5150	4950–5620
350+430+512	5480	5300–5700
348+430	5750	5700–6000
245+978*	6080	5920–6420
243+978†	6450	6150–6800
244+397+555	7180	6700–Infra-red

*These filters are of half standard thickness.
†The filters are of standard thickness, i.e., 0·25 in = 6·25 mm.

The following combinations yield a high intensity monochromatic radiation (*796*).

TABLE 9.12

Monochromatic Filters and Sources of Radiation

Monochromatic Wavelength A.U.	Type of Discharge Lamp	Type of Filter
2537	Hg	Chance OX7 or Corning Red Purple Corex + Chlorine
3076	Zn	Corning Red Purple Corex + Picric acid
3130	Hg	Corning Red Purple Corex + Potassium chromate
3261	Cd	Corning Red Purple Corex + Potassium chromate
3650	Hg	Wratten 18A or Chance OX1
3776	Tl	Corning Red Purple Corex + Schott GG2
4047	Hg	Corning Red Purple Ultra
5068	Cd	Wratten 61
5350	Tl	Wratten 62
5461	Hg	Wratten 77
5780	Hg	Wratten 22
5893	Na	Wratten 23
6362	Zn	Schott RG1 + RG2
6438	Cd	Schott RG1 + RG2

Bibliography Reference: (*595*)

9.16. Ultra-Violet Filters

All filters operating over a region of the spectrum other than luminous are coloured filters. Colouring agents are the oxides of Ti, V, Cr, Mn, Fe, Co, Ni, Cu, all of which show an absorption characteristic which is of interest in a particular range of the spectrum. For ultra-violet filters (3650/63 A.U.) nickel oxide (Wood's) glass is the most popular. It is used as the outer (filtering) bulb of the commercially called " black " lamp, because it looks black at first sight. Actually, it is very dark purplish-red. It cuts off nearly all the luminous energy (cf. Chap. 7, Table 7.20). The 2537 A.U. radiation is selectively transmitted by a Chance OX7 filter. The above mentioned metal oxides have a broad absorption band. Using rare earths as a colouring agent results in a sharp absorption band (*259*, *661*). Most of the ultra-violet transmitting glasses, although opaque to luminous radiation, are transparent again in the very dark red or infra-red region, respectively, according to chemical composition and thickness of the filter. If this range of the spectrum must be suppressed, combinations, as instanced by those given in the foot-note to the 5461 A.U. line in Table 9.8, will be satisfactory. Christiansen filters for the ultra-violet region have been described recently (*2422*, *2423*).

Bibliography Reference: (*530*)

9.17. Infra-red Filters

Nearly all dyed gelatine and many types of both clear and coloured glass filters, whatever their particular spectral range may be, transmit infra-red radiation more or less freely. Glass filters, either singles or compounds, can be made to cut off at specified wavelengths. Blue, blue-green, and green filters usually begin transmission at wavelengths greater than 7600 A.U. If blue filters are used in photo-electric colorimeters the infra-red transmission should be prevented from reaching the photosensitor by adding an infra-red absorbing filter. Infra-red transmission can be designed to extend up to about 40,000 A.U. (4 μ). Infra-red transmitting filters sometimes also transmit small quantities of purple light, i.e., a mixture of luminous extreme red and luminous extreme violet : they also usually transmit in the ultra-violet. Infra-red absorbing filters must be made of heat-resisting glass : if ordinary glass is used thermal breakage is bound to occur due to the great heat generated in the glass by the absorption of the infra-red energy. Transmission curves of plastic materials (Cellophane, Nylon, Polyvinyl alcohol, Furane lacquer, and others) are given by E. R. Blout, *et al.* (*1638*). *Bibliography References*: (*536, 1513, 1514, 1539, 1540*)

9.18. Atmosphere

Haze, fog, dust, steam, or any other medium causing a turbidity in the atmosphere through which the radiant energy must pass on its way from the source of radiation to the photosensitor or its optical system cause the intensity of the beam to be reduced considerably, depending on the wavelength of the radiation under transmission.

As a general rule, long-wave radiation undergoes less attenuation than does short-wave radiation. Since the distances covered in industrial photo-electric practice do not exceed perhaps 20 to 30 feet, it may safely be said that infra-red radiation has no particular advantage over long-wave luminous (orange, red) radiation.

E. O. Hulburt (*660*) showed that up to about half a mile the infra-red sensitive photographic plate had no advantage over the unaided eye, which may also be taken to be characteristic of the photosensitor operating with either luminous or infra-red radiation.

Ultra-violet radiation is heavily reduced in its intensity by haze, fog, steam, etc. For wavelengths smaller than 4000 A.U. the radiant energy is reflected by the solid or liquid particles suspended in air, and only a very small amount is transmitted. The average sizes of the particles are (*36, p. 306*) :

Smoke : in general 0·001–0·1 μ, i.e., 10–1000 A.U.,
Smoke : from burning oil : 1 μ max., i.e., 10,000 A.U.,
Haze : in general 0·001–0·1 μ, i.e., 10–1000 A.U.
Fumes : in general 0·1–1·0 μ, i.e, 1000–10,000 A.U.,
Fumes : in industrial smelter fumes up to 100 μ, i.e., 0·1 mm.,
Dust : in general 1–10 μ, i.e., 10,000–100,000 A.U.,
Fog : 5–50 μ, i.e., 0·005–0·05 mm.

If the particles are small relative to the wavelength of the incident radiation there are but small losses due to scattering. Larger particles act as reflecting bodies, thus reducing the transmitted energy.

In clear air the absorption of luminous and infra-red rays, the latter as far as 20,000 A.U. (photosensitor range), is negligible and independent of the wavelength of the radiation : this is not the case in the ultra-violet region. The absorption coefficient for radiation of 2100 A.U. wavelength is about 125 times the absorption coefficient at 3000 A.U. (*660, 661*).

Bibliography Reference: (*2348*)

9.19. Aqueous Filters

The absorption of a liquid for monochromatic light is characterized by the absorption coefficient β, viz., $I = I_0 \cdot e^{-\beta d}$, where I_0 is the incident intensity of light, I is the intensity of the light beam after passing through the liquid filter of thickness d (cm.). The passage through the liquid results also in the beam being scattered. The fraction of light scattered at right angles to the light pencil is proportional to I, namely αI, where α is the scattering coefficient for the particular liquid. (cf. Chap. 14.1, also *805*, *806*). In general the scattering coefficient increases with decreasing wavelength. For water (*662*) the relation is given in Table 9.13.

TABLE 9.13

Scattering Coefficients for Water

Wavelength A.U.	Scattering Coefficient $\times 10^{-7}$	Wavelength A.U.	Scattering Coefficient $\times 10^{-7}$
2500	34·4	4500	2·53
3000	14·8	5000	1·66
3500	7·5	5500	1·03
4000	4·06	6000	0·79

9.20. Powder Filters

These have extensively been described by Pfund (*663*), Plummer (*664*), and others : they are used in infra-red work. A typical transmission curve is shown in Fig. 9.4, the particle size of the powder being

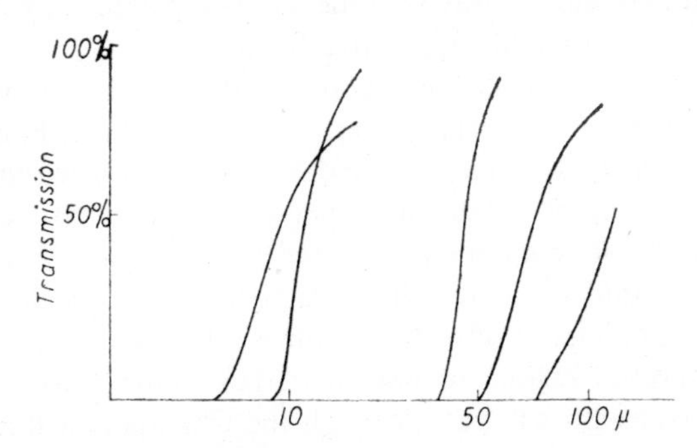

Fig. 9.4. Spectral characteristics of some powder filters.

880 A.U. The tenets of the preceding section are borne out and confirmed by this curve. Plummer (*loc. cit.*) produces such filters by

fuming magnesium oxide on nitrocellulose ; Pfund (*loc. cit.*) by distilling selenium on the same carrier material. These filters transmit from 5000 A.U. to 100,000 A.U.

Bibliography Reference: (*535*)

9.21. Filter Factors

In calculations with filters or mirrors care must be taken not to forget the transmission and reflexion coefficients, Radiant energy, after striking the mirror, always loses a certain quantity of energy which must be supplied by the light source : the same holds for filters. The general relation is $I_s = (1/L)I_p$ where I_s is the intensity emitted by the (light) source, I_p the intensity needed on the photo-cathode, and L are the total losses incurred by passing through optical filters, dusty atmosphere, dirty cover glasses or lenses, reflexion from mirrors, etc. The total loss L is the product of the various individual loss factors. If, for instance, the total loss results in the intensity on the photosensitor being reduced to one quarter of the required intensity the loss can be balanced, according to the square law, either by using a (light) source of four-fold the intensity or, if permissible, by reducing by half the distance between the source and photosensitor.

9.22. Christiansen Filter

Although a Christiansen filter (named after C. Christiansen (*665*, *666*) who discovered this particular effect in 1884) is not commonly used in industrial routine or shop work, it is a useful tool in laboratory practice and may find its way into the workshop some day, perhaps in modified and more readily applicable form.

Principally, it is a dispersion compound filter based on the fact that one component of that filter, viz., granulated homogeneous optical glass, does not change its index of refraction within practical limits of temperature, while the other component, viz., an organic liquid which at ordinary temperatures has the same refractive index as the glass granules, changes its refractivity very considerably. The identity of the indices of refraction is limited to a very narrow band λ_0 within the spectral region for both materials. Luminous radiation of the same wavelength will pass through the Christiansen filter without incurring any losses worth noticing. If the indices of refraction differ by reason of a change in temperature then the region of transmissivity is shifted from λ_0 to λ' and it will totally cut off radiation of wavelength λ_0 which it has passed previously.

A practical filter which is capable of transmitting a strong beam of radiation has been described by McAlister (*667*, *668*, *p. 104*). giving the following details for optimum operation :

Size of glass granules :	0·5 to 2·0 mm. ;
Type of glass :	low-dispersion boro-silicate crown glass ;
Liquid :	a 9% CS_2 in benzene, the CS_2 being a highly dispersive medium. Weigert (*669*) suggests the use of methyl benzoate.

For work in the ultra-violet region of the spectrum, v. Fragstein (*670*) recommends the use of granules of clear fused quartz in a mixture of

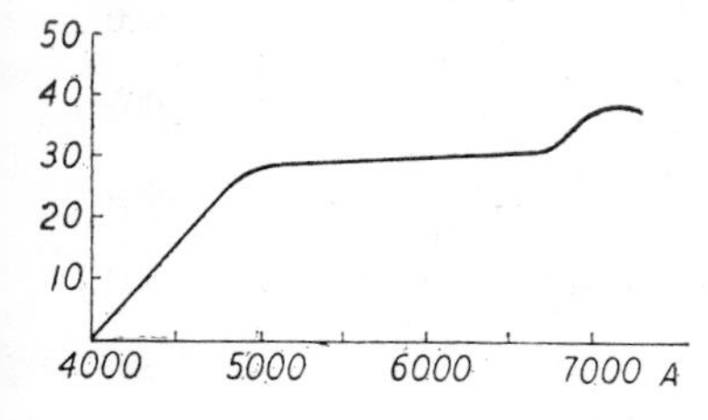

Fig. 9.5. Transmission curves of two sheets of Polaroid—axes parallel.

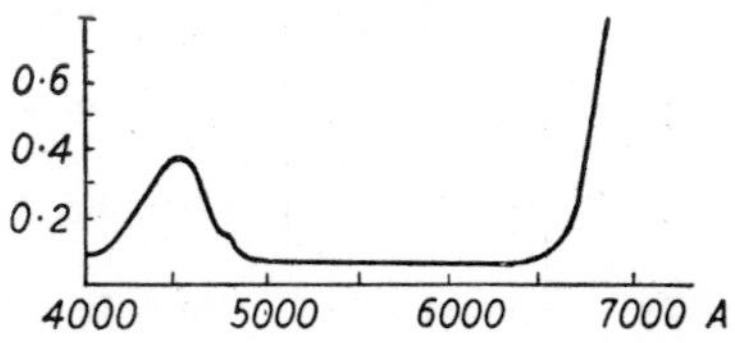

Fig. 9.6. Transmission curves of two sheets of Polaroid—axes crossed.

44% ethyl alcohol and 56% benzene. This Christiansen filter covers the region from 3000 to 3700 A.U. (*2422*, *2423*) and is particularly suited for isolating the 3650 A.U. band. G. J. Minkoff and A.G. Gaydon (*2422*) have succeeded in isolating the 2537 A.U. line by means of a Christiansen filter composed of crushed fluorite (CaF_2) in 43% pure carbon tetrachloride (CCl_4) and 57% ethyl alcohol (*665*, *666*, *670*, *2440*).

Another combination was described by Denmark and Cody (*671*). The cell is 7·5 mm. thick and contains ethyl salicylate. The grain size of the optical glass ($n_0 = 1{\cdot}523$) is about 0·7 mm. With the temperature varying between 22° and 57° C. the transmitted light varies from 5730 to 4330 A.U.

The Christiansen-Weigert monochromator (*669*) produces monochromatic light of any desired wavelength by varying the temperature of the liquid.

9.23. Dyes for Gelatine Filters

In the following Table the chemical composition is given of dyes as used in the manufacture of filters (*672*).

TABLE 9.14

Dyes for Gelatine Filters

Wratten Filter No.	Colour	Dye	Concentration p.p.m.
12	yellow	Auramine	100
22	orange	Chrysoidine	1000
32	violet	Complementary Scarlet	1250
44	blue-green	Iodobenzoine 92	5000
45	blue-green	Azine Scarlet	2000
50	blue	Eosin Blue	1000
53	green	Tetraiodofluorescinate of Sodium*	1000
58	green	Rose Bengal	1000
62	green	Phloxine B.A. Extra	1000
77	green	Pinatype Carmine	500
78	bluish	Pinatype Carmine	2000
86	yellowish	Acid Chrome Blue 2R	400
91	deep red	Methyl Violet BBR	400

* The Erythrosin (pure) of the No. 53 filter is replaced in more recent types by the disodium ferrous salt of nitroso-beta-napthhol sulphuric acid, called Naphthol Green for short.

9.24. Polaroid Filters

Polaroid is a cellulosic film exhibiting polarizing properties by means of small, needle-shaped dichroic* crystals which are uniformly orientated and dispersed in great numbers in the cellulosicmed iums. The light transmitted by Polaroid at maximum visibility (5550 A.U.) is

* Dichroism is the property of certain crystals to exhibit different colours when viewed in different directions.

99·8% polarized. Fig. 9.5 shows the transmission of two Polaroid plates superimposed with their axes parallel, while Fig. 9.6 represents the transmission with the axes crossed (*675*, *676*, *677*). The degree of polarization for the luminous range is given in Fig. 9.7 (cf. Chaps. 11.13, 4.36).

Bibliography References: (*426*, *586*, *1165*, *1577*, *2068*, *2096*, *2132*)

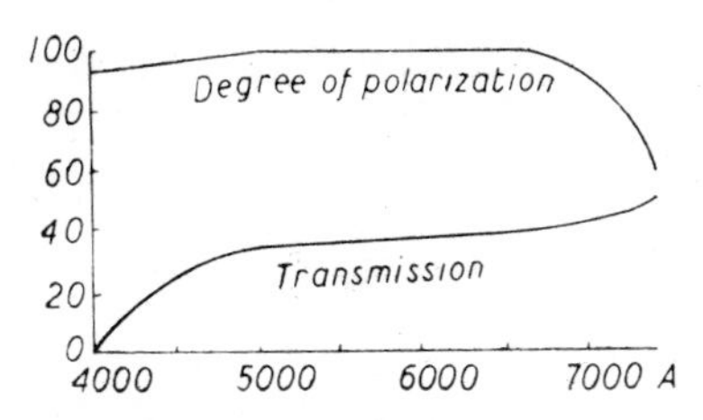

Fig. 9.7. The degree of polarisation of Polaroid for the luminous range.

9.25. Heat-Absorbing Filters

Heat-absorbing filters must be mounted in frames allowing for free movement of the highly expansive glass.

TABLE 9.15

Heat Absorbing Filter (*Chance Bros.*)

Type	Integral Heat Transmission	Integral Light Transmission	Transmission % at A.U.					
			5000	7500	10000	22000	29000	35000
ON13 2 mm.	13%	64%	max.	15	2	20	10	2
ON20 2 mm.	14%	88%	max.	50	7	10	15	2
ON20 3 mm.	8·5%	87%	max.	as above				
ON20 0·5 mm.	39·0%	91·3%	[ON20] $n_D^{20} = 1{\cdot}505$					
ON20 6 mm.	4·5%	81·0%						

9.26. Achromatic Vision Filter

In some cases it is necessary to exclude the values of colour (cf. Chap. 19.5) and simply match the relative brightness or luminosity, lustre, or any other such optical property of the material concerned.

A filter of the achromatic vision type is the Wratten No. 90 or Ilford Nos. 811 or 812. The Wratten filter is one of the best in that it removes nearly all colour from the object without materially affecting the relative luminosity of the various colours. The Ilford No. 811 filter converts the colour sensitivity of a panchromatic plate, Fig. 8abc.

Special purpose filters are described by various authors (***36, p. 364*** ; ***528, 673, 674, 1103***).

9.27. Using Coloured Light

The lack of red rays in the spectrum of a mercury lamp (the radiations at 6720, 6910, 7080 and 7730 A.U. are of negligible energy) gives the possibility of building a very selective photo-electric relay. A caesium photosensitor or a thallium light-sensitive resistor has the maximum sensitivity in the dark red and near infra-red part of the spectrum. If the photosensitor is screened with a type OX1 (Chance) filter of 2 mm. or more thickness, no light will be admitted to the cell between 4000 and 6700 A.U. The visible line spectrum of the mercury discharge lamp extends from 4047 to 5790 A.U. which means that this light will not affect the photosensitor. An incandescent lamp of suitable type is used as a light source. The continuous spectrum of this lamp is cut off at wavelengths which should coincide with, or at least approach closely to, the limits of the filter (4000 to 6700 A.U.) by using an identical filter in front of the lamp. This gives double protection as no light is emitted by the lamp which would be within the forbidden range, viz., 4000–6700 A.U. Good transmission takes place both in the ultraviolet and infra-red region.

9.28. Mutual Agreement between Source of Radiation, Filter, Colour of Object, and Photosensitor

When the need arises to eliminate the influence of the general illumination on the cell, four types of selective devices are generally at the disposal of the engineer, viz. :

(*a*) a steady light beam whose energy is emitted on a very narrow band of wavelengths, the latter being different from the wavelengths of the general illumination ;

(*b*) a pulsating light beam, produced by mechanical or electrical means, the light of the beam having a wavelength equal to, or different from, the light used for general illumination. If vapour discharge lamps are A.C. operated and provide the general illumination the frequency of the pulsating light beam should be distinctly different from double the A.C. frequency ;

(*c*) a baffle tube or pin-point diaphragm ; the former must be long enough to exclude light from sources other than the one actuating the photosensitor, but at the same time the baffle must be wide enough to admit the required flux. The diaphragm can be used instead of a baffle.

(*d*) a balanced two-cell circuit.

Very often coloured objects, or chemical or physical processes involving a change of colour must be controlled by photo-electric gear. It is, then, essential to harmonize all components so that :

(1) a maximum change is caused in the light flux falling on to the photosensitor ;

(2) certain variations in the manufacturing process affect the photo-electric control system whereas others do not.

9.29. Attenuation of Radiation

The fact must be borne in mind that the radiant energy undergoes attentuation by the selective effects of filter and photosensitor, respectively. The product of the energy of the radiation at a certain wavelength emitted at a given colour temperature, times the transmittance of a filter, times the relative response of the photosensitor to this wavelength, is proportional to the photo-electric current as it would be measured by exposing the cell to the filtered radiation of the source.

Bibliography Reference: (*2367*)

PART II

CHAPTER 10

PROTECTIVE DEVICES

"No sane industrialist questions the spending of money on a good maintenance engineer. From the standpoint of accident prevention, it is just as essential to spend money on seeing that the human machine is studied, cared for and understood."

(*Mr. G. Tomlinson, Parliamentary Secretary to the Minister of Labour, in a speech to the Royal Society for the Prevention of Accidents ; London, November, 1944.*)

The protection of the machine operator from accidents due to insufficient or unworkable guards has been made the object of many learned investigations and has become an integral part of modern legislation. It is very fortunate that the aspects and interests of employer and employee coincide in this matter and also cover the intentions of the legislator.

An industrial accident is a serious affair not only for the injured person who may suffer bodily for a long period or be disabled for life, but who also suffers a financial setback which may seriously disturb all future decisions concerning the welfare and the education of his family. It also has a more or less pronounced effect on production in the department in which the affected person worked, depending upon the type of work and the ability and willingness of the injured person's shopmates to take over part of his routine work.

Taking the broad view the invalided person is a liability to the working and producing capacity of the nation as a whole.

During the last 110 years legislation, being conscious of these basic facts, has succeeded in passing a series of Factory Acts the trend of which is to safeguard the workman as well as the nation against industrial accidents. Sir Robert Peel's Health and Morals of Apprentices Act, 1802, is of great importance for later developments as it led to the institution of Factory Inspectors. These Inspectors found that one of the greatest evils to which people employed in factories are exposed is the danger of receiving serious and even fatal injury from machinery (*742*) and they recommended " boxing off of dangerous parts of machinery " (*743*).

It was not until 1833 that offenders against the law which demanded machinery to be fenced, should be heavily fined. Lord Ashley wished that negligence in safeguarding machinery by mechanical means, if causing death from accident, should be sufficient reason to try the employer for manslaughter.

The Factory Act, 1833 (3 & 4 Will., IV, Chap. 103) amongst other important rights, empowers the Inspector to order machinery to be fenced. The Factory Act of 1844 (7 & 8 Vict., Chap. 15) legislates much on the lines the Inspectors had recommended in the decade between the two Acts. Modern legislation on Safety in Factories is embodied in the Factory Acts of 1905, 1924, and 1937.

10.1. Mechanical Safeguards

The Factories Act of July 30, 1937, Part II, Section 14, Sub-Sections 1 and 2, gives a full account of the basic functions a protective device is expected to fulfill if it is to be within the classifications defined by the law.

Mechanical devices have a double purpose, viz., (*a*) " to prevent the exposure of a dangerous part of machinery whilst in motion " ; and (*b*) to remind the workman, visually and factually, of the ever lurking danger and also of the presence of certain measures taken to safeguard him from this danger.

There is, however, a group of cases which makes the workman abandon all precautionary measures and accept the probability of meeting with an accident rather than work a little slower but safer. This point of view reveals as regrettable an attitude as does the factory girl who denied herself the benefit of a protective cap, maintaining that she " preferred to have an accident rather than to look a fright " (*744*). And this after she had had a minor scalping accident!

In the workman's case it is not a misunderstood and distorted sense of beauty, but a misguided desire for maximum efficiency, output and thereby increased wages.

There is, however, the genuine case of a mechanical safeguard being unsuitable for the performance of certain operations. Either the work-piece or the jigs are too bulky, or a power press is used for many different types of work which would entail as many different safe-guards, some perhaps of very costly and yet clumsy design.

It is in such cases that the above quoted sub-section 2, al. B., becomes effective and provides the legitimate background for the introduction of photo-electric relays as a means and essential element of the protective fencing of machinery.

10.2. Photo-Electric Protective Devices

The extraordinary adaptability of the photo-relay as compared with the rigidity in design as well as construction of mechanical fences makes the electronic device appear to be the *non-plus-ultra* of protection. The utilization of the photo-electric cell affords a high degree of adaptation to the existing needs of the workshop.

Attention must be drawn to a possibly indiscriminate use of such a device. The workman is well acquainted with and accustomed to the mechanical guard with its robust structures making a rattling noise sometimes, and then again, working with that little pleasant sound of tinkling metal gives the operative the assuring certainty of the presence of a tangible danger and of an even more tangible and therefore effective safeguard against it. Moreover—and not the least important—the material safeguard continuously reminds the man of the danger.

This psychological effect is not effective when a photo-electric relay is used. The only visible means of protection and security is the light ray passing from the lamp to the photosensitor across, or in front of, the object or space to be guarded. Light, for the ordinary man, is a natural commodity, inherent in the routine of a 24-hours day, and is subconsciously acknowledged as the result of an experience which is as old as vision. Suddenly this perception of light is moved from the sub-conscious background of its existence to full consciousness and, what is more, its characteristics have undergone so drastic a change that the ordinary man finds it hard to make use of it. Light, as far as he knows and has ever experienced or read about, is the means of illumination. But here, light is used in the apparently compact form of a pencil or beam or sheet. This beam, too, has a certain solid—and therefore reassuring—appearance which speaks very much in favour of the photo-electric device, but it is, nevertheless, immaterial and intangible. Therefore the machine operator might feel let down by this silent and motionless beam.

It is the task of the works engineer to acquaint the man with the outstanding efficiency and reliability of photo-electric devices, and to disperse the suspicion against its silent, yet most watchful behaviour. For this reason only visible light should be used.

Photo-electric protective devices are characterized by a practically unlimited number of different cases efficiently covered by merely a few types of photo-relays and by the wide range of applications one and the same type can be adapted to by making minor alterations in the set-up as a whole or in the constructional details of a component or an accessory.

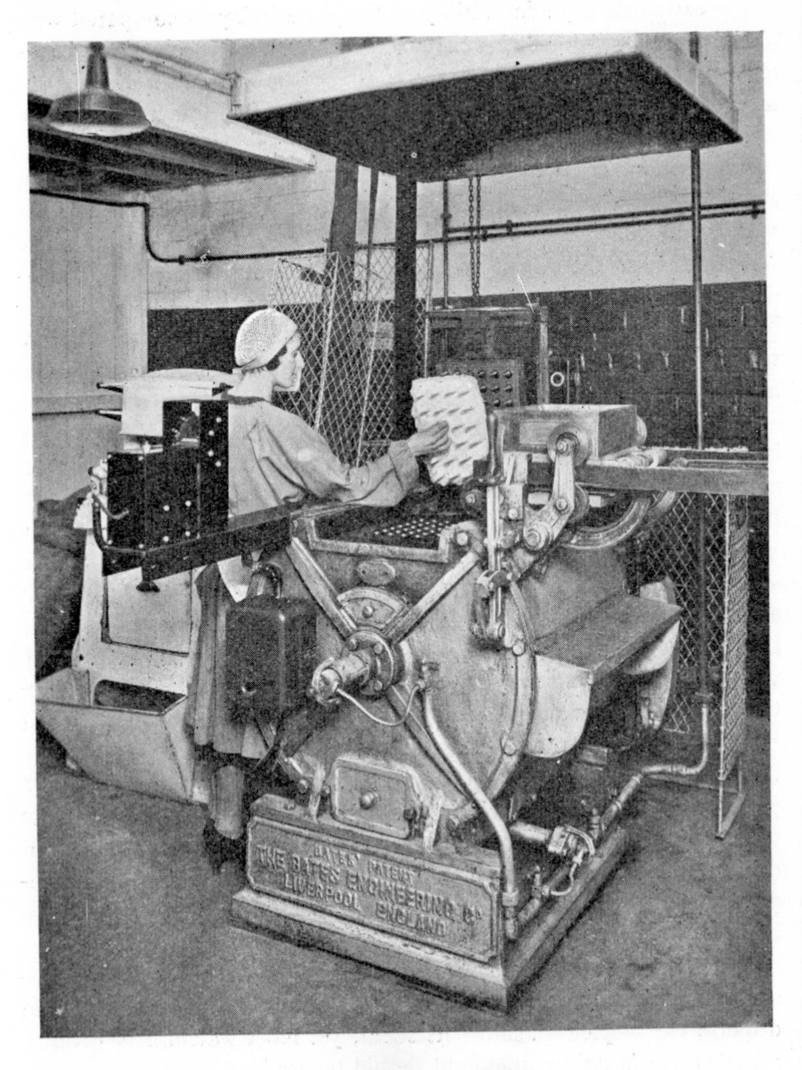

Fig. 10.1. Protection of operator's arm by photo-cell equipment: the press cannot close while the spot of light (on the upper arm) is intercepted.

Power presses, circular saws, machine planes ; dangerous corners, in narrow gangways, doors, passages, and crossings, etc., are protected by photo-electric relays (Fig. 10.1). A pencil or a sheet of light, transmitted freely through the air, or conducted through special optical media (cf. Chap. 6), is harnessed and put to the task of protecting the productive capacity of workmen as well as machinery. Calenders, laundry ironers, and similar machines are not only stopped but the direction of motion may be reversed when an object enters the danger zone. A photo-electric safeguard may be devised to be operative during the downwards movements of a machine, for instance of a power press, but to be ineffective during its upward movement, thus saving considerable time in not unnecessarily interrupting the smooth working of the machine.

What might perhaps be called the most essential feature of a photo-electric safeguard is the possibility of interlocking it electrically with the main switch or any other electrical control gear in such a way that an interruption of the normal function of the photo-relay causes the machine to be switched off the mains. This action takes place either if an object obstructs the path of the light beam, or if the operative should try to tamper with the apparatus in order to increase the output of his machine. The machine also stops if the electrical circuit of the photo-electric device should fail for any reason whatsoever.

From the Safety Engineer's point of view the photo-relay indubitably is preferable to any other device. The ingenuity of the engineer will find many applications the effects of which will not only reduce costs, time of production, rejects, and accidents, but at the same time will increase production and guarantee a high-quality output (*745*).

Bibliography References : (*500, 1310, 1380, 1953, 1963, 1973, 2264, 2401, p. 114 2406*)

10.3. Light Beams

The protecting medium is either a light beam or, in special cases, a light curtain (cf. Chap. 6). Generally, non-selective, i.e., white light will be used, but a necessity may arise for using monochromatic or modulated light in order to discriminate between the general illumination and protective light rays. Modulated light (cf. Chap. 7) will only rarely be used, but monochromatic light is easily adapted to the lighting routine in the workshop. Since the advent of mercury discharge lamps with or without colour correcting media in the form of luminescent powders, it has become general practice to instal this type of light source for industrial illumination. The spectrum of the bulb-shaped clear or phosphorescent mercury discharge lamp is deficient in red rays. An orange or light red ray recommends itself as an actuating medium. If sodium discharge lamps are used for general illumination, a blue or violet light ray will prove successful.

The application of infra-red radiant energy as actuating medium in protective devices is restricted to such cases where it is desirable to conceal the presence of a protective device as, for instance, in all property protecting equipment when, for obvious reasons, luminous radiation is not desirable. As already mentioned, non-luminous radiation should not be used where man is the object of protection.

10.4. Spatial Protection—the Aniseikon

Spatial supervision and, derived from it, spatial protection was usually performed by a scanner of the mechanical or electronic type, or a number of photosensitors was employed each viewing a section of the whole space to be protected. The Aniseikon* can be made in two types ; the one, using an optical system of a focal length different for each part of the binocular, resulting in the object being imaged at unequal sizes which, in turn, upsets a balanced two-cell circuit (*85*). This type of Aniseikon is capable only of detecting objects or conditions alien to the original set-up. It cannot, however, detect motion if the image of the moving object was part of the original silhouette on the photosensitor. If an object starts moving in a room where it has been before without the object or its image on the photosensitor varying its size, and it is desired to detect the motion of the object, it is necessary to introduce a *réseau* which, in a sense, imitates the structure of the human retina (*746*).

The image of an object, projected by the lens of the eye on to the retina, covers a certain number of photo-receptors (cf. Chap. 3), each of which conveys a stimulus to the higher brain centres. If a change occurs in the position of the image other photo-receptors will be stimulated and the result of this action is the perception of motion.

The physical interpretation and imitation of this psycho-physiological process led V. K. Zworykin to the invention of the iconoscope which might be interpreted as an immensely enlarged retina with a

* Aniseikonia is a pathological condition in which the images which reach the consciousness through the two eyes are not of identical shape and size (ikon = picture, image ; iso = same ; an = not).

relatively small number of light sensitive elements (10,000 photocells to the square centimetre).

Another suggestion was made by A. Fitzgerald (*746*) who interposed a screen of alternate opaque and transparent small squares of equal

Fig. 10.2. Aniseikon in combination with a reseau. Any combination of two of these reseaux will give an aniseikon effect regardless of the position of the individual reseau.

size between the image and the photo-cathode. There are, however, serious disadvantages to this type of grating which make its practical application questionable.

The Aniseikon, using an identical binocular system in combination with a *réseau* instanced in Fig. 10.2, is a foolproof device. The two gratings are not complementary—on the contrary they are widely different as to both the size and shape of the elements and their relative position. The pattern of the two gratings is distinctly different. It will be useful to arrange generally for the small elements of the one grating to be located where the large elements of the other screen are positioned, thereby enhancing the sensitivity of the device. There is limitation neither to size nor shape of the image and it is by no means conditional that the image must not exceed the area of a certain element.

The size of the smallest element is kept down as much as possible in order to enhance the scope and range of the instrument.

Bibliography References: (*1233*, *1367*, *2290*, *2290*, *2306*, *2320*, *2387*)

Fig. 10.3. Photo-cell and relay guarding an operator's arm. The lamp and cell housings are shown by the arrows.
(*Courtesy of the Westinghouse International Corpn.*).

10.5. Power Presses

The engineer responsible for the protection against accidents of his machine operators will, when initially considering the type of machine, nearly always decide in favour of a power press (Fig. 10.3). His decision is based on two facts which, however, are not always realized correctly, viz., (1) that the power press represents the most commonly used type of machine, and (2) that, except for calenders, the power presses claim the lion's share in industrial accidents. In many cases, the engineer will be confronted with the necessity of adapting an already existing

Fig. 10.4. Mechanical guard to press, operated by photo-cell equipment. The light beam is shown by the rectangular area on the operator's body.

installation and providing a photo-electric protective device for a power press the mechanical safeguard of which impedes efficient operation.

The more elegant way of adapting a press with photo-electric guards is to replace the trip pedal by a solenoid of sufficient power and stroke. The coupling of the solenoid acts either direct on the coupling rod or on the lever of the press, Fig. 10.4. If the necessary stroke is greater than provided for in the usual range of commercial solenoids, a D.C. magnetic coupling will have to be used, Fig. 10.5.

A pot magnet rated at between 50 and 75 watts is fixed to the coupling rod which has been reduced in length. The casing of the magnet carries a cylindrical brass tube acting as a guide for the armature which is connected to the trip pedal and a small spring will balance the weight of the armature. The press operator has to exert the same pull as in the case of a purely mechanical control. When the photosensitor is illuminated the relay will " make " the circuit, the magnet keeps the armature attracted in position and the operator, pulling down the trip pedal, pulls down the coupling rod also. If, however, the photosensitor has been eclipsed, the relay will " break " the circuit and actuating the trip pedal results in " no action ".

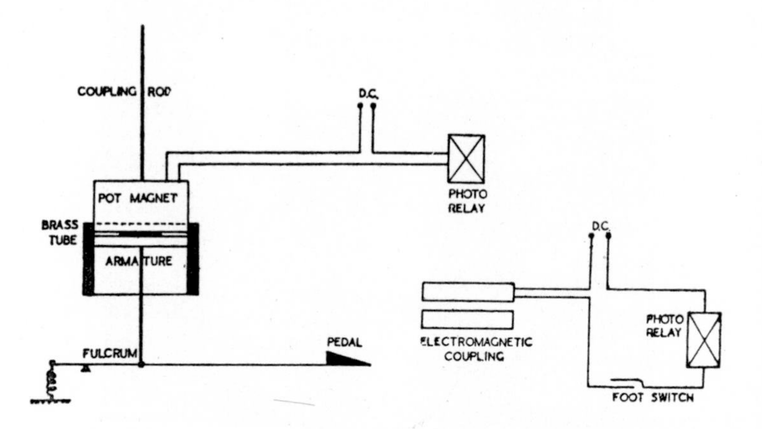

Fig. 10.5. Solenoid safety coupling between trip pedal and press.

Fig. 10.6. Foot switch replacing the trip pedal of Fig. 10.5.

With new presses the coupling between the trip pedal and the punch is of the electromagnetic type. The mechanical trip pedal, actuated by the foot of the machine operator (necessary pressure up to 40 to 50 lb.), is replaced by an electric foot switch, Fig. 10.6. The light beam or light curtain is thrown across the press just in front of the punch. If an object, for instance a tool, or the work-piece, or the operator's finger, approaches the punch too closely, it will obscure the photosensitor and the relay will disengage the coupling with the effect that the moving parts of the press immediately come to a standstill. For slow working presses and heavy work the coupling may be allowed to be disengaged by the photo-relay only when the punch is on its down-stroke. The relay does not break the circuit when the punch is on its up-stroke, i.e., when no harm can come to an object by approaching the punch too closely.

Bibliography Reference (1853)

10.6. Calenders

Calenders of any description, in particular laundry ironers, are easily and most efficiently controlled by photo-relays. The light ray is projected across the work table parallel and close to the rollers of the calender, Fig. 10.7.

When the hand of the operator moves in the direction of the arrow until it intercepts the light ray, a double-throw relay is energized thereby reversing the revolution of the rollers so that the hand of the operator cannot be pulled-in by the rollers. The forward motion of

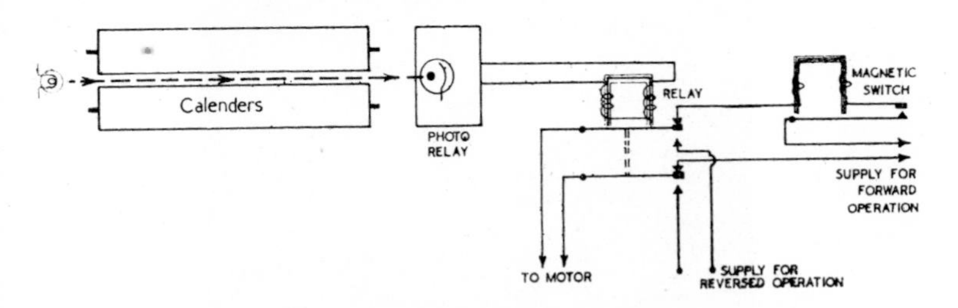

Fig. 10.7. Photo-electric control of calenders.

motor and rollers is not automatically restored when the light ray falls again on the photosensitor after the obstructing object, i.e., the operator's hand, has been removed. The motor can be set moving in the correct direction only by manually throwing a switch *MS*. This is an additional factor of safety. The circuit is wired as shown in Fig. 10.7. The current becomes zero upon the light ray being obscured.

The sequence of operations is :

(1) light on photo-relay ; photo-current flowing.

(2) electromagnetic relay is energized ; supply connected to motor for forward running.

(3) magnetic switch must be closed manually ; motor running.

(4) light interrupted ; photo-relay obscured ; no photo-current flowing.

(5) electromagnetic relay released ; this action reverses the motor.

(6) The interruption of the forward motor circuit also opens the main switch.

Fig. 10.8. Protection of guillotine operators (*Courtesy of the Westinghouse International Corpn.*).

(7) The obstruction is now removed ; light falls again on to the photo-relay.

(8) The relay is energized again and switches the motor from reverse to forward run.

(9) However, the motor cannot start automatically, because the switch is a manual one and must be closed first.

(10) Only after the switchhas been closed by hand can the motor start again. (Fig. 10.8.)

10.7. Protection of Tools

As already mentioned in the Introduction, the application of protective devices to safeguard expensive and complicated tools is very often a sober and economical proposition. The delay in the flow of production through breakage and consequent replacement of a tool which, in many cases, takes two or more weeks to make, amply justifies the installation of a photo-electric protective relay the costs of which are easily covered by the continuity of production. High-power tools, for instance, those used in large presses, lend themselves to being equipped with protective gear which prevents the punch from entering on the down-stroke if a pressing from the previous operation should stick to the punch which, in the case of metal being pressed or punched,

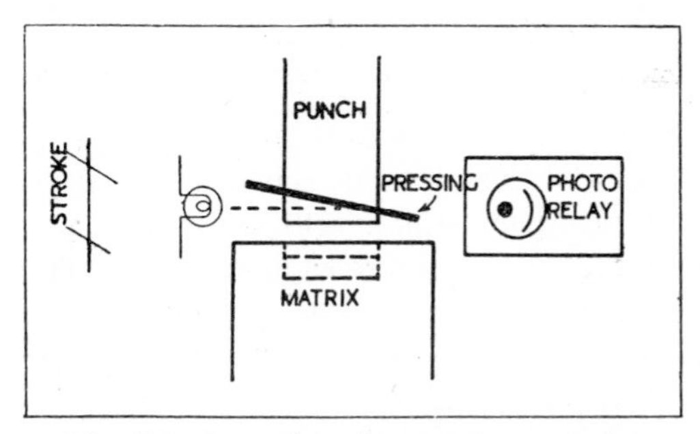

Fig. 10.9. Protection of a stamping press die.

might easily break the matrix and the punch as well. A ray or curtain of luminous or infra-red radiation is thrown across the die and the photo-relay is so adapted that the light ray, after being partially obscured by the punch moving downwards, still receives enough radiant energy so that the relay is not actuated, Fig. 10.9. If an object, moving with the punch, causes a further eclipse of the light source, the photo-relay will be energized and stop the machine, at the same time giving an alarm signal to the machine operator.

10.8. Fire Prevention

In nearly every case a fire is heralded by a more or less intense development of smoke depending on the type of object and ventilation. Very often smoke is already present without the temperature having risen appreciably or flames having developed. It is therefore correct to use a photo-electric system of smoke detection in order to prevent a fire from getting a hold.

This principle is used in the protection of ships, enclosed transformers, motors, generators, etc. (*26, p. 271*; *747*). The smoke indicator, as devised by Lange-Buchholz, is fitted between the points *A* and *B* of the cooling pipes, Fig. 10.10. If smoke develops the light beam in one of the compartments will be obscured and the then

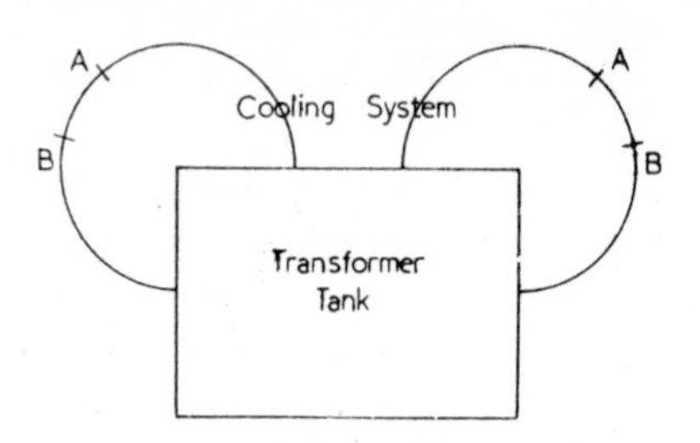

Fig. 10.10. Photo-electric protection of transformers by the Lange-Buchholz smoke indicator.

unbalanced two-cell circuit will actuate the relays. The circuit makes use of two photo-e.m.f. cells controlling a high-sensitivity relay of the double fixed contact solenoid reset (Weston 705) type which actuates two double-pole double-throw power relays (Weston 712), each capable of switching a non-inductive load of 2 amps. at 230 V A.C. The relay circuit is fed by 6 V D.C. which may be supplied through a rectifier. The circuits controlled by the 712 type relays may be connected to alarms or to electromagnetic valves of carbon dioxide cylinders which, when turned on, discharge immediately into the smoke-generating tank. A very sensitive circuit reacting to a change of 0·1% in the illumination has been described by Hull (*229*).

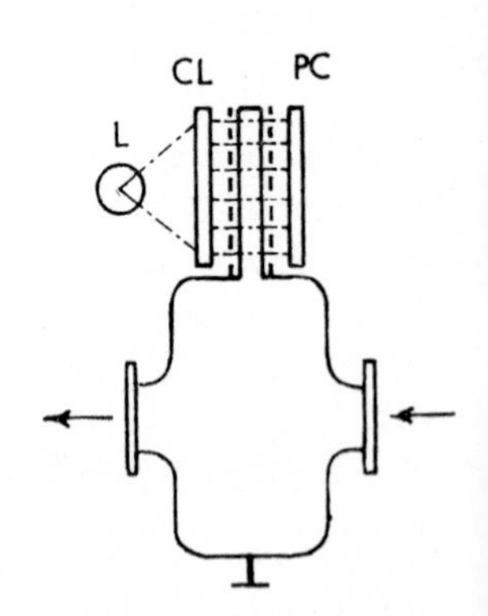

Fig. 10.11. Buchholz relay for detecting high temperature in transformer tank.

The Buchholz relay can also be placed between the transformer tank and the conservator (*748*). It will then act on the presence of gas bubbles in the oil, the bubbles being indicative of an abnormal and dangerous temperature. A glass tube may be fitted into the top outlet of the relay, Fig. 10.11. An opaque tube is slipped over the glass tube, the former having a series of six to ten apertures of about $\frac{1}{8}$ inch diameter so arranged that the light of a lamp *L*, when passing through the tubes, is intersected in as many single beams as there are apertures. A cylindrical lens *CL* will provide a uniform illumination of the tubes. Bubbles will ascend to the top of the gas relay which in this case is the tube and will, in passing through the tube, interrupt each light beam. If the photosensitor is circuited in an A.C. amplifier the modulated light beam can be made to operate a relay.

A fire and flame detector was designed by P. B. Weisz using the characteristic ultra-violet (*2537* A.U.) radiation as energizing agent (*1603*).

For smoke control as an aid to correct combustion cf. Chap. 15. The photo-electric protection of a gas line was described by J. A. Setter (*1689*).

Bibliography Reference (*1964; 2170*)

10.9. Protection of Sightless Machine Operators

J. O. Kleber of the American Foundation for the Blind has developed a photo-electric safety control for electric sewing machines to assist

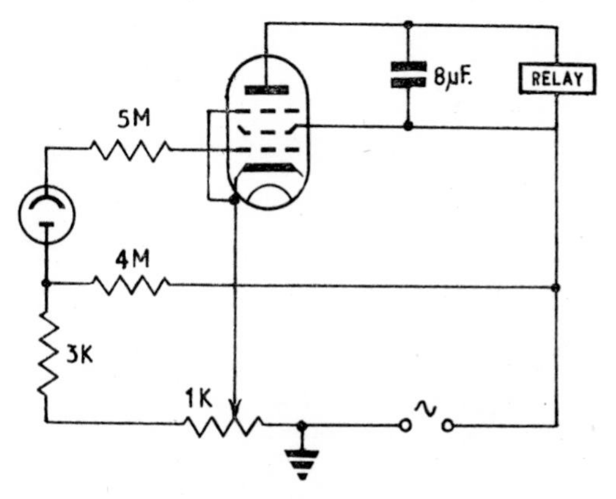

Fig. 10.12. Circuit of protective relay for blind operators.

blind people in their work and, at the same time to protect their fingers from being injured by the needle (*749*). The circuit used is shown in Fig. 10.12 and the relay is so arranged that it closes whenever the light ray is off the cell.

The technique employed in the case of sightless machine operators differs from the one employed when protecting workers with normal sight. When protecting the latter, the distance between the dangerous object or the danger spot (the needle of the sewing machine, the rolls of calenders, etc.) and the light ray is relatively large. The case of the blind worker, however, demands this safety space to be reduced in order to allow his fingers to come as close as possible to the spot where the actual operation takes place and yet to guarantee him absolute freedom from possible injury. It is obvious that the above principle can be applied to any type of machine provided that suitable modifications are considered.

Another sensory aid for the blind uses the principle of reflexion (*2462*), and other methods (*2611*).

10.10. Intrusion Detector

The protection of property is not always a violation of the principles of J. J. Rousseau, solely guided by " selfish interests " ; on the contrary it is very often in the public interest that property must be safe-

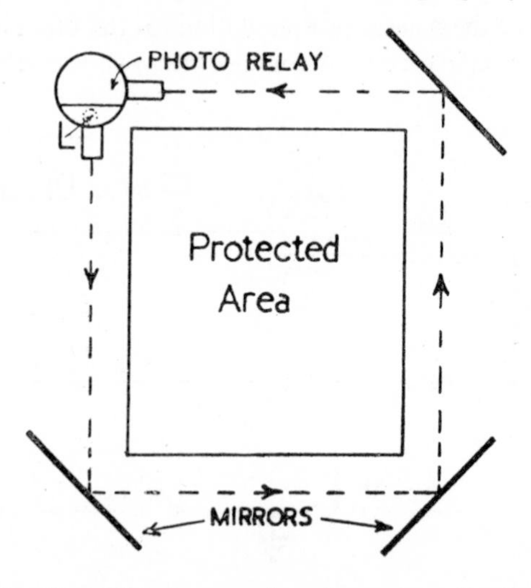

Fig. 10.13. Photo-electric protection of an area against intruders.

guarded. Precious stones for industrial applications, expensive tools, laboratories, safes, entire plants, are protected against intruders by two different methods, viz., boundary protection, Fig. 10.13, and area protection, Fig. 10.14. In both cases the use of a non-luminous, in particular of an infra-red light source is advisable since it might not be in the interest of complete safety to advertise the presence of protective devices by using beams of luminous radiation. If, in the former instance, a beam of modulated radiation is thrown around the object or room or building, the whole set-up is complicated by the use of a modulator,

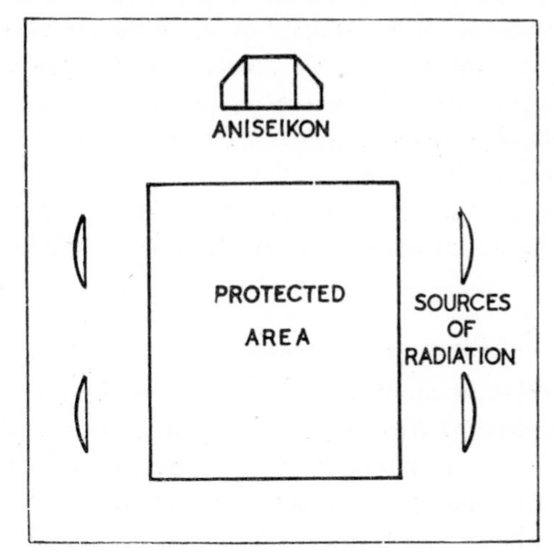

Fig. 10.14. Non-luminous protective system with aniseikon.

but the receiving unit and amplifier being designed for A.C. amplification are much simpler and safer in operation than a D.C. amplifier.

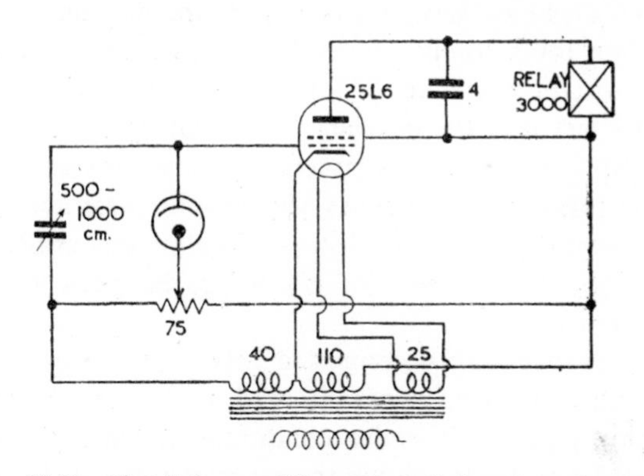

Fig. 10.15. Circuit for amplifier with static beam on photo-cell.

A further advantage may be seen in that the fluctuations and variations in the intensity of the daylight do not influence the photosensitor if modulated radiation is used. (cf. Chap. 7.)

For the amplification of a static beam of radiant energy the circuit (*750*) of Fig. 10.15 will give satisfaction. The D.C. output of the photosensitor is amplified by the 25L6. The variable capacitor and variable resistor permit of controlling the sensitivity of the circuit.

Area protection is easily obtained by using the aniseikonic principle. No rays are thrown around the object, but for good irradiation a number of (infra-red) light sources is provided. They must be well concealed behind infra-red filters (cf. Chap. 9) and mounted in light-tight luminaires on high masts.

The detection of an intruder can be utilized to sound an alarm, switch on the lights or even take an infra-red photograph of the intruder.

Bibliography References: (*1192, 1197, 1775, 1925, 1964, 2195, 2232, 2387*)

10.11. Control of Electrostatic Discharges

There is a certain number of industrial processes where static discharges are caused by friction. After a period necessary for the accumulation of a sufficiently high charge, the sparking potential is reached and the discharge takes place. Electrostatic charges are often originated by the friction between a transmission belt or rope and its pulley or in chemical works, for instance, between the rollers of medical plaster spreaders and the sticky rubber compound. The latter case deserves attention, because the air in the machine, being saturated with benzine or other inflammable vapours, often is ignited to the detriment of the machine and explodes, seriously damaging the machinery and holding up production for a comparatively long period. If protective devices of the rake or comb type are of little or no avail advantage should be taken of the fact that the discharge potential becomes reduced when the spark gap is enclosed in a practically exhausted atmosphere. The atmospheric pressure in the spark gap should preferably be identical with the critical degree of exhaustion. For air this critical value is a pressure of less than 1 mm. of Hg when the electrodes are about 465 mm. apart.

The vacuum spark-gap is connected between the source of the static electricity and earth, i.e., in parallel with the natural path of the discharge taking place in it under conditions which are insufficient to allow a spark to bridge the gap in the external atmosphere. A luminous glow will fill the discharge tube. A photo-relay detects this phenomenon and either gives a signal to the machine operator or automatically switches on an additional exhaust fan to clear the machine of obnoxious or explosive fumes.

Arrangements can also be made to signal to the engineer the sparking of a commutator and thus prevent the commutator from being burned.

Another interesting arrangement is based on the afore-mentioned static discharge. The vertical radiators of transmitting stations collect static charges which from time to time discharge through a spark gap to the ground. The power of the generator plant follows the spark through the ionized gap to the ground and remains connected to earth through this short-circuit, thereby interrupting the transmission. In 1934, a photo-relay was first installed at WLW Cincinnati Transmitting Station (*751*) in order to watch the gap for discharge sparks. When energized by the light of the spark the power of the generating plant is shut off and, is restored again after the gap has been de-ionized by the natural air currents.

Bibliography References: (*1376*, *1856*, *1944*, *2282*)

10.12. Detection of Noxious Gases and Vapours

The detection and quantitative determination or indication of toxic gases is not only prescribed by law,* but also is in the interest of both workmen and management. Noxious gases are very often the unavoidable by-products of industrial processes which, in themselves, are quite harmless. A large number of chemical plants are utilizing processes involving either the use or the production of a toxic gas or toxic liquid, some of the latter having a very low boiling point so that volatilization takes place at ordinary room temperatures, a fact which the workman accepts for organic solvents rather than for mercury. In the mining industry most hazards occur through explosions, methane being the dreaded and most dangerous ingredient of fire damp.

In a number of pamphlets the Department of Scientific and Industrial Research has laid down standard methods and apparatus for the detection of toxic gases in industry (*752*). The official methods may be altered, for instance, " by means of a comparator using coloured glasses as standard, of a photo-electric colorimeter, or of an optical densitometer. . . ." Coloured glass disks showing colour standards and percentages of gas content in air by a number of steps, are available.†

The sensitivity of chemical detection methods varies from one to a hundred p.p.m. according to the type of gas. Although individual

* In England, the Chemical Works Regulations, 1922 (regulation 7), made under Section 79 of the Factory and Workshop Act, 1901, covers the ground.

† The Tintometer, Ltd., The Colour Laboratory, Milford, Salisbury, England.

workers, as a result of their physiological constitution, can stand different quantities of noxious gases before experiencing serious trouble, the average man will stand up well to the average figures in Table 10.1. The "Threshold Value of Pathological Sensitivity" (*1267, 1268*), i.e., the lower limit of irritation, represents that concentration of a noxious gas which, after several hours exposure to it, causes but slight symptoms. This minimum concentration is, however, active enough to cause an irritation or painful sensation in its characteristic manner. The chemical methods do not lend themselves to checking continuously and automatically the contents of noxious gases in air, as the indicating agent is not reversible and must be replaced after every indication.

TABLE 10.1

Lower Limit of Irritation (Threshold Value of Pathological Sensitivity).

(A short analysis of the physiological effects of noxious gases on the human system is given by J. B. S. Haldane and J. I. Graham (*753 ; pp. 153, sqq.*)).

Gas or Vapour	Aniline $C_6H_5NH_2$	Arsine AsH_3	Benzene C_6H_6	Carbon bisulphide CS_2	Carbon monoxide CO	Chlorine Cl
Pts. by Volume 1 : mg./litre	200,000 0·02	250,000 0·013	10,000 0·35	120,000 0·025	12,000 0·008	1,000,000 0·003
Limit of Detection p.p.m.	0·3		1·2	12, 2		
Photo-electric Method of Detection				(*769, 756*)		
Number of Steps in Lovibond Colour Disk			1			

Gas or Vapour	Hydrogen cyanide HCN	Hydrogen sulphide H_2S	Nitrous fumes (N...)	Phosgene $COCl_2$	Sulphur dioxide SO_2	Carbon dioxide CO_2	Mercury Hg
Pts. by Volume 1 : mg./litre	100,000 0·012	150,000 0·0101	100,000 0·03	1,000,000 0·004	100,000 0·03		2×10^7 $7{\cdot}7 \times 10^7$ 0·00025 0·0001 (*1609*)
Limit of Detection p.p.m.		8		5		100	0·004
Photo-electric Method of Detection	(*771*)	(*770*)	(*772, 773*)			(*774, 775*)	(*707, 768*)
Number of Steps in Lovibond Colour Disk	6, 4	4	1		4		

Physical methods are the basis *par excellence* of automatic detection. A photo-cell absorption analyzer has been devised by V. F. Hanson

(*754*, *755*) and adapted by S. Silverman (*756*, *757*) for the detection of carbon bisulphide. The range of concentrations covered is 2 to 200 p.p.m. by volume, and the time required for an individual determination usually is less than 60 seconds with an accuracy of 1 per cent. If continuously run with a resolving power of 5 to 10 seconds the accuracy will approach 4 p.p.m. The circuit used by Silverman is shown in Fig. 10.16. The light source is a mercury quartz burner and the photocells are of the sodium type.

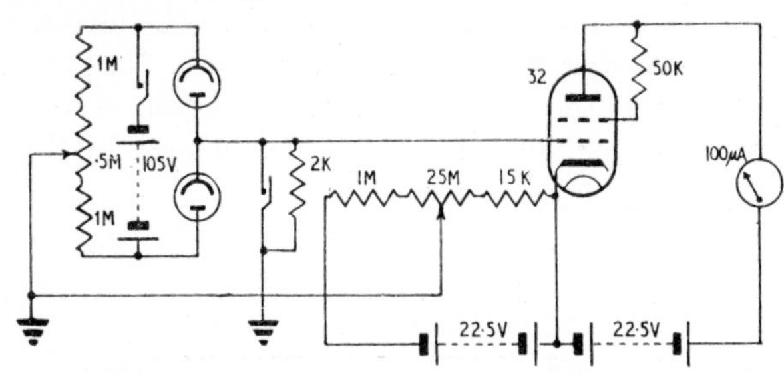

Fig. 10.16. Circuit for the detection of carbon bisulphide.

The physical method is based on the absorption by the gas of radiant energy of certain wavelengths which are characteristic for a certain gas, thus making the method a specific detection. An interesting and very effective method and apparatus for recording the results of

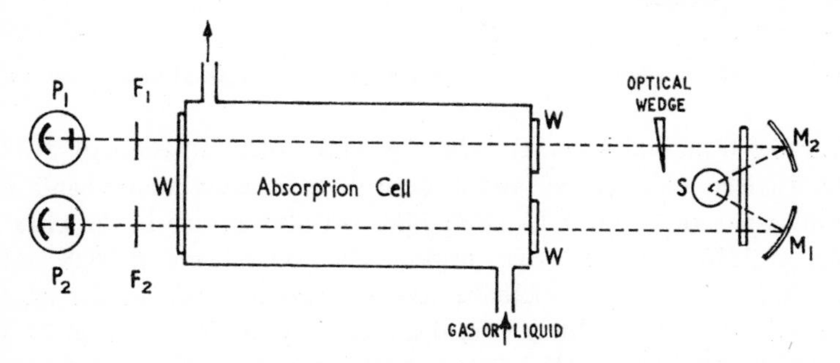

Fig. 10.17. Photo-cell absorption analyzer for carbon bisulphide detection.

gas analyses was developed for the infra-red region (*775*). The optical section of the instrument is shown in Fig. 10.17, adapted for use with photosensitors. The original instrument works with bolometers. If the source *S* emits in the infra-red, the windows *W* may be made from silver chloride, lithium fluoride, sodium fluoride, or quartz: for ultra-violet radiation quartz will be used. When gas, absorbing in the wavelength region transmitted by filter F_2, but not transmitted by filter F_1, enters the absorption cell the bridge is unbalanced. The unbalance voltage is then amplified and recorded.

The circuit can be so modified as to introduce two sources of radiant energy, Fig. 10.18. The one, S_1 for instance, emits its energy on a narrow band centring at λ A.U. which peak is identical with or very close to the absorption band of the gas to be detected. The other source S_2 must not emit within the range of S_1. A suitable two-cell circuit is then balanced if no absorption takes place. The presence of a trace of the suspected gas will unbalance the circuit. The windows, filters, sources, and photosensitors must be adapted to the optical characteristics of that particular gas.

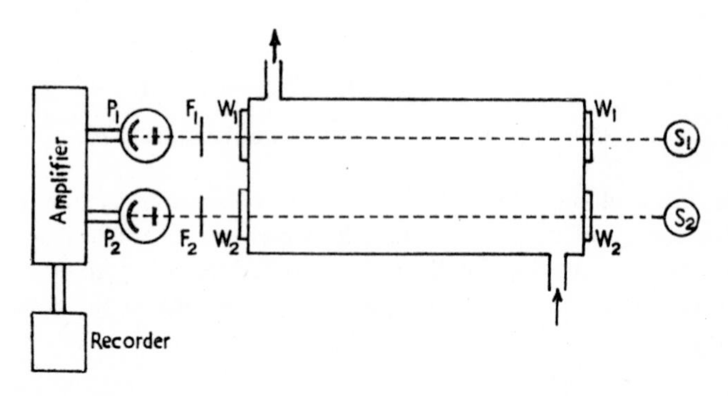

Fig. 10.18. Modification of optical arrangement for two radiant energy sources.

Carbon bisulphide strongly absorbs ultra-violet radiation of 3132 A.U. wavelength ; benzene and its derivatives have an intense band in the infra-red at 14,800 A.U. (*758*, *759*), but also absorb in the ultra-violet at 2590 and 2601 A.U., respectively, and toluene at 2628 and 2668 A.U. (*776*, *777*) ; methane has absorption bands in the near infra-red (*760*), New bands were discovered by W. H. J. Childs *761*) and W. V. Norris and H. J. Unger (*762*), but absorption was found neither in the near and middle ultra-violet (*763*), nor in the luminous region nor in the far ultra-violet (*764*) down to 1965 A.U. In the still remoter region of from 1450 to 850 A.U., Duncan and Howe (*765*) found the absorption spectrum of methane to be continuous. Mercury vapour has many absorption bands in the far ultra-violet (*766*), for instance at 1850, 1807, 1694, 1403 A.U. and a very intense absorption line at 2537 A.U. The French Patent 632396 is based on the principles of spectral analysis and quotes the following characteristic regions of absorption in various vapours.

TABLE 10.2

Vapour	Characteristic absorption region
benzene	2300 to 2680 A.U.
phenol	2350 to 2780 A.U.
aniline	2600 to 3000 A.U.
carbon bisulphide	2800 to 3650 A.U.
formaldehyde	2700 to 3500 A.U.
methane	1600 to 1800 A.U.
carbon dioxide	1450 to 1750 A.U.

The photo-electric gas detector often utilizes the fact that gases and vapours are less transparent to infra-red radiation than is air (*767*). (cf. Chap. 14.)

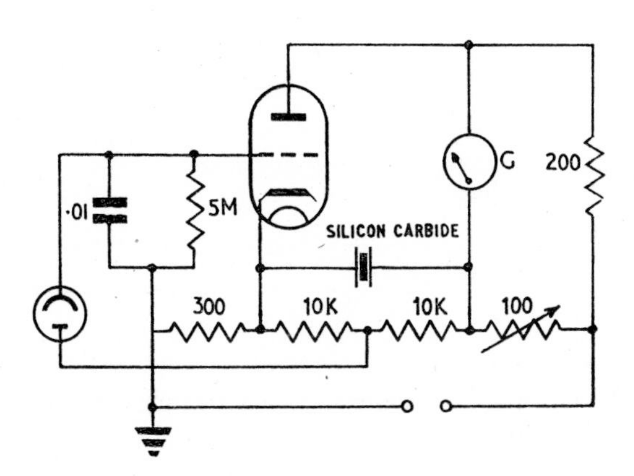

Fig. 10.19.

Behrens described how a laboratory method using a non-reversible moist indicator can be adapted for continuous indication in industrial practice in the case of hydrogen sulphide. The usual method employs moistened lead paper which when brought into contact with hydrogen sulphide turns black. This change is readily translated by a photo-sensitor into alarm signals, etc. Lead-paper must not be dry or it will lose sensitivity (*778*). Behrens (*770*) uses a strip of paper, similar to ticker tape, soaked in lead-acetate $Pb(OAc)_2$, the strip moving slowly and continuously, or by steps, in a stream of air between the light source and a photo-relay. The formation of black PbS affects the illumination of the photosensitor.

Chemical detectors for various gases are listed in Table 10.3.

TABLE 10.3

Gas or Vapour	Chemical Detector	Reaction paper in the presence of gas
CO		
in traces	solution of palladium chloride	turns black
in quantities	ammoniacal sol. of AgOH	black precipitate
Cl_2	solution of silver nitrate	turns black
	fluorescein paper	turns red
	o-tolidine in HCl	turns orange-red
SO_2	blue litmus	turns red
H_2S	lead acetate	turns black
PH_3	solution of $AgNO_3$	turns black
$COCl_2$	p-dimethylamino benzaldehyde-diphenylamine	turns yellow
Hg	activated selenium sulphide (yellow) (*779, 799*)	turns black

Lester and Ordung (*771*) describe an elegant method for the detection of hydrogen cyanide in air by means of a self-contained, portable detector, capable of detecting 10 p.p.m. HCN. The photo-electric instrument uses methaemoglobin as the reagent (*780*). Another highly sensitive circuit, Fig. 10.19, is applicable to the detection of all those gases or vapours which have no natural spectral absorption band overlying the resonance line of the mercury vapour discharge lamp (2537 A.U.) which is used as a light source. Hydrogen, oxygen, nitrogen, ammonia, and water vapour can be tested. Ozone does not conform to the above stipulation ; it must not even contaminate any of the gases under examination. (cf. Table 10.2.)

The absorption analyzer, as patented by V. F. Hanson (*754, 755*) operates at the following sensitivities, viz. :

TABLE 10.4

	p.p.m.		p.p.m.
Mercury (approx.)	0·0001	Phosgene	5·0
Tetraethyl lead	0·13	Acetone	5·0
Xylene	0·2	Ethylbenzene	5·0
Monochlorobenzene	0·3	Pentachlorethane	7·0
Aniline vapour	0·3	Hydrogen sulphide	8·0
Perchlorethylene	0·5	Trichlorethylene	10·0
Toluene	1·0	Carbon bisulphide	12·0
Benzene	1·2	*n*-heptane	25·0
Vinyl acetylene	2·0	Gasoline	50·0

Reactions with chlorinated hydrocarbon vapours are given in a booklet published by the Air Hygiene Foundation of America (*786*). There are few chemical reactions between benzene vapours C_6H_6 (i.e. benzol in the States and on the European Continent) and an indicator : the indicator mostly used is formaldehyde in sulphuric acid giving a red coloration of varying saturation (*752, 787, 788*).

British Standard 2740 : 1956 describes simple smoke alarms and alarm metering devices. These instruments are designed to give an alarm when the emission of black or grey smoke exceeds a chosen Ringelmann shade.

***Bibliography References*:** (*407, 415, 429, 440, 469, 1228, 1500, 1842, 1971*)

CHAPTER 11

PRODUCTION CONTROL

It is difficult to classify and subdivide the available matter and to select the correct instances here more than in any other chapter of this book. The quoted applications are typical of a group rather than of individual cases. The method of continuously measuring the diameter of wire is also applicable to yarn ; that of controlling the feed of brass rods into automatic machines is easily adaptable to controlling the feed of pulverized coal to the burner head, etc. The arrangement of the various sub-sections will, therefore, lack somewhat in uniformity, a defect of which the author is fully aware and asks the indulgence of the reader.

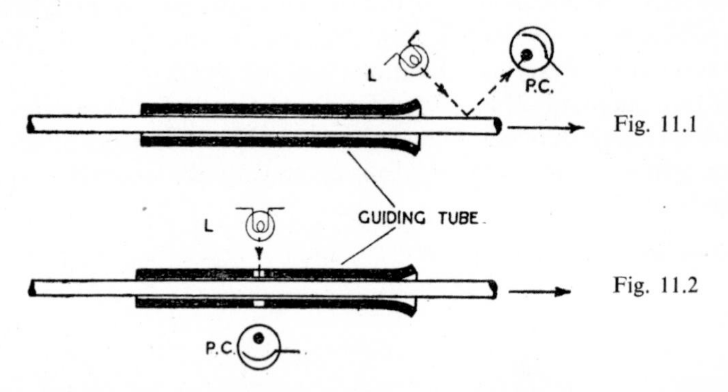

Fig. 11.1. Feed control by reflexion can indicate a stoppage in the flow of material.
Fig. 11.2. Photo-electric feed control: the light passes to the cell when the flow of material ceases.

11.1. Feeder Control

Any material which is fed in rods or wires to a lathe can be made to indicate when all of it has been used up and also when no new material is fed to the machine by a fault in the feeding mechanism, Fig. 11.2. If control by reflexion is employed, Fig. 11.1, then not only might the missing of new supplies be detected but also a stoppage in the feed.

The rods or wires have no clean surface but are mottled with stains of rust, dirt, and grease. The steady light ray from a lamp *L* will therefore be modulated but have no set frequency. The photo-electric circuit, if designed with a capacitor in the grid circuit of the amplifier valve (cf. Chap. 23, Fig. 28d), will amplify only the A.C. output of the photosensitor ; with steady light on the cell, as caused by a stopping rod, the circuit does not respond.

Bibliography References : (*1185, 1729, 1776, 1777, 1778, 1798, 1807, 1808, 1811, 1817, 1819, 1825, 1827, 1833, 1840, 1848, 1882, 1906, 1918, 1967, 1976, 1980, 1984, 2058, 2071, 2072, 2081, 2091, 2094, 2112, 2116, 2149, 2151, 2157, 2190, 2245, 2247, 2251, 2254, 2255, 2256, 2266, 2268, 2401, pp. 113, 118*)

11.2. Textile Machines

In textile and other machines (*943*) it is essential to stop the driving motor when the thread or web breaks. The photo-electric stopper for textile machines (*1405*) uses a small aluminium or plastic shield threaded

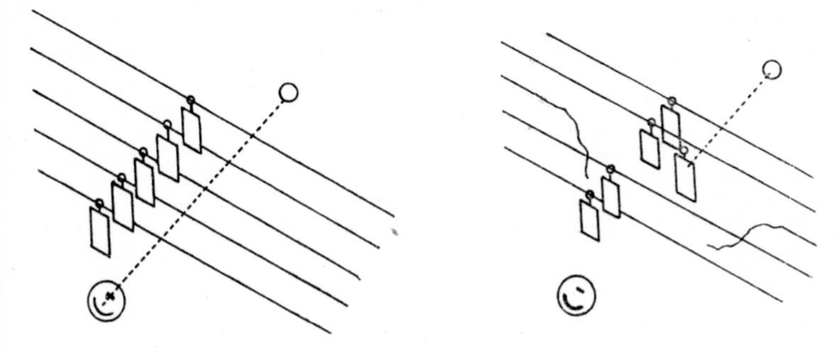

Fig. 11.3. Photo-electric stopper for textile machines, operating by breakage of threads.

on to each individual thread. When this breaks the shield either drops or is lowered by the thread, but in each case interrupts a light ray, thereby energizing a photo-relay. Long banks of such shields can be mounted within the path of vision of one photosensitor, Fig. 11.3.

A photo-electric yarn tester (*949*) makes use of an arc of Dow metal* as an indicator. This arc swings between the light source and a photosensitor transforming the constant light beam into a number of impulses

* Dow metal is the trade name of a group of magnesium alloys manufactured by Dow Chemicals. These alloys generally contain over 85% of magnesium and have a specific gravity of 1·8 (aluminium 2·7).

which is correlated to the number of holes in the arc, Fig. 11.4. A uniselector switch moves according to the number of impulses received and actuates a recorder.

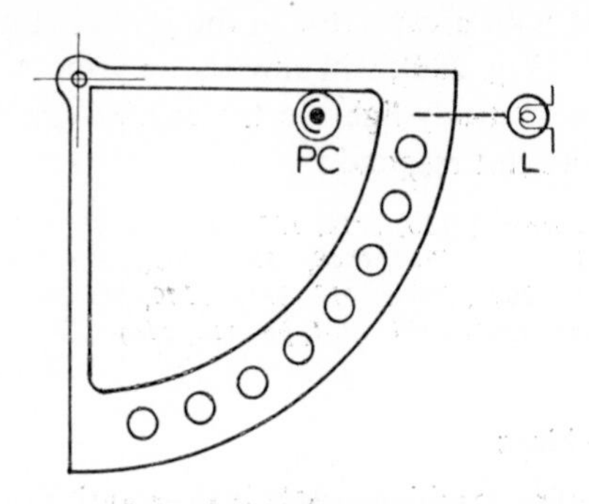

Fig. 11.4. Light metal indicator for yarn testing.

An autographic load-elongation recorder for testing single textile (or other) fibres has been described by Sookne and Rutherford (*950*) who used a magnetically damped analytical balance with "chainomatic" control to provide a constant rate of loading and so of elongation.

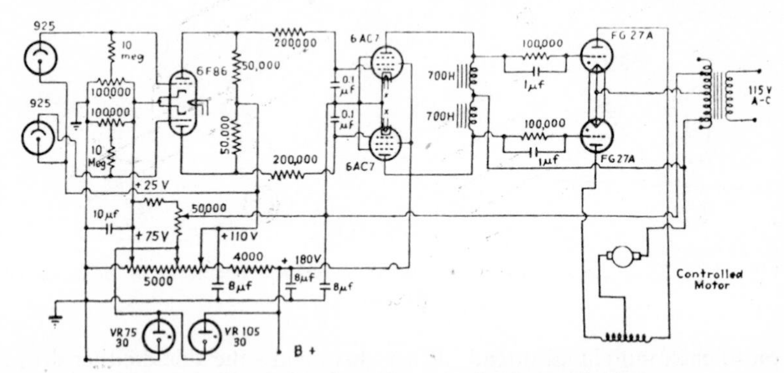

Fig. 11.5. Circuit for elongation recorder for textile fibres.

The circuit used is shown in Fig. 11.5. An assembly for automatically measuring the rate at which metal flows when heated under stress creep uses two identical glass grids ruled with opaque horizontal lines 1/250 inch apart. At the outset of the investigation the glass grids are so arranged that the respective rules coincide. Light from a lamp is therefore transmitted and strikes a photosensitor (*1121*). The one grid is fixed ; the other, which is fastened to the wire or rod under test, will move according to the elongation. The transmitted light will show fluctuations in intensity which are recorded by the photosensitor and permit of being interpreted in terms of elongation (*1294*). The principle of the two identical grids has also been used in turbidimetric work (*442*) and in measuring mechanical vibrations, (cf. Chap. 18.15.)

Bibliography References: (*547*, *567*, *1121*, *1180*, *1720*, *1798*, *1813*, *1816*, *1817*, *1821*, *1825*, *1863*, *1900*, *1901*, *1920*, *1928*, *1936*, *1939*, *1976*, *1980*, *1990*, *1991*, *2015*, *2016*, *2017*, *2021*, *2258*).

11.3. Loop Control

In many instances loops of material must be maintained between the reel and the cutting table. This method of control can be applied to a variety of materials such as fabric, steel strip (*945*), rubber (*944*), paper, and others. In the case or rubber sheeting, three photosensitors are used, Fig. 11.6. The lower, *PC*, stops the pay-off-reel motor if the loop approaches the floor below a safe distance. As

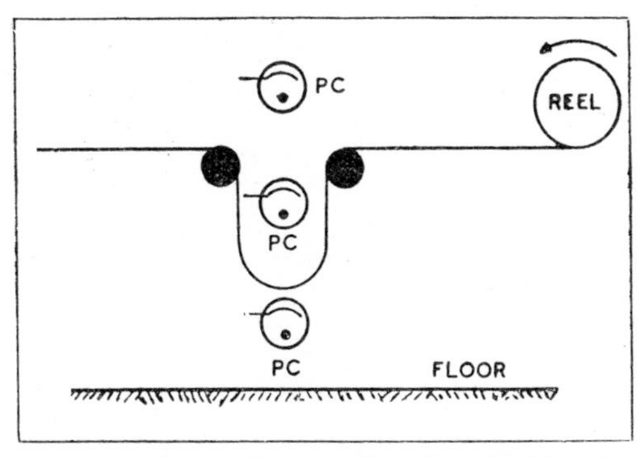

Fig. 11.6. Three photo-cells controlling flow of rubber sheeting.

the rubber stretches it will reach *PC* and restart the reeling motor. The photosensitor *PC* on the top immediately stops the whole machinery, i.e., reel and conveyor, if the sheet breaks and, being caught in the reel, sweeps around into the air. The same end can be achieved with one photosensitor if the loop is arranged to obscure one half of the photo-cathode if in its normal position. When the loop lengthens it will totally obscure the photosensitor, but will permit the full light beam to strike the cell if the loop shortens. Two separate motors can be made to operate different sections of the conveyor system to slow down or speed up the feed of the material and thus maintain the loop at its correct length.

Bibliography Reference: (*1923*)

11.4. Optical and Photographic Industry

Amongst the many standard applications in these industries some newly developed methods are of outstanding interest and importance.

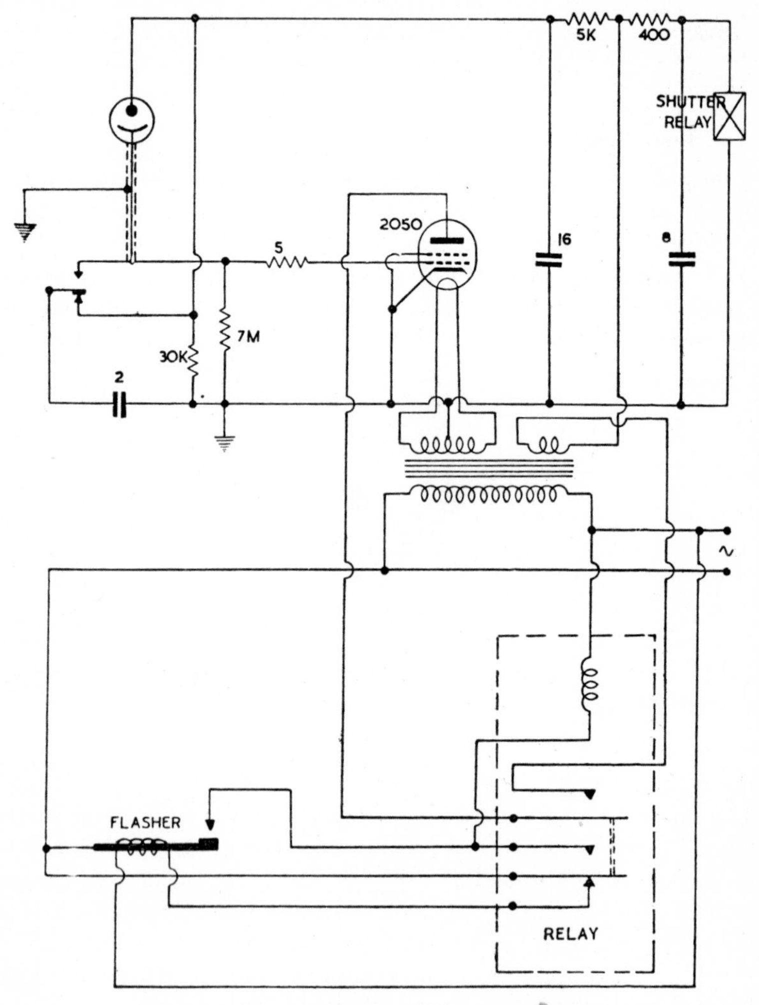

Fig. 11.7. Circuit of photo-electric shutter tester.

Optical lenses are coated with magnesium fluoride in order to reduce reflexion from the surface of the lens. A photo-electric instrument is used to measure the diminishing intensity of reflected light. The instrument also indicates the end-point of the coating process (*946*). This method is applicable also to measuring the film (1/200,000 inch thick) which is applied to finished plastic lenses for the same reason (*1276*).

The stop values of lenses are determined photo-electrically and are correct, stop for stop, regardless of the design and construction of the lens. In the United States this process is well on the way to be adopted as national standard procedure for calibrating lenses (*946*, *1604*, *1687*).

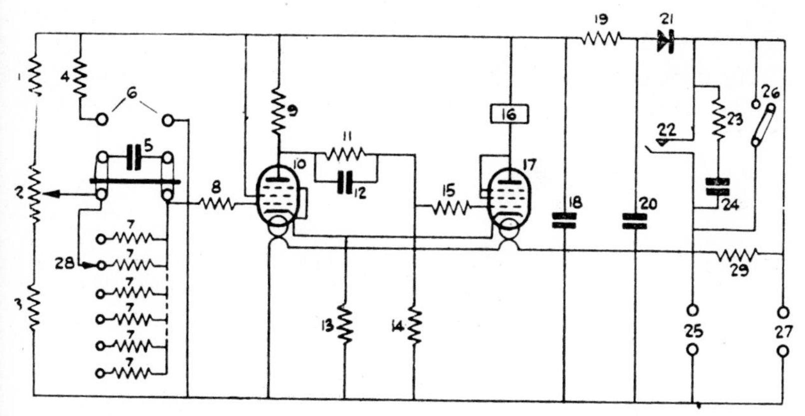

Fig. 11.8. Circuit for photo-electric photographic exposure control.

In the photographic industry the process of recovering the silver precipitated in the hypo-bath is too well known to need description (*572*, *79*, *p. 350*; *2453*). A photo-electric contact black and white printer control is described by Penther and Weiske (*948*) and a control for colour printing by J. Robins and L. E. Varden (*1465*). Once the correct printing time has been determined (for methods and instruments cf. Chap. 14) for a given negative, the circuit ensures that all prints made from that negative will have uniform density regardless of variations in lamp intensity due to changes in filament temperature.

A circuit for photographic exposure control is shown in Fig. 11.8. The exposure is proportional to both the intensity of light and time. The photo-cell is so placed that it receives light which has been reflected from the subject matter that is going to be photographed. This automatically takes into account any variations in light intensity which might be due to the deterioration of the lamps, reflectors, differences in distance, etc. A complete cycle is started by a press button. At the end of the cycle, either the camera shutter is closed or the studio lights turned off. In the manufacture of photographic cameras the electronic shutter-tester (*1416*, *1686*) is of great value Fig. 11.7.

A photo-electric exposure meter for photomicrography is described by Alder (*2602*) and others (*2603*, *2605*) and for industrial radiography by Dighton & Herz (*2600*). Automatic exposure control is discussed by Bruck *et al.* (*2604*).

Bibliography References : (*572*, *1206*, *1338*, *1368*, *1782*, *1818*, *1852*, *1862*, *1908*, *1911*, *1917*, *1933*, *1951*, *1959*, *2018*, *2289*).

11.5. Printing Presses

The damage done to printing presses by breakage of the paper web can be averted by using the web as a diaphragm between a light source

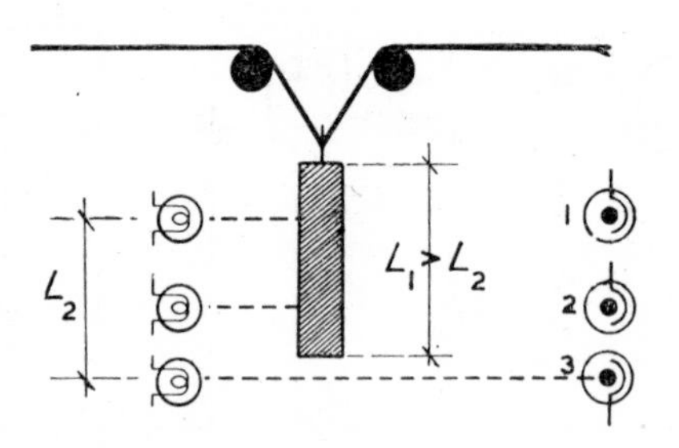

Fig. 11.9. Photo-cells arranged to maintain constant tension.

and a photo-relay. When the web breaks it wraps around the printing cylinder, causing damage to it. The photo-relay must be of the quick-acting type and the cycle of " seeing " the broken web and stopping the printing press must need less time than it takes the broken web to reach the printing cylinder. If the equipment is to work on the reflexion principle, difficulties may be encountered if the web is of low reflectivity, for instance, if it is brown paper. If the paper breaks, some exposed part of the machinery may have a very outstanding stray reflexion which can be used to energize the photo-relay. Aniseikonic detection (cf. Chap. 10) which does not depend on differences in reflexion but actually " sees " the object (*85*), is an essential and reliable method.

Bibliography References : (*548*, *1177*, *1180*, *1194*, *1761*, *1794*, *1795*, *1823*, *1845*, *1847*, *1881*, *1899*, *1906*, *1910*, *1918*, *1928*, *1929*, *1955*, *2035*).

11.6. Tension Control

The system indicated in Fig. 11.6 can be adapted to keep the tension of wire, rope, yarn, etc., constant. A weight carried by the material, Fig. 11.9, fulfils two tasks : firstly, it keeps the material under tension, and secondly, it acts as a target eclipsing one or a number of light pencils. The photo-relays are wired as instanced in Fig. 11.10. Eclipsing the photo-relays 1 and 2 means that the tension is at its correct value. If only relay 1 is obscured the tension is too big;

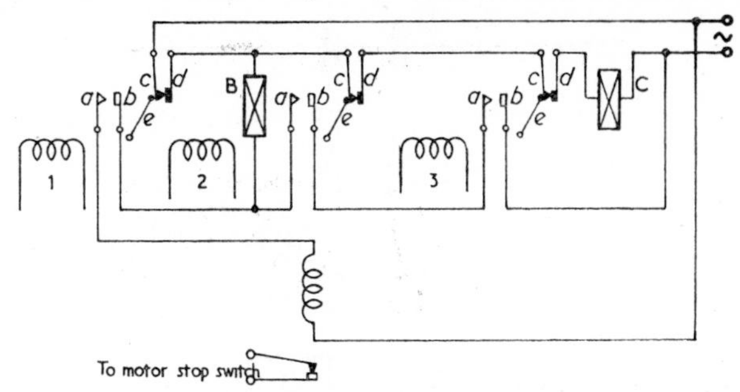

Fig. 11.10. Schematic of tension control equipment (see text).

if all three light sources are eclipsed the tension is too small. If the tension has been much too high and might result in breakage, all three photo-relays are energized at once and the machine is stopped.

Photo-relays eclipsed	Tension	Action	Gear
1 + 2	correct	none	A
1	too big	release	B
1 + 2 + 3	too small	increase	C
none	none or dangerous	stop	D

The circuits for the various actions are as follows where 1, 2 and 3 are the coils of the photo-relays. If the photosensitor of a relay is eclipsed the armature *e* keeps the contacts *c*, *d* closed and *a*, *b* open.

Circuit	Gear is energized
$R - c_1d_1 - c_2d_2 - \ldots (c_3d_3$ open)	none; no closed circuit
$R - c_1d_1 - B - a_2b_2 - a_3b_3 - S$	B
$R - c_1d_1 - c_2d_2 - c_3d_3 - C - S$	C
$R - D - a_1b_1 - a_2b_2 - a_3b_3 - S$	D

Bibliography References: (*1727, 1901*)

11.7. Thickness Control

The thickness of wire can be checked continuously and too thin or too thick material marked and rejected by the layout shown in Fig. 11.11. The wire moves between four guiding reels which are no more

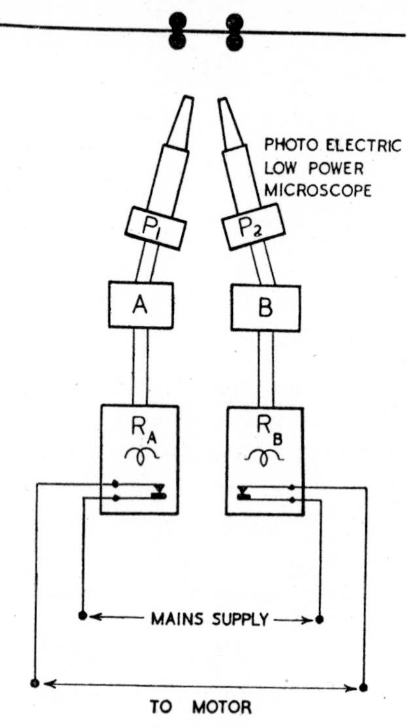

Fig. 11.11. Photo-electric microscope for continuous checking of wire or yarn thickness.

than about ½ inch apart in order to warrant a fixed position of the wire under observation. A low-power binocular microscope is used to project the image of the wire on to the photosensitors P_1 and P_2. The one circuit, P_1, for instance, is wired for negative action (cf. Chap. 5), the other, P_2, for positive action. The sensitive area of the photosensitor in the negative circuit must be identical in size and shape with the image of the piece of wire under inspection. The cathode area of the other photosensitor must be as wide as would be the image of a wire of maximum tolerable thickness. Following these two conditions the illumination on the photosensitors, and the consequent relay actions, are :

Diameter of wire	Photosensitors P_1	Photosensitors P_2	Relay A (neg.)	Contacts	Relay B (pos.)	Contacts	Motor circuit
normal	obscured 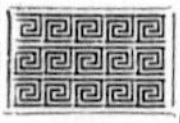	illumin. 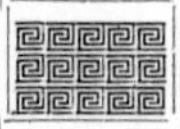	current	closed	current	closed	closed
too thin	illumin. 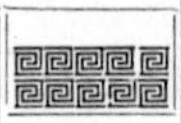	illumin. 	no current	open	current	closed	open
too thick	obscured 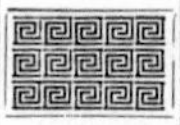	obscured 	current	closed	no current	open	open

Any type of microscope will do as long as the working distance, i.e., the distance of the object lens from the wire, is such as to suit the individual circumstances. Working distances may range from 50 to 120 mm. with corresponding magnifications of from 50 to 4 according to the optical system (cf. Chap. 18). Indirect electronic micrometers measure the shadow of thin wires (*1671*).

The photo-relays must be of the quick-acting type. The usual speed of fine wire drawing is 800 to 1200 ft.p.m. At the Spencer Wire Co. (U.S.A.) this speed has been increased to between 2000 and 2500 ft.p.m. If an irregularity extends over a length of 3 ft. the photo-sensitors will receive a light impulse lasting only 0·07 sec.

The thickness of textile fibres can be determined by different methods, one of which makes use of notched frames, the number of notches varying with the thickness of the thread (*212, p. 235*). The standard yarn is wound on one frame and the specimen yarn on another, both frames having the same number of notches. The tightly wound frames are used as an optical filter, the variation in the transmittance of the frame as a whole being a measure of the diameter of the single thread. This method is applicable to any type of yarn since only the proportion of the light transmitted between the individual threads is measured. Obviously a light source of low intensity must be used in order to prevent the material from becoming translucent. If coloured material is to be examined in this way the light source should emit monochromatic radiation of a wavelength which is complementary to the colour of the fibre. The checking of air-conditioning filters for impurities (dirt, dust) is carried out on a similar basis (*1417*).

Bibliography References : (*1720*, *1727*, *1779*, *1849*, *1850*, *1974*)

11.8. Transport Band Control

Finished articles rolling off the production line may be large objects like cars which it is easy to supervise, or they may be small articles made in tens of thousands per hour, for instance, envelopes, paper bags, etc. Stoppage of the transport mechanism can spoil a large proportion of the output if the production of the machine is not stopped instantly. The machine must be clear of the one finished article before the next one is released. Since one object follows the other at a certain distance, two photosensitors can be arranged to supervise an inclined plane or part of a conveyor belt so that the one photosensitor is always covered by one object when the other photosensitor is not obstructed. One photosensitor (P_1) is wired for positive, the other (P_2) for negative action, and the amplifiers supply time-delay relays which in turn control the power relays. The circuit of the motor control switch is so connected with the contacts of the relays that the motor is stopped when either P_1 is not obscured or P_2 is eclipsed for a period greater than the temporal distance between two adjacent objects passing a given point. The negative action photosensitor is mounted close to the machine, the positive-action photosensitor close to the assembly table or packing table. The time delay must be greater than the temporal distance between two adjacent objects. If five objects are delivered per second then the delay will be $\frac{1}{4}$ sec.

Bibliography References : (*1777*, *1819*, *2144*, *2165*)

11.9. Control of Fluid Flow

The position of a float in a tapered transparent tube is controlled by two light beams, the one being projected across the top of the float, the other across the lower end of it (*951*). The light rays strike two photosensitors which are connected in parallel, Fig. 11.12. As the float moves the illumination on either the one or the other photosensitor is altered, the change energizing the valve motor which is reversible and runs at full torque all the time. Other features of the instrument, which was developed by the Brooke Engineering Co., are a lock-in circuit indicating the direction in which the float has moved if, as the result of a surge in the fluid, it has left the light beams ; anti-hunt compensation will control the speed of the motor proportional to the instantaneous distance of the float from its neutral position ; automatic shut-down of the machinery if breakage or failure of any essential part of the circuit occurs. (cf. Chap. 22).

Bibliography References : (*502*, *1128*, *1868*, *1956*, *2011*, *2045*, *2189*)

11.10. Control of Spray Guns

In spray shops where mass-produced objects, for instance, car bodies, receiver cabinets, etc., are continuously passing through it is essential for the spray guns to be stopped when the one article has been sprayed, and started again when the next object has moved into position. Although the time interval may be only a few or even

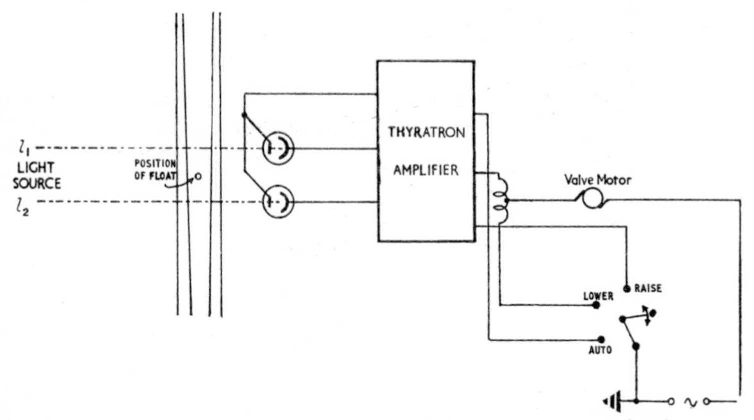

Fig. 11.12. Schematic circuit for the control of fluid flow—*Brooke Engineering Co.*

fractions of a second, in the aggregate the amount of paint saved by this method is an economic detail which cannot be overlooked. This control is achieved by the object interrupting the controlling light beam upon entering the range of the spray gun. The gun is switched on by the action of the obscured photo-relay and it is switched off again when the object has passed and the light beam is admitted to the photosensitor. If a two-colour spray is used another photosensitor and light source are stationed at the correct point where, when the object passes, another spray gun begins to coat the object with the second colour.

Bibliography References : (*1774, 1871, 2021*)

11.11. Measuring Steel Plate

The width of red-hot steel plate can be measured from a safe distance (20 ft.) by a method devised by E. D. Wilson (*954*). A system of mirrors is arranged, Fig. 11.13, to reflect the image of the moving hot steel plate on to the " measuring mirror ". The image of five white lines on a black cardboard is projected on to the same mirror as a reference and superimposed on the image of the steel plate. When the steel plate has the correct width its image fills the space between the five lines and the plate is sent on to be rolled into sheets. When the plate is too narrow the rolling mill operator applies additional pressure.

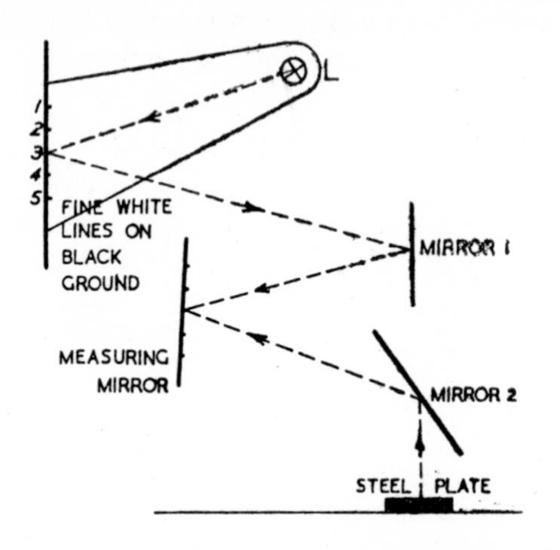

Fig. 11.13. Arrangement for optical measurement of steel plate thickness.

This procedure can be made fully-automatic if the " measuring mirror " is constructed as shown in Fig. 11.14. This mirror now consists of two silvered strips separated by a strip which is transparent and whose width is identical with the correct (imaged) width of the steel plate. A photo-relay watches the mirror and as long as the image of the steel plate is within the transparent central area no light will reach the relay and pressure will be applied to the plate to bring it to the correct dimension. The width of each of the two silvered (reflecting) strips is half the tolerance allowed for " correct " steel plate. The image of the plate, upon being superimposed on the transparent central area and the two silvered strips, will reflect light into the photo-relay which action will stop the application of pressure. When the steel plate has been fed on to the conveyor, the plate being too wide, its image will spread over the silvered strips and cover part of the non-silvered, i.e. transparent marginal strips. Other photo-relays, positioned behind these marginal elements, will pick up the incident energy and actuate an auxiliary gear or stop the conveyor.

Instead of using mirrors as in Fig. 11.13 any optical system will serve the same purpose as long as the same ends are achieved. A simple telescope can be used for scanning the steel plate from a safe distance. The path of the light rays within the telescope tube is intersected by a diaphragm, the latter being a negative of the mirror described in Fig. 11.14. Two transparent bands border the opaque central strip and the rest of the diaphragm also is transparent, Fig. 11.15. The place of the eye-piece is taken by a compound photo-e.m.f. cell. The one cell covers the area *ABCD*, another cell the area above, and yet another

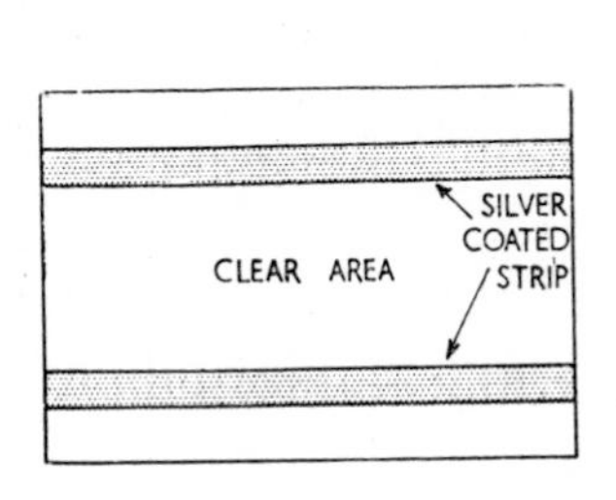

Fig. 11.14. Measuring mirror used in method shown in Fig. 11.13.

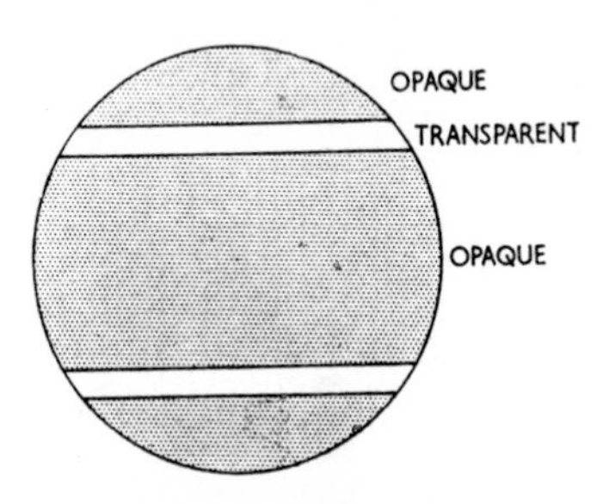

Fig. 11.15. Diaphragm used in place of mirror of Fig. 11.14.

cell the area below *ABCD*. The centrally situated photosensitor is wired for negative action : as long as the image of the steel plate is too small it will be located on the opaque part of the diaphragm and therefore the pressure of the rolling mill will increase. On reaching the two

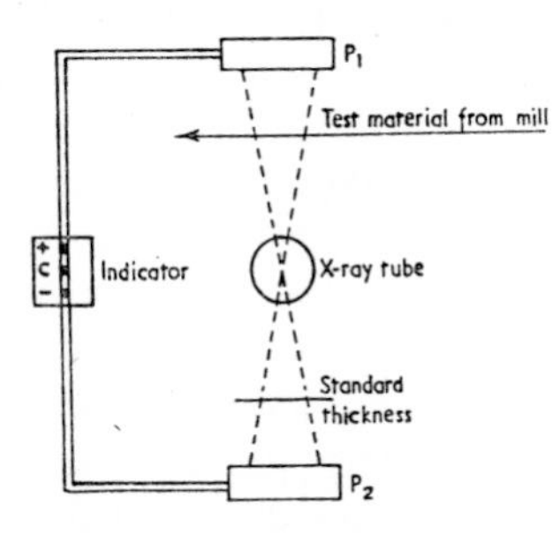

Fig. 11.16. Detection of thickness variation by X-ray measurement.

transparent strips this photo-relay will be de-energized. If the steel plate is too wide its image will reach into the segment-shaped photocells which action will stop the mill motor.

Variations in the thickness of hot or cold strip or sheets of metal, glass, rubber, plastics, paper, etc., can be detected by a method devised by H. M. Smith (*729*). A two-port X-ray tube, Fig. 11.16 is so arranged that one part of its radiation goes through a piece of material of standard thickness ; the other part of the X-rays continuously goes through the moving material under test. The photo-electric X-ray detectors are described in Chapter 13 and are connected to result in a central " correct " position from which the pointer can deviate to either side, thus indicating a " plus " or " minus " deviation if the instantaneous thickness of the material is greater or smaller than normal. It may prove necessary to protect the equipment from radiant

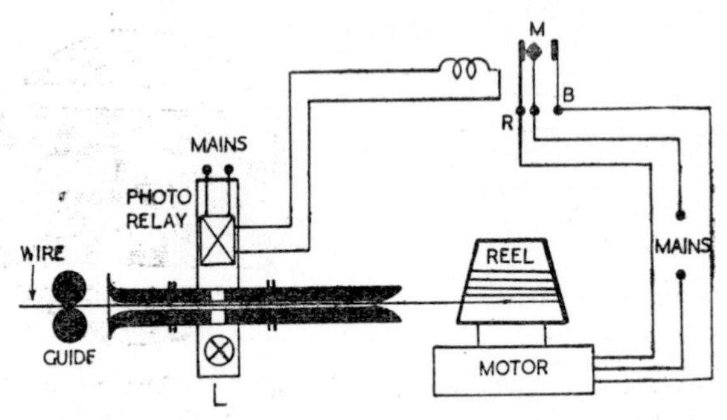

Fig. 11.17. Photo-electric control of wire-reeling: contacts RM drive the reel and contacts BM brake the reel.

heat by applying forced draught. Photosensitors for relative high ambient temperature (up to 100° C.) should be used. If photo-e.m.f. cells are used in such equipment the aluminium-based selenium cell, exerting a selective filtering action on X-rays (*1412*), will prove interesting and useful.

The high sensitivity of certain type photosensitors in the infra-red region of the spectrum make these cells useful in the detection of non-luminous heat-rays emitted by bodies at temperatures as low as 200° C.

Wire reeling machines can successfully be controlled by photosensitors. As long as the hot wire is drawn through the guide, Fig. 11.17, the motor contact remains closed. When the wire is cut at the proper length, or when the wire breaks, the illumination on the photosensitors is reduced to practically nil and the relay switches off the motor. The reeled wire can be thrown off if the motor is momentarily braked (*955*).

Bibliography References : (*545, 1949*)

11.12. Cutting Steel Rods

The cutting to proper length of metal or steel bars, plate, etc., can conveniently be arranged by using photo-electric control gear. The distance between the photosensitor and the shears must be equal to the desired length of the cut wire. Only the time delay of the shear movement has to be taken into account, the electromagnetic relays operating with a lag of from 0·005 to 0·01 sec.

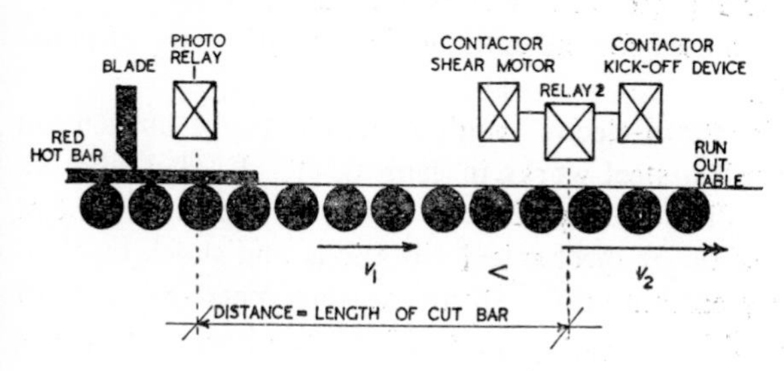

Fig. 11.18. Photo-electric control of mechanical shears and run-out table in steel milling.

One of the first equipments at a steel works was installed at the Bethlehem Steel Company's plant in Lebanon, Pa., U.S.A. (*956*, *957*). The scheme is shown in Fig. 11.18. The construction or performance of the apparatus can be easily changed according to different types of production. The red hot bar, travelling at a speed of 15 miles or more per hour, passes under a photo-relay which is energized by the radiant energy emitted by the material. The relay closes the circuit of a power relay or contactor which in turn sets the shear moving, but stops when the blade is just short of touching the bar. Instead of using a preset automatic timer to release the blade for the cutting performance, an additional photo-relay is recommended to give the impulse for cutting, thus taking care of any changes in the speed of the rod and preventing the lengths from being cut unequal. The distance D of the photo-relay 2 from the shear determines the length of the cut bar : this length can easily be varied by giving the relay 2 another position along the run-out table. When the bar has reached the photo-relay 2 the shear moves down, cutting the bar to its exact pre-determined length. The rolls of the run-out table, at the far end of relay 2, move the cut bar at a greater speed V_2 than the bar had had all along the table until it has been cut. Because $V_2 > V_1$ the cut bar will be moved away from under photo-relay 1 before the new supply of red hot bar will reach relay 1. This reduction in the illumination of relay 1 is made use of in resetting the blade and allowing it to move up to its " open " position. Not until the bar to be cut moves into the correct position in front of relay 1, will the shear be actuated and caused to move down as before.

The above mentioned increase in speed from V_1 to V_2 moves the cut bar along for a certain distance until it comes in front of the " clearing " or " kick-off " device which pushes the hot bar from the table down to another conveyor. This device is not necessarily actuated by a photo-relay but by a timer *T* preset to any convenient time period.

Similar systems are used for the cutting of full-width strips of paper or textile web (*958*).

Anti-microphonic photo-electric equipment will prove efficient in places like rolling mills, steel works in general, etc. F. H. Gulliksen has overcome the difficulties experienced with photo-electric control equipment due to sonic or mechanical vibrations and shock by completely and securely earthing not only the various metal cabinets of amplifiers, photo-cell housing, and parts of the amplifier circuit, but by also earthing the cathodes of the photosensitors (*1291*). More details are given in chap. 29.2.

Bibliography References : (*545*, *560*, *1870*, *1897*, *1991*)

11.13. Follow-up Mechanisms

Automatic curve followers were amongst the earliest applications of photosensitors (*961*, *p. 155* ; *962*). John Fies has described how a black and white chart, moving between a photosensitor and a light source, can be made to control the full-automatic operation of a power plant. As a fact the Llano River station of the Texas Power and Light Company is controlled by such a device.

Time-cycle process controls (programming controls) are devised to regulate to a predetermined programme, external conditions such as power generation, temperature, pressure, or any manufacturing process such as casting, flame cutting, high speed moulding, etc.

Most systems of follow-up mechanisms (*945*, *963*, *964*, *965*, *1668*) use full-size templates around which the probing light ray is guided. The circuit is so adjusted that no sideways movement of the cutting tool, in this case a gas cutting torch, results as long as the spot of light is half on the white and half on the black area (or line) of the template (*1418*, *2463*). This is achieved by a bridge circuit feeding into a double triode which in turn controls another double triode in whose anode circuits are the respective D.C. windings of two saturable reactors. The current flow in these reactors is equal as long as the output of the bridge, when applied to the one grid of the first double triode, is equal to the output which is applied to the other grid. The one arm of the bridge is formed by the scanning photosensitors.

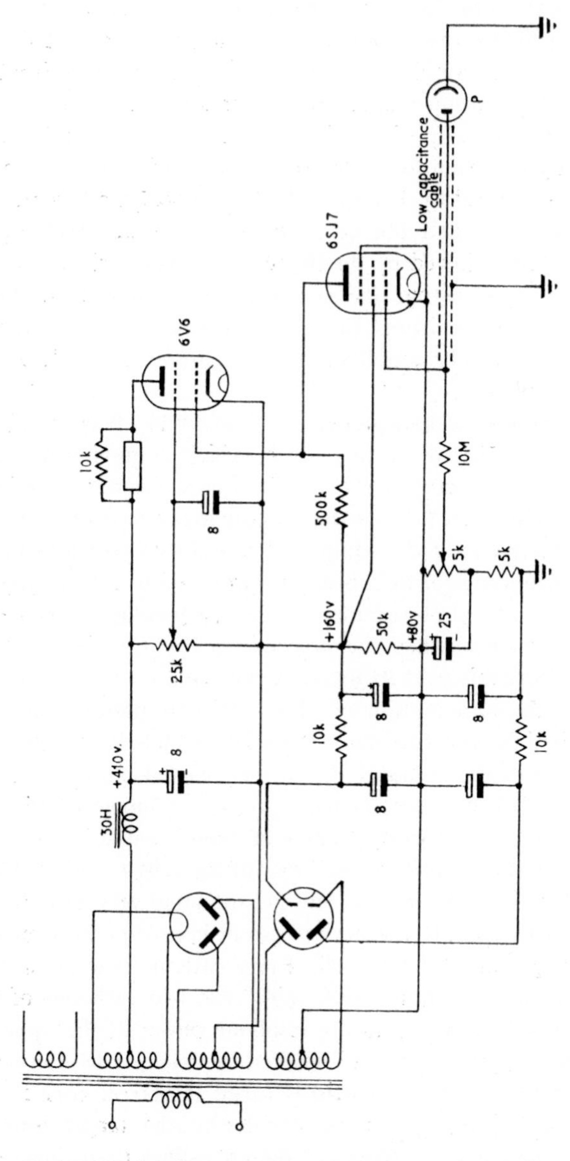

Fig. 11.19. Amplifier for scanner of follow-up mechanism.

Lastly, the D.C. steering motor will be driven in one or other direction according to which of the reactors is carrying more D.C. If the D.C. through both reactors is the same the motor will not rotate. If the spot of light moves towards the white paper or towards the black area (or line) one or the other reactor will carry more instantaneous current and the motor will rotate in such a direction that the spot will return to its normal position, i.e., centred on the demarkation line.

Distinctly different solutions to the problem of follow-up mechanisms were suggested by Tucker and Collins (*2425*) and by D. S. Walker (*966*), who eliminated the necessity of having actual-size templates. The line to be followed by the flame cutters is inscribed on two guide drums each representing one axis of a Cartesian system. The modus of inscribing these drums causes the torches to cut either straight lines or curves. The amplifier of the scanner, Fig. 11.19, is of the direct coupled type.

The follow-up mechanism described below has been developed with the aim of tracking down any object which is moving in space. The device can prove useful as a drive of automatic cameras filming objects moving at high speed, once the pick-up relay has located the object the reference point of the equipment will always be trained on it.

The surroundings of the object are projected by a wide-angle optical system on to the photosensitor PC_1 of the pick-up relay the contacts of which are open when the object is not within the field of view. When it enters this field its image is projected on to the cell PC_1, thus decreasing the illumination on this particular photosensitor. As the relay is wired for negative action the load contacts 10, 20, 30, are closed. The making of the contacts 10, 20, has started motors M_A and M_R, Fig. 11.20. Other optical systems project an image of the target on PC_2 and PC_3, respectively. Each of these consists actually of two independent photosensitors, viz., PC_2 of the cells L and R, and PC_3 of the cells U and D. Every two cells are mounted very close together, or the respective elements of every cell can be housed in the same envelope, thus forming a kind of twin-cell. Every cathode is a flat disk (end or thumb type cell or photo-e.m.f. cell). The two cathodes of the twin-cell are spaced according to the resolving power of the optical system and the maximum distance it is desired to watch. The interval between the two cathodes (about $\frac{1}{8}$ inch) is called the target zone : the target zone of PC_2 is arranged perpendicular to the target zone of PC_3. These two target zones represent the cross-lines (hair-lines) of a gun-sight.

The working principle of the locator is as follows : The image of the object is projected on PC_2 and PC_3, covering part of the respective cathode of either L or R of PC_2, and part of U or D of PC_3. The

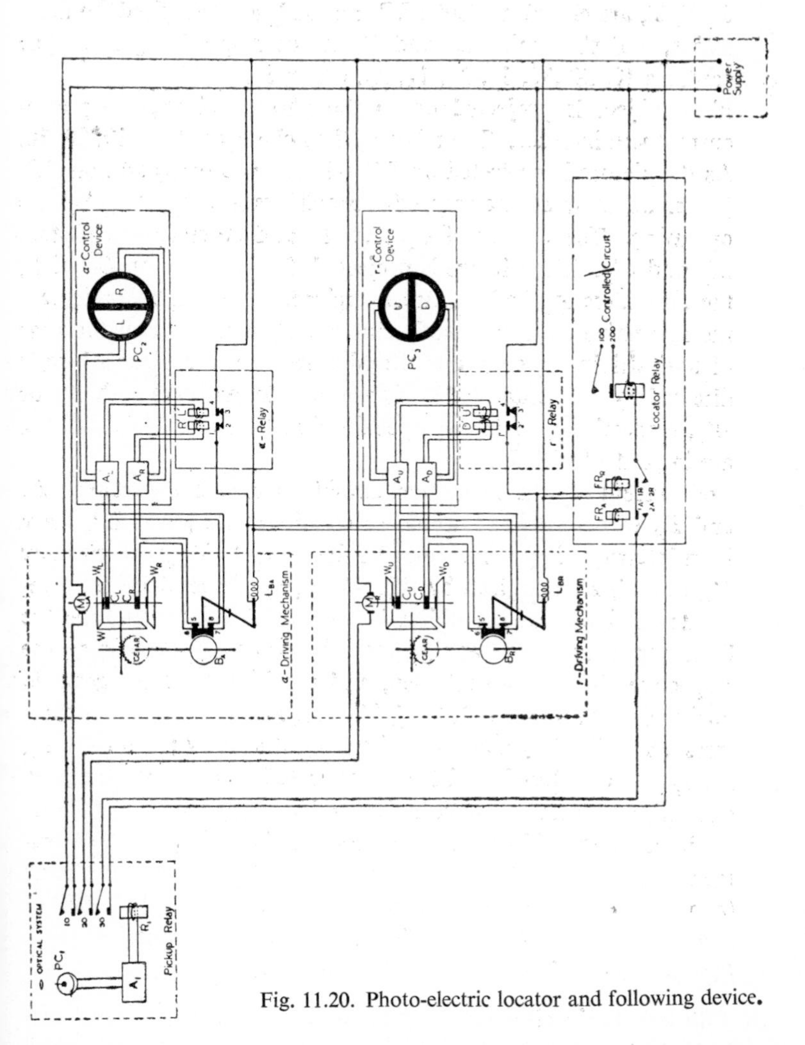

Fig. 11.20. Photo-electric locator and following device.

mechanical arrangement is so designed that the device always tries to avoid the image of the object being on any of the photo-cells, and moves as long as a shadow (i.e., image) decreases the light input. The movement stops only when the image is in the target zone.

No object in the field of view :

The three photosensitors are fully and equally illuminated : no current flows. The contacts 1, 2, 3, 4, 5, 6, 7, 8, 1′, 2′, 3′, 4′, 5′ 6′, 7′, 8′, are closed, the coils LB_A and LB_R are energized from the mains, and the brakes B_a and B_r fix the respective gears. The contacts 10, 20 ,30, 1_A, 2_A, 1_R, 2_R, are open.

If an object is projected on to the photosensitors, the photo-current will increase. The relay R_1 then closes contacts 10, 20, 30. As the picture is projected on PC_2 (either on L or R) and on PC_3 (either on U or D) the respective amplifiers A_L, A_R, A_U, A_D, are operating. The closing of contacts 10 and 20 starts the motors M_A and M_R. If the image is projected, for instance, on L and U, the amplifiers A_L and A_U are energized. The amplifiers actuate the respective electromagnetic clutches C_L and C_U, and the gear of both driving mechanisms A and R revolve in a sense which is directed by the contact of W (wheel or friction disk) with W_L or W_U, respectively, or in the opposite direction when W_R and W_D are in contact with W.

The current of the respective amplifiers causes the brakes B_A and B_R to open when the power circuits of LB_A and LB_R have been interrupted by the opening of the contacts 1, 2, (energized by L'), and 1′, 2′ (energized by D'). When by virtue of these movements the image of the object is brought to the target zone the light input increases again, the photo-current decreases, the respective clutches are released, and the brakes fix the gears in position as the contacts 1, 2, 1′, 2′, close again. This action energizes the coils FR_A and FR_R of the locator relay ; contacts 1_A, 2_A, 1_R, 2_R, are closed, and the contacts 100 and 200, respectively, close a power circuit which indicates that the object is in the line of sight. As the object moves further on, the action of the instrument starts again. Contacts 30 can be fitted to a delaying relay (about $\frac{1}{2}$ sec.) so that its closing by the action of PC_1 cannot actuate LR before the relays FR_A and FR_R are adjusted. PC_2 and PC_3 are mechanically fixed with the respective horizons.

A fully-electronic circuit of simple design, Fig. 11.21, uses two identical phase-shift circuits and gaseous triodes or tetrodes. The output of both thyratrons is fed into the coils of a split-field motor *M*. Other circuits are described by Müller et al. (*961*), Cockrell (*967*), Ryder (*1680*), and others. Boyd (*2431*) described a curve-follower for the reproduction of photographically recorded oscillograph signals.

A new type follow-up mechanism has been devised by T. M. Berry (*1278*). Polarized light is used as the connecting medium between the primary and secondary mechanism. Two beams of light pass through

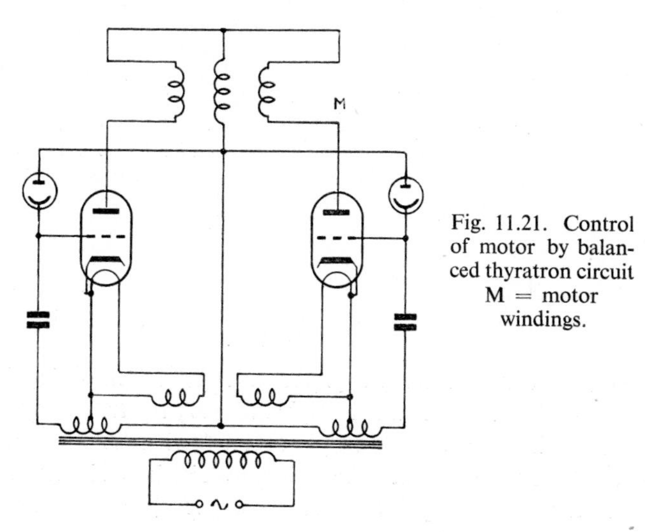

Fig. 11.21. Control of motor by balanced thyratron circuit M = motor windings.

the primary polarizer and strike photosensitors after each having passed through a secondary polarizer, the planes of polarization being at right angles to each other. The photosensitors are connected in a balanced two-cell circuit. If the primary polarizer is at an angle of 45 degrees to each of the two secondary polarizers, an equal amount of light will fall on each photosensitor and the circuit is balanced. If this angle changes, i.e., decreases or increases, the circuit will be unbalanced and thereby control the direction and speed of the servo-motor. A motor control system, using polarized light, has been described by H. R. Hartig (*1410*) (cf. Chap. 9.24). For further applications, (cf. E. R. Schwarz (*2442*).)

Bibliography References : (*454*, *550*, *1377*, *1577*, *1704*, *1723*, *1767*, *1810*, *1904*, *1927*, *1938*, *1948*, *1954*, *1988*, *2007*, *2013*, *2032*, *2039*, *2047*, *2125*, *2152*, *2211*, *2234*, *2267*, *2272*, *2275*, *2279*, *2291*, *2405*).

11.14. Testing of Electricity Meters

The stroboscopic effect of apparent motion is utilized in comparing the r.p.m. of a disk under test with the r.p.m. of a standard disk.

This method has been applied to the testing of watt-hour meters (*968*, *969*, *970*). The periphery of the standard disk has n notches. A paper disk has a number n' of black sectors printed on a white background and is fixed on the test disk. A light ray from an incandescent lamp is projected on a photo-relay, the light being modulated by the

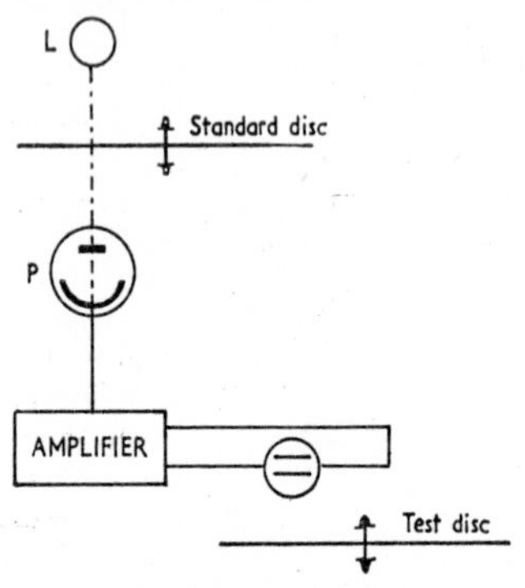

Fig. 11.22. Photo-electric method of testing electricity meters.

teeth of the standard disk, Fig. 11.22. After amplification in A the modulated light feeds a stroboscopic lamp L', the frequency of whose light output is identical with the product nN, where N is the number of r.p.m. of the standard disk. If the paper disk is viewed in the modulated light of the neon lamp L', the stroboscopic effect becomes evident. The general formula is $nN \overset{<}{\underset{>}{=}} n'N'$ where N' is the number of r.p.m. of the test (paper) disk. In the present case $n = n'$. There are three cases possible, viz. :

$N = N'$ The test disk apparently stands still ; both disks are in step.

$N < N'$ The test disk apparently rotates in the direction of its own rotation, the degree of apparent forward motion being a measure of its excessive speed. The disks are out of step, the test disk is leading the standard disk.

$N > N'$ The test disk apparently rotates in a direction opposite from its own rotation, the degree of apparent reverse motion being a measure of its (now reduced) speed. The disks are out of step, the test disk lagging behind the standard disk.

To calculate the error of the test disk, the number n of the notches (or teeth) on the standard disk must be known. If the test disk is out of step $\pm m$ notches per rotation, the ratio $\pm m/n$ is the exact value of the percentage error. This method can be applied to any type of apparatus having rotating parts.

Another instrument for meter testing is the electronic load regulator designed by Lenahan (*971*). The circuit is reproduced in Fig. 11.23.

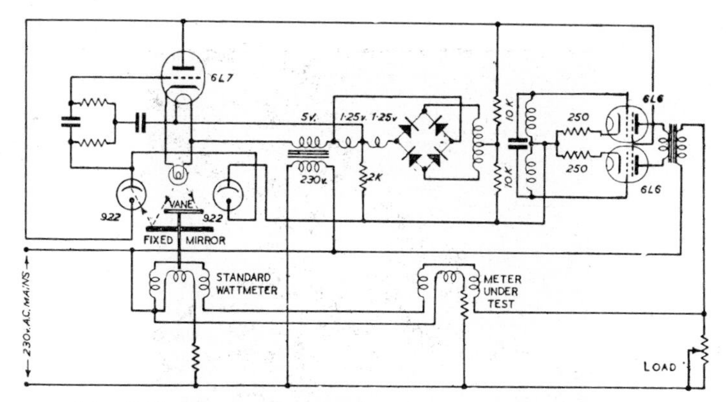

Fig. 11.23. Meter testing circuit with automatic load regulator.

A photo-electrically controlled dynamometer loader has been described by Proctor (*972*) and was abstracted in Electronics (*973*). A photo-electric system of megawatt telemetering is described in the *Electrical Times* (*2464*).

Bibliography Reference : (*1789*)

11.15. Register Control

The field of register control is so wide that it is impossible to allow it more than a few sections in a book which is not entirely devoted to this important subject. Gulliksen and Vedder (*398*) have described various methods and the technical literature of the last ten years is replete with references to register control.

From the application to postage stamp perforating and cutting 400-stamp sheets at the rate of 200 sheets per minute (*974*), the photo-electric control ranges from motors responding to printed marginal register marks (*975*), over controls which correct the side shifts of paper or textile fabrics in high-speed roll-winding machines (*976*), to packaging machines which cut the wrapper correct and in the same position (*79*, *977*, *978*) ; practically any industrial serial process can be made controllable by photo-electric register control.

The photo-electric control on the four-colour rotogravure press of the *Philadelphia Inquirer* positions the four different colour impressions within narrow limits at a web speed of approximately 10,000 ft.p.m. Each colour unit in the press is fitted with two photo-electric scanning heads. One head scans the margin of the web of paper as it

Fig. 11.24. Arrangement for automatic control of paper registration.

moves through the press. On this paper are register marks equally spaced and printed simultaneously with the first colour impression. The second scanning head is arranged to scan a disk attached to the printing cylinder. When the index marks on the paper and the disk are accurately in register the two scanning heads produce synchronous impulses. However, if the paper gets ahead of, or falls behind, the disk on the printing cylinder the two sets of impulses are not synchronized. A net control voltage is produced and relayed through thyratrons to a pilot motor which advances or retards the position of the paper with respect to the printing cylinder until synchronism is achieved. In printing the remaining two colours the same method is used, employing different register marks laid down by the successive colour impressions (*979, 980*). To maintain the lateral displacement of the web within given limits two photo-relays are mounted at one edge of the web opposite from the light source in such a way that one photo-sensitor is always covered and the other uncovered when the web is in

Fig. 11.25. Two-circuit rotary selector switch (*British Thomson-Houston Co. Ltd.*).

the correct position. Any lateral movement will result in either covering or uncovering both photosensitors simultaneously. This change in the original condition will energize a warning device and/or cause an automatic control to adjust the web.

Control of paper registration in wrapping machines actually begins when a small register mark is printed in the margin of the web. The length of this mark is about ½ inch, the width varying with the tolerance limits allowed by the characteristics of the process and the web, the width of the marks usually being twice the dimension of the tolerated deviations from " normal ".

As the web is fed to the wrapping machine the register mark passes the photo-electric scanner, Fig. 11.24. As each mark passes, a light impulse is either reflected or transmitted into the photosensitor. The duration of this impulse is extremely brief, mostly of the order of 100 microseconds (10^{-4} sec.) or even less. Due to stretch and slip of the

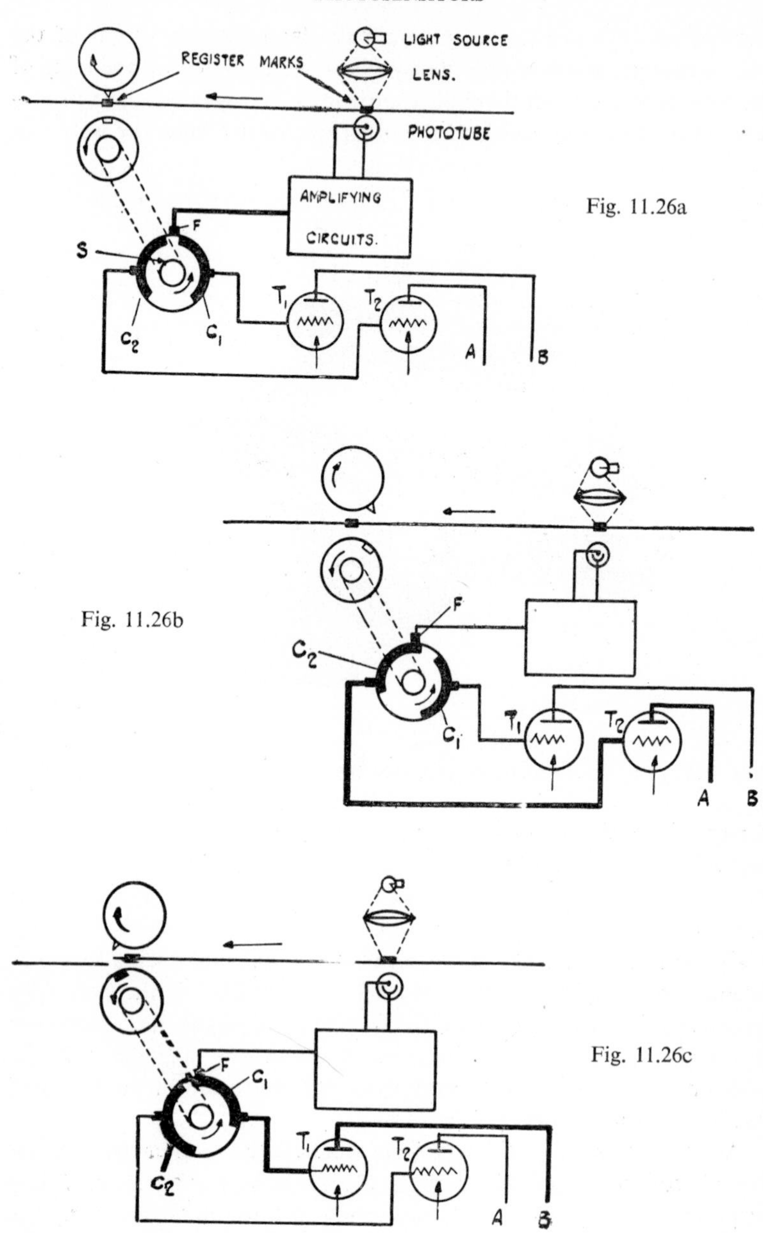

Fig. 11.26. Schematic of register control equipment: (a) mark on web in register with cutting knife; (b) register mark leading; (c) register mark lagging.

web it must be fed to the cutter of the wrapping machine at a variable, yet controlled speed, thus compensating for the above mentioned shortcomings of an elastic web. Not only must the speed control decide that the speed has changed but also how, i.e., in which direction. The control equipment is capable of recognizing whether the instantaneous speed is greater or smaller than it should be and takes corresponding action. This is done by driving a two-circuit rotary selector switch, Fig. 25, from the cutter shaft either direct or by a chain or gear train. In Fig. 11.26a, b, c, the three characteristic cases are represented, viz., web in register with knife ; register mark leading ; register mark lagging behind. Accordingly, the rotary switch will connect neither, or the one or the other control circuit, respectively.

Figure	Relative Position of register mark and cutting knife	Amplifier connected via brush F and contact	to circuit	Effect on web
a	correct	—	—	none
b	mark in front of knife	C_2	T_2	retarded
c	mark behind knife	C_1	T_1	advanced

A suitable mechanical equipment gears the various motors. One such arrangement is instanced in Fig. 11.27. Two types of change are possible, viz., the space change which brings the web back immediately into register, and the speed change, which is permanent. The latter is effected by the motor M_2, the former by the motor M_3. Running these small motors for the correcting period alters the ratio of the respective differentials (A or B) and a small decrease or increase in the speed of the drawing rolls results in a correct position of the register mark. If the feed rolls are small a compensating roll may be used instead of the complicated mechanical gearboxes. A mechanical-electrical differential system is discussed by Cockrell (*978*). Two-way control has successfully been employed in maintaining an accuracy of $\pm$ 1/64 inch at speeds of 500 ft.p.m. and more.

To avoid heavy wear of the differentials the web may be fed with such a varying speed that the accumulation of five to eight or ten plus-or-minus errors results in one correcting action of the differentials. This greatly reduces the number of actions and saves maintenance costs.

The two-way control discussed above is essential for high-speed machines where the web is moving at speeds greater than 50 ft.p.m.

To prevent the web from being fed at too great and too small a speed, a phenomenon which is called " hunting ", a system has been devised which by creating a dead zone provides an efficient anti-hunting equip-

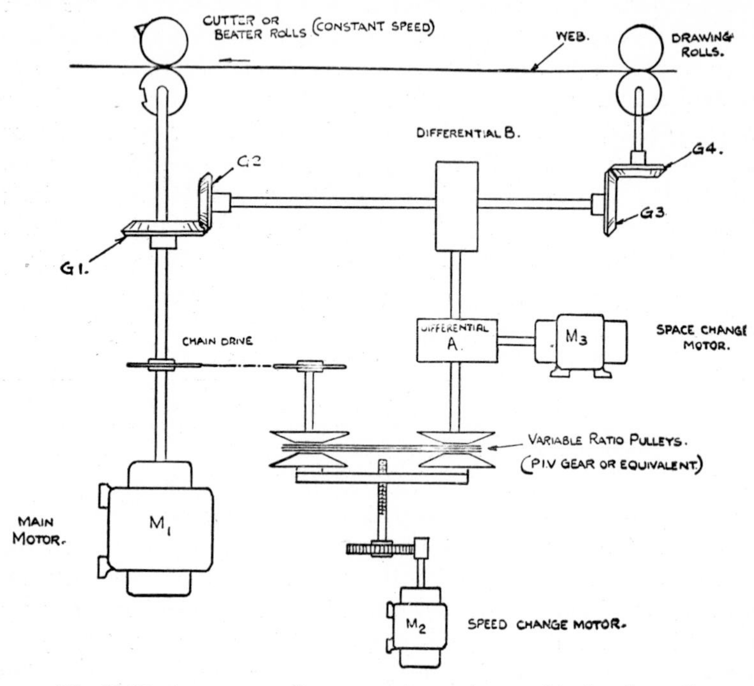

Fig. 11.27. Arrangement for automatic speed control in drawing mill.

ment. The register mark is allowed to move within a given area without causing control operation. This area is the " dead zone " and must be at least double the width of the register mark.

For speeds below 50 ft.p.m. a one-way control will be effective. It is principally the same method as described above with the exception that the rotary switch has one control only and controls but one circuit. The system is similar to the method of intermittent-feed (*vide supra*). Continuously-fed web is fed to the machine slightly faster or slightly slower than required. Thus an error is purposely introduced. The accumulation of the small errors results in the register mark operating the control gear which, since the errors are only unidirectional, i.e., either positive (overfeed) or negative (underfeed), need be only of the one-way type.

G. M. Chute has described in detail the operation and function of the register control equipment developed by the General Electric Company. (*981*, *2607*), Fig. 11.28.

Another and rather different application of the principle of register control was discussed by E. H. Vedder before the A.I.M.E. (*982*, *1692*).

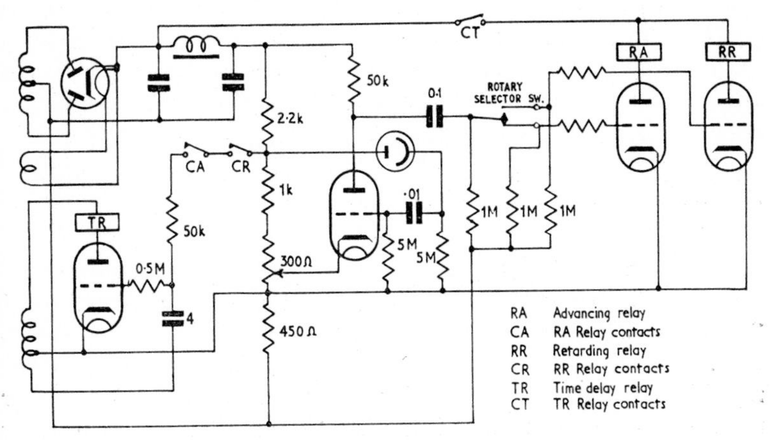

Fig. 11.28. Circuit of register control equipment (*General Electric Co.*)

The introduction of high-frequency heating into the process of tinning strip steel has necessitated an automatic control device to keep the heat supply (H.F. generator output) within such limits that the flow line is produced at a certain position in the heating coil. The flow line is characterized by the physical change of the tin which causes the optical properties of the tin surface to exhibit a distinctive change. The surface of the tin changes from matt to bright, i.e., from diffusing to reflecting, along the flow line. This difference in the reflective qualities of the tin is utilized in controlling the high-frequency output of the heating generator. The line of partition is equivalent to the register mark printed on the paper web of packaging machines. When the line moves away from the high-frequency coil (because too much heat has been developed), the power output will be reduced, and vice-versa.

Yet another, and again very different application of register control was developed by the General Electric Co. (*638*, *1366*) for the operation of continuous weft straightening in the textile industry. Two scanning heads control the angle between weft and warp threads, respectively. When they are askew the one scanner will count more threads per time unit than the other. The different frequencies produced by the passing threads—being unequal in number per scanner—are fed into a frequency-sensitive circuit the output of which controls the operation of the straightening motor.

A number of new circuits designed for high speed web and side register control using thyratrons, selsyns, and saturable reactors are now used for direct motor control in packaging and wrapping machines (*2607*). A photo-electrically controlled servo-mechanism (*2608*) and an automatically recording magnetic balance (*2613*) also use photo-electric gear.

Bibliography References : (*547*, *567*, *583*, *1183*, *1202*, *1308*, *1366*, *1809*, *1810*, *1835*, *1866*, *1904*, *1928*, *1940*, *1943*, *1946*, *1947*, *1950*, *1961*, *2207*, *2281*, *2609*).

11.16. Production Testing

In most testing or measuring methods on a production line basis a " pointer " instrument, for instance a galvanometer (*1408*, *1444*) is used. In many cases the output of the object under test can be made repetitive at regular short intervals ; it is then a matter for the designer to utilize a cathode-ray tube instead. The output of the object under test will result in a curve on the screen of the C.R. tube, the shape of

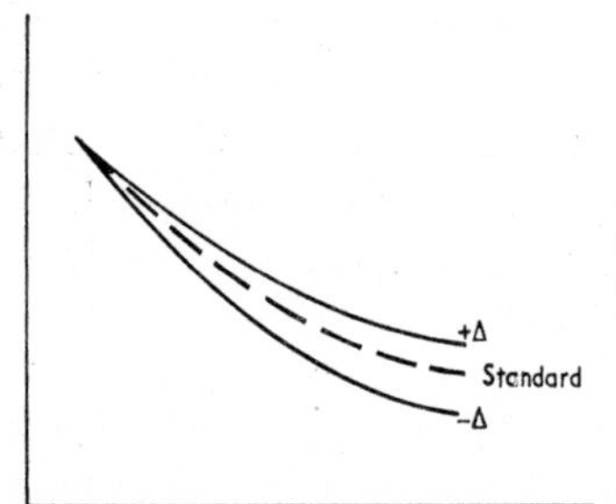

Fig. 11.29. Mask for c.r.t. control of production, showing permissible deviation from standard

the curve being characteristic and representative of the correct operation or design of that object. Certain tolerance limits will be allowed before an object is rejected for failing to reach, or overreaching, the standard curve, Fig. 11.29. If a mask is cut from an opaque material to suit a particular characteristic and the screen of the C.R. tube is covered with it, then the curves of all objects which can be passed " correct " must appear in the cut-out of the mask. All curves appearing outside the admitted plus-minus tolerances will not be seen as they are covered by the opaque mask (*1605*).

L. L. Antes (*983*) has described how such a cathode-ray outfit can be equipped with a photo-relay to watch out for curves appearing within the cut-out of the diaphragm. A brief list of potential applications will illustrate the wide flexibility of the device :

Checking the frequency response of microphones, amplifiers, filters, etc. ;

Checking the colour of objects having identical shape ;

Checking the characteristics of electronic valves.

The cycle of internal combustion engines (*1442*) can automatically be controlled by such a device. A pressure operated pick-up (*1250*), a quartz crystal for instance (*984*), is inserted in, or securely fixed to the wall of the engine cylinder. German practice is described in the F.I.A.T. Final Reports (*2434*). The diagram, as picked up by the crystal, is reproduced on the screen of a cathode-ray tube by connecting a time base to the X-electrodes and the piezo-electric output of the pick-up to the Y-electrodes. The ideal cycle of a four-stroke petrol engine (*985*) is shown in Fig. 11.30. An appropriate mask will reveal any deviations from the permitted tolerances. If the characteristic curve of an engine is known it can be used as a standard in petrol tests. A pressure-time-curve indicator (*1414*) is marketed under the name " Pressuregraph " (Fig. 11.31). This instrument produces in picture form a linear pressure-time curve which may be used to test or record pressures occuring in any machine having static or dynamic pressures. Static pressures will appear as a line on the screen of the CRT the width of this line being proportional to the pressure. Dynamic pressures will appear as pressure-time curves.

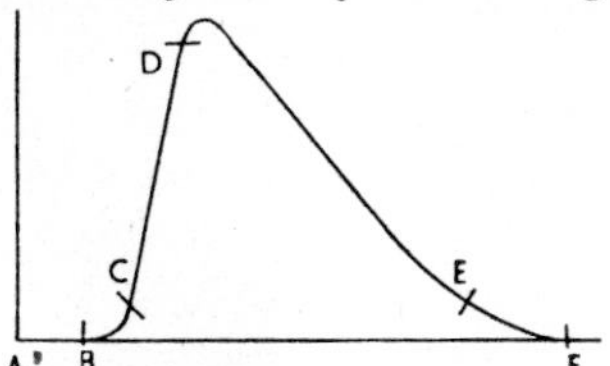

Fig. 11.30. Ideal cycle of 4-stroke petrol engine: A
A: Origin of coordinates
B: Start
C: Compression
D: Explosion
E: Exhaustion
F: Suction

A synchronizer is connected to the crankshaft of the pump or engine being investigated and provides a timing voltage which, when connected to the cathode-ray oscillograph, synchronizes the engine speed with the CR sweep, thereby steadying the produced curve at any position on the horizontal plane of the screen : the synchronizer can be rotated through 360 degrees.

The pick-up contains a pressure actuated diaphragm which controls the electronic circuit. The following ranges will practically cover all types of engines.

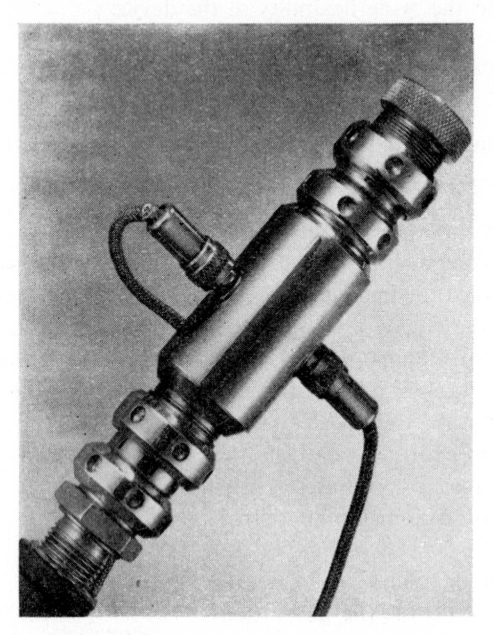

Fig. 11.31. " Pressuregraph " pressure indicator.

Thickness of Diaphragm. inch.	Pressure Range lb.
0·002	from 0 to 25
0·006	from 0 to 50
0·010	from 0 to 100
0·015	from 0 to 500
0·030	from 0 to 2000
0·045	from 0 to 6500
0·060	from 0 to 10,000

Diaphragms can be readily removed and interchanged. For temperatures up to 300° C. the pick-ups are cooled by natural air currents For operating temperatures up to 750° C. the pick-ups are water cooled.

In Diesel operation the Pressuregraph is being used to show the timing of injection together with the pressure rise of compression and the additional pressure created when the fuel is fired. Due to the negligible inertia transient pressure waves of micro-seconds duration causing erratic engine performance can be visually noted. The Pressuregraph can be applied to investigations of all types of internal combustion engines, e.g., Diesel engines, two- and/or four-stroke petrol engines ; chemical processing cylinders ; gas or air lines ; compressors; air or liquid pumps, etc.

H. C. Weber (*986*) has measured the pressure existing in large guns, during firing, by means of piezo-electric material.

A different pressure operated pick-up was used by Robertson (*372*) whose indicator takes advantage of the fact that the intensity of a beam of light reflected from a spherical mirror varies with its radius. A highly polished metal diaphragm is inserted in the wall of the combustion chamber or cylinder. Variations in pressure across the diaphragm will deform it into a spherical segment the radius of which will be inversely proportional to the pressure in the combustion chamber. The amplifier is of the direct current type and can be used at any engine speed and the output can be made visible on a cathode-ray tube.

A photo-electric pressure gauge is described by Kerris and Weidmann for measuring very rapidly changing pressures. (*1677*). The photosensitor is illuminated with varying intensity by a pencil of light directed by a mirror.

In some cases photo-electric control can be achieved in processes which have none of their characteristic features directly convertible into luminous radiation, but which are controlled by other electronic devices. The cathode-ray tuning indicator (the " magic eye " of the radio receiver) is of use in some cases. This tube contains a triode on which is mounted a control electrode and a target in the form of a disc coated with luminescent material. The area of target which luminesces under the electron bombardment is controlled by the negative bias applied to the grid, and a shadow on the target, caused by the control electrode, varies its angle with the grid voltage (Fig. 11.32). The usual shadow angle has a maximum angular width of about 100°, but if a separate D.C. amplifier is used the angle can be extended to nearly 180°.

The basic circuit for a tuning indicator type 6E5 is shown in Fig. 11.33. Another tuning indicator, type 6AD6G, has two independent control electrodes, casting shadows on opposite sides of the target electrode (Fig. 11.34a). The control grids may be supplied from independent circuits (Fig. 11.34b). The 6T5 tuning indicator has a control which casts an annular shadow (Fig. 11.34c).

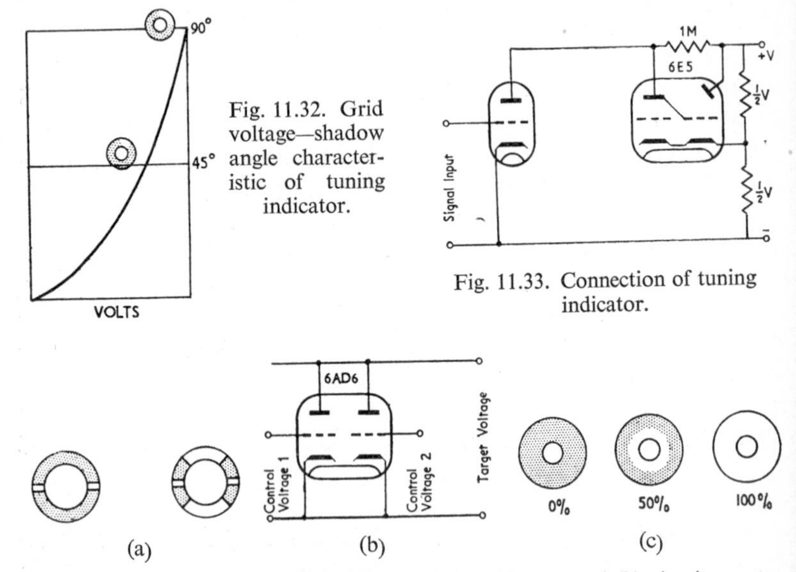

Fig. 11.32. Grid voltage—shadow angle characteristic of tuning indicator.

Fig. 11.33. Connection of tuning indicator.

Fig. 11.34. (a) Double shadow of 6AD6 tuning indicator, and (b) circuit arrangement; (c) annular shadow of 6T5 tuning indicator.

An example of the application of the 6E5 is shown in Fig. 14.13.

Other examples of photo-electric control are given in references *988*, *908*, and *2610* (a photo-electric r.f. welding control unit).

Bibliography References : (*472*, *473*, *474*, *475*, *476*, *477*, *478*, *574*, *1054*, *1179*, *1183*, *1235*, *1333*, *1527*, *1545*, *1574*, *1742*, *1749*, *1754*, *1755*, *1757*, *1785*, *1821*, *1828*, *1829*, *1831*, *1864*, *1869*, *1877*, *1883*, *1885*, *1886*, *1893*, *1912*, *1930*, *1941*, *1952*, *1958*, *1962*, *1975*, *1986*, *1992*, *1993*, *1996*, *2001*, *2004*, *2023*, *2027*, *2139*, *2274*, *2296*).

11.17. Roller Hearth Furnace

The General Electric Company, Ltd., has equipped a 100 kW roller hearth furnace with a photo-relay which warns the operator when a charge, after travelling through the furnace, reaches a position near the exit door in readiness for being discharged. The relay also stops the movement of the furnace hearth while the charge is withdrawn, and restarts the cycle when a new charge enters the hearth (*897*).

Bibliography References : (*1188*, *2122*, *2123*, *2171*)

11.18. **Cement**

The fineness of cement is measured by utilizing the scattering effect which the finely dispersed particles exercise on a light beam passing through a suspension of cement in castor oil or liquid paraffin. This method was developed at the University of California, Berkeley, and

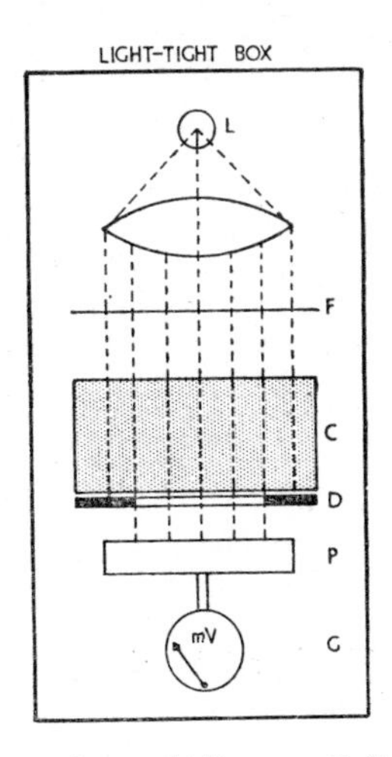

Fig. 11.35. Diagram of suspension turbidimeter. L light source, F filter, C vessel of liquid, D diaphragm, P photo-cell.

is based on the conception of the " specific surface " (*2437*), i.e., the surface area of particles expressed in units of area per unit of volume or weight, for instance in cm^2 per $cm.^3$, or in $cm.^2$ per gram. The smaller the particles, the greater is the " specific surface ".

A light beam is made to pass through a suspension of the powder (cement, dust, carbonaceous matter, powders) in a proper vehicle. The resulting reduction in the intensity of the light beam is a function of the " specific surface " and, therefore, of the fineness of the particles. The diagram of the Suspension Turbidimeter is given in Fig. 11.35. A light-box encloses the light source with collimating lens and optical filter, the container (or a micro-slide), a diaphragm, and the photosensitor. The microammeter may be calibrated in units of " specific surface ". Another optical method for the determination of the surface of powders in suspension was developed by H. Baumann (*1642, 1643*).

Bibliography Reference : (*1966*)

11.19. Accelerated Weathering

Plastic and rubber materials take a long time if they are to be tested for weathering under natural conditions. The simulation of alternating rain and sunshine makes it possible to carry out weathering tests in the laboratory with an acceleration factor of from 10 to 11. The results of the weathering tests are measured by photo-electric equipment. Reference should be made to the original paper for details of equipment and procedure (*1262*).

11.20. Photo-electric Switch

A huge rotating mandrel on a hose-wrapping machine is controlled by a light beam which extends the full length of the machine. As the operator moves along the 50 ft. long mandrel he can stop the machine from any point where he stands by simply moving his foot forward and interrupting a light beam.

Another instance is given by industrial hand (hot air) dryers which are switched on by placing the hands in any of the drying compartments (*1463*).

Bibliography References : (*2155*, *2156*, *2164*, *2261*, *2384*)

CHAPTER 12

ASSEMBLY CONTROL

A rather obvious application has been discussed in *Electronics* (*1024*). Each set of jig-saw puzzles passes between a light source and a photo-relay. If every piece of the puzzle is in position no light reaches the photosensitor of the relay and the set is passed on to the conveyor. If, however, one or any number of pieces is missing from the set the light, striking the photo-relay, will cause a trap door or chute to open and the defective set is diverted to a scrap bin.

Other instances for the inspection of goods for missing items are the rejection of bottles, the corks or labels of which are missing or misplaced, or the contents of which have undergone a change resulting in an optical characteristic or quality different from the one set up as standard, e.g., discoloration ; clear liquids turning turbid ; suspensions settling or emulsions disintegrating, which means that opaque or translucent liquids become transparent, etc.

Boxes filled with breakfast cereals are inspected regularly for coupons which the customers expect to find in each box (*1025*). The light ray is projected through a slit on to the coupon which, when in the right place at the right time, will intercept the light beam and keep the photo-relay obscured. This system can be developed into a register control. The coupon is lifted from its stack by means of a pneumatic lever and placed in the box. The movement of this lever is controlled by the box intercepting another light pencil. Finally, the interior of the box is inspected for the coupon. It is obvious that the principle of register control can be employed in various ways for controlling assemblies of packaged, tinned, and canned goods, or of complicated parts of machinery, the photo-relay watching out for any particular piece to be placed in the right place at the right time.

In many cases luminoscopic or fluoroscopic methods will be called upon to investigate assembled objects and to inspect for missing parts (Chaps. 13 and 18).

CHAPTER 13

LUMINESCENCE

13.1. Theoretical Considerations

The earliest ascertainable date in the history of luminescence* is the year A.D. 1602, when the Italian shoemaker and adept of alchemy, Vincenzo (sometimes named Pietro) Casciarola of Bologna, discovered the phenomenon of inorganic phosphorescence (BaS) (*680*, *681*). Yet it took 300 years before the foundations were laid for a scientific treatment of the subject (*1295*, *1296*, *1297*, *1403*). Thomas A. Edison, in 1896, made the first practical application of luminescence—he built the first fluorescent lamp. Recent research (*614*, *688*, *693*, *694*) into the problems presented by the phenomena of phosphorescence and fluorescence, respectively, was inaugurated by the advent of the cathode-ray tube.

The theory of luminescence (*682*) is based on the Quantum Theory (*387*). A molecule, when absorbing radiation of a frequency ν, can only absorb a photon whose energy $E = h\nu$. If this energy is re-emitted, it can be done on the same or on a smaller frequency ν_1. In either case, the emitted energy is an integral photon, no fractions of a photon being allowed. The energy E_1 of a radiation on a smaller frequency ν_1 is, therefore, smaller than E.

The Quantum Theory provides for a molecule to exist in certain energy states only : no arbitrary states are possible. The lowest of these states is the " ground state " E_0 or *filled band*. The influx of a quantity of energy raises the molecule to a higher, or " excited " state E_1, E_2 or *conduction band*, the excitation level being a function of the absorbed energy. The return of the molecule from any excited state (conduction band) to the ground state is accompanied by the emission of the previously absorbed radiant energy. Since a molecule has only discrete levels E_1, E_2, etc., it can absorb or emit only radiations of certain frequencies. It is obvious that the molecule, having absorbed a certain energy $E = h\nu$, cannot re-emit a greater energy $E' = h\nu'$,

* Xenophon of Colon (530 B.C.) had already noticed phosphorescence. Cleidamus, a Greek philosopher (5th century B.C.) also noticed the phosphorescence of the sea.

which means that the frequency of re-emission cannot be greater than that of the absorbed energy. It can however be smaller, i.e. its wavelength can be longer, if $E' < E$. This is Stokes' law, which holds for practically all substances, stating that fluorescent (re-emitted) radiation always experiences a shift towards the red (long-wave) end of the spectrum with respect to the wavelength of the absorbed radiation (*256*). This complex of phenomena is called fluorescence. In 1935, Prilezhaeva (*184*) found a case of Anti-Stokes behaviour in anilin vapour, the fluorescence frequency of which was 1·1 frequency units " greater " than the excitation frequency. No satisfying explanation has been proffered (*1621, p. 6*). Stokes' law is represented in Fig. 13.1, showing that while fluorescence must follow Stokes' law, yet phosphorescence—which also follows it—may " include " the excitation wavelength.

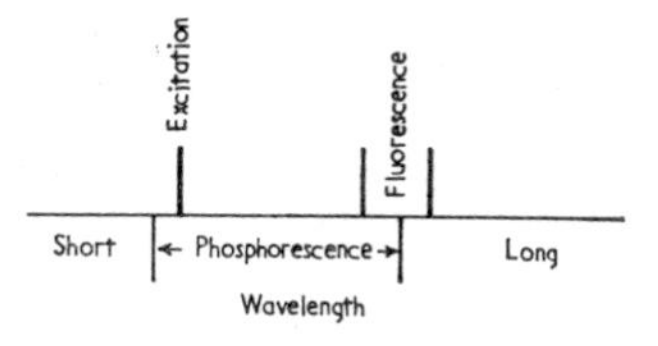

Fig. 13.1. Diagram to illustrate Stokes' law.

If a fraction of the excited molecules behaves differently from what has been described above as a normal procedure, another effect can be noticed. This phenomenon, called phosphorescence, is characterized in that the excited molecule does not pass directly from its excited level E_n (conduction band) to the ground level E_0, but remains for a period of time on a metastable level, whence it returns to the ground state. This return is accompanied by a re-emission of radiation (*683, 684*).

The exciting radiation can be luminous, ultra-violet, or X-rays. Other sources of excitation, although at present of less importance to the production engineer, are cathode rays, alpha rays, beta rays, friction, ultrasonic waves, chemical processes, thermal processes, etc. The fluorescence can be luminous or non-luminous (*1621, pp. 501, 601*).

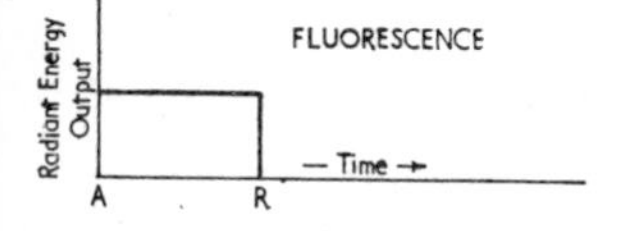

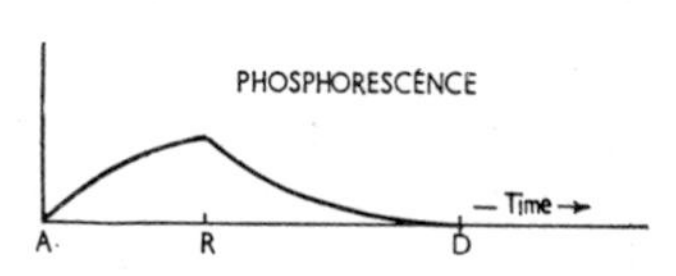

Fig. 13.2. The characteristics of fluorescence and phosphorescence.

A graphical representation of the characteristics of fluorescence and phosphorescence respectively is given in Fig. 13.2. Although the real nature of the difference between these two phenomena becomes clear only when explained in terms of the Quantum theory, it must suffice here to give the definition based on the effect rather than on its cause, viz.,

A substance, emitting light after the excitation process has come to an end, is said to show the phenomenon of phosphorescence ;

A substance, emitting light only while the excitation process lasts, is said to show the phenomenon of fluorescence.

The afterglow is the light emitted by the luminescent substance after the exciting source of radiant energy has been removed or its emission stopped. Thus, for all purposes, fluorescence is characterized in that there is no measurable ($<10^{-8}$ sec.) afterglow, while the afterglow of phosphorescent substances has a life from fractions of a second to many hours, and in some cases even weeks (*1657*, *Table 8*).

Bibliography References : (*554*, *1129*, *1224*, *1373*, *1504*, *1566*, *1587*, *2402*)

13.2. Notation

The author would like to draw the attention of the reader to the notation of the characteristics of fluorescence as suggested by DeMent (*376*). $[\Lambda]^{\lambda}_{\text{solv.}}$ represents the characteristic colour Λ of fluorescence when the phosphor is excited by the wavelength λ and is dissolved in a solvent, for instance, water, alcohol, etc. $[\Lambda]^{3650}_{H_2O}$ = Green means that the phosphor, when in aqueous solution and excited by long ultra-violet energy of wavelength 3650 A.U. emits light of a green colour. $[\Lambda]^{2537}_{-}$ = Blue means that the phosphor, when in the solid state (the negative sign indicates the absence of a solvent) and excited by 2537 A.U., emits blue light.

13.3. Constitution

Synthetic phosphors* are represented by the constitutional formula : $AB + M + F \rightarrow$ Phosphor, where,

- *A* may be : barium, beryllium, cadmium, calcium, magnesium, rubidium, sodium, strontium, zinc ;
- *B* indicates that one of the following compounds has been formed : borate, carbonate, molybdate, oxide, phosphate, selenide, silicate, sulphide, tungstate ;

* A " phosphor " is a substance exhibiting the phenomenon of luminescence. " Phosphorus " is the name of the chemical element known under the symbol P. In order to avoid ambiguities the phosphor is sometimes called " luminophore ".

M is a heavy metal, added as a necessary impurity (*683, 685, 686, 687*), viz., antimony, bismuth, cobalt, copper, iron, lead, manganese, nickel, silver, tellurium, tin, uranium, zinc ;

F is a flux, e.g., sodium borate, sodium chloride, sodium sulphate.

If the phosphor is of the inorganic type, the solvents *A* and *B* are inorganic and the impurity *M* is metallic, the flux being inorganic likewise. In organic phosphors, the solvents *A* and *B* are organic and so is the flux *F*, but the impurity *M* is either an organic compound or a metal. The phenomenon of luminescence is based on the presence of an impurity *M* which acts as activator, but sometimes has a quenching effect. This is borne out by Table 13.1. The presence of nickel in as low or even lower a concentration as 1 p.p.m. quenches the phosphorescence of ZnS or ZnCdS without materially affecting the fluorescence.

TABLE 13.1

Activators and Quenchers

Phosphor	Impurity				
	Ag	Cu	Mn	Fe	Ni
CaS	*a*	*a*	*a*	*a*	*a*
SrS	*a*	*a*	*a*	—	*a*
MgS	—	—	*a*	.	.
ZnS	*a*	*a*	*a*	*q*	*q*
CdS	*a*	*a*	*a*	*q*	*q*
$CaWO_4$	—	—	—	*q*	*q*
Zn_2SiO_4	—	*q*	*a*	*q*	*q*
$Cd_2B_2O_4$	.	*q*	.	*q*	*q*

NOTE : *a* means activator ; *q* means quencher ; — means no effect; means that nothing has been published up to 1943 about that case (*614*).

The absorption and luminescence bands, respectively, of a phosphor are characteristic not for the type, but only for individual compounds. This is borne out in Table 13.2 which gives the respective data for ZnCdS.

A material highly resistant to electron burn was described by G. L. Hunt, an investigator on the Combined Intelligence Objectives Committee (*1462*), who found the phosphor in use in German factories. It is of the zinc sulphide-zinc selenide type. The fluorescence is green with 10^{-5} to 10^{-6} Cu impurities, or blue with 10^{-4} to 10^{-5} Ag impurities. An increasing content of ZnSe causes the emission to move to the red end of the spectrum. It has but a short afterglow and is excited by long ultra-violet rays as well as by electrons. A Ni-killer suppresses the afterglow. For high-voltage cathode-ray tubes a zinc-oxide phosphor is used exhibiting cream, yellow, and green colours.

TABLE 13.2

Luminescent Colour and Ratio of Mixture

Per cent. Cd		0	20	40	60	80
Long-wave Limit of fundamental absorption A.U.		3460	3720	4115	4450	4820
Peak of Fluorescence band-with A.U.	Cu	5200	6100	6400	6600	7000
	Ag	4450	4800	5100	6000	6700

TABLE 13.3

Intensity of Fluorescence and Concentration of Quencher

Phosphor	Activator	Quencher			
		conc. %	Fe	Ni	Cu
$ZnSiO_4$	Mn	0·00	100	100	100
		0·01	78	78	88
		0·1	30	16	23
$CdSiO_3$	Mn	0·00	100	100	100
		0·01	77	90	50
		0·1	15	70	0
$MgWO_4$	—	0·00	100	100	100
		0.01	93	100	99
		0·1	83	100	87

Bibliography References : (*1232*, *1335*, *1568*, *1569*)

The intensity of fluorescence depends, among other factors, on the concentration of the quencher as is shown in Table 13.3 (*614*). The relation between the wavelength of the exciting radiation and the excited fluorescence, is given in Fig. 13.3.

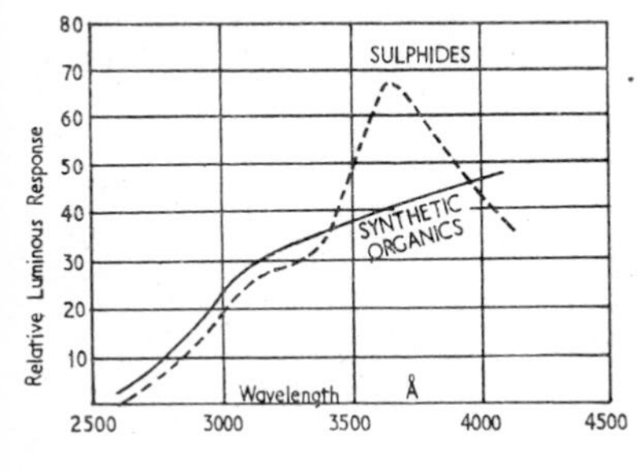

Fig. 13.3. Wavelength—intensity characteristic of fluorescent materials.

13.4. Excitation

As a general rule organic phosphors are best excited by radiation in the near ultra-violet, i.e., at 3650–63 A.U., and the inorganic phosphors, both synthetic and natural, by the powerful 2537 A.U. line and by still shorter waves.

TABLE 13.4

Luminescence and Excitation Wavelengths (*683*)

Types of Inorganic Phosphor	3650 A.U.	2537 A.U.	X-Rays	Cathode Rays	α-Rays (from Radium)
Sulphides ZnS, $ZnCdS$	very good	slight to fair	very good	very good	very good
Tungstates $CdWO_4$, $MgWO_4$	almost nil	very good	good	good	very slight or nil
Silicates Zn_2SiO_4 $ZnBe_2SiO_4$	very slight	very good	fair	very good	very slight or nil
Borates $Cd_2B_2O_4$	poor	very good	very slight	moderate	very slight
Phosphates $CdPO_4$, $ZnPO_4$	poor	very good	very slight	good	very slight or nil

The various spectral regions from the ultra-violet to the infra-red are given in Table 13.5.

TABLE 13.5

Spectral Ranges

Range A.U.	Name	Action
1200 to 2000	Schumann rays	ozone forming
2000 to 2950	far ultra-violet	bactericidal
2804 to 3132	Dorno (biotic) region	antirachitic
2950 to 3820	near ultra-violet	fluorescence
3820 to 7660	luminous	light, colours
7660 to 14,000	near infra-red	photographic
14,000 to 500,000	medium infra-red	heat
500,000 to 4×10^6	far infra-red	heat
2950 to 9×10^5	solar radiation reaching the earth.	

Certain phosphors respond to excitation with both 3650–63 A.U. and 2537 A.U. ultra-violet, the fluorescence colour in many cases being different, for instance :

TABLE 13.6

Luminescent Colour and Excitation Wavelength (*689*)

Phosphor	Exciting Wave-length	
	3650 A.U.	2537 A.U.
Cinchophen hydroiodide	strong orange red	dull violet
8-hydroxyquinolene	strong purple	strong violet
Oxyquinolene sulphate	strong crimson	dull purple
Pyrophosphate (ferric)	deep rose	blue

Other substances show no change in colour, for instance, quinine, quinine bisulphide, quinine salicylate.

A rather wide variety of phosphors responds to still shorter radiation, namely to X-rays which cover the spectral range from 100 A.U. to 0·01 A.U. For most industrial purposes a wavelength of the order of magnitude of 10 A.U. is sufficient and satisfactory. In the following Tables a range of materials is compiled which exhibit the phenomenon of luminescence on being excited by luminous, ultra-violet, or X-rays.

TABLE 13.7 (*350*, *614*, *690*)

Fluorescence by Ultra-Violet Excitation

Phosphor	Activator	Excitation long-wave limit A.U.	Excitation peak A.U.	Emission range A.U.	Emission peak A.U.
Calcium tungstate $CaWO_4$	Pb	2900	2720	3800–7000	4400
Calcium sulphide CaS	Bi	4200	3650		4750
Magnesium tungstate $MgWO_4$	—	3200	2850	3800–7200	4800
Zinc Cadium Sulphide: ZnS (80), CdS (20)	Ag		3650	4200–5900	4880
Calcium sulphide CaS	Cu	4200	3650		5100
Zinc sulphide ZnS	Cu	4300	3300		5200
Strontium sulphide SrS	Cu	4400	3650		5350
Zinc Cadmium Sulphide: ZnS (90), CdS (10)	Cu		3650	4200–6500	5410
Strontium sulphide SrS	Mn	4200	3650		5550
Zinc orthosilicate Zn_2SiO_4	Mn	2960	2537	4500–6200	5630
Zinc Cadmium Sulphide: ZnS (50), CdS (50)	Ag		3650	4900–7000	5690
Zinc sulphide ZnS	Mn	4500	3300		5850
Cadmium silicate $CdSiO_3$	Mn	3200	2400	4300–7200	5950
Zinc beryllium sil. $ZnBe_2SiO_4$	Mn	3000	2350	4500–7200	5950
Calcium sulphide CaS	Mn	4200	3650		6000
Cadmium borate $Cd_2B_2O_4$	Mn	3600	2300	4000–7200	6150
Magnesium silicate $MgSiO_3$	Mn	2800	2537	5000–7400	6800
Calcium sulphide CaS	Ni	4200	3650		7800
SYNTHETIC DYES					
Alpha-naphthol $C_{10}H_7ON$			4000	3900–5600	4190
Fluorescein acid $H_{20}C_{12}O_5$			3650	4500–5600	4800
,, ,, alk.			3650	5000–6000	5270
Erythrosine $C_{13}H_{14}O_6N_2$			3650	5000–6000	5600
Eosin G extra $C_{20}H_8O_5Br_4$			3650	5400–6400	5800
Rhodamine 6G $C_3H_4ON_2S$			3650	5500–7000	5800
Magdala Red $C_{30}H_{21}N_4Cl$			3650	5500–6600	5940
Rhodamine 3B			3650	5500–7000	5950
Rhodamine B extra			3650	5500–7000	6050

TABLE 13.8

Fluorescence by X-Ray Excitation

Phosphor		Emission		
		Short-wave Limit A.U.	Long-wave Limit A.U.	Peak A.U.
Fluorspar	CaF_2	2400	3640	2840
Willemite	$ZnSiO_4$	2270		3420
Zinc sulphide (synth.)	ZnS	3610		3800
Lead sulphate (*691*)	$PbSO_4$	2660		3970
Uranium ammonium fluoride	$UO_2F_2.3NH_4F$	3800	4400	4100
Zinc sulphate	$ZnSO_4$	3510		4260
Scheelite	$CaWO_4$	3750	4800	4330
Cadmium phosphate	$Cd_3(PO_4)_2$	3000		4440
Quartz	SiO_2	3910		4480
Cadmium ammonium bromide	$CdBr.2NH_4Br$	3260		4500
Potassium platinocyanide	$K_2Pt(CN)_4$	4120	4900	4500
Sidot blende	ZnS	4120	5090	4500
Balmain's paint	CaS	3510		4690
Barium platinocyanide	$BaPt(CN)_4$	4420	5090	4800
Calcium platinocyanide	$CaPt(CN)_4$	4550	5090	4800
Benzoic acid	$C_7H_6O_2$	2950	4500	3900 (min.)
beta-naphthol sodium sulphonate		3300	4900	3900
Diphenyl	$C_{12}H_{10}$	2960	5000	even distrib.
Phenol	C_6H_6O	2960	5000	3080, 4850
Naphthalene	$C_{10}H_8$	3300	4500	3460

Tables 13.7 and 8, respectively, are arranged to show increasing wavelengths in the column marked " emission peak ".

Zinc oxide ZnO, ordinary salt NaCl, potassium bromide KBr, potassium iodide KJ, benzene C_6H_6, and other substances also emit ultra-violet fluorescence. Most of the substances in the above Table emit non-luminous short-wave fluorescence upon irradiation with X-rays. The following, however, do not emit ultra-violet fluorescence upon X-ray excitation, viz., barium chloride $BaCl_2$, beryllium chloride $BeCl_2$, cadium sulphide CdS, and others.

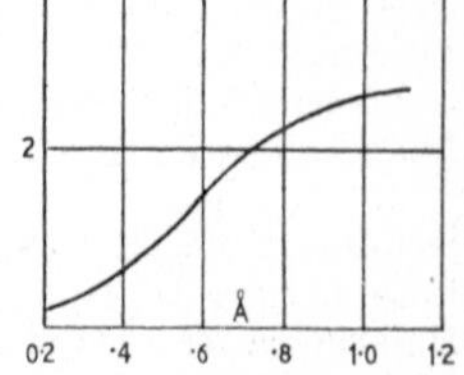

Fig. 13.4. Effect of X-rays of different wavelengths on fluorescence.

The effect of X-rays of different wavelengths on the intensity of the fluorescence is shown in Fig. 13.4 (*692, p.* 71).

There are a number of materials exhibiting phosphorescence when excited by X-rays or ultra-violet rays.

TABLE 13.9

Phosphorescent Materials

Phosphor		Excitation wavelength
Acetamide (techn. grade)	C_2H_5NO	2537 A.U.
Aluminiumacetate	$Al\,(C_2H_3O_2)_2OH$	2537 A.U.
Benzoic acid	C_7H_6O	X-rays
Diphenyl	$C_{12}H_{10}$	X-rays
Diphenylamine	$C_{12}H_{11}N$	X-rays
Resorcinol	$C_6H_6O_2$	X-rays
Sodium acetate (techn. grade)	$NaC_2H_3O_2$	2537 A.U.
Theobromine	$C_7H_8O_2N_4$	X-rays
Zinc acetate	$Zn\,(C_2H_3O_2)_2$	2537 A.U.
Zinc sulphide	ZnS : Cu	3650 A.U.
Zinc Cadmium sulphide	ZnS (82) CdS (18) : Cu	3650 A.U.

Most of these materials exhibit a green fluorescence. Commercially available products are listed in Tables 13.10 and 13.11. Both are excited at 3650 A.U.

TABLE 13.10

Commercial Phosphors

(Sterling Brand ; Made in England)

Type	Dominant wavelength of luminescence A.U.	Luminescent Colour	Afterglow
fluorescent	4600	B	none
	5150	B–G	none
	5400	G	none
	5600	Y	none
	6000	O	none
	6300	O–R	none
	6750	R	none
	7000	Deep Red	none
phosphorescent	4400	V	12 hours
	4500	V	12 hours
	4800	B–G	12 hours
	5200	G	4 hours
	5400	G	4 hours
	5650	Y	3 hours

TABLE 13.11

Commercial Phosphors

(Cal-Lux Brand : Made in U.S.A.)

Code 36/....	Type	Excitation	Range of Luminescence A.U.	Dominant Colour	Rate of Decay
51	phos.	L ; C ;	4670 to 6670	O	slow
2	phos.	L ; C ; UV ;	4480 to 5600	B	slow
38-B	phos.	C ;	4210 to 6600	G	slow
50	fluor.	C ;	4000–5000 ; 5300–6000	B-White	fast
30-2A	fluor.	C ;	4210 to 6020	B	$<10^{-8}$sec.
19-Cl	fluor.	C ; UV ;	4050 to 6856	Y–G	fast
19-Cl-L	phos.	UV ;	4050 to 6856	Y–G	slow
16	phos.	C ; UV ;	5760 to 6420	R	<5 sec.
20	fluor.	UV ;	4770 to 6040	Y–G	fast
33	fluor.	UV ;	5500 to 6320	Y	fast
34-D	fluor.	UV ;	5890 to 6500	R	fast
34-DO	fluor.	UV ;	5740 to 6650	O	fast
6	phos.	L ;	5500 to 6400	Y	slow

NOTE : L means : luminous rays
C means : cathode rays
UV means : ultra-violet rays
SLOW means : decay lasts from a few seconds up to 4 to 5 hr.
FAST means : decay lasts a few milliseconds

A new phosphorescent material* (*695*) has two peaks of sensitivity in the excitation, viz., 3200 A.U. and 4360 A.U. The maximum of phosphorescence is in the blue-green at 5070 A.U., i.e., near the wavelength of maximum scotopic vision (q.v.). The afterglow is accelerated by infra-red irradiation, but quenched by illumination with red light.

Another advance in luminescent materials was made a short time ago when V. Arkadiev (*1038*) produced a screen which became fluorescent under the direct impact of radio waves.

Bibliography References : (*523, 524, 541, 542, 1225, 1226, 1391, 1392, 1393, 1541, 1542, 1543, 1567, 1575, 1580, 1581, 1582, 1583, 2396*).

13.5. Chemical Notes

The pigment vehicle and solvent of organic or inorganic luminous materials, respectively, must be transparent to the exciting radiation and must be stable, which means that neither its chemical nor physical

* Produced and marketed by the Fluorescent Pigments Corp., New York.

composition is allowed to change under the impact of the exciting energy. Chemically, the reaction of these substances must be neutral; physically, the optical qualities must not deteriorate, for instance, no discoloration must take place. Suitable vehicles are the methacrylate, vinylchloride, vinyl-acetate, and cyclohexanone resins, polystyrol, and similar substances. For organic fluorescent materials the author used a commercially available solvent of the " acetate " type, and a nitro-cellulose medium which were both neutral. These vehicles were found to be very suitable for the acridines, flavines, rhodamines, etc.

Some organic radicals (*696*) act as activator, others as inhibitor or quencher of the luminescent phenomenon in organic substances. Activating radicals are :

amino– $-NH_2$; hydroxy– $-OH$; carboxyl– $-COOH$;

Quenching radicals are :

nitro– $-NO_2$; benzoyl– $-C_6H_5CO-$; acetyl– $-CH_3CO$;

Amongst the inhibitors are the bromides, chlorides, some iodides, nitro-benzene $C_6H_5NO_2$; hydroxy-benzene (phenol) C_6H_5OH ; methoxy-benzene $C_6H_5OCH_3$; methyl-benzene (toluene) $C_6H_5CH_3$ (*689*).

Bibliography References : (*1064*, *1101*)

13.6. Stroboscopic Effect

The electric discharge in a gas or vapour is a process with no thermal inertia. The output of radiation follows the frequency of the operating current. The discharge lamp is, therefore, a source of flickering light, the flicker having exactly double the frequency of the operating alternating current. Moving objects, seen by the light of a flickering source, show the phenomenon of stroboscopy. Depending on the duration of the afterglow, luminescent substances may also exhibit the stroboscopic effect, especially when the phosphors are used as coatings in low-pressure fluorescent tubular lamps. Taking the stroboscopic effect as 100% for the electric discharge in mercury and for all phosphors having an afterglow less than 10^{-8} sec., Table 13.12 (*350*) represents the stroboscopic characteristic of the various phosphors.

The relative brightness of the above phosphors, when excited under constant and equal conditions, is as shown in Table 13.13.

TABLE 13.12

Stroboscopic Effect

	Deviation from Mean Light Output %
Bare Mercury Discharge Lamp	100
Calcium tungstate	90
Magnesium tungstate	35
Zinc silicate	20
Zinc-Beryllium silicate	20

NOTE: The deviation from the mean output for low-wattage tungsten lamps is:

40 watts	13
100 watts	5
above 100 watts	negligible

TABLE 13.13

Relative Brightness

	%
Zinc silicate	100
Magnesium tungstate	63
Calcium tungstate	35
Zinc-Beryllium silicate	33

The effectiveness of the phosphors is instanced by the figures of Table 13.14 (*697*).

TABLE 13.14

Luminous Efficiency

Phosphor	Lm/W
Willemite $ZnSiO_4$ (native)	100
Zinc silicate (synthetic)	70
Magnesium tungstate	35
Zinc-Beryllium silicate	32
Cadmium silicate	30
Cadmium borate	23
Calcium tungstate	21

The spectral distribution of the luminous radiation from various phosphors, when excited by the 2537 A.U. line, is compiled in Table 13.15 (*697*)

TABLE 13.15

Spectral Distribution of the Luminous Radiation of Phosphors

Phosphor	luminous colour	$\lambda_{max.}$	% spectral energy relative to $\lambda_{max.}$				
			4500 A.U.	5000	5500	6000	6500
$CaWO_4$	blue	4400	98	60	24	8	2
$MgWO_4$	blue	4800	86	97	56	26	9
$ZnSiO_3$	green	5250	1	33	48	4	0
$(Zn_2Be)SiO_3$	yellow-white	5950	1	9	68	99	55
$CdSiO_3$	yellow-pink	5950	2	2	30	99	45
CdB_2O_5	pink	6150	1	2	7	92	69

An analysis and graphs of the spectral distribution of the luminous radiation of 45 various phosphors were published by Leverenz (*690*).

13.7. Sources of Ultra-Violet Radiation (cf. Chap. 7.19).

Bibliography References : (*1891, 2216*)

13.8. Filters

In some cases it will be necessary to use filters and their spectra will be different according to where the filters are used. Fundamentally, there are two places in a set-up where filters are used, (Fig. 13.5.) The " Short-wave filter " *FS* transmits freely the radiation of the source *R* necessary to excite the luminescence of the object. The "long-wave filter" *FL* is interposed between the luminescent object *L* and the receiver *Re* (observer, photo-cell, etc.) in order to prevent any short-wave radiation, which might not have been intercepted by the object, from reaching the eye of the observer. A long-wave filter, for instance, must be inserted if the radiation which is utilized in producing luminescence is not entirely confined to the non-luminous region of the spectrum, but extends into the luminous (violet, blue)

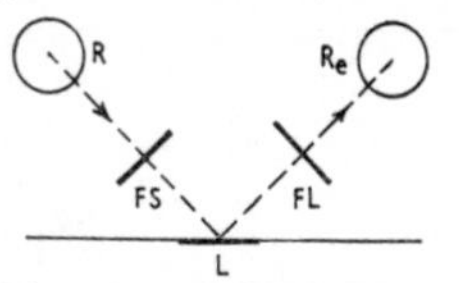

Fig. 13.5. Arrangement of short and long wave filters.

end. In this case a filter glass must be used which does not transmit the luminous rays of the radiator, but allows the eye or photo-cell to be reached by long radiations only. The *FS* filters should preferably be of the heat-resisting type. A recommended range of filters is given in Table 13.16.

TABLE 13.16

Range of Filter Sets

Short-wave Filter				Make		Long-wave Filter			
Code	transmitted range A.U.	peak at A.U.	%			Code	transmitted range A.U.	peak at A.U.	%
597	3100–4150	3650	87	1	1	038	4100—I.-R.	5200–7200	85
986	2500–4250	3650	75	1	1	368	4400—I.-R.	5200–7200	85
586	3300–3870	3600	30	1	2	Green	4500—I.-R.	5350	80
584	3100–3930	3590	55	1	2	16Y	4000—I.-R.	5500–	90
OX1	2900–4000	3650	84	2	3	4	4500—I.-R.	5000	90
OX7	2300–4300	2560–4000	87	2	4	401	4200—I.-R.	5600	90
18A	3100–4000	3650	55	3	4	108	4600—I.-R.	5100	90
UG1	3000–4000	3650	75	5	5	GG5	4100—I.-R.	4600	98
UG5	2300–4400	2500	40	5	5	GG7	4500—I.-R.	5000	98
		3000	95		5	VG5	4450—I.-R.	5250	90
		3250	98						
		3650	85						
BG24	1850-5500	2509	66	5					
		3000	90						
		3650	98						
		4000	96						
		4500	50						

(Other Wratten filters are : Nos. 5, 8, 9. other Ilford filters are : Nos. 107, 110, 111, 404, 406, 407, 805, 809)

NOTE :—Makers of Filters :

(1) Corning Glass Works, U.S.A.
(2) Chance Bros., Smethwick, Birmingham, England
(3) Wratten, Eastman Kodak, England ; U.S.A.
(4) Ilford, England
(5) Schott & Gen. ; Jena ; (Schurmann Corp., U.S.A.)

If a heat-resisting intermediate filter must be used the Aklo type Corning glass 395 with an ultra-violet transmission of 70% at 3650 A.U. will be of good service. A heat-absorbing heat-resisting British glass is Chance's type ON20 with a heat transmission of only 14% and a transmission in the luminous region of 88%.

13.9. Photo-electric Cells

Photo-electric cells usually have their peak or peaks of sensitivity in the luminous or infra-red region. A few types, however, are commercially available for the direct detection of ultra-violet rays.

Photo-electric cathodes made of pure metal extend their range of sensitivity into the far ultra-violet. These cells are useful not only in the instrumentation of technical research, but also in the solution of medical, biological, and meteorological problems. The rather small absolute sensitivity of pure metal cathodes is compensated by the use of high-sensitivity amplifiers.

TABLE 13.17

Ultra-Violet Sensitive Photo-electric Cells

Type	Cathode	Spectral Range	Max. Sensitivity	μA/Lm	Code	Make
		A.U.	A.U.			
G	Cd	2500–2950	2600	<0·1	UDG7	1
G	Cs_2O	3000–12000	3650(7500)	100	CMG8	1
V	K on Ag_2O	2500–7000	3500	2	KMV6	1
V	Cs–Mg	2750–7000	3300	0·75	WL770	2
V	U	2800–3200	2975			2
V	Zr	2000–3150	2340		WL767	2
V	Th	2000–3675	2550		WL773	2
V	Ta	2000–3000	2400		WL775	2
V	Pt	. . –2000	<1700		WL789	2
V	Sb–Cs	2000–7000	3650	20–50	QVA38	3

NOTE: Makers: (1) G.E.C. (England);
(2) Westinghouse Lamp Co. (U.S.A.);
(3) Cinema-Television, Ltd.—CINTEL (England) (*2445*)

Other cathode materials affording a long-wave limit in the ultra-violet, are Au (about 2500 A.U.), Ag (about 2700 A.U.). All these materials are highly sensitive in the far ultra-violet. (*vide* Chap. 4).

13.10. Mutual Agreement

Best overall efficiency will be attained if the respective maxima of radiation source, filters, luminescent material, and photosensitor or human eye or, in general, recording or receiving apparatus, either actually coincide or occur within a narrow band, and if it can be assumed that the relative sensitivity remains fairly constant within that range. This means that the long ultra-violet radiation (3650 A.U.) is best registered by a caesium oxide cell. The second peak of caesium cells, occurring at about 7500 A.U., can be cancelled by the use of appropriate filters, or it may be utilized by employing a luminescent material emitting in the far red. The sensitivity in the ultra-violet can be increased by making the bulb from Corex D glass or quartz (*25*). If the caesium oxide cell is used in both ranges at once an effect can be attained as with an intensifying screen (barium-platinocyanide screen or calcium tungstate screen) in X-radiology (*699*). The ultra-violet energy causes a maximum photo-current which may still be increased by intercepting by a dark red luminescent material any ultra-violet energy not striking the photosensitor. The dark red luminescence is then " seen " by the photosensitor (by virtue of its second peak in the 7500 A.U. region), thus causing an additional increase in the photo-current.

If no direct observation of the ultra-violet energy is required by any particular method or task the agreement between the maximum emission of the radiator and the maximum susceptibility of the luminophore is necessary as well as the agreement between the peak output of the luminescent energy and the maximum sensitivity of the photosensitor. The following combination is an instance.

Excitation	Luminescent material	Peak Output at	Photosensitor type
at 2537 A.U.	Zn_2SiO_4	5630 A.U.	PA2-Green ; peak at 5650 A.U.

Other photosensitors in this range are : EEL Cells (5500 A.U.) ; Weston Photronic (5800 A.U.).

13.11. Industrial Applications of Luminescence

Only in recent years has a certain group of phenomena, termed " Luminescence ", been applied to industrial problems (*1651*). This is not only due to methodological achievements but also to improvements in the performance of sources of ultra-violet energy. While the research worker in the laboratory has at his command a wide variety of elaborate methods and apparatus, the production engineer will give preference to a set-up which allows of a wide range of applications and uses as simple methods and as robust appliances as ever possible.

The modern forms of mercury vapour discharge lamps are just the source of radiant energy the engineer has been waiting for. These lamps operate at a high efficiency, viz., 38 to 45 and more Lm/W, have a long life (up to 5000 hours), a high overall power factor (0·75 to 0·98) and are both electrically and mechanically well fitted for the somewhat rough handling in workshops.

Bibliography References : (*462*, *1125*, *1155*, *1162*, *1201*, *1378*, *1381*, *1383*, *2379*, *2386*).

13.12. Fluorescence Analysis

The fluorescence analysis is one of the most sensitive chemical methods. Although lack of space forbids even a short description of the methods and advantages of the fluorescence analysis*, a few data will readily prove the above statement (*1621*).

TABLE 13.18

Detection Limits of Fluorescence Analysis

Fluorescent Material	Detectable Concentration
Quinine in water	10^{-10}
Uranium in water	10^{-11}
Aesculin	10^{-12}
Anthracene in alcohol‡	10^{-10}
Fluorescein	10^{-10}
Eosin	10^{-8}
Peroxides	$1{\cdot}2 \times 10^{-8}$
Aluminium	10^{-7}
Arsenic	10^{-7}
Saccharine	$1{\cdot}6 \times 10^{-7}$
Boric Acid	$5{\cdot}0 \times 10^{-7}$
Bromine in hydrochloric acid	10^{-6}
Coal tar pitch in asphalt	$2{\cdot}0 \times 10^{-5}$

* There is an enormous literature on this subject. Radley and Grant (*700*) quote more than 2000 references ; Dhar (*701*) more than 2500.

‡ Pure anthracene has a blue fluorescence at 4047 and 4358 A.U. Commercial anthracene exhibits a green fluorescence due to the presence of naphthacene in the molecular lattice. Naphthacene, in this case, must be considered an impurity " Pure " chemicals are of A.R.-quality.

13.13. Detection of Mercury Vapour

The phenomenon of mercury vapour being opaque to ultra-violet rays is utilized in the detection of traces of mercury vapour. This is the most sensitive method known at present and is used in the chemical, smelting, metal-mining, and electrical apparatus industry.

A zinc silicate screen or an anthracene screen will detect mercury in an ore at the ratio of one in a hundred thousand. An ore, suspected to be mercuriferous, is powdered and heated strongly and the suspected vapours are allowed to pass between an ultra-violet source emitting at 2537 A.U. and the screen. Vapours other than of mercury cast no or only a very hazy shadow on the screen ; mercury vapour, even in as low a concentration as 10^{-5}, casts a very dense shadow. The same dense shadow appears if a sample of air from a room, in which mercury has been volatilized at N.T.P., is drawn between the ultra-violet source and the screen (*1662*, *1663*, *2471*). The General Electric Co. (*703*) has produced a mercury-vapour detector for use in industrial plants, measuring directly concentrations as high as one part in 5×10^5 parts of air by volume and as low as $2{\cdot}5 \times 10^{-8}$ p.b.v.: the accuracy is about 5%. The toxic limit of mercury vapour for humans is 1·2 parts of mercury vapour in 10^5 parts of air. A different toxic limit was given by C. Goodman (*704*), viz., 0·05 p.p.m. by volume (i.e., 0·25 mg/m^3). The G.E. detector works at the remarkable rate of $\frac{1}{2}$ cubic foot of air per minute (*705*).

A highly sensitive portable mercury-vapour detector of simple design (*706*, *1404*), which is also sensitive to any light-blocking medium such as smoke, fly-ash, haze, fog, etc., uses a Wheatstone bridge circuit, one resistor being replaced by a triode. The method used is based upon the scattering of the 2537 A.U. (resonance) line by Hg-vapour (*707, p. 590* ; *708*). The lower limit of detection is of the order of 10^{-9} p.b.v. (cf. Chap. 10, Table 10.1 and following text). A silicon resistor across the cathode-anode of the triode effectively reduces fluctuations due to changes in the mains voltage.

The same methods can conveniently be adapted to act as a safety valve in vacuum plants. High vacuum installations, for instance, those for neon tube pumping, are very sensitive to contamination by mercury

Note on silicon-carbide resistors :

The resistance of Thermistor silicon-carbide resistors (Trademarks, for instance, Atmite, Metrosil, Thyrite) is an inverse function of the applied voltage. The current is proportional to the *n*-th, for instance fourth, power of the applied voltage. The theory of silicon-carbide resistors is discussed in detail in a publication by the Automatic Telephone and Electric Co., Ltd. (*709*). They are used in the control of voltage-selective circuits, in the protection against voltage surges, in the stabilization of power voltages, etc.

vapour. It is easy to arrange for an ultra-violet sensitive photo-relay to be mounted behind the quartz tube, an appropriate part of which masked by a diaphragm. The aperture in this diaphragm has an area equal to the projected area of the photo-electric cathode ; one dimension of this cathode, which may be of rectangular, square, circular, etc., shape, being equal to the diameter of the glass tube. The radiation (2537 A.U.) is allowed to pass through the aperture in the diaphragm, traverse the gas stream in the tube, and fall on to the photosensitor.

TABLE 13.19

Optimal Combinations between Photosensitor and Fluorescent Screen

Material of Fluorescent Screen		Photosensitor	
	max. A.U.		*max.* A.U.
Zinc silicate	5630	Westinghouse PA2-Green	5650
Calcium tungstate	4400	RCA-926 ; GEC-KG7 ;	4400
Anthracene	4358	RCA-926 ; GEC-KG7 ;	4400
Cadmium borate	6150	BTH-PV921 ; SeS or CdS cells (80% at 6150 A.U.)	5500
(All the above excited at 2537 A.U.)			
Zinc sulphide : Ag	3800	RCA-931A	3750
(Excited by X-rays)			

A minute trace of mercury vapour will obscure the ultra-violet beam, causing the photo-relay to operate, i.e., to close a valve before the mercury vapour can reach it. If it is difficult to obtain ultra-violet sensitive photosensitors recourse may be had to the transformation by a fluorescent screen (*vide supra*) of the 2537 A.U. radiation into luminous radiation. In such cases coincidence between the maximum spectral sensitivity of the photosensitor and the peak emission of the fluorescent material must be approximated as closely as possible. There must be no additional phosphorescent effect (afterglow) and the fluorescence afterglow of the screen must be negligible as compared to the action time of the relay. The mechanical basis of the fluorescent screen can be any transparent material which is not affected by the ultra-violet radiation (insolation). It need not be transparent to ultra-violet radiation if the uncoated surface of the fluorescent screen is next to the photosensitor and the coated surface turned towards the radiant source.

In many other cases the fluorescent screen can be replaced by a fluorescent filter, e.g., by Uranium Crown glass or Canary glass, exhibiting a strong greenish-yellowish fluorescence, or by Clear Blue Fluorescing 014 (Corning Glass Works) which is a colourless transparent glass exhibiting a strong blue fluorescence. Both should be excited by radiations shorter than 3100 A.U., preferably 2537 A.U., although the 3650 A.U. band also gives the characteristic, but rather weak, fluorescence. When these fluorescent filters are used they should be sandwiched between the photosensitor and another filter that excludes luminous radiation from the photo-cell. Such filters are of the Red Purple Corex A No. 986 (Corning), or UG5 (Jena) type, etc., and are defined by a high transmission in the far ultra-violet (<3100 A.U.).

Bibliography Reference : (*2109*)

13.14. Detection of Flaws, Cracks, etc.

The many methods of crack detection in materials used industrially have been greatly enriched by the use of fluorescent substances. The technique is simple and is well suited for mass inspection. According to the shape of the test object some methods show definite advantages over others. Small plain objects are tested by the " duochromatic " method, developed by the author. A 1% solution of 3 : 6-dihydroxyphthalimide in petroleum ether* is colourless in daylight or incandescent light, but shows a strong blue colour when irradiated with long-wave ultra-violet light. A drop of this liquid is applied to the test object where it spreads out evenly, or the object can be dipped into the fluorescent indicator. The volatile liquid vaporizes within one or two seconds, but is retained longer in crevices, cracks, and flaws. The time needed for vaporizing the petroleum ether can easily be controlled by selecting a suitable boiling range†. When viewed in ultra-violet light after the liquid has volatilized the dry surface will appear a yellowish colour, the cracks standing out in bright blue against the yellow background, which is due to the capillary action of the fissures. After a very short time, varying from two to three seconds for the low-boiling point petroleum ethers and up to one to two

* Dissolve 1 gm. of 3 : 6 -dihydroxyphthalimide in 127 cm.^{3} of alcohol abs. and dilute with petroleum ether puriss.

† Ranges available : below 40° C. ; 40–60° C. ; 50–60° C. ; 60–80° C. ; 80–100° C. ; 100–120° C. ; above 120° C.

minutes for the high boiling ethers, the liquid will have totally disappeared. No residues which are harmful to glass, plastics, ceramics, metals, textile fibres, etc., are left on the surface of the object. The inspection need not be carried out in complete darkness, but can be effected in daylight if an ultra-violet inspection unit is used.

Other methods employ anthracene dissolved in petroleum jelly or in medicinal paraffin. The surface is covered with the jelly, or paraffin. The petroleum jelly by itself has a violet-blue to sky-blue fluorescence depending on the degree of purity. The surface is then wiped clean. The petroleum jelly will be retained in flaws and cracks, if any, and reveal its presence by a strong blue fluorescence. This method is often employed in grinding, polishing, honing workshops, etc., because it indicates any cracks which might have been cut open during the polishing process. Larger flat surfaces of metallic or other smooth-surfaced bodies are inspected by the " brushing method ". An inorganic fluorescent powder is brushed over the surface to be inspected and this is then wiped clean. One or more grains of the finely ground powder (*710*) will remain in the crevices and give away their position by exhibiting a bright coloured light when viewed under the ultra-violet source (*711*, *712*, *713*).

Bibliography Reference : (*1127*)

13.15. Petroleum Industry

The application of luminescent phenomena to problems in the petroleum industry is discussed in a paper by de Ment (*714*).

13.16. Mining

Certain minerals exhibit a vivid fluorescence the colour of which is characteristic for the mineral and its source. A source of ultra-violet radiation is now a tool of the prospector and miner just as are his pick-axe and shovel, except that it is infinitely more delicate. A mineral mixed with waste or gangue material which either does not fluoresce at all or has a fluorescence different from that of the mineral, will stand out clearly when irradiated with ultra-violet rays and an appropriate, yet very simple, apparatus can be designed for automatically picking out and separating the ore from the dead stone (*715, p. 41*).

No data other than the general rule can be given because the minerals vary in their fluorescence colour and intensity not only with the intensity and wavelength of the exciting ray (long or short u-v or X-rays), but also with their origin and mineralogical structure so much so that the experienced miner can often tell the origin of a mineral by judging from its fluorescence colour.

13.17. **Irradiation**

The mercury arc is a source of bactericidal radiation (*716*). This is used, for instance, in the brewing industry for sterilizing water ; in the dairy industry not only for sterilizing water (*1437*), but also producing a high vitamin D content in the milk. The polykymatic discharge tube usually consumes 700 to 1200 watts supplying sterilized water at an hourly rate of up to about 2800 litres (625 gallons). The monokymatic low pressure mercury-in-quartz discharge tube is the most efficient, powerful and economical source of bactericidal and germicidal radiant energy.

13.18. **Infra-Red Image Converter (Image Changer ; Infra-red Telescope, Light Transformer)**

If it is desired to produce luminous radiation by the impact of infra-red rays on a suitable material, the Zworykin-Morton electron-image tube (Image Converter) must be resorted to (*1674*, *2472*). It consists of an infra-red sensitive cathode and a fluorescent screen, (Fig. 13.6a). A means is provided (*717*, *718*, *719*) which focuses the electron-image from the cathode on to the screen. The cathode is sensitive to infra-red energy. The electron-image tube is capable of transforming infra-red images into luminous images. The industrial application lies in " viewing " infra-red images of the interior of melting pots, furnaces, kilns ; night driving ; optical pyrometry (at temperatures down to 350° C.) ; control of operations which are carried out in the dark ; in inspecting goods emerging from a kiln for evenness of temperature distribution, etc. (cf. 13.19).

Early image converters based on this principle have been built in England by Pratt (*2452*, *2488*) (E.M.I., Ltd.), by Coeterier and Teves (*720*) in Holland (Philips Gloeilampen Fabrieken, Eindhoven), in Italy by Malatesta (*1266*), in the United States by Farnsworth (*2447*) and Zworykin (2448), in Germany by Kluge (*2449*) and Schaffernicht (*2450*), and elsewhere by others (*1440*, *1640*, *1641*). The Dutch workers used an electron-optical system known as the " long magnetic lens " (*159*). The cathode consists of a platinum film on top of which a quartz film is deposited. This system is covered with a film of silver oxide and is sensitized with caesium. The anode is made up of the same elements, but bears a nearly transparent film of zinc silicate or calcium tungstate instead.

The English design of static infra-red image converters is very simple and effective. The tube consists of an approximately 40 mm. length of Pyrex glass, 50 mm. in diameter. The ends are closed with plane glass windows about 2 mm. thick. The one window is coated with a semi-transparent silver-caesium cathode with its range extending into the infra-red to about 13,000 A.U. A Willemite (zinc silicate) screen is deposited on a thin glass disk and mounted inside the glass tube at a distance of about 5 mm. from the photo-cathode. The plain glass window is the ocular, the cathode window the objective of the image converter.

German practice is described in the BIOS Final Reports (*2433*, *2438*).

A modern development of the static type image converter, i.e., a tube where the position of the electron beam with respect to the tube walls does not alter, is the dynamic image converter where the electron beam is deflected across the tube (*1440*, *1640*, *1641*) so that a time axis is added to the picture and, as a further extension of this, a series of discrete pictures can be produced by using suitable deflexions of the beam.

The dynamically-operated image converter tube can be used instead of rotating drum cameras or mirrors in high-speed photography. Due to the character of the luminescent screen the image of the transient phenomenon will persist sufficiently long for a photograph of it to be taken. Comparative writing speeds are :

drum camera	200 metres/sec.
rotating mirrors	350 to 2000 metres/sec.
image converter (dyn.)	100,000 metres/sec.

In Fig. 13.6a the Mullard type ME 1200 is shown and in Fig. 13.6b an arrangement of the magnetic lens. The photo-cathode must be of the S- type. Magnification is $\times$ 3, and resolution is 200 lines/cm. The anode voltage is 6 kV and the sensitivity of the S_{-1} surface is 20 μA/L at a colour temperature of 2700° K. In the type ME1201 a grid is introduced which will blank the screen and permit exposures of 10^{-8} sec., or less. The effective cathode area is a circle of 1 inch diameter. Curved screens should be used whenever possible to avoid pin-cushion distortion. Max. length : 240 mm. ; max. diameter : 130 mm. (*2597*).

A practical application of such an instrument which transforms an invisible infra-red image into a green (zinc silicate) or blue (calcium tungstate), i.e., luminous, image may also be found in tin-plating works.

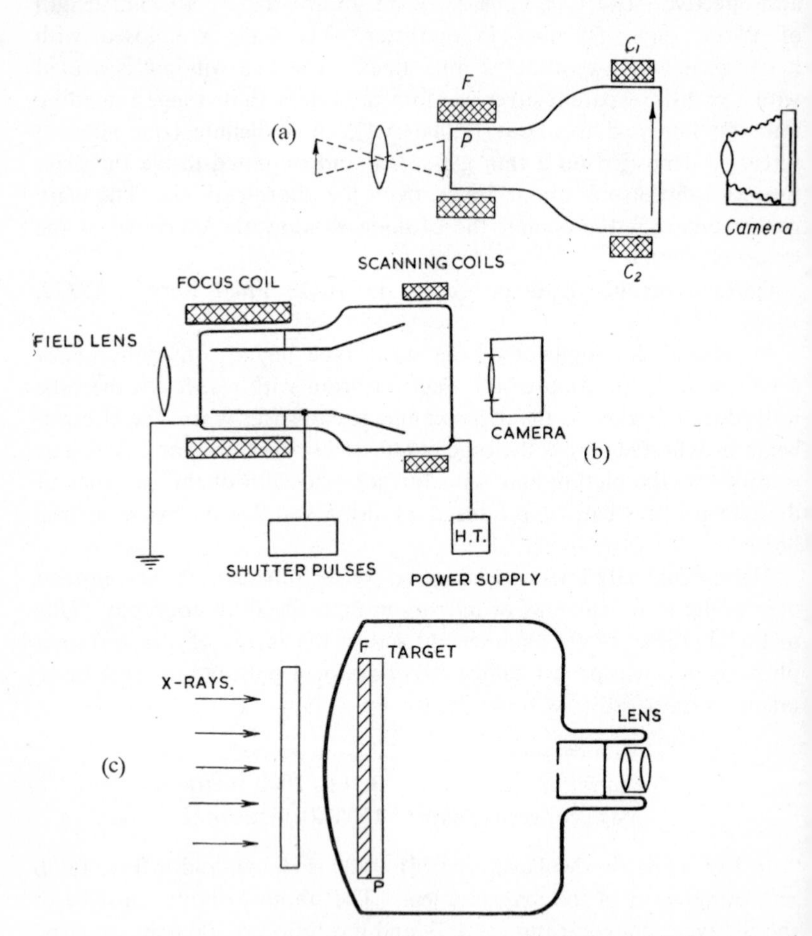

Fig. 13.6. Outline diagrams of Image Converters: (a) Magnetically focused and deflected tube; (b) Tube Type ME1201 with special electrode for high-speed photography; (c) X-ray intensifier tube. (*Mullard Ltd.*)

The procedure of using infra-red irradiation for the detection of porosity in tinplate was developed by H. J. Taffs of the International Tin Research and Development Council. An account of the photographic method is given by Clark (*36, p. 276*).

It is obvious that a combination of the two principles will result in a very useful apparatus for tin-plating works. A " light transformer " will allow a continuous inspection to be carried out, a task which will become the more important as the introduction of electronic tinning control progresses (*721*) (cf. 11.15). Porosity of the tinplate shows as a dark field or dark spots against the white or light coloured tinplate of perfect surface. The infra-red radiation strikes the continuously moving sheets or strips of steel under an oblique angle. A photosensitor, having its peak of sensitivity at, or close to, the maximum emission of the fluorescent screen of the " light transformer " is used in scanning this screen for dark patches. If a certain ratio, which may be termed the " limit of porosity ", is reached a photo-relay is energized and actuates the electronic tinning controls.

The image converter can also be used in the inspection of lubricating oils which have been used in internal combustion engines. The initially clear oil, after a certain time, becomes blackened by soot, dust, and the products of carbonization. As King (*5*, *723*) points out it is the high temperature, especially in air-cooled engines, which causes the formation of hard carbonaceous matter, resulting in an increase of internal friction which, if neglected, may reach the point where seizure takes place. The regular inspection of the oil, if carried out in non-selective light, will give a falsified picture as both carbonaceous matter and other impurities are opaque to luminous radiation. This is not so if infra-red irradiation is used, because only the carbonaceous matter is opaque to infra-red radiation. This phenomenon can be made use of in producing an image of the oil on the fluorescent screen of the " light transformer " or in directly scanning the oil by means of a photosensitor which covers the infra-red range of the source of radiation. Image converters for the conversion of ultra-violet images into visible ones are under development at present.

The image converter has developed into an important instrument in photographic practice. Equipment has been built for astronomical photography in which the photo-electrons are accelerated in the image converter by applying 20-40 kV. By this means, objects can produce an electronic image in great detail within four minutes compared with a previous exposure time of six hours for a photographic plate . (*2596*)

The use of an infra-red image converter as an electronic ocular for infra-red spectroscopy is described by Carsen and Wilson (*2606*). The spectral distribution in the red and infra-red (1.2μ) of sources of radiation can be investigated by means of photo-multipliers with a S_4 photo-cathode (approx. 6200 A.U. threshold). An image converter with a S cathode and blue fluorescent screen (ZnS:Ni) in front of the standard multiplier (*2598*) will give suitable results. The time response of the image converter is sufficiently rapid to cause only small distortion at 400 c/s. (*2599*)

Bibliography References : (*578, 579, 1354, 1762, 1775, 1780, 1924, 2086, 2088, 2223, 2262, 2284, 2355, 2356*).

13.19. Thermography

It has been known since the beginning of the last century that phosphorescence, excited by radiations from the ultra-violet range of the spectrum is in some cases readily extinguished by the incidence of infra-red rays (*684, 722, 724*). In practice, this general statement will be restricted to a few cases of optimal conditions. When using a zinc sulphide with an excitation peak at 3650 A.U., the infra-red radiation of between 9000 and 14,000 A.U. will effect the most marked extinction. Calcium sulphides have a higher infra-red limit, about 17,500 A.U. The action of the infra-red depends on its wavelength, but is independent of the time of exposure to, and the intensity of, the infra-red radiation ; in other words the phosphoro-extinction is governed by the Bunsen-Roscoe reciprocity law (time $\times$ intensity is a constant) (*725, 726*).

In a German Patent (*727*) a very effective phosphor is described having a strong lasting afterglow which is very susceptible to infra-red radiation. It is a zinc-cadmium sulphide phosphor with a CdS content up to 15%, using copper as an activator*. Maximum excitation at 3500 A.U. to 5300 A.U., maximum emission at 5550 A.U., extinction wavelengths between 5300 and 15,000 A.U.

Another phosphor has already been described (*695*) which can be used in phosphoro-extinction methods, but it must be borne in mind that it is the red (not the infra-red) portion of the spectrum which causes the afterglow of this particular phosphor to be extinguished.

In the British Patent 391374 and in the French Patent 742894 (1932) it is proposed to use the phosphoro-extinction method when determining the distribution of temperature at the surface of a hot body (cf. Chap. 16). An image of the hot surface is projected on to a previously excited phosphorescent screen where the phosphorescence will be extinguished pro rata of the incident heat energy. This image can

* A phosphor (max. emission at 5650 A.U.) for infra-red extinction is manufactured by Messrs. Thomas Tyrer, Ltd., London.

be scanned by a photo-relay ; temperatures below or above a given limit are then used to energize an alarm or control gear.

The above described phenomenon of quenching luminescence by the impact of infra-red radiant energy is different from the phenomenon called stimulation which, at a first glance, is very much like the quenching process. The phosphor is first excited in the ordinary way by blue, ultra-violet, or alpha-rays, respectively (*1633*, *1635*), and then emits the visible afterglow as usual. After this luminous afterglow has died down completely, or nearly so, the phosphor is stimulated with infra-red radiation (*1634*) upon which the so " excited " phosphor will emit luminous radiation.

Heat and heat distribution of objects can be recorded over a wide range of temperatures, making use of sensitive phosphors. A screen is coated with specially prepared phosphors and a curved metal mirror is used to focus the heat radiation of the test object on the screen.

In a related technique, phosphors are coated directly on the object to get a " contact " picture of the heat distribution which can then be photographed or filmed. Phosphors are available that show a 20 to 25% change in brightness for each degree Centigrade of change in temperature. Thermography can be used over a very wide range of temperatures reaching from about —180° C. to 500° C.

Bibliography References : (*1226*, *2403*)

13.20. Fluoroscopy

The method of X-raying an object (*1298*, *1299*) and viewing its silhouetted image on a fluorescent screen is called fluoroscopy. The luminescent image can be viewed either by an observer or by photo-sensitors (*728*). The fluoroscopic method of inspection has advantageously been applied to spotting a foreign body in packaged goods, like food, tobacco, or candy ; spotting air bubbles in cast metal ingots ; determining the filling level in tins, canisters ; detection of internal flaws especially in light alloy castings, inspection of oranges and other fruit (*1623*), etc. An instance of this type of inspection is the X-raying of a filled hand grenade in order to locate any irregularities that may exist (*3*, *4*).

Another instance of loaded ammunition being inspected by high-voltage (1,000,000 Volts and, at other plants, 2,000,000 Volts) X-ray equipment is quoted in Chemical and Metallurgical Engineering (*1039*). Voids in TNT-filled shells are indicated even when the steel of the shell is 2 inches thick. Up to 4000 shells have been X-rayed in 24 hours with one machine.

The alignment of elements which are enclosed in an outer casing can be checked as, for instance, in metalized or metal electron valves. Golf balls, cored arc carbons, wires, cables, small ammunition, shell and grenade fuzes, car tyres, etc., are more instances where fluoroscopic methods are used with advantage.

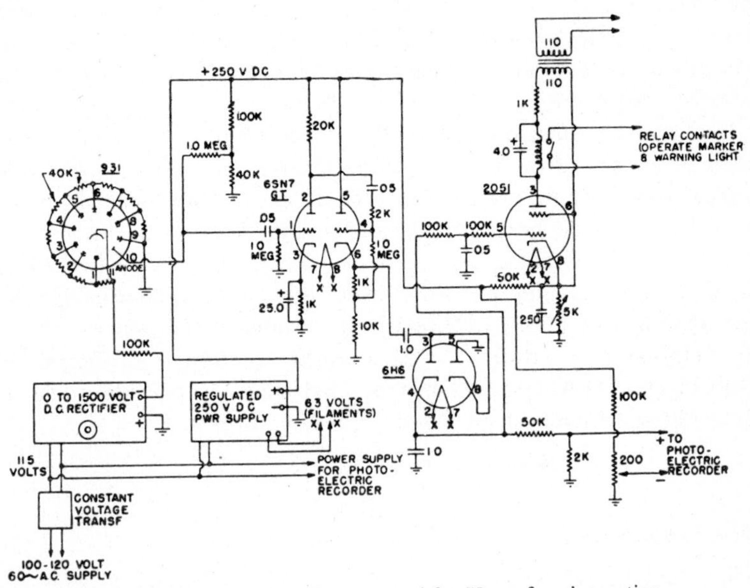

Fig. 13.7. Circuit of equipment used for X-ray fuze inspection.

The screen for fluoroscopic observation is usually of the zinc sulphide type which has been treated in such a way as to reduce phosphorescence.

An outstanding combination of method and apparatus is described by H. M. Smith (*729, 1652*). The X-ray sensitive phosphor is applied directly on the outside of a photosensitor the cathode of which is insensitive to X-rays. The luminescence peak must coincide with, or approach as closely as possible, the maximum wavelength of the spectral sensitivity of the cathode material. Smith, in using a RCA-931A which has its maximum sensitivity in the region of 4000 A.U., employed a phosphor emitting in the violet or ultra-violet portion of the spectrum. For optimal conditions the phosphor must be ZnS : Ag or $CaWO_4$. Another binding condition is the total absence of phosphorescence.

Readily measurable are X-ray intensities that cause the phosphor to produce an amount of light sufficient for 10^{-7} lumen to be incident on the cathode of the 931-A. Much less than this amount is sufficient if the light is blue, viz., about 10^{-4} μW. The circuit shown, Fig. 13.7, was used for fuze inspection.

A photo-electric exposure meter for industrial radiography (range of X-rays between 40 and 200 kVp) makes use of photo-multipliers and two different types of fluorescent screens. The meter can be used with or without the normal X-ray intensifying screens (*2600*).

The penetrating power of alpha-particles is within reach of industrial inspection methods and it is probably only a matter of a few years development before non-destructive inspection by both X-rays and alpha-particles will have become generally adopted methods. Blau and Dreyfuss (730) have developed a radiometric method using a multiplier photo-electric cell in radioactive measurements. The source of the alpha-particles is placed on a photometer bench, the radiation, after penetrating the test object, is intercepted by a fluorescent screen the fluorescence of which is measured by the multiplier photosensitor. A standard light source is also placed on the photometer bench and is moved along it until the photosensitor produces the same deflexion in the measuring instrument as when viewing the fluorescent screen. The distances on the photometer bench allow the intensity of the radium to be calculated according to the inverse square law, or to measure the thickness of the material under inspection. The fluorescent screen with the highest yield (about 80%) is a copper-activated zinc sulphide phosphor (*731*).

Curran and Baker (*2446*) have described a similar method which proves useful in the detection of alpha particles as encountered in radiation laboratories (stray radiation). The measurement of the scintillation effect of fluorescent screens caused by the impact of alpha particles is carried out with a photo-electric multiplier. This arrangement is a specific detector for alpha particles since the fluorescent screen is insensitive to simultaneous beta and gamma radiation.

Bibliography References : (*431*, *434*, *558*, *1732*, *1786*)

Photo-electric multipliers are used in the field of radio-active particle counting and radiation detection. A scintillation counter consists of a photo-electric multiplier which is brought in close contact with a fluorescent crystal or screen. If the receptor, i.e., the screen or crystal, is struck by the radio-active particle, a feeble scintillation is produced.

The sensitivity of the photo-multipliers and their inherent amplification is such that even one single particle can be counted reliably. Scintillation counters are employed for the detection and measurement of alpha, beta, gamma, roentgen, ultra-violet ,and infra-red energies. If the photo-cathode of the multiplier tube is not directly sensitive to the incidence of particles or radiations, detectors, i.e.. screens or converters must be used in front of the cathode (*cf. 23.14*).

13.21. Luminoscopy

There are certain substances whose luminescent colour is characteristic for a certain condition which may be classed as the critical characteristic for " acceptance " or " rejection ". Such a case is the inspection of shell eggs. Fresh eggs show a red fluorescent shell while stale eggs have a distinctly blue fluorescence. Besides basing visual inspection on this phenomenon (*388*) it is quite easy to design a photo-electric mechanism which rejects blue fluorescent eggs but passes the red ones.

Summer has now shown that the biological premisses do not hold (*2601*). The red fluorescence is due to ooporphyrine which is located in the shell. Exposure to strong light or longwave ultra-violet radiation will oxidize the porphyrin and change its fluorescence colour to blue while the interior of the egg remains unchanged. If kept excluded from radiation the shell will still fluoresce red, even after months, but the contents will have gone stale a long time ago. The fluorescence test is not a reliable test for freshness or staleness of eggs, although many authors still maintain this point.

Bibliography References : (*1502, 1505, 1509, 1510, 1511*)

13.22. Measuring Instruments

Photo-electric ultra-violet meters are not always readily available on the market. The necessity of measuring the output of lamps or the intensity of any ultra-violet radiation may, sometimes arise and present a delaying problem to the workshop engineer.

Photo-electric ultra-violet meters are simple instruments. The basic principle is shown in Fig. 13.8a (*732*), and its application to a practical circuit in Fig. 13.8b (*733*), An instrument for measuring the 2537 A.U. line of low pressure mercury discharge tubes has been devised by Luckiesh and Taylor (*734*). The interesting feature is the combination of an ordinary lightmeter, using a photo-e.m.f. cell, with a special filter.

This is a compound filter consisting of a quartz disk and an ordinary glass disk, the fluorescent material being sandwiched between these two. The optical properties must be selected as shown in Table 13.20.

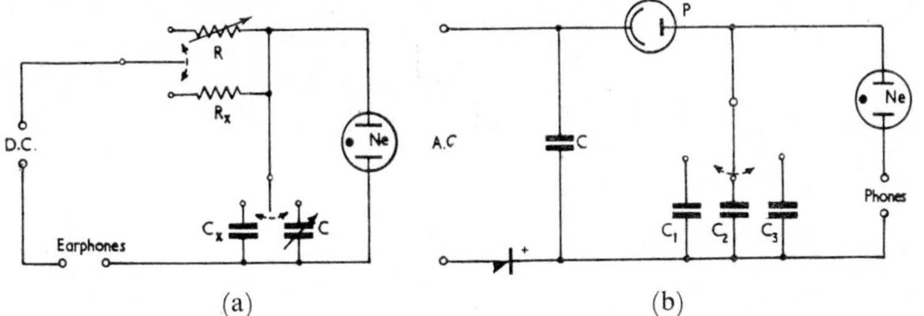

Fig. 13.8. Photo-electric ultra-violet light meter (a) basic circuit (b) practical form.

TABLE 13.20

Quartz-Glass Filter

Spectral transmission of Quartz disk : uniform ;

Spectral transmission of Glass disk : no transmission for $\lambda < 3000$ A.U.

Phosphor (Zinc meta-silicate): Excitation maximum at 2537 A.U.; no reaction to radiation > 3000 A.U.

Two readings must be taken, viz., one by placing the filter with the quartz disk topmost, on top of the light meter, and another by placing this filter with the glass disk on top. In the first case the ultra-violet radiation from the lamp excites the material the fluorescence peak of which should coincide with the maximum sensitivity of the photo-e.m.f. cell in the light meter. In the second case the glass disk, which is now placed between the source of radiation and the fluorescent substance, will permit no radiation shorter than 3000 A.U. to reach the fluorescent material which is not excitable by radiations that might be transmitted by the glass ($\lambda > 3000$ A.U.). The difference of the two readings, when taken as described above, is a direct measure of the intensity of the 2537 A.U. energy. Less than 1% of the differential deflexion is due to wavelengths other than 2537 A.U.

An improvement on this type of filtering ultra-violet from luminous radiation is in the use of a thin coat of a neutral nitro-cellulose lacquer in which picric acid (2-4-6 trinitrophenol $C_6H_3O_7N_3$) or, better still, picrolonic acid (3 - methyl - 4 - nitro-1-p-nitrophenyl-5-pyrazolone, $C_{10}H_8N_4O_5$) has been dissolved. The author has been working with these two solutions since 1937 and always attained satisfactory results (*1419*). A saturated solution of picrolonic acid in ethyl alcohol puriss. is mixed (2·5 to 5 p.b.v.) with a neutral thinner and this mixture added to the neutral nitro-cellulose stock. For spraying a 1 : 1 ratio will be satisfactory. The lacquer is of a slightly lemon-yellowish tinge. It is sprayed on one side and the fluorescent material on the other side of the quartz disk.

An ultra-violet intensity meter for use in workshops was described by Andrews (*735*). The photo-cell used is a WL-775, the tantalum cathode being insensitive to radiation longer than 3000 A.U., Fig. 13.9.

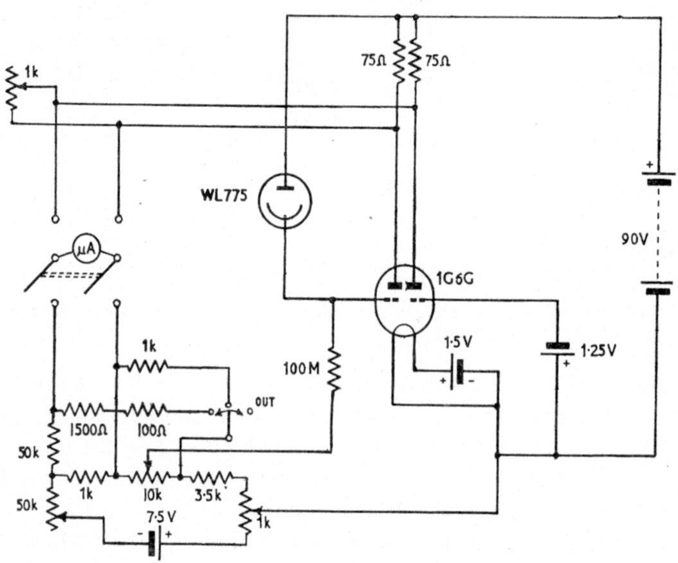

Fig. 13.9. High-sensitivity photo-electric meter for u-v radiation below 3000 A.U.

Another type of fluorimeter, as described by W. Koch (*736*), is used in the estimation by comparison of riboflavin and thiamin.

The standard unit of luminescence is called " Fluorescent Unit ". This is the luminescence produced by 1 mg radium element of 1 cm^2 on barium-platino cyanide screen ($BaPt(CN)_4$).

A fluorimeter for measuring the intensity of fluorescence (*1626, p. 826*) of liquids is described by Krebs and Kirsten (*737*).

An ultra-violet lamp housed in a cylinder open at both ends provides the light which passes through four 0.47 × 2.5 cm. vertical slits. The cells for holding the liquid whose fluorescence is to be determined are supported on two platforms of an " elevator ". Part of the fluorescence from the liquid enters two photocells contained in housings after it passes through filters. The filters may be selected to transmit a part of the fluorescent light without transmitting too much of the light diverted toward the photocells from the ultra-violet beam by the liquid. A liquid which does not fluoresce will then have a reading of almost zero on the meter.

A photo-electric photometer for luminescent materials was developed by Teele (*738*).

In medical as well as in industrial roentgenology it is of the utmost importance to provide extreme uniformity between films for maximum analytic value. Euler *et al.* have developed an electronic timer for the control of X-ray exposure which operates on the principle that the exposure time must be adapted according to the individual object under inspection. As the mechanical dimensions of the individual objects, although of the same type, are at variance with one another, it will be necessary for the exposure time to be adjusted in each case individually. This seemingly complicated and tedious procedure is made time saving and fully automatic by means of the simple arrangement shown in Fig. 13.10. Euler *et al.* (*739*) concluded that the fluoroscopic image of the object is the only means which correctly reproduces,

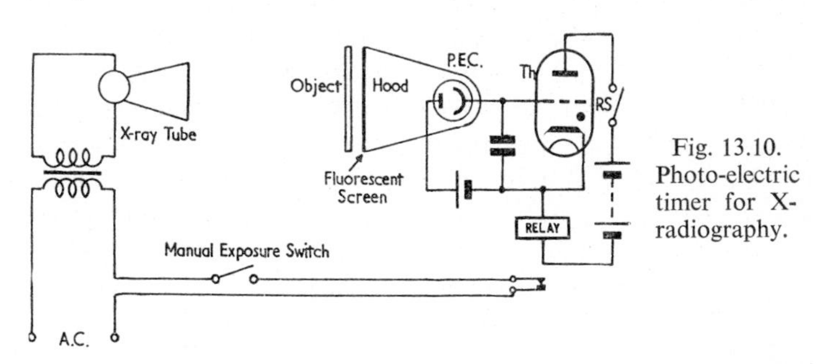

Fig. 13.10. Photo-electric timer for X-radiography.

and is a measure of, the density of a particular object. The photosensitor scans a certain area of the fluorescent X-ray screen (*2426*), and the photo-electric current so produced charges the capacitor to a given amount which process, according to the intensity of the luminescence, takes varying lengths of time. When the capacitor is charged it discharges through the thyratron, thereby firing it and causing the load contacts of the relay *R* to open : this interrupts the exposure. Since the contacts must remain open the thyratron must be D.C. operated and a resetting switch must break the anode circuit before the manual exposure switch is thrown.

Bibliography Reference : (*445, 462, 515, 2498*)

13.23. Metal Cleaner

When appraising the degreasing qualities of metal-cleaning compounds use is made of the bright fluorescence exhibited by mineral oil under the incidence of ultra-violet radiation (*740*). The metal parts to be cleaned are treated with the solvent and then viewed under ultraviolet irradiation. The minimum visible amount of residual oil, i.e., the lower limit of visual observation, is 0·000004 gram of oil per cm^2. If records are to be made, this method can be combined with one given for recording the colour of opaque objects (*741*) or a photoelectric instrument may be used in the detection of luminescence which might be too weak to be " seen " visually.

13.24. Detecting and Measuring Minutest Quantities of Oxygen

A method of measuring the production of very small quantities of oxygen, in fact of 10^{-9} cm^3/sec of O_2 at atmospheric pressure, is based on a phenomenon discovered by H. Kautsky (*1400*). He found that certain dyes become phosphorescent upon irradiation by a tungsten lamp. Pringsheim, Franck and Terwood, in a paper read to the American Chemical Society (Symposium on Fluorescence and Luminescence ; September 11, 1945), showed that the afterglow of the dye trypaflavine (acriflavine) adsorbed on silica gel, when it is contained in a highly evacuated glass container, is not affected by the introduction of H_2, N_2, CO, CO_2, CH_4, or any of the rare gases, but is quenched to about one half of its maximum intensity by the addition of O_2 of 5×10^{-5} mm. pressure (*1401*, *1402*). A low-voltage projection lamp (6 V, 18 A) has been used by the investigators to excite the phosphor. The phosphorescent light is picked up by a type 931-A photomultiplier cell (*1049*).

Bibliography Reference : (*1557*)

CHAPTER 14

CHEMICAL INDUSTRY

14.1. Various Applications

A particularly interesting field of useful applications of photo-electric control will be found in the chemical industry. Here the photo-sensitors' qualities of exceeding the sensitivity of the human eye in both luminous and non-luminous spectral regions come into their own.

Inherent in many chemical processes is a more or less drastic change in such optical properties as refraction, opacity, turbidity, selective absorption (i.e., colour) of the substances concerned, but physical changes also occur as, for instance, the formation of lather, fumes, sedimentation, precipitation, liquefaction, evaporation, solidification, etc. There are many cases where a change in a certain quality will be better ascertained by using non-luminous, viz., ultra-violet or infra-red, radiant energy rather than luminous rays as a stimulating medium which is then " sensated " by the proper type of photosensitor. In other cases, where there is no inherent change in optical properties, such a change can be brought about by using an indicator, i.e., a chemical substance which changes its initial colour under given specified conditions. There are also " physical indicators ", viz., measuring instruments as, for instance, thermometers, barometers, electrical and other instruments, the position of their indicating element (pointer, mercury or other liquid column, etc.) being watched by a photo-relay.

Photo-electric methods have gained for themselves a wide field in analytical chemistry. To mention only the more important sections in which photo-electric methods of measurement are successfully applied, it may suffice to enumerate colorimetry, densitometry, spectrophoto-metry, nephelometry, polarimetry, measurement of lustre, gloss, reflectancy, transparency, etc., etc. (*796*).

A thorough study of the qualities of a substance as revealed under luminous, ultra-violet, or infra-red irradiation, respectively, will dis-close what type of photo-electric equipment must be used in order to get optimal results. The following section is but a very brief and in-complete account of what has been achieved during the last ten years ;

in fact, a kaleidoscopic picture is presented rather than a proper survey which would take many times the space allocated to this section.

A very simple circuit for the detection of colour changes as experienced in reactions with chemical indicators is shown in Fig. 14.1. This circuit (*795*) operates from the A.C. mains, but a full-wave rectifier

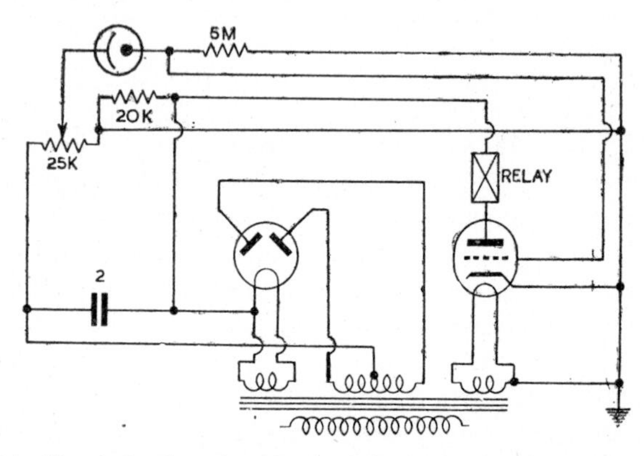

Fig. 14.1. Circuit for detection of colour change in chemical indicators.

supplies D.C. for the photo-cell circuit. The potentiometer can be adjusted to determine the degree of discoloration of the indicator at which indication is desired. In principle the discoloration method can be operated in different ways, for instance, by using single sheets of filter paper impregnated with the indicator and being replaced after each test ; by using self-impregnating paper tape which, before moving in front of the photosensitor, passes through a solution of an appropriate indicator (*770*) ; by employing some reversible chemical process envolving a reversible change of colour. Some indicators must be kept damp in order to exhibit maximum and quantitatively correct indication. In such cases a 10 to 15% admixture of glycerol will prevent the paper from becoming dry.

One of the first applications of a photo-relay in controlling a production process by observing colour changes inherent in the processed material was made in the plant of the Papeteries Navarre in France, where the colour of the cooking pulp controls the steam valves of the digester. This method is based on the close relationship between the degree of cooking and the colour of the liquid. Any type of photoelectric circuit which is designed to be operated by fluctuations of incident radiant energy can be made to control the above described and any similar process. A circuit as shown in Fig. 14.2 can be used either for recording the fluctuations due to changes in colour or density or turbidity, i.e., transmissivity (if the valve is of the grid-controlled type) or it can be employed in controlling directly the process by actuating a relay switch or any industrial control gear (if the valve is of the trigger type, e.g., a thyratron).

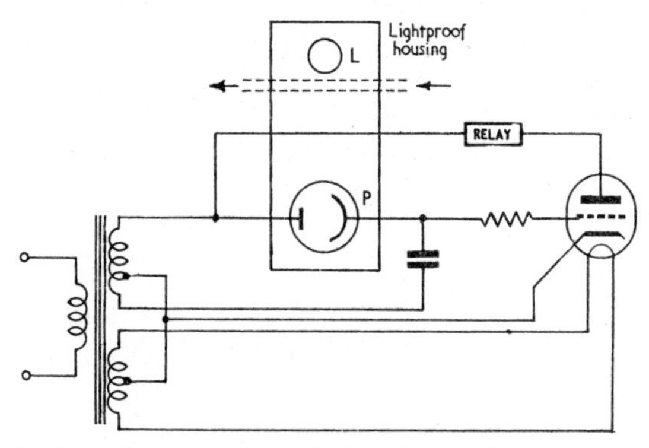

Fig. 14.2. Scanning head and circuit for a colour controller.

V. Sukhikh (*805, 806*) developed a photo-electric colorimeter and nephelometer with a cylindrical or annular photosensitor. It is particularly suitable for the automatic control and inspection of continuous processes where the optical properties of a liquid (colour or

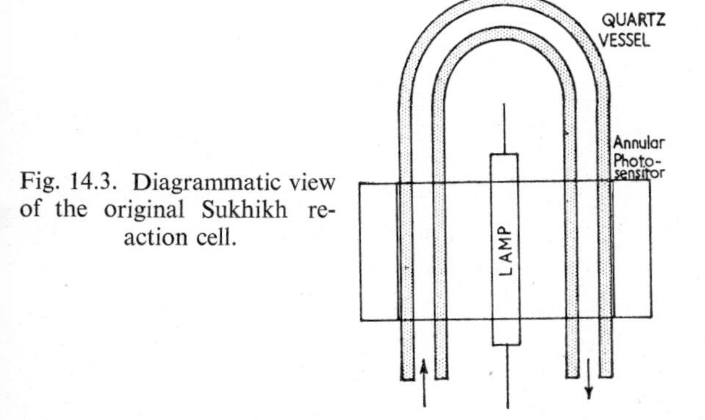

Fig. 14.3. Diagrammatic view of the original Sukhikh reaction cell.

cloudiness, i.e., turbidity) become changed during the course of a reaction. The Sukhikh reaction cell, Fig. 14.3, consists of two concentric tubes of a suitable transparent material, e.g., fused quartz, organic or inorganic glass. The diameters of the tubes differ just sufficiently to cause the liquid to flow in a thin layer between a light source which is at the centre, and a cylindrical photosensitor. The disadvantage of this arrangement becomes obvious at once, viz., its lack of ventilation of the light source, which may prove disturbing in many cases. An inverted arrangement uses in the centre a non-directional photo-cell, for instance, a RCA 928 or a Visitron type R85, and an annular light source on the outside of the flow cell. If a straight tubular light source must be employed, for instance, sodium or mercury discharge lamps, the original arrangement must be adhered to. The cell, however, will conveniently be constructed as is shown in some detail in Fig. 14.4.

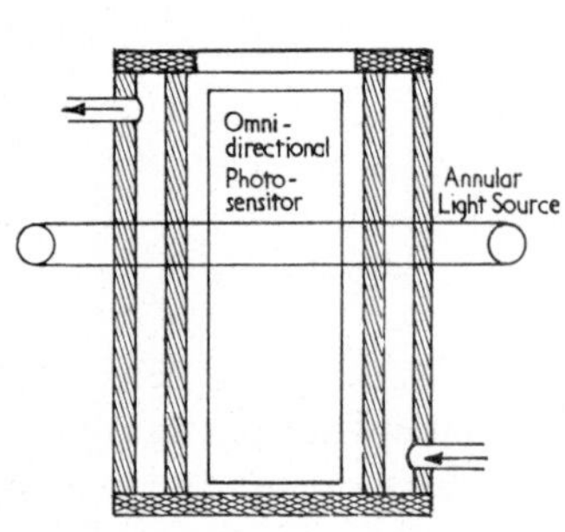

Fig. 14.4. Inverted reaction cell.

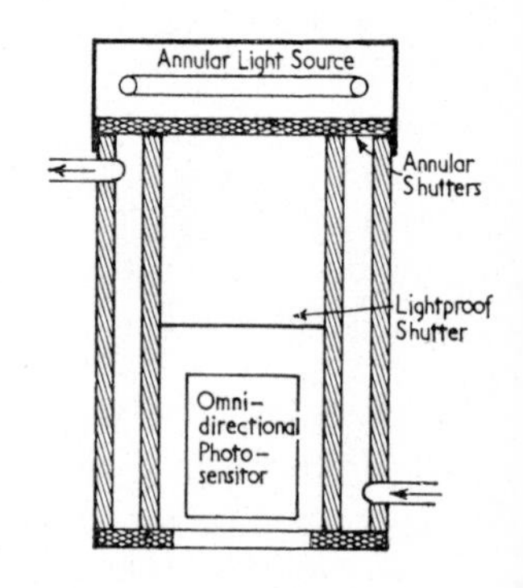

Fig. 14.5. Inverted reaction cell modified for measuring the Tyndall effect.

This instrument is also used for measuring the intensity of scattered light (Tyndall effect). A cylindrical cell is fitted into the space inside the cylindrical element. Parallel rays of light are directed axially on to the surface of the liquid in the cell, Fig. 14.5. The cylindrical photosensitor is now affected only by the light scattered by particles in the liquid. Sukhikh has also described a tyndallometer which, by the addition of an ordinary photosensitor, measures the transmitted light (cf. Chap. 9.19). Another instrument measuring the Tyndall effect is described by S. Silverman (*442*).

A photo-electric nephelometer requiring no amplifier is used in the measurement of the growth of bacteria (*E. coli*). The incident light is scattered by the culture (5×10^7 bact./ml) and produces a photocurrent of 12μ amp (*2618*).

For current determinations of the moisture content of steam, a system like the one patented under B.P. 484144 will be useful. Its principle is based on the fact that the transparency of steam varies as the moisture content of the steam changes. Another important instrument is the Water Hardness Tester (*1269*, *1270*, *1271*) which permits the determination of water hardness to be carried out continuously, a feature which becomes particularly valuable in supervising the feed water of boilers in laundries, etc. It is obvious that a modification of this simple apparatus lends itself not only to measuring the hardness but also to keeping it constant or within set limits by controlling the electromagnetic valves of drums or tanks containing the softening agents. The general principle involved in testing water for hardness is the formation of a quantity of lather, this quantity being in a known relation to, and a measure of, the hardness of the water under test. The hardness of natural water is due to the presence of simple inorganic substances, such as calcium or magnesium bicarbonates and other compounds of these elements. Soft water is a *conditio sine qua non* not only in the textile and laundry industry, but also in tanning and leather works, paper mills (*797*), in the brewing industry, steam raising plants, etc.

Water must be free from bacteria if it is to be fit for human consumption. The most generally adopted sterilizing agent is chlorine in the form of sodium hypochlorite NaOCl. Quite a number of different systems and apparatus for automatic chlorination have been developed (*397, pp. 118 et. seq.*; *798*, *800*, *801*), all of them being based on the detection of residual chlorine by the orthotoluidine reagent which, by the shade of its yellow to orange-red discoloration, indicates the amount of residual free chlorine in water (*752*).

Mercury vapour is detected by the discoloration of selenium sulphide (*779*, *799*). Sensitivity : 0·125 p.p.m. Ozone absorbs at 3130 Å and is detectable by this effect (*1661*).

The determination of organic matter present in sand filters, as used in water purification, is made by digesting the sand in diluted sodium hydroxide NaOH and viewing the resulting colour by a photosensitor (*802*, *804*).

Sewage is analyzed and controlled by measuring its turbidity and colour (*803*). The turbidity of water or any other liquid is measured with a device the arrangement of which is shown in Fig. 14.6. The light from the lamp is made into a parallel beam by the lens and, after traversing the tubular flow-chamber, is focused by a second lens on to the diaphragm D which is so placed that the focus lies exactly in the plane and centre of the pinhole behind which is a photosensitor PR placed so that the diameter of the light cone equals the diameter of the circular photosensitor, in this case preferably a photo-e.m.f.

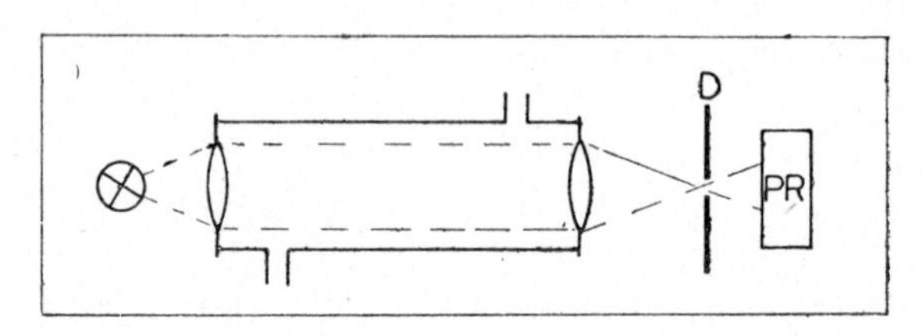

Fig. 14.6. Device for measuring turbidity in liquids.

cell. The instrument is adjusted with clear water (or with pure air) in the flow-chamber. Any degree of turbidity will cause a deviation of the beam by dispersion, resulting in a displacement of the focus, thus causing the circuit to become unbalanced. The attenuation by absorption of part of the transmitted light is considered a secondary effect in this arrangement (*807*). Another circuit for measuring the turbidity of a liquid uses two photosensitors, the one, PC_2, measuring the degree of turbidity, and the other, PC_1, acting as compensation. The cells are in opposition and are connected to the individual measuring coils C_1C_2 of a differential galvanometer DG or electronic recorder Fig. 14.7 (*808*). Turbidimetry in the infra-red has been described by

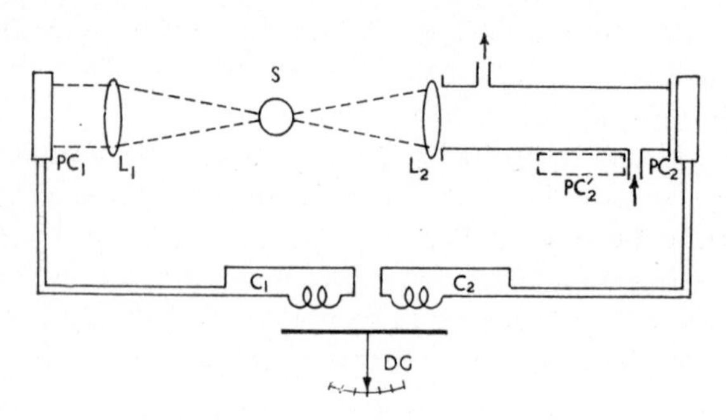

Fig. 14.7. Another arrangement for measuring the turbidity of a liquid.

Barnett (*809*). In stationary as well as ship engines the steam condensate very often contains some of the lubricating oil in the form of an emulsion. This water cannot be used again in the boiler until the oil has been removed. A two-cell circuit, Fig. 14.8, with the cells in opposition and having a cathode-ray indicator as measuring instrument, is used in detecting the balance point. The National Bureau of Standards has produced standards of turbidity for oil-in-water emulsions ranging from 0 to 2 p.p.m. of oil (*810*).

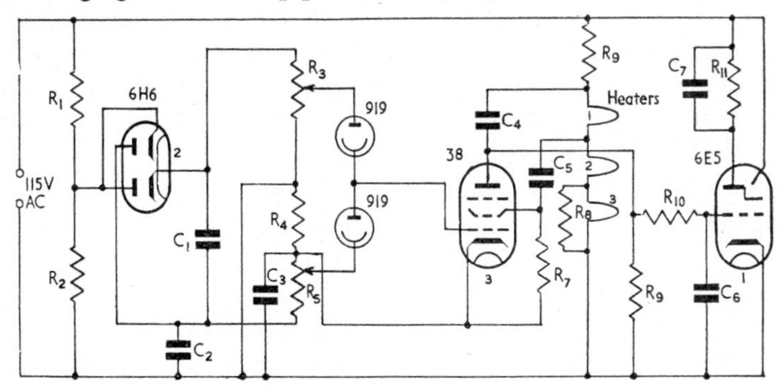

Fig. 14.8. Sensitive circuit for matching measurements (*Courtesy RCA*).

In general, the degree of turbidity is expressed as the turbidity of an emulsion of Kieselguhr in water. This arbitrary, yet accepted, standard unit of turbidity is exhibited by an emulsion of 1 mg. of Kieselguhr in 1 litre of distilled water.

Changes in humidity can be made visible by observing a patch of cobaltous chloride $CoCl_2$ that is blue-green when dry, but changes to pink with increasing humidity.

Bibliography References : (*407, 408, 409, 410, 414, 417, 419, 420, 421, 422, 423, 424, 429, 432, 433, 434, 435, 572, 600, 1149, 1175, 1374, 1536, 1557, 1869, 1877, 1881, 1889, 1909, 2138, 2148*).

14.2. Detection of Freon

Freon-12 (known in Britain as Arcton and on the Continent as Frigen), is the trade name of difluorodichloromethane. This, and other substituted methanes are used in large-scale as well as domestic refrigeration. The only disadvantage of Freon is its ability to leak through porous metal which would be considered quite impervious and safe for other gases or vapours. Another property of difluorodichloromethane is its inclination to produce, by decomposition when in contact with flames or hot surfaces above 300° C., traces of carboxychloride $COCl_2$ (phosgene)* and carboxyfluoride COF_2 which, however, was hotly disputed by the makers of Freon (Frigen). Extensive investigations in

* An indicator for phosgene is *p*-dimethylamine benzaldehyde.

this matter and careful analyses of difluorodichloromethane have given definite proof (*812*) that no noxious gases are produced. It decomposes easily, however, into HCl and HF.

Since Freon is a rather expensive refrigerant the detection of traces of Freon vapour in air is highly desirable. One method, which is objectionable because an open flame is employed (*vide supra*), has the advantage of being a physical method, no replacements of indicators after detection being necessary. An alcohol flame heats a copper burner. When difluorodichloromethane is present, copper halogenides are formed, colouring the flame green : this method is extremely sensitive. The change can be observed by any type of photo-electric equipment. If suitably designed, the objection might be reconsidered if proper care is taken to prevent the highly active decomposition products from entering into the atmosphere of a room. The open flame is harmless as Freon is neither combustible nor explosive.

Another system of detection has been developed by the Linde Eismaschinen, using a chemical method. A U-shaped tube of silicon-containing material, for instance porcelain, or fused quartz, Fig. 14.9, is heated to about 800° C. To prevent thermal losses most of the U-tube is lagged. The tube ends in a flask which is partly filled with

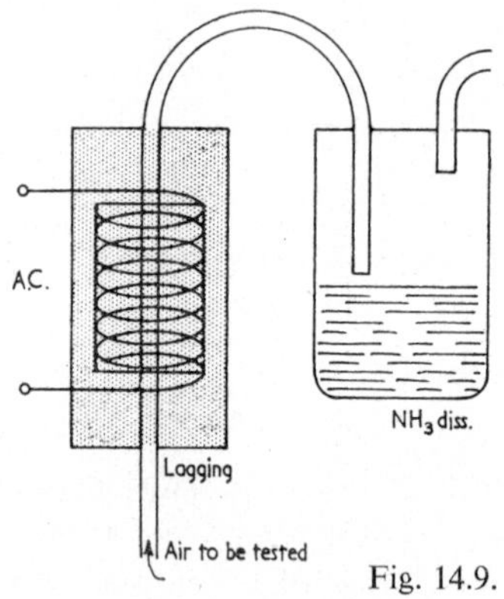

Fig. 14.9. A Freon detector.

ammonia water. If difluorodichloromethane contaminates the air, silicon fluoride SiF_4 is formed in the hot tube. Upon coming in contact with the moist ammonia atmosphere, the silicon fluoride becomes hydrolysed and breaks up into hydrofluoride HF and hydrosilicon H_4Si. The chlorine derivatives hydrolyse and form HCl. In the presence of NH_3, the following are precipitated in the form of a fine white fog : NH_4Cl, NH_4F, Si. This precipitation can easily be detected by photo-electric equipment.

Bibliography Reference : (*1415*)

14.3. Ultra-Violet Absorption Analysis

In German chemical works photo-electric devices were used in controlling the maturing process of a certain type of explosive. It is essential for the agitators, as used in this process, to be switched off immediately when a little white foam appears in the centre of the tank around the driving shaft of the agitator (*811*). This particular spot is constantly watched by two photo-cells in a compensated circuit. The general layout is shown in Fig. 14.10. The amplifier A, is supplied with

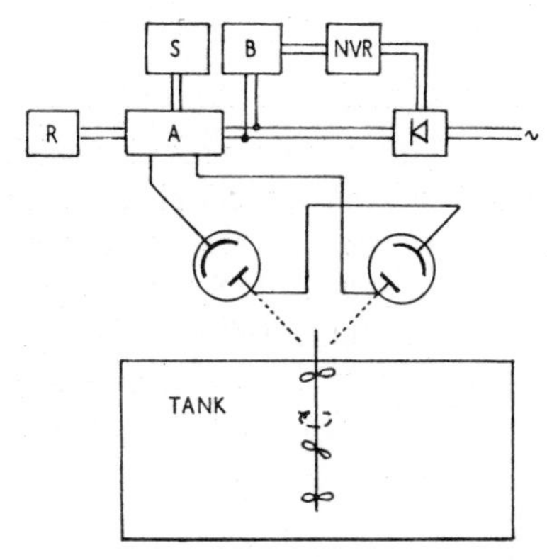

Fig. 14.10. Block diagram of control circuit used in the manufacture of explosives. A. amplifier R. recorder S. Signal B. battery NVR. no-voltage relay

D.C. (rectified A.C.) which, in case of mains failure, is fed into the system from a battery of accumulators B.

Ultra-violet sensitive photosensitors are essential in the control and measurement of the output of therapeutical, germicidal, and other sources of ultra-violet radiation. Therapeutical generators usually operate over a region the lower limit of which is characterized by the erythemal (Dorno) range. The latter comprises the waveband from 3200 to 2800 A.U. The germicidal action of ultra-violet radiation (*1288*) becomes evident when wavelengths from 2700 to 2000 A.U. (*1289*, *1620*) are used. Data on germicidal action have been published in many periodicals and textbooks. An interesting comparison, valuable for works managers and welfare officers, shows that in a 4000-cubic-foot room the germicidal action of low-pressure ultra-violet sources is so intense that the old-fashioned exhaust fans will be superseded to avoid the expense and inconvenience of fan ventilation if not for the more obvious reason of saving and safeguarding the health of the worker (*611*, *2413*, *2414*).

TABLE 14.1

Watts per ultra-violet radiator	Equivalent to air changes
4	10
8	40
15	45
30	100

Ultra-violet radiators are widely used in dairies for sterilizing water (*1437*) which is based on the germicidal action of ultra-violet rays below 2700 A.U. After a few seconds exposure to ultra-violet radiation the natural potency of 10 U.S.P. units per quart of milk* is increased forty-fold, viz., to 400 U.S.P. units per quart (*813*). Orange juice also gains by irradiation with ultra-violet energy and the treated products can be kept suitable for human consumption over a period of many months.

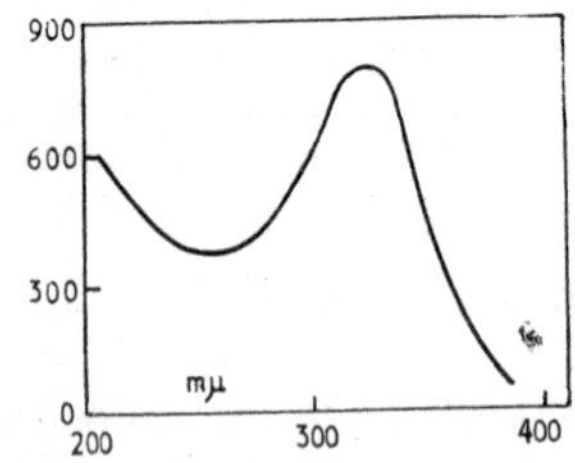

Fig. 14.11. Spectral absorption curve of Vitamin A. (*Courtesy of Ind. Eng. Chem. Anal. Ed.*)

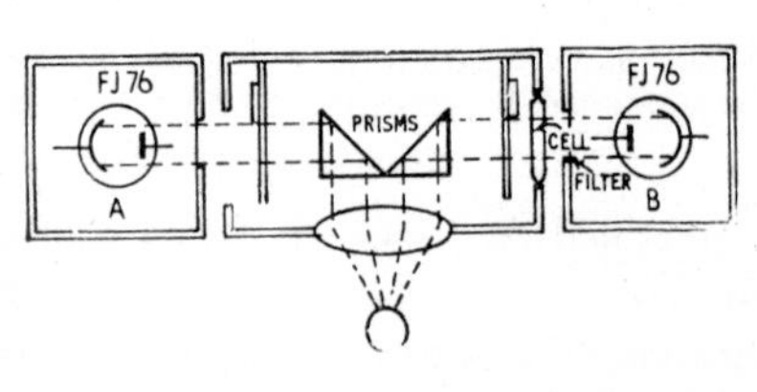

Fig. 14.12. Diagram of photo-electric absorptiometer for measuring Vitamin A content. (*Courtesy of Ind. Eng. Chem. Anal. Ed.*)

The continuous control of cod-liver oils for the presence of vitamin A (*1441*), or the control of synthetically produced vitamin A is made possible by the fact that vitamin A strongly absorbs the 3280 A.U. line.

* The destruction of an enzyme (lipase) in milk is due to blue light but not to the ultra-violet radiation in the solar radiant energy.

It was found (*826*, *827*) that the absorption of vitamin-A-containing materials is directly related to, and can be made a measure of, the potency of that particular material. The ultra-violet absorption of vitamin A varies with the nature of the solvent (*828*, *829*). The spectral analytical method is admirably suited for that purpose as well as for the control of the production of vitamin D by the action of ultra-violet radiation of 2804 A.U. wavelength.

The absorption spectrum of vitamin A has its maximum at 3280 A.U., Fig. 14.11, but it is possible that another maximum is reached in the short ultra-violet region (shorter than 2000 A.U.). A photo-electric instrument for measuring vitamin A by means of absorption analysis was used in the investigations by McFarlan, Reddie and Merrill (*830*). The circuit of the instrument, Fig. 14.12, was designed by F. H. Shepard, Jr. (*345*) and is based on the circuit shown in Fig. 14.13.

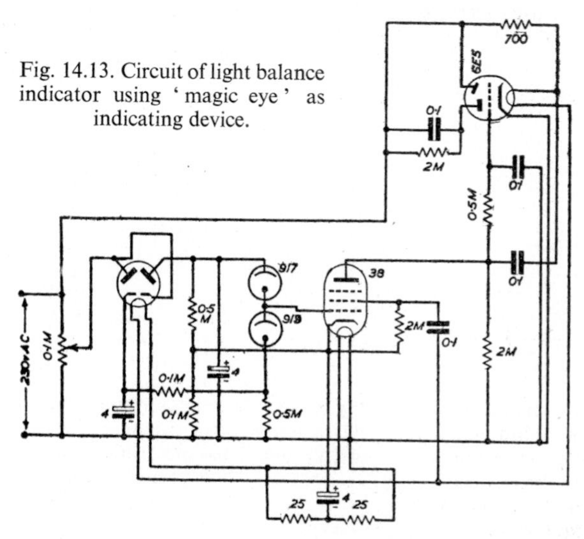

Fig. 14.13. Circuit of light balance indicator using ‘ magic eye ’ as indicating device.

The light source is a sodium arc filtered through a 5-mm. Corning Red Purple Corex-986 filter. The transmission maximum lies between 3200 and 3500 A.U., respectively, and the resulting radiation is perfectly monochromatic (3303 A.U.). The optical system is made of fused quartz. In order to eliminate false values by the infra-red radiation of the sodium arc it is necessary to chose photosensitors of a type insensitive to infra-red radiations : this is a condition since the ultra-violet filter transmits freely in the infra-red. Photosensitors with a S-4 cathode surface are suitable.

The circuit and the method developed reduce the time required for a complete measurement to less than two minutes. The accuracy attained is 1% and better, and the range of the instrument for $\log(I_0/I)$ is from 0·1 to 1·0. The relation between the concentration of vitamin A and the logarithm of the intensities is a straight line within the above range.

An ultra-violet photometer for the analysis of solutions, using the 2537 A.U. line as a source of radiation, was described by I. M. Klotz (*837*) who also worked by the substitution method, using two absorption cells and a diaphragm with variable shutter which may be directly calibrated in the units to be measured, Fig. 14.14.

Similar methods and instruments are used in measuring other vitamins. A fluorimeter can be adapted to measure the aneurin-vitamin B_1. Vitamin C (ascorbic acid) can also be determined by photo-electric methods (*814*, *815*, *1697*, *2412*).

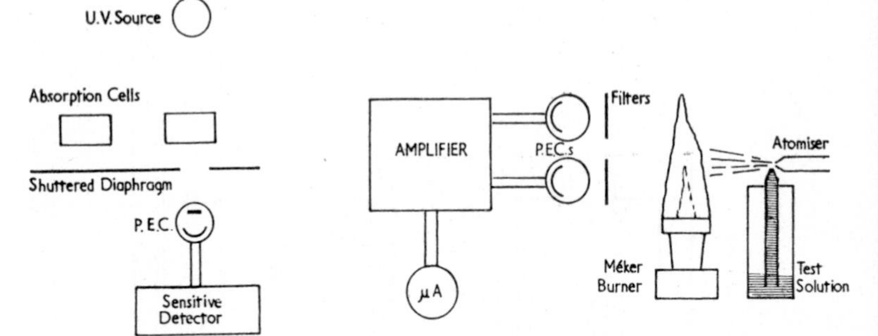

Fig. 14.14. Block diagram of ultra-violet photometer. The shutter may be directly calibrated in the units to be measured.

Fig. 14.15. Flame photometer. One filter transmits the radiation of Na, the other of K only. The filters exclude any radiations from elements other than Na or K.

Photo-electric colorimetric methods (*2415*) are applicable to many other chemical problems on the condition that a variation in an optical characteristic can be established. A list of references on the subject of photo-electric methods in analytical chemistry has been compiled by R. H. Muller (*238*). Such methods also play an essential part in the petroleum industry. Diller, Gray, and Wilson (*816*) have built a specific colorimeter with which they have succeeded in measuring the colour of petroleum products. They have introduced a new system, viz., "photo-electric colour" for the measurement of the colour of lubricating oils (*427*, *714*, *817*, *818*).

The intensity of sodium or potassium radiation which is emitted when an aqueous solution is atomized into the flame of a Meker burner can be measured by means of a flame photometer, the general construction of which employs two photosensitors, one sensitive to each particular radiation (*831*), Fig. 14.15.

Bibliography References: (*404*, *412*, *413*, *415*, *428*, *529*, *530*, *599*, *1051*, *1063*, *1379*, *1503*, *1516*, *1517*, *1521*, *1572*, *1858*, *2292*).

14.4. X-Ray Absorption Analysis

Chemical analysis is still a matter for the laboratory in most cases. New developments in method and apparatus, however, have equipped the industrial worker with the means of accurately and quickly carrying out his routine analyses. X-ray absorption is the latest method in chemical analysis, and equipment utilizing this phenomenon was developed independently by Morgan (*832*) and by Smith (*729*, *1652*) (cf. Chap. 13.) The expediency of method and apparatus for chemical analysis by X-ray absorption (*833*) is well proved by the fact that in practical applications the instrument is quickly adjusted and trouble-free, that results are obtained almost instantaneously, and that the sample is not changed in any way. The instrument uses a multiplier photo-cell coated with an X-ray sensitive phosphor. The basic equation of the instrument is $\log(I_0/I) = \log(i_0/i) = km$, where

I, I_0	..	intensities,
i, i_0	..	photo-electric currents,
k	..	a constant,
m	..	the mass of the sample.

The quantities with the index zero refer to measurements with an empty cell; those with no index refer to the cell filled with the liquid under examination. The X-ray absorption by a homogeneous material is $I = I_0 \exp(-\mu x)$, where

I	..	intensity after passing through a thickness x of the material,
I_0	..	intensity of the incident radiation,
μ	..	X-ray absorption coefficient,
x	..	thickness of the absorbing material.

The expression $\exp(-\mu x)$ stands for the Naperian base ε to the power $(-\mu x)$. The sensitivity of the instrument is well demonstrated by the fact that, if a pile of 100 sheets of paper is X-rayed, a difference of one sheet is readily indicated on the meter.

14.5. Other Applications

The photo-electric circuit of Fig. 14.16 was devised by Davenport (*821*, *822*) and used for indicating the concentration at any instant of a temperature-controlled coloured solution the concentration of which

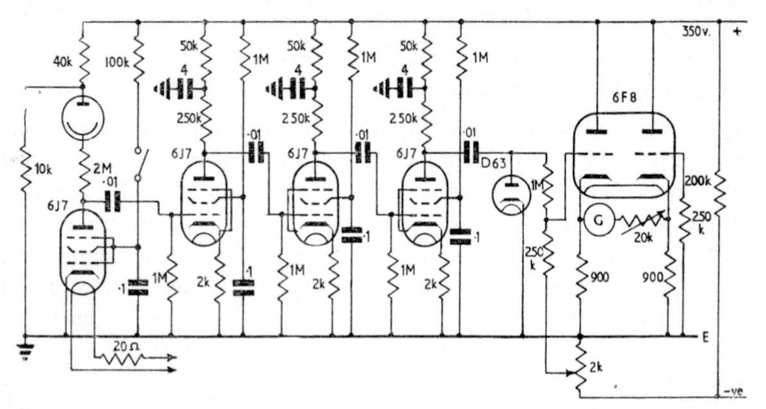

Fig. 14.16. Circuit based on logarithmic amplifier circuit for indicating concentration of solutions.

varies with time when its optical density changes between 0 and 3. The circuit is based on the logarithmic amplifier circuit developed by R. E. Meagher and E. P. Bentley (*382*).

A photo-electric saccharimeter uses sodium light which is sent through the two halves of a polarizer (*823*, *824*). The polarization planes are perpendicular to each other, thus forming a half-shadow angle of 90 degrees. The light then passes through the polarization tube and analyzer and is directed on to the photosensitors of a two-cell balanced circuit in such a way that the light from one half of the polarizer reaches one photosensitor, while the light from the other half is thrown on the other cell.

A circuit suitable for the measurement of the sugar content in beverages, concentration of syrups, etc., has been devised by F. H. Sheperd, Jr. (*345*).

An opacimeter for use in chemical analysis was described by Evans and Silberstein (*825*). Fundamentally, it is based on the substitution method of comparison, using a photo-e.m.f. cell ; the lay-out is very simple, Fig. 14.17. A heat filter is used in order to avoid an increase in the ambient temperature over 45° to 50°C. which would be detrimental to the photosensitor. This filter is either a glass filter or a cuvette with a 4% copper sulphate solution. A standard cell is inserted first and the galvanometer or microammeter is adjusted to read zero. Then

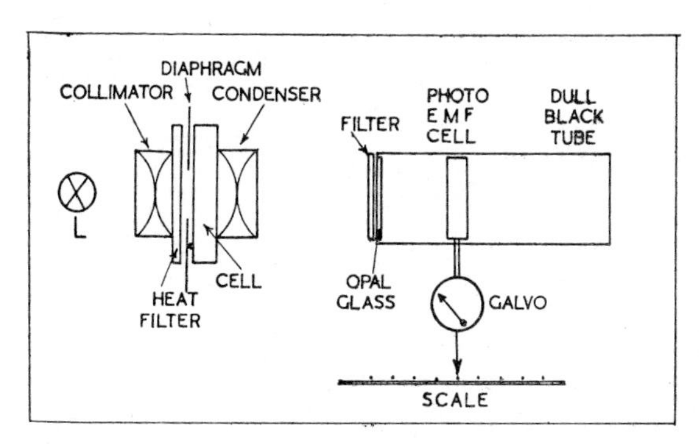

Fig. 14.17. Diagram of an instrument measuring the concentration at any instance of a coloured solution the concentration of which varies with time. (*Courtesy J. Sci. Instr.*).

the specimen cell is substituted for the standard and the new reading taken is a measure of the opacity. If the distance of the photosensitor from the zero position (standard cell inserted) is measured when the test cell is *in situ*, this distance can be read directly on a scale and is a measure as explained above.

A spectrograph exposure control is described in *Electronics* (*2465*).

Joseph G. Baier (*834*, *835*) describes a microdensitometer for rapid turbidimetric (scopometric) determinations. Only very minute quantities of solution (1 c.c.) are needed for exact determinations. The balanced bridge circuit is of well-known design. When the equilibrium of the electronic circuit is upset by a difference existing between standard and test specimens, respectively, an optical wedge is employed to alter the light transmitting qualities of the window to such an extent and in such a way that the circuit is balanced once more, Fig. 14.18. A 0–20 microammeter will indicate the conditions (balance or unbalance) of the circuit, equilibrium being indicated by the zero position of the measuring instrument. The amount of movement of the optical wedge is an exact measure of the amount of light absorbed by the specimen under test. The spectral characteristics of optical wedges are discussed in a paper by M. H. Sweet (*334*). The resistor R in Fig. 14.18, is of such a resistance as to limit the maximum current to slightly less than full-scale deflexion of the pointer. This circuit actually is a development, or rather combination, of two circuits, the one developed at the RCA-Laboratories (Fig. 19.4), the other by D. G. Fink (Fig. 19.5). Another microdensitometer was described by L. Raitiere (*1688*).

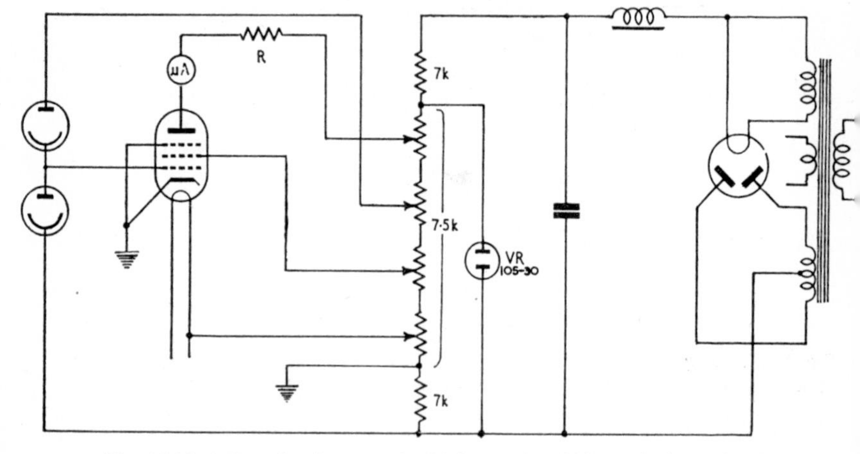

Fig. 14.18. Micro-densitometer for high-speed turbidimetric determinations.

For the quantitative determination of " hard " water, films formed on transparent glass plates during detergent processes such as commercial dish-washing, J. L. Wilson and E. E. Mendenhall (*836*) have devised a photo-electric photometer of very simple design. A method for the observation of the rate of dissociation of N_2O_4 by shock waves (Schlieren technique) uses for irradiation of the gases different wavelengths which are selectively absorbed, namely 2537 A.U. by N_2O_4 and 4358 A.U. by NO_2 (*2612*).

The contamination of air with CS_2 vapour constitutes a serious health hazard. The detection of minute quantities of carbon disulphide is best carried out by the physical process that is based on the specific absorption of the 3122 A.U. line in CS_2 vapour. The photo-electric part of the instrument designed for this purpose is shown in Fig. 14.19. The ventilated head houses the polykymatic straight quartz burner producing the full Hg spectrum at high intensities. The control choke (starting current 3.5A, running current 2.5A, continuous 24-hours rating) is separated from the tube by means of a double-walled partition which protects the choke from the heat of the burner by an air current flowing between the double walls. The position of the quartz tube is universally adjustable.

The tunnel-shaped part of the instrument houses the two translucent quartz absorption tubes of 800mm length which, on the far end, carry two cells of 1cm and 3cm depth, respectively. At both ends of each

Photo-cell and Amplifier

Liquid filters

Air outlet

Absorption Tubes

Air inlet

Filters

U-V Source

Choke

Fig. 14.19. Carbon disulphide detector (cover removed). (*Courtesy: Barber Medico-Electronic Laboratories Ltd.*)

absorption tube an air inlet is provided for the air under inspection to be passed through the one tube. The other tube is left open or may be sealed, containing plain air without any trace of the substance in question, in this case, carbon disulphide. The near end of the two absorption tubes is supported by a filter stage which carries a heat absorbing, heat resisting filter of the ON20 type (Chance Bros.) and, in series with it, an ultra-violet transmitting filter of the OX7 type (Chance

Bros.). This filter is opaque to luminous radiation, but transmits freely the ultra-violet. The liquid filters are of the type described in chap. 9.19. Two photo-electric cells of the UNG7 (GEC) type are wired in a balanced circuit and any unbalance caused by a difference in absorption due to the presence of CS_2 in the one quartz absorption tube will cause the amplifier to produce the proper control signal.

Bibliography References ; (*467, 533, 587, 1193, 1228, 1340, 1341, 1356, 1519 1520, 1525, 1535, 1571, 1784, 1836, 1894, 1907, 1915, 1971, 1972, 2040, 2041*).

14.6. Automatic Titration

One of the earliest applications of automatic photo-electric control to a chemical industrial process was described in 1928 by Müller and Partridge (*838*). Another circuit was developed in the laboratories of the General Electric Company (*839*) and a working model exhibited

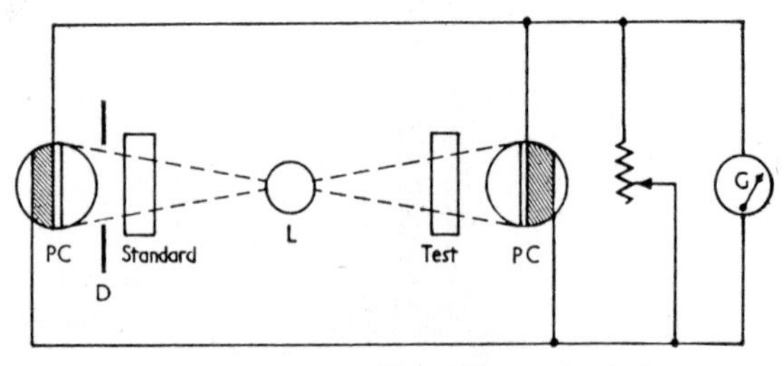

Fig. 14.20. Balanced selenium-on-iron cells used in a circuit for automatic titration.

in the Science Museum in London. A two-cell circuit, using selenium-on-iron front-wall cells matched a reference solution against the test sample (*840*), Fig. 14.20.

The fundamental idea of automatic titration is simple enough. A single-cell or two-cell circuit, as used in colorimetric work, is employed in the detection of colour changes, if any. In the load circuit a relay actuates a burette release, for instance, a pinchcock, Fig. 14.21. The relay should respond to changes in current of 1% and less. The light used should have a wavelength corresponding to the absorption maximum of the indicator. There are two types of indicator, viz. the " monochromatic " and " dichromatic " type, respectively. The first is represented, for instance, by Martius Yellow which is colourless before the reaction but turns yellow at a certain characteristic *p*H value. The other type is instanced by substances like tetra-iodo-phenol-sulphone-phthalein which is yellow before, and blue after the reaction has taken place. Here, the two colours are complementary.

With other indicators the " opposition " may be less than 180°, for instance, violet-yellow, red-blue, green-violet, etc., which means that these colours are less than a semi-circle apart in the colour circle ; they are not exactly complementaries.

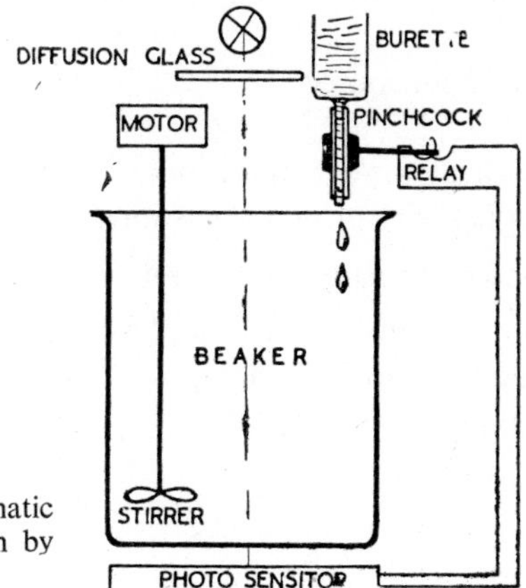

Fig. 14.21. Automatic control of titration by photosensitor.

The general rule provides for two actions as follows :

NEGATIVE ACTION : The colour change at indication value causes the light beam either to be cut off completely from the photosensitor, or the intensity of the beam to be reduced to such an extent that the photo-electric current decreases below the holding current of the relay. The latter is then released and opens the auxiliary (titration) circuit.

POSITIVE ACTION : The colour change at indication value causes the radiant flux striking the photosensitor to increase so that the photo-electric current will increase above the operating current of the relay. The latter is now energized and will close the auxiliary (the titration) circuit.

For negative action it is essential for the deciding factors to agree in the way indicated below:

Frequency of light source
Filter,
Colour of indicator *before* indication,
Maximum sensitivity of photosensitor,
} .. C_0

Colour of indicator *after* indication .. .. .. C_{180}

This negative action is equivalent to a " forward circuit " (cf. Chap. 5) which results in a decrease in photo-current output when the light input is decreased. When the other type of electrical action is necessitated by some special conditions, i.e., that a decrease in light input must result in increasing the current output, the " reverse circuit " will be used.

For positive action the above colour agreement is altered as indicated, viz. :

Frequency of light source, Filter, Colour of indicater *after* indication, Maximum sensitivity of photosensitor,	} C_0
Colour of indicator *before* indication	C_{180}

This positive action is equivalent to the " forward circuit ".

Table 14.2 suggests co-ordinated types of indicators, filters, light sources, and photosensitors.

TABLE 14.2

pH — Indicators

*p*H Value	Indicator			Light source type (*see* *p. 427*)	Photo-sensitor type (*see p. 428*)	Filter type (*see* *p. 428*)	Action	Notes (*see* *p. 429*)
	Type (*see* *p. 427*)	Colour before indication	Colour after indication					
0·0–1·0	A	pink	green	d	v, viii	ν, ξ	+	
0·1–3·2	B	yellow	violet	a	i		−	(3)
1·0–2·0	C	colour-less	pink	a, d	v, viii	ν, ξ	−	(1)
2·0–3·2	D	colour-less	yellow	b	ii	α, β	−	(2)
3·0–4·8	E	yellow	blue	a	i		−	
3·0–5·0	F	orange	blue-v.	a	i		−	
4·0–5·6	G	colour-less	yellow	b	ii	α, θ	−	
4·4–6·0	H	red	green	b	v, viii		+	
5·0–6·0	K	yellow	purple	a	i		−	
5·0–7·0	L	violet	yellow	d	ii	ζ, ε	−	
				d	iii	ξ, η	+	
				a	iii		+	
5·0–8·0	M	red	blue	c	iv		−	
				d	iv, vi, vii	θ	−	
				d	iii	κ, λ	+	
				d	ii		+	
6·0–7·2	N	yellow	blue	a	i		−	
6·0–12·0	P	o-red	violet	c	iv		−	
				d	iv	ζ, η	−	
				d	ii	δ, κ	+	
7·0–8·6	Q	yellow	violet	a	i		−	
8·0–9·6	R	yellow	blue	a	i		−	
9·0–11·0	S	brown	green	d	iv	μ	−	
9·3–10·5	T	colour-less	blue	a	i		−	
10·0–12·0	U	colour-less	yellow	b	ii	α, β	−	
				d	ii	δ, ε	−	
				d	ii		−	
11·0–13·0	S	green	violet	d	ii		+	(4)
				d	v	ν, ξ	−	
12·0–12·4	V	blue	red-purple	c	iv, vi, vii		+	
				d	iv, vi, vii	γ, μ	+	

In Table 14.3 some of the more important Adsorption Indicators together with the appropriate optical equipment are listed.

TABLE 14.3

Adsorption Indicators

Indicators			Light source type (*see below*)	Photo-sensitor type (*see p. 428*)	Filter type (*see p. 428*)	Action	Notes (*see p. 429*)
Type (*see below*)	Colour change from	to					
AA	red	green	*b*	v, viii		+	
BB	purple	violet	*c*	iv, vi, vii		+	
			d	iv, vi, vii	γ, μ	+	
CC	yellow	blue	*a*	i		—	
DD	orange	pink	*a*	i		—	
EE	pink	orange	*a*	i		+	
FF	colour-less	yellow	*b*	ii	α, β	—	(*2*)

Key to Tables 14.2 and 14.3

Indicators :

- *A* Haematoxylin
- *B* Methyl Violet
- *C* Quinaldine Red
- *D* Martius Yellow
- *E* Tetra-Iodo-Phenol-Sulphone-Phthalein
- *F* Moir's improved Methyl Orange
- *G* 2 : 5-Dinitro-Phenol (γ)
- *H* B.D.H. " 4460 " Indicator
- *K* Cochineal
- *L* Phenyl-α-Naphthylamine-Azo-o-Carboxy-Benzene
- *M* Litmus, or Azolitmin
- *N* Nitrazine Yellow
- *P* Alizarine Red S
- *Q* Diphenol Purple
- *R* Thymol Blue
- *S* Alizarine Blue S
- *T* Thymol Phthalein
- *U* Alizarin Yellow GG
- *V* Brilliant Cresyl Blue

		Indicator for :
AA	Alizarin	Nitrates
BB	Biebrich Scarlet	Bromides
CC	Bromo-Phenol Blue	Chlorides
DD	Dibromo-Dimethyl Fluorescein	Chlorides
EE	Dibromo-Fluorescein	Orthophosphates
FF	Tartrazine	Silver with Halides

For fluorescent indicators cf. the catalogues of the chemical manufacturers, and Pringsheim and Vogel (*614, p. 117*)

Light Sources :

- *a* Sodium Discharge Lamp
- *b* Mercury Discharge Lamp
- *c* Neon Discharge Lamp (positive column or hot-cathode type has a many times greater output than the cold-cathode type)
- *d* Incandescent Lamp

NOTE : *a* is monochromatic
b is heterochromatic,
d is panchromatic.

Photosensitors :

i S-4 type cells.
ii Hydrogenized Potassium (thick film) type (Osram KG7)
iii Potassium on Silver Oxide type (Osram KMV6)
iv S-1 type cells
v Selenium-on-Iron (photo-e.m.f.) type (Photronic)
vi Thallium Sulphide (light-sensitive resistor) type
vii Selenium bridge (light-sensitive resistor) type (*Radiovisor*)
viii Copper-Oxide (Front-wall photo-e.m.f.) type (*Westinghouse*)

Filters :

	Manufacturers :						
Type	Chance Bros.	mm	Corning Glass Works	Wratten	Ilford	Jena	mm
α	Didymium Crown ON12	4			205+302	BG20 or BG11	2 8
β			512 or 592		205+302	BG20 or BG11	2 8
γ			244+555	88**A**, 70, 70, 91		RG8	2
δ	Potblue	4			501	BG24 or BG1 or BG3	2 2 1
ε			555	39	305	BG1 or BG2	2 2
ζ	Pale Yellow OY3 or OY5	2		5 + **ND**	109, 111	GG11 or OG1	2 2
η			348 or 349	22, 23**A**, 23A, 23B	202, 201	OG2 or OG5	2 2
θ			242			RG2	2
κ			554	47	304	BG12	2
λ	OB1	2			601		
μ			241 or 242 or 243 or 244	29 29	205 205	RG2 RG2 RG1 RG1	2 2 2 2
ν	Pale Yellow OY5 or OY7	2		3,5,5+**ND**	107, 109	GG14 or GG11	2 2
ξ			351 or 352	5 + **ND**	111	OG4 or GG11	2 2

NOTES : The harmonizing is based on filters made by Chance Bros. or Corning Glass Works. The other filters are alternatives, the transmissivities of which are approximations to the filters in the first or second column, respectively, It will be advisable to request from the manufacturers an individual transmission sheet for the filter purchased. This will not be necessary where the filters are made to standardized specifications as laid down in the manufacturers' catalogues. Corning's adopted standard thicknesses are : ¼ inch unpolished or 5 mm. polished. The latter has been adopted in these Tables.

When two or more filters are quoted, equivalents are given in the sequence of the main columns, e.g. :

OY7 = 5N5 = 109 = GG11 ;
OY5 = 16 = 111 = OG1

Filter 5N5 has a relatively low transmission.

NOTES TO TABLE 14.2:

(1) Filter is to be used only with *d*-type lamp.
(2) Filter has no transmission in the yellow region.
(3) The S_4 type cell is here more efficient than the S_1 type cell. Best is the Selenium-on-Iron photo-e.m.f. cell the sensitivity of which exceeds the above mentioned (for the spectral range of a Sodium Discharge Lamp) viz.:

Cell type	Max. Sensitivity at A.U.	Abs. Response at max. sensit. μA/μW	Rel. Sensit.		Abs. Response at 5893 A.U. μA/μW
i	4000	0·02	72%	=	0·0144
iv Vac.	8000	0·01	41%	=	0·0041
iv Gas	8000	0·1	41%	=	0·041
v	5893	0·0460	100%	=	0·04600

When monochromatic or heterochromatic light sources are used the current output of the photo-e.m.f. cells is less than with the same illumination from panchromatic (tungsten) lamps. For correction factor see manufacturers' lists and Chap. 4.

(4) A blue filter, e.g., types δ or ε can be used with advantage.

GENERAL NOTE :

When using a panchromatic light source the correct choice of photosensitor and filter decide whether the action is positive or negative, and so does agreement between either the BEFORE or AFTER colour and the colour of the monochromatic light source.

In general the combination of photosensitor plus amplifier plus indicating instrument exceeds visual work by a factor of eight to ten (*841*), especially in spectral ranges where the eye is less sensitive.

Only two of a great many more instances are quoted in which the determination of the instantaneous *p*H values is of the greatest importance and therefore demands for a testing method that is continuous. The first instance refers to the production of water equivalent in ion content to distilled water (*p*H = 7) by using two beds of melamine-derived synthetic resin, the one dissolving the salts in the water to the corresponding acids, while the second bed absorbs these acids. This particular process has been developed by the American Cyanamide Co. (*842*). The other instance is taken from the paper industry where the *p*H value of the liquors is automatically controlled to limits within ± 0·15 *p*H. The liquids must be mixed with alkaline solutions before being used a second time and kept at a constant *p*H (*843, 844*). Electronic *p*H meters using glass electrodes attain a high accuracy, namely, 0·02 *p*H (*645, 846*). The photo-electric methods are no less accurate as can be seen from Table 14.4.

TABLE 14.4

Mean Precision of pH Determination

Indicator	pH-Range*	Filter	Precision
Thymol Blue (acid range)	1·2–2·8	a	0·02 *p*H
Bromophenol Blue	2·8–4·6	c	0·04
Methyl Red	4·4–6·2	a	0·04
Bromocresol Purple	5·2–6·8	c	0·02
Bromothymol Blue	6·0–7·6	c	0·02
Phenol Red	6·8–8·4	b	0·02
Cresol Red	7·2–8·8	c	0·02
Thymol Blue	8·0–9·6	c	0·03

* The *p*H ranges are taken from the catalogue of the British Drug Houses, Ltd.

The compound filters are made up of three individual filters, viz. :

(a) .. Wratten 12 + Wratten 58A + Chance Blue-Green 6 ;
(b) .. Wratten 21 + Wratten 58 + Chance Blue-Green 6 ;
(c) .. Wratten 22 + Wratten 59 + Chance Blue-Green 6.

The above instances illustrate the versatility and usefulness of photoelectric methods and equipment in the chemical industry. The instances have been selected from the production and workshop engineer's point of view, the laboratory chemist having at his command a much wider range of more complicated and variegated instruments and methods.

Bibliography References : (*418, 430, 437, 438, 1062, 1321, 1322, 1323, 1914, 2363*)

CHAPTER 15

COMBUSTION CONTROL

Combustion control (*1424*) is mainly concerned with two tasks, viz., the control of flue gases, and the control of smoke, respectively.

15.1. Control of Flue Gases

The importance of proper carbon dioxide control is shown in the nomogram of Fig. 15.1 (*885*). Lowest fan loads and lowest chimney losses, expressed in " lb. fuel per lb. fired " are indicated in type by

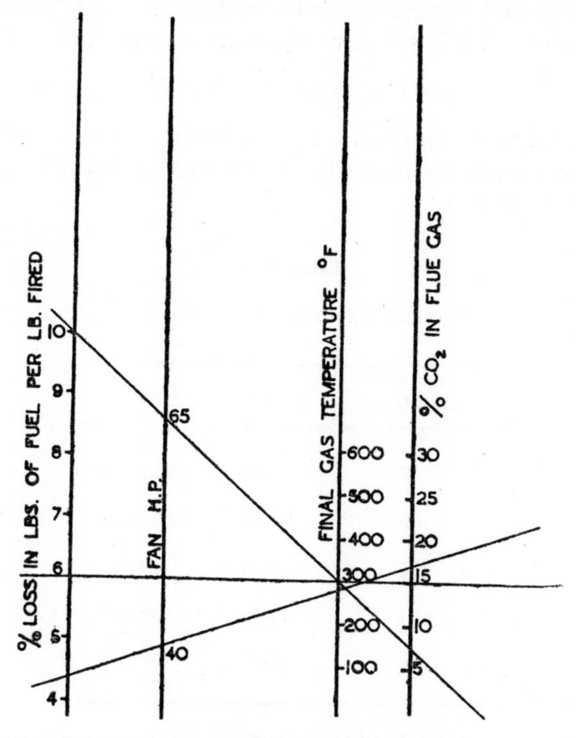

Fig. 15.1 Nomogram of chimney losses and fan loads expressed in lb of fuel per lb fired.

a family of graphs as represented by Fig. 15.1. This means that chimney losses are minimized by reducing the final gas temperature and allowing for a maximum CO_2 content. Excess air is expressed in the increasing load on the induced draught fan. This and incomplete combustion are the essential factors in flue waste.

In flue gas control advantage is taken of the thermal conductivity of carbon dioxide being less than that of other components. The greater the percentage of carbon dioxide in the flue gases the less conductive will be the gas volume under instantaneous observation. The carbon dioxide content of flue gases can be determined by various methods, the resistance method being the one mostly used and giving continuous readings or recordings (cf. methane detection, Chap. 17). This is based on the phenomenon that the thermal conductivity k of a gas, in this case of CO_2, varies with the temperature. The thermal conductivity of a gas is the amount of heat (in gram-calories) that passes per second through one cubic centimetre of that gas when the temperature gradient is 1°C./cm. The thermal conductivity of a gas is:

$$k = 1{\cdot}603\ \eta c_v\ [\text{g.cal.cm.}^{-1}.\text{sec}^{-1}.\ \text{deg.}^{-1}]$$

where η . . . viscosity, c_v . . . specific heat at constant volume. For carbon dioxide the thermal conductivity at different temperatures is given in Table 15.1.

TABLE 15.1

Thermal Conductivity of Carbon Dioxide

Temperature deg. C.	k × 10^{-5}	Authority
0	3·43	(*52, p. 54*)
100	5·06	(*52, p. 54*)
282	6·78	(*863*)
507	11·78	(*863*)
555	14·19	(*863*)

More data for carbon dioxide as well as for Freon are reported by Sherratt and Griffiths (*377*), Table 15.2.

TABLE 15.2

Thermal Conductivity of Carbon Dioxide and Freon.

Temperature	100° C.	150° C.	200° C.	250° C.	300° C.
Carbon dioxide	5·50	6·49	7·48	8·47	9·45
Freon	3·30	3·97	4·63	—	—

The thermal conductivity increases with rising temperature. The specific heat of carbon dioxide is :

$$c_v = 0{\cdot}165 + 0{\cdot}2125d + 0{\cdot}34d^2 \qquad (52, p. 61)$$

where d is the density of carbon dioxide. The density of a gas, being a function of its temperature, is lastly a function of the thermal conductivity. The viscosity of carbon dioxide is listed in Table 15.3 (*52, p. 34*).

TABLE 15.3

Viscosity of Carbon Dioxide

Temperature deg. C.	Viscosity $\eta \times 10^{-6}$
0	137
100	184
300	268

As the carbon dioxide content of the flue gases varies, so does its ability to conduct heat from an incandescent platinum wire, the temperature of which is proportional to the carbon dioxide content. The electrical resistance of the wire is a function of its temperature and, therefore, lastly of the amount of CO_2 in the flue gases. This method is easily adapted to a much higher degree of sensitivity and accuracy by exploiting the phenomenon laid down in the radiation formula. For pure metals the resistance is roughly proportional to the absolute temperature T, viz., $R = cT$ which when substituted in the formula for the purpose of this discussion shows that the radiant energy emitted from the incandescent platinum wire is proportional to the fifth power of its resistance. The emissive power E of the radiation at dominant wavelength varies as the fifth power of the absolute temperature of a Planckian radiator, $E = \text{const.}\ T^5$ or, after substitution, $E = \text{const.}\ R^5$. This fifth-power law accounts for the high sensitivity of all such arrangements.

The identical platinum wires are enclosed in cells of heat-resisting glass, or better still of fused quartz (Vitreosil). The wires are primed to a low degree of incandescence, either A.C. or D.C. being used for this purpose. The wire in the sealed chamber is enclosed in a standard atmosphere of a known amount of carbon dioxide in the air, the other filament being mounted in an open specimen cell permitting a constantly changing volume of flue gases to contact the platinum wire. The free length of the wire must be shorter than the distance between the inlet and outlet if the specimen cell is of the semi-enclosed type. The open type cell is shown diagrammatically in Fig. 15.2.

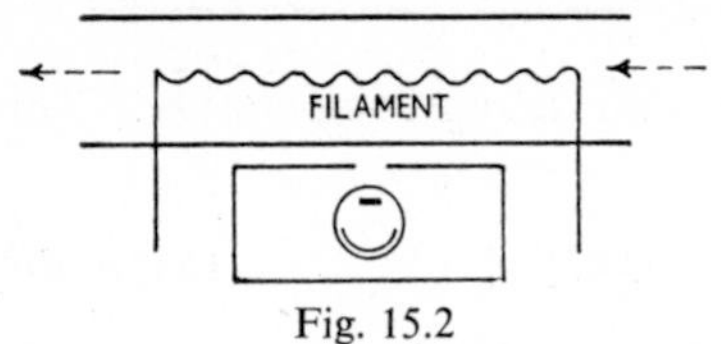

Fig. 15.2

Bibliography Reference : (*469*)

15.2. Smoke Control

Smoke control, the battle cry of the Smoke Abatement Society, is an economical factor of the utmost importance. Smoke controlling equipment not only charts the instantaneous densities of smoke, but also gives alarm signals and/or operates the fuel supply or draught controls in order to ensure perfect, i.e., smokeless, combustion. Detection has been so perfected that preventive measures have either been taken automatically or the change in smoke density has been signalled to the boilerman for manual operation of the controls before the smoke which was detected in the flue uptake has reached the top of the stack.

The general arrangement of photo-electric smoke control equipment is shown in Fig. 15.3. A light beam is thrown across the flue or uptake and received by a photosensitor. Two observation holes of three to five inch in diameter are cut in the wall of the flue or stack or, as preferred by others, in the duct close to the induced draught fan inlet. These windows are closed by a disk of plate glass which requires continuous cleaning. This is done either by providing for a natural draught or a compressed air system. Water jet cleaning and/or mechanical wipers of the kind used on the windscreens of cars have also been suggested but were found less successful in practice (*1683*).

The colour of the light source is peaked preferably in the short-wave region of the luminous spectrum. Orange or red light has too great a penetrating power through dense haze or smoke. The infra-red radiation of the light source should be filtered out or photosensitors used which are not sensitive to infra-red radiation (*1691*).

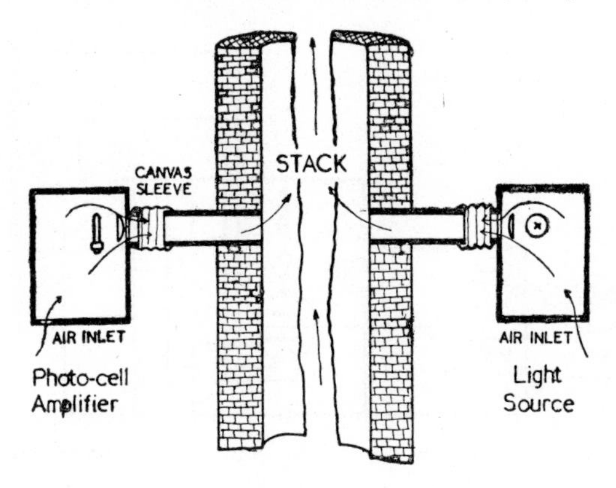

Fig. 15.3 General arrangement of smoke control equipment

The circuit of a very sensitive smoke detector was described by Hull in 1929 (*229*). The basic idea of this two-cell circuit, Fig. 15.4, is to strike the photosensitors with 1000-times the intensity which would be required to start the thyratron. Therefore the change of one unit, i.e., 0·1% in one cell will cause the thyratron to operate.

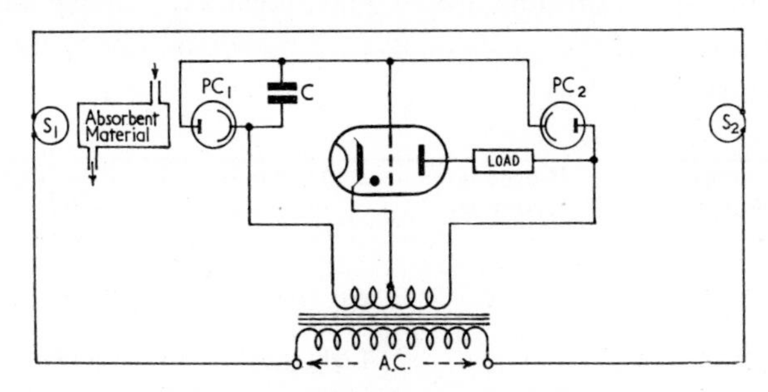

Fig. 15.4 Sensitive smoke detector (Hull)

A circuit using not industrial but ordinary radio valves is given in Fig. 15.5 (*886*). One photo-cell receives the light directly from the lamp, the other photosensitor after the beam has passed through the stack or the breeching.

Smoke detectors can be made to indicate and remedy as well as to record any deviations from the optimal working conditions. An operation recorder marks only qualitative deviations, showing that the flue gases are off colour and also records the duration of this condition. The density recorder gives quantitative and directional charts, which

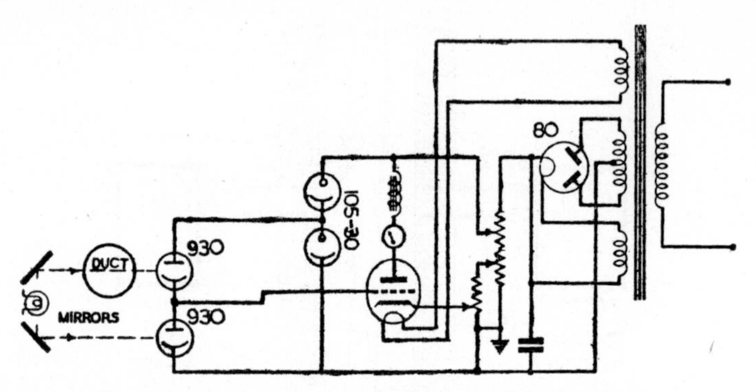

Fig. 15.5. Detection of smoke in air-conditioning duct.

means that the amount the gas is off colour is recorded and also whether it is darker or lighter than normal (*887*). The measuring instrument can be calibrated in the Ringelmann Smoke Chart Numbers which are schematically shown in Fig. 15.6.

The correlation of optical density with the nature and quantity of smoke is discussed in a Report published by the Fuel Research Board (*1646*). In the layout as used by the investigators, " smoke numbers " are used instead of the numbers of the Ringelmann Chart, the correlation being as follows :

Smoke Number	Ringelmann Number	Description of smoke	Percentage Black
0– 2	0	No smoke	0
3– 4	1	Light grey	19·0
6– 8	2	Darker grey	40·7
10–12	3	Very dark grey	60·3
14–16	4	Black	79·8
18 and over	5	Dense black	100

The following passage is an excerpt from the Report (pp. 8, 9): " The difference in the structure of the particles observed under the microscope would lead one to expect a change in density. This was roughly checked by determining the bulk density of the material. Some of the sample for analysis was weighed and introduced into a

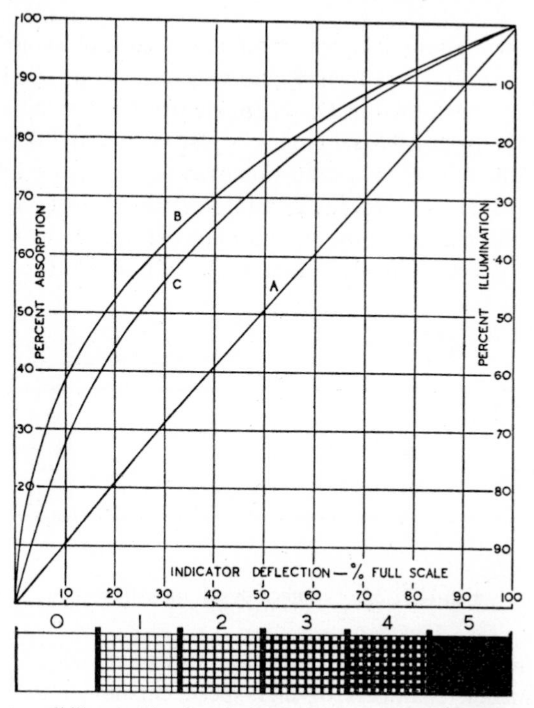

Fig. 15.6. Photo-cell illumination in relation to meter reading and Ringelmann Scale. A: Photo-voltaic cell; B: Photo-emissive cell; C: Photo-voltaic cell, 1000Ω load.
(*Radiovisor Parent Ltd.*)

small glass cylinder of known dimensions. After gently shaking until no further diminution in volume was observed, the height was measured and the bulk density calculated. The highest bulk densities are associated with the smokes of lowest optical density. This is in agreement with the result of the microscopical examination, since high bulk density is consistent with a close structure, and low bulk density with a more flocculent structure.

Experience with the same fuel at other loads suggests that the difference in the apparent densities of the particles for the two series is probably due to the difference in load rather than fuel.

The change in the apparent density might be expected in view of the chemical analyses. High carbon and tar contents would produce a loose flocculent structure and a high ash content would result in close packing, as well as a higher true density."

The measurement of smoke has been discussed in detail by Shaw (*2461*).

Photo-electric equipment for combustion control is not restricted to coal or coke fires but to any fuel which develops smoke. Smoke indicators have been used in Diesel engine plants. The clearness of the exhaust smoke from a Diesel engine is just as safe and dependable an indicator of the quality of combustion as is the smoke in the stack of a boiler plant (*888*). To prevent moisture in the exhaust gas from condensing on the glass window of the photosensitor head the use of a heating coil is recommended, Fig. 15.7. Photo-electric devices are

Fig. 15.7. Smoke indicator cell for exhaust gas.

used for routine and test field investigations to measure the radiation from combustion chambers of high-speed engines of the Diesel and Otto type, respectively (*889*).

Photo-electric instrumentation is also used in the accurate control of boilers (*2619*).

The principle of smoke control apparatus is also applicable to the control and measurement of dust (*1650*).

Bibliography References : (*492*, *1056*, *1058*, *1246*, *1759*, *1815*, *1857*, *1889*, *1972* *2227*, *2401*, *p. 116*).

15.3. Flame Control

Explosions of pressure-fed heating equipment, consequent to combustion failure, are eliminated when photo-electric control is used to watch over burners of oil, gas or pulverized coal. The general layout is the same with all three types of burners, the difference in arrangement being caused by the type of fuel. It is the luminous radiation of the flame which is observed by a photo-electric relay. A blue-sensitive cathode should be used. Other principles used in flame control are not safe as, for instance, the control by radiant heat, because there is

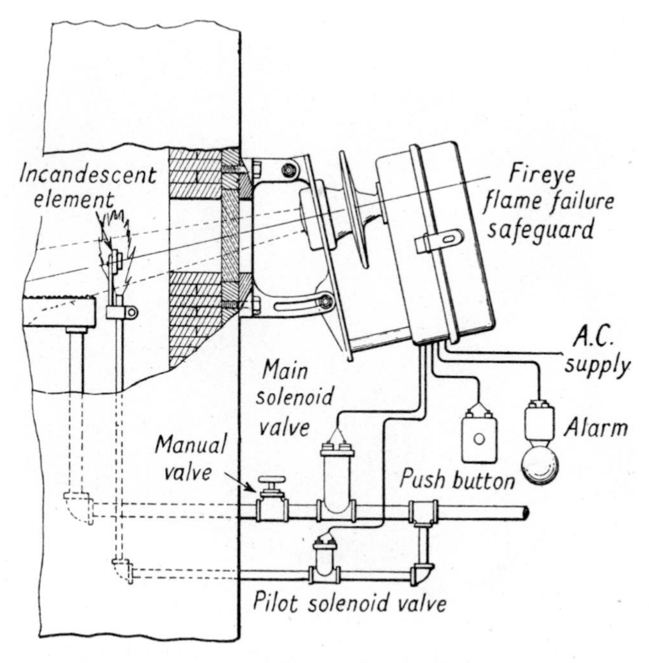

Fig. 15.8. Diagram of 'Fireye' flame failure safeguard.

still a substantial amount of heat radiation in the flame chamber when the flame itself has failed already. In watching non-luminous gas flames a clever trick has been used in rendering the flame—or an indicator in its path—luminous.* A little disk of about half an inch in diameter is clamped to the burner and brought in steady alignment with the photosensitor, Fig. 15.8. The element is of a special refractory material and becomes incandescent or turns non-luminous immediately as the gas flame is burning or failing. The photo-electric relay is made to control the solenoid valves of the pilot as well as

* Introduced by the Combustion Control Corporation (U.S.A.). (See also *2620*, *2621*).

of the main flame. An external view of the safeguard unit is shown in Fig. 15.9.

If luminous gas flames are used as pilots no refractory disk need be inserted in the path of the pilot flame : its own incandescence controls the valves through a photosensitor circuit (*2460*). A luminous gas flame

Fig. 15.9. View of combustion control unit. (*Combustion Control Corpn. Inc.*)

shows a continuous spectrum, superimposed over which is a line spectrum of four main lines, viz., at 5800 A.U. (dark yellow), 5100 A.U. (green), 4700 A.U. (blue), and 4300 A.U. (violet), respectively. These wavelengths are approximate only and indicate regions rather than individual values. They are, however, representative of the gas flame.

Either one or more photosensitors can be used to control both pilot and burner flame, or each photo-relay may control one flame separately. The general circuit, using two photosensitors, Fig. 15.10, has, at least in the main points, the same operation programme as the circuit using one cell only.

Photosensitors used in the control of high temperatures, smoke, burner flames, etc., are usually exposed to rather high ambient temperatures. Although water-cooling of photocells has not only been proposed but actually carried into effect (*849*), the general application of this feature is still remote and development will probably be sought along lines other than that of forced cooling. A first indication is the development of photo-electric cells for ambient temperatures of 100° C.

A complete cycle of operations, Fig. 15.10, starts with the thermostat switching on the mains which opens the pilot valve. A spark bridges the gap and, ordinarily, ignites the pilot flame. If no ignition follows

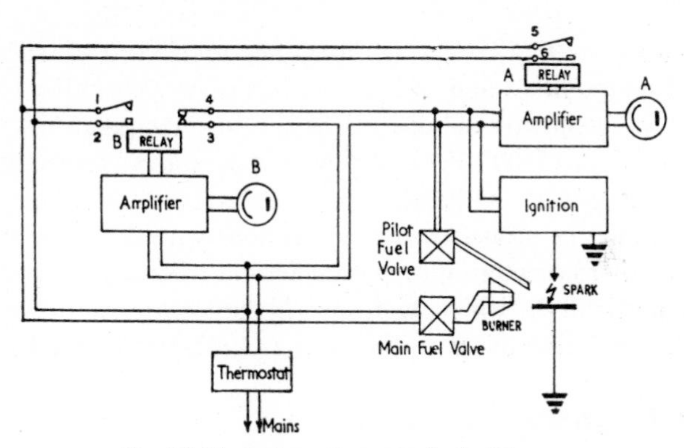

Fig. 15.10. Automatic control of oil burner.

the preliminary process is not repeated but an alarm circuit (not shown in Fig. 15.10) can be energized by a time delay relay if, after the spark has been generated, no ignition follows. When the gas flame has been ignited by the spark, light falls on the photosensitor *A*, sufficient to close contacts *5*, *6* of relay *A*. This operation completes the circuit of the fuel valve and the fuel is ignited by the pilot flame. Sufficient light is now produced to energize the photo-relay *B*, *B*, which is insensitive to the small amount of light from the pilot flame. The energized coil of relay *B* opens contacts *3*, *4*, thus breaking the circuit of the gas valve and, at the same time, closes contacts *1*, *2* which keeps up the flow of the fuel. The opening of *3*, *4* also breaks the circuit of the high-sensitivity relay *A*, thus preventing it from being overloaded. When the fuel fails the flame is extinguished. Relay *B* is de-energized, contacts *1*, *2* are now open, thus shutting down the fuel valve ; contacts *3*, *4*, are closed and have reset the photo-relay *A*, *A*, for controlling the ignition. More details are given by Steiner and Ravensbeck (*890, p. 214*). The manually lit system (Wheelco Instrument Co.) uses only one photosensitor to control the oil flame (*891*).

Bibliography References : (*1340, 1341, 1523, 1524, 1703, 1764, 1773, 1801, 2307*)

CHAPTER 16

TEMPERATURE CONTROL

The photo-electric devices for the measurement and subsequent control of temperature and of heat producing or consuming processes (*1040*) are conveniently subdivided as for low temperatures, i.e., up to about 600° C. (1100° F.) and high temperatures, respectively. In some applications it is the device which is built on photo-electric principles while the measurement itself is done with the more orthodox methods of thermometering or pyrometering, whereas in the majority of cases, particularly where high and highest temperatures are concerned, the operation of measuring uses a photo-electric method (*953*).

16.1 Low Temperature Control

The electric mercury thermometer is a well known instrument. It suffers, however, from two serious disadvantages, namely, that its contacts, once they are set and fused, make the thermometer useful only within a certain set range and give indication only at pre-arranged

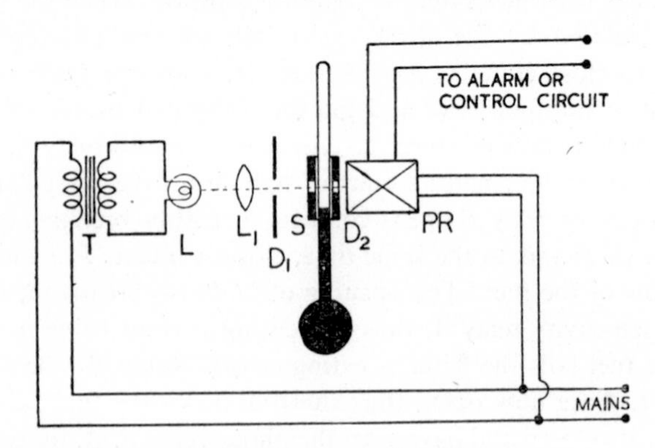

Fig. 16.1. Low temperature control by glass thermometer

levels of temperature which, for an individual instrument, are practically unalterable. This type of thermometer lacks a high degree of accuracy because wire contacts impede the free flow of the mercury column.

The arrangement shown in Fig. 16.1 avoids all these disadvantages of the more usual type electric thermometer and adds a new feature, namely that of adaptability to any range of temperature. A low-voltage lamp L throws a narrow beam of light (optical system L_1, pinhole diaphragm D_1) through the narrow slit S of a tubular diaphragm D_2 which slides up or downwards on the circular stem of the thermometer. Since any type of liquid thermometer (mercury, alcohol, or any other suitable liquid) covering any range up to about 600° C. can be used and any type or range is easily substituted for another, the great advantage of this system becomes obvious. The tubular diaphragm is self-arresting and can be set to any desired degree of temperature. If the measuring column is below the slit S the light-ray passes through the slit striking the photosensitor of the photo-electric relay PR which can be wired for positive or negative action, respectively (cf. Chap. 5). The rising column obstructs the free transmission of the light-ray and reduces its energy (in the case of the column being transparent to light, and coloured) or totally cuts it off (in the case of a mercury thermometer), thus causing the photo-relay to act.

If a mercury thermometer is used any type of light source will do provided the light source and photosensitor are within reasonable limits of a spectral agreement (cf. Chap. 9). Things become a little complicated when coloured liquids are used, for instance alcohol coloured with methyl violet or methyl red. The absorption spectrum of the former is shown in Fig. 16.2, and it becomes evident that coloured light, peaked between 5000 and 6000 A.U. must be used in order to get a reasonable extinction when the light ray passes through the thermometer column. The most suitable filter to be used for the light source in connection with methyl violet dyed alcohol thermometers is the Wratten 61 N green filter. The high transmissivity in the red of the thermometer column, which is fairly well represented by a Wratten 36 Methyl Violet B.B.R. filter, can be suppressed for safety reasons by an Ilford 803 (Red Absorber) filter. It is, of course, possible to have the alcohol tinted by a more suitable dye and to use a complementary filter between the light source and the tubular diaphragm. Other substances for colouring alcohol are of the rosaniline type, and in the U.S. Pat. 2151984 (*848*) aromatic phosphates are used as indicating media

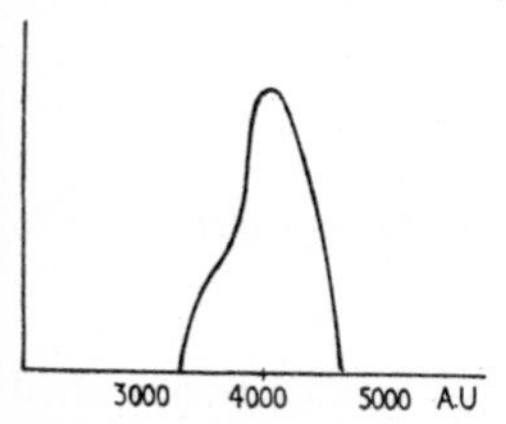

Fig. 16.2. Absorption spectrum of violet-coloured alcohol

in thermometers, manometers, etc. These substances, heated to above 150° C. without decomposition or discoloration, are represented by diphenyl-o-chlorophenyl phosphate, di-o-xenyl phenyl phosphate, phenyl ditolyl phosphate, etc., and are coloured with dyes of the thioindigoid type, for instance Helindone Pink FF. Filters and their dyes are discussed in more detail in Chap. 9.

The arrangement of Fig. 16.1 provides for only one level of temperature to be indicated. For properly controlling the process, of which the temperature is a characteristic, it is necessary to know not only that the temperature has reached a certain level, but also to be informed if and when the temperature is still fluctuating. For this purpose an arrangement as in Fig. 16.3a must be chosen. The distance

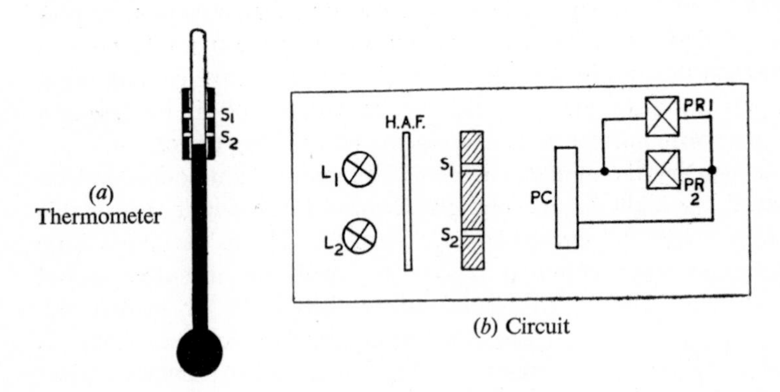

Fig. 16.3. Low temperature control by multi-level thermometer

between the two slits S_1 and S_2 determines whether one or two optical systems and photosensitors are to be used. If one photosensitor is sufficient the circuit of Fig. 16.3b can be employed. The coils of the electromagnetic relays PR_1 and PR_2 are connected for positive action, relay PR_1 releasing when the photosensitor is totally eclipsed, and PR_2 releasing at a value intermediate between zero and a set maximum. These values are generally related to the temperature as set out in Table 16.1.

If the indication is to be in the reverse, i.e., when the temperature decreases below a certain level and continues to do so, arrangements are made according to Table 16.2. The circuit can still be of the forward type, but the load contacts are now working in the reverse sense.

TABLE 16.1

Positive Circuit

Temperature	Slit S_1	Slit S_2	Photosensitor
too low	not obstructed	not obstructed	fully illuminated
correct	not obstructed	obstructed	half illuminated
too high	obstructed	obstructed	obscured

Photo-current	Relay 1	Relay 2	Load contacts 1	Load contacts 2
maximum	energized	energized	open	open
medium	energized	released	open	closed
zero	released	released	closed	closed

TABLE 16.2

Negative Circuit

Temperature	Slit S_1	Slit S_2	Photosensitor
too high	obstructed	obstructed	obscured
correct	not obstructed	not obstructed	half illuminated
too low	not obstructed	not obstructed	fully illuminated

Photo-current	Relay 1	Relay 2	Load contacts 1	Load contacts 2
zero	energized	energized	closed	closed
medium	energized	released	closed	open
maximum	released	released	open	open

If a photo-electric cell is used any simple circuit will operate an appropriate relay ; either a hot or cold cathode valve can be used to control the electromagnetic relay. If a thyratron is used in the circuit no relay may be needed at all.

Thermometers reading up to 600° C. are made from borosilicate glass and have a mercury column in a protective atmosphere of inactive gas under high pressure.

It is sometimes possible that the photo-e.m.f. cell attains a temperature in excess of 45° to 50° C. simply by being subjected for a considerable time to radiations from the light source.

The output and characteristics of the cell may vary with ambient temperatures above a certain critical range which, for nearly all commercial makes, is 45 to 50° C. Exceptionally an ambient temperature of up to 100° C. is admissible. Undue heating of the cell by radiation from the source of heat or light, respectively, must be avoided or at least reduced to the safe value. If necessary a water-cooled fixture (*849, 850*) must be designed for the photo-e.m.f. cell.

There is a certain variation in cell output when the cell is exposed to constant illumination. Investigations have shown fatigue to be responsible for errors up to about ± 10° C. under unfavourable conditions (*147, 148*).

The greater part of the change due to fatigue occurs during the first sixty to ninety seconds, the response being steady afterwards.

All photosensitors, just as other electronic devices, show individual characteristics despite—or because—of being a mass-produced commodity with certain generally maintained features. It is quite possible that cells from different batches have a more or less pronounced

Cells examined	unusable for accurate work	errors up to +10° C.	errors up to +5° C.	Observer
9	1	6	2	Hall (*147*)
10			9	Land (*148*)

characteristic of a certain type which makes a particular cell unusable or alternatively exceedingly well suited for a given purpose. The user of photosensitors will be well advised to select the cell he wants from about a dozen he has carefully tested under actual operating conditions (*1487*), or to buy the cell from the manufacturer after discussing the circumstances of usage and operation. From instances, quoted by T. Land and A. J. Hall (*147*, *148*), the following give a fair picture of what might be encountered when measuring temperatures with photo-e.m.f. cells.

TABLE 16.3

Thermindex Paints (Made in Britain)

Type	Colour change from	Colour change to	at deg. C.	at deg. F.
G 87-R	pink	lavender	80	176
E 102-P	pink	blue-violet	115	239
GG 55-P	mauve pink	bright blue	140	284
E 91-P	dull blue	green	145	293
69-P	light tan	bronze green	150	302
E 91-P	dull blue	black	155	311
E 94-P	bright violet-blue	bright green	155	311
G 97-P	blue	dark green	160	320
E 106-P	red-orange	brick red	205	401
G 75-P	light blue	fawn	210	410
F 41-P	ochre-yellow	brick red	225	437
E 106-P	red-orange	brown	230	446
E 94-P	violet-blue	olive green	230	446
E 104-P	greenish-white	grey	235	455
69-P	light tan	purple brown	240	464
E 106-P	red-orange	black	245	473
E 93-P	grey-blue	buff	275	527
E 6-P	scarlet	brick red	285	545
E 94-P	violet-blue	dark grey	285	545
E 93-P	grey blue	creamy white	290	554
E 94-P	violet-blue	light grey	290	554
E 106-P	red-orange	medium grey	295	563
G 87-R	pink	light brown	295	563
E 94-P	violet-blue	light brown	300	572
E 102-P	pink	grey	310	590
69-P	light tan	indian red	310	590
GG 55-P	mauve-pink	grey	315	599
F 21-P	white	brownish yellow	320	609
E 106-P	red-orange	dirty white	335	635
E 94-P	violet-blue	buff	340	644
E 6-P	scarlet	grey-brown	370	698
E 59-P	mauve	fawn	400	752
G 6-P	red	brown-grey	410	770
E 6-P	scarlet	yellow	440	824
G 6-P	red	yellow	490	915
E 59-P	mauve	grey	515	958
E 59-P	mauve	white	560	1040
G 6-P	red	orange	575	1067
E 6-P	scarlet	orange	625	1157
G 6-P	red	green	800	1472

Efkalin Paints (Made in U.S.A.)

Type	Colour change from	Colour change to	at deg. C.	at deg. F.
2 P-R	yellow	orange	40	104
3 P-R	green	brown	50	122
5 P-R	rose	brown-grey	70	158
1 P-R	red	brown-blue	85	185
4 P-R	yellow	red	115	239
B : P-P	red	yellow	140	284
C : P-P	red	grey	170	338
6 : P-R	red	brown-blue	185	365
7 : P-R	red	brown-blue	240	464
D : P-P	red	brown-blue	280	536
E : P-P	red	brown-blue	310	590
F : P-P	red	brown-blue	390	734

16.2. Heat-Sensitive Paint

The temperature of objects, the very nature of which makes the use of a thermometer undesirable, can be determined with a fair degree of accuracy by heat-sensitive substances. A set temperature is indicated by a change in the colour of the indicator. Heat-sensitive substances, exhibiting a certain colour change, were invented in 1880 by Meusel. They usually are double iodides of mercury with other metals, for instance : the double iodide of mercury and copper is of scarlet colour ; it turns almost black at 87° C. The double iodide of mercury and silver is yellow, but turns red at 45° C.

It is the range of temperatures up to about 800° C. which is reliably covered by colour-changing heat indicators. Some of these materials have a reversible action, which means that they change back again to the original colour when the temperature, after having reached its peak, returns to normal. Heat-indicating chemicals are very useful when applied to such materials as plastics, wood, glass, fibre, rubber, etc., or in cases when the temperature of the material is insufficient in order to emit radiation of wavelengths that can be detected by photo-sensitors. Some suggestions for applications are : bearings, resistors, switches, shafts, transmissions, tanks, joints, piping, fuses, electric wiring, dielectric heating, infra-red baking and drying, etc. (*851*)

The colour change at a well defined temperature lends itself to operate a photo-relay of suitable design. In the preceding Tables the colour changes of heat indicators are listed against the respective temperature.

Reversible indicators are marked R, permanent indicators P. Photosensitors used for this type temperature measurement or detection must be insensitive to infra-red radiation. Either the correct type of cell or heat-excluding filters must be used.

The heat distribution in a sheet of any material can be made visible either by using a paint of wide range or by using image converters. If records are desired the object can be photographed on an infra-red sensitive plate (*36, p. 270, 1457*).

16.3. High Temperature Control

The wavelengths of the energy radiated by a hot body approach the luminous spectrum when the temperature rises up to and above a certain critical value. Fig. 16.4 shows the relation between the relative

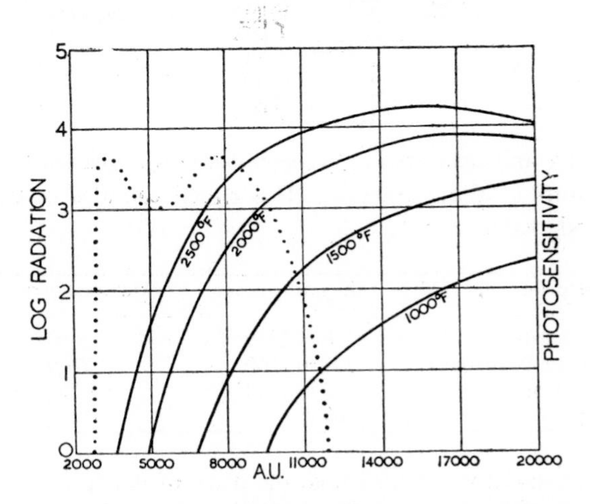

Fig. 16.4. Relative energy radiated by a body at various temperatures. Response of photosensitor shown dotted line

energies emitted from a hot body at various temperatures and the corresponding wavelengths (*852*). This diagram will be helpful in selecting the correct type photosensitor for a certain temperature range when the colour response of the photosensitor is a known quantity.

A highly sensitive circuit, using phase-shift as a means of control, is described by H. J. Reich (*156, p. 456*). The photosensitor, taking the place of the resistor in the basic phase-shift circuit (cf. Chap. 5), is controlled by the light reflected from the mirror of a galvanometer,

Fig. 16.5. The combination of a galvanometer and photo-electric relay is typical of a whole group of different circuits. A thermocouple* in the oven or furnace energizes the galvanometer. Any change in temperature causes the light beam to be deflected from the cathode of the photo-sensitor, the latter being connected for positive action. This circuit

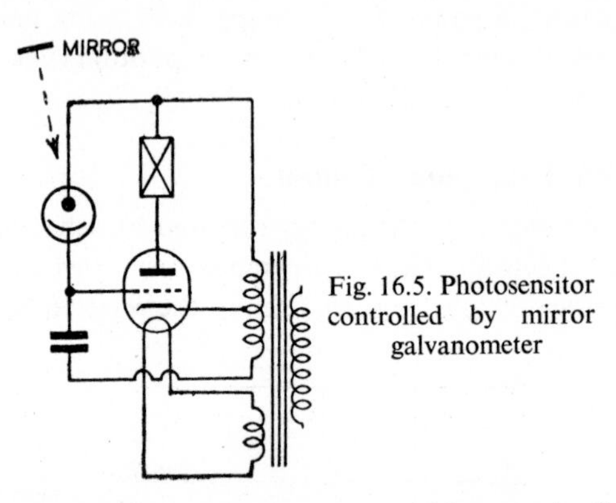

Fig. 16.5. Photosensitor controlled by mirror galvanometer

is so sensitive and accurate as to keep constant within a tenth of a degree a temperature of about 1000° C. This circuit can also be used with a cold cathode valve, Fig. 16.6.

* Thermo-couple (*853*)	Operating range	Max. temperature
Pt—PtRh	0 to 2650° C.	3100° C.
Chromel P—Alumel	−300 to 2200	2450
Iron—Constantan	−300 to 1400	1800
Copper-Constantan	−300 to 650	1100

The photosensitor can also take the place of the variable resistor in one arm of a Wheatstone Bridge. The light variations on the photo-sensitor produce grid variations in the amplifier triode, a 6J5 which, in turn, deflects the pointer of the galvanometer (*856*). A still more sensitive photo-relay was described by Zabel and Hancox (*855*). A diaphragm having a V-shaped aperture is fixed in front of the photo-sensitor, Fig. 16.6, so that more or less light can strike the cell as the mirror of the galvanometer moves one way or another. The incident light controls the amount of current flowing through the thyratron. If the current capacity of the thyratron does not allow for the whole heater current to be controlled by the valve, the thyratron may be

* On Thermo-couples for infra-red, Roess and Dacus (*854*).

shunted by a resistor R_1 which carries a large proportion of the heater current, Fig. 16.7. R_2 is the heater, and R_3 a limiting resistor which protects the valve from being overloaded. The thermo-couple is of the constantan-chromel type ; the other junction is held at zero degrees.

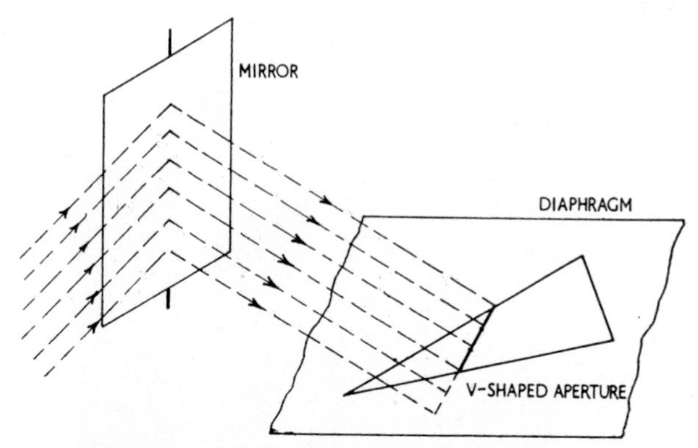

Fig. 16.6. Control of relay by V-shaped diaphragm

The sensitivity of the galvanometer is 40 MΩ, its resistance is 80 ohm. With this circuit the furnace temperature was maintained constant at 880° C. within a limit of 0·06° C., i.e. within an accuracy of 0·0075 %.

The pyrometer (*857*) is an instrument which directly measures the temperature of a hot body by utilizing the heat radiation from that

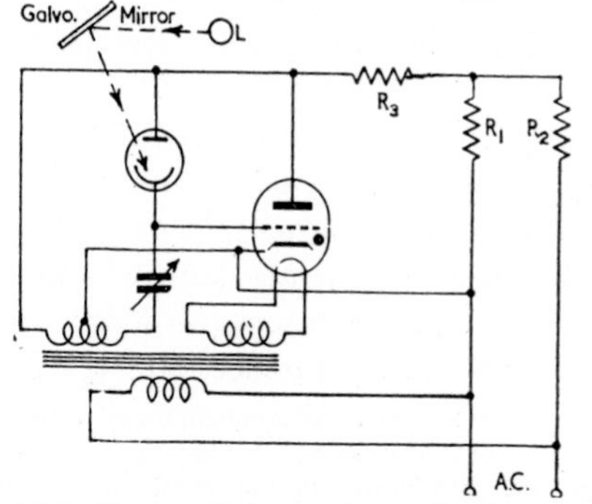

Fig. 16.7. Circuit of photo-relay and galvanometer

object. The instrument indicates and/or records the temperature of red hot objects in steel mills (*801*), of cement, clinker, etc. The pyrometer, when installed at the kiln, or furnace, or mill, is adjusted and calibrated and then left to itself to produce records or give signals.

A form of pyrometer head and the indicating meter are shown in Figs. 16.8a and b. A portable photo-electric pyrometer, utilizing a photo-e.m.f. cell, was described by Hubing (*859*).

A different method, first mentioned by L. R. Koller in a lecture before the American Chemical Society at the Buffalo Meeting in 1931

Fig. 16.8*a*. Pyrometer head with cover open to show adjustable aperture. (*British Thomson Houston Co.*)

(*858*) utilizes the phenomenon expressed by the general formula $\Phi = T^n =$ const., where Φ is the total radiation, T the absolute temperature and $n > 1$. This formula shows that the radiation varies proportionally to the n-th power of the temperature of a hot body.* Therefore, the direct observation by a photosensitor of the roof or walls of the furnace† or some object in the furnace, not necessarily of the charge

* Stefan-Boltzmann Law: The total hemispherical radiation Φ over all wavelengths at T° K. is $\Phi = \sigma A T^4$. The emissive power E of the radiation at the dominant wavelength varies as the fifth power of the absolute temperature. The emissive power of a Planckian radiator is $E = \beta T^5$. The energy radiated at a given wavelength λ is expressed by Wien's Law, viz., $J_\lambda = c_1/\lambda^5 \left\{ \exp(c_2/\lambda T) \right\}$.

† The minimum area of observation suitable for a given maximum scale temperature is $A = kd^2/R^T$, where A is area in sq. in., d distance in inches of the hot body from the photo-electric pyrometer, R_T relative photo-cell response for the temperature T, k an empirical constant (*857*). Photo-electric pyrometers are of the nature of 12th or 13th power instruments (*853*).

itself, will reveal a change in radiation, i.e. in temperature, much faster and more accurately than a thermal instrument. There is, of course, no upper limit to the temperature being observable by photo-electric pyrometers, the lower limit being at about 800 to 1000° C. This lower value is determined by the relative response of the photosensitor to

Fig. 16.8*b*. Typical measuring instrument for pyrometer indications. Note limits marked on dial. (*British Thomson Houston Co.*)

red and infra-red radiation, respectively (Fig. 16.8A). Infra-red photo-sensitors are now available whose longwave limit extends up to 35,000 A.U. and even more. This feature, in turn, extends the pyrometrical range towards the lower temperatures.

It is appropriate to mention in passing a report of Dr. John Johnstone, Director of Research of the U.S. Steel Corporation (*13*), who says that savings of as high as 50% in the life of refractory brick lining in open-hearth furnaces were attained when the temperature of the furnace was accurately controlled and maintained at controlled temperature.

The photo-electric principle can be employed in the automatic control of heaters for valve stems, rivets, welds, etc. The optical system of the photometer projects the image of the object to be heated onto the light-sensitive cathode (*860*), Fig. 16.9. As shown in Table 16.4 the intensity of the radiation at a certain wavelength changes exponentially with the temperature (*864*). The intensity of radiation at any wavelength is given by Planck's formula $R_\lambda = c_1/\lambda^5\{\exp(c_2/\lambda T) - 1\}$. Calculated values of Planck's formula are tabulated in various special

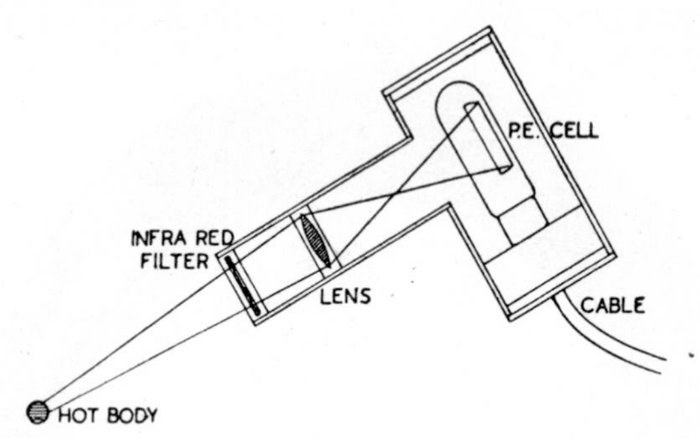

Fig. 16.9. Head of photo-electric pyrometer

works and textbooks (*861, 862, 863, pp. 238–242, Table 2*). Table 16.4 is a brief abstract of data calculated from Planck's formula, covering the ranges most likely to be met in industrial applications of photo-

TABLE 16.4

Intensity of Radiation at given Wavelengths

Wavelength λ in A.U.	y	q	Wavelength λ in A.U.	y	q
5000	4·0193	0	9500	1·3141	5
5500	3·3970	1	10000	2·1651	5
6000	1·9367	2	10500	3·3613	5
6500	8·1810	2	11000	4·9598	5
7000	2·7366	3	11500	7·0055	5
7500	7·6093	3	12000	9·5275	5
8000	1·8235	4	12500	1·2538	6
8500	3·8710	4	13000	1·6031	6
9000	7·4357	4	14000	2·4361	6
			15000	3·4188	6

electric instruments. In the above Table the general formula for R_λ, as given above, is transformed into one which better suits the purpose of tabulation, viz. $R_\lambda = y \,.\, 10^q$ erg/cm²/sec./μ and the values are listed accordingly.

TABLE 16.5

Monochromatic Intensity of Hemispherical Radiation of a Perfect Radiator (Planckian Radiator)

HIGH TEMPERATURES

T° K.	800		1000		1200		1400		1600		1800		2000	
λ A.U.	*A*	*n*	*A*	*n*	*A*	*n*	*A*	*n*	*A*	*n*	*A*	*n*	*A*	*n*
4000	1·28	−2	1·00	2	3·9	4	2·8	6	6·8	7	8·2	8	6·0	9
4500	1·04	0	3·00	3	6·0	5	2·67	7	4·6	8	4·17	9	2·45	10
5000	3·3	1	4·2	4	5·0	6	1·53	8	1·97	9	1·44	10	7·1	10
5500	5·3	2	3·50	5	2·74	7	6·1	8	6·3	9	3·80	10	1·62	11
6000	5·2	3	2·02	6	1·08	8	1·86	9	1·56	10	8·2	10	3·10	11
6500	3·44	4	8·5	6	3·36	8	4·61	9	3·31	10	1·53	11	5·21	11
7000	1·69	5	2·84	7	8·6	8	9·9	9	6·1	10	2·53	11	7·91	11
7500	6·6	5	7·9	7	1·90	9	1·84	10	1·02	11	3·83	11	1·11	12
8000	2·13	6	1·88	8	3·71	9	3·14	10	1·55	11	5·39	11	1·46	12
9000	1·43	7	7·6	8	1·08	10	7·21	10	2·99	11	9·03	11	2·19	12
10000	6·17	7	2·21	9	2·41	10	1·33	11	4·78	11	1·29	12	2·86	12
15000	3·18	9	3·46	10	1·70	11	5·30	11	1·25	12	**2 43**	**12**	**4·15**	**12**

TABLE 16.6

Monochromatic Intensity of Hemispherical Radiation of a Perfect Radiator (Planckian Radiator)

LOW TEMPERATURES

T° K.	373		400		500		600	
λ A.U.	*A*	*n*	*A*	*n*	*A*	*n*	*A*	*n*
10000	7·6	−2	1·03	−1	1·32	3	1·58	5
15000	3·7	3	2·08	4	2·46	6	5·94	7

NOTE: When using the figures of Tables 16.5 and 16.6, respectively, it must be borne in mind that they refer to the ideal case of the radiating object being a Planckian Radiator (Black Body). In practice such a condition is not readily approximated. A furnace, for instance, would radiate like a Perfect Radiator if, when the interior of the furnace is viewed through a SMALL aperture in its wall, no details were discernible in the furnace. A trick can be used to create those conditions artificially which make applicable the Black-Body Laws. This trick is often used in the pyrometry of liquid metals, for instance, of liquid steel. A small tube of refractory material, closed at one end, is introduced into the molten metal and kept immersed in it for sufficient time to acquire the temperature of the melt. The closed-end tube gives a very good imitation of the theoretical Planckian Radiator if the photo-electric pyrometer is used in sighting on the bottom of such a tube (*853*). The closed-end tube can also be used in brick and other kilns, etc., if sufficient care is taken that the tube has acquired the temperature of the kiln and that only the bottom of the tube is inspected. Small muffles produce the necessary conditions much better than other types or sizes of furnaces and no auxiliary tubes are needed.

In Table 16.5 the monochromatic intensity of hemispherical radiation at high temperatures is listed, while some values for the low range of temperatures are given in Table 16.6. In Planck's formula the unit of $d\lambda = 1$ cm. Then, Planck's formula can be reduced to the form $R_\lambda = A \cdot 10^n$ erg/cm²/sec. The values of A and n at various temperatures (in deg. K.) are given for various wavelengths expressed in A.U. The figures in **bold type** are the respective maxima occurring at the indicated wavelength.

The energy radiated, for instance, at 7000 A.U., is

$2{\cdot}84 \times 10^7$ erg/cm²/sec. at 1000° K.
$8{\cdot}6 \times 10^8$,, at 1200° K.
$9{\cdot}9 \times 10^9$,, at 1400° K.
$7{\cdot}91 \times 10^{11}$,, at 2000° K.

The energy radiated in this instance has been increased by a factor of nearly 30,000 when the temperature has been only doubled, i.e. raised from 1000° K. to 2000° K. Use of the above facts has been made in photo-electric pyrometers, for instance as described in the B.P. 472146 and 472147.

TABLE 16.7

Brightness-Absolute Temperature Relation

T° K.	Brightness B in Lightwatts/cm²	$\log_{10}B$
2000	0·0706	−2·8490
2080	0·1137	−1·0556
2160	0·1767	−1·2473
2240	0·2665	−1·4257
2320	0·3910	−1·5922
2400	0·5595	−1·7478
2480	0·7827	−1·8936
2560	1·0730	0·0306
2640	1·443	0·1594
2720	1·910	0·2809
2800	2·486	0·3956
2880	3·192	0·5040
2960	4·040	0·6068
3040	5·060	0·7042
3120	6·262	0·7967

The relation between the brightness B and the temperature T of a Planckian Radiator has been determined by Caldin (*865*). The value of log B is very nearly linearly proportional to $1/T$, viz. $\log B = 4.2750 - 10860/T$ (*866*, *867*).

According to H. K. Work (*868*) the observation of the flame at the mouth of a Bessemer converter enables the operator to know the instantaneous state of the charge at any time. Usually, the operator at any production machine has a more or less numerous arsenal of scientific instruments and aids at his command to control his particular

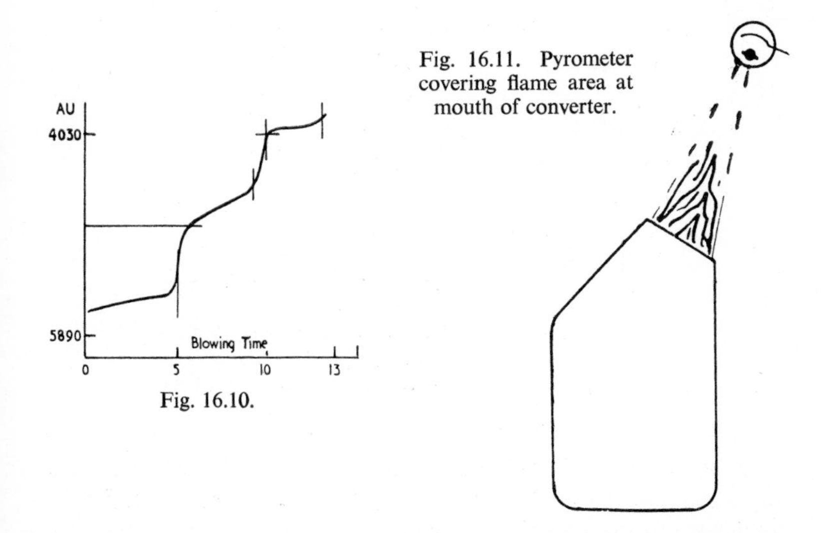

Fig. 16.10.

Fig. 16.11. Pyrometer covering flame area at mouth of converter.

part of production. " The Bessemer process stands out as an anomaly. Here the control depends on just one man—the blower." Fig. 16.10 shows schematically the spectral distribution of luminous radiation from the flame of the Bessemer converter as a function of the blowing time. The diagram refers to the fact that the colour of the flame changes as the metallurgical process passes through its various phases, and that each characteristic phase is represented by a certain range of wavelengths in the spectrum of the flame. At the beginning of the blowing, the colour of the flame is yellowish-orange, approaching the colour of the sodium discharge lamp. At the end of the blowing process the colour has moved towards the blue end of the spectrum.

The field of view of the photosensitor encloses the whole flame, Fig. 16.11. If the size of one cell is not sufficient to cover the entire area, two or more photosensitors must be used in parallel. The unit is set up about 60 feet from the converter. The filter influences the shape of the recorded graph so that an appropriate filter (*1272*, *1273*) must be selected and not changed if one graph is to be compared with another. If the end of the blow process is to be indicated by a signal a combination of two filters is used instead of the one infra-red filter. This combination is a heat-absorbing filter, e.g. of the Corning 397 Aklo type, and an ultra-violet absorbing filter, e.g. of the Corning 338 Noviol Yellow type, Fig. 16.12. The end of the blow is indicated by a

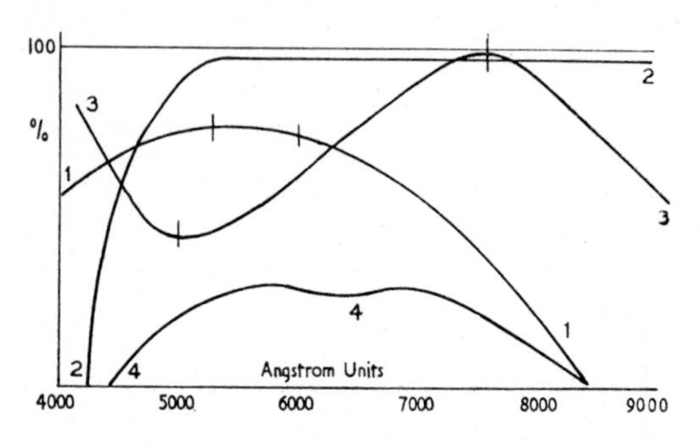

Fig. 16.12. Filter combination used in controlling Bessemer converter. 1: Heat absorbing. 2: Ultra-violet absorbing. 3: Photo-sensitor response. 4: Total response.

" no photo-current " condition in the circuit which can be evaluated for either positive or negative operation. The same method is also applicable to the basic Bessemer process. The Bessemer flame control was developed at the Jones & Laughlin Steel Corporation (*1272*). The advantages of this control are a narrow range of temperature of the steel at the end of the blow ; an improvement in freedom from surface defects and a sound structure in the centre of the billets and bars ; a high degree of workability and machinability (*871*).

A collection of useful data and observations made on the converter flame was published by Naeser and Krächter (*202*). Since it was shown by numerous investigations (*872*) that the quality and uniformity of steel depends on interrupting the blowing process at the correct moment, a characteristic which changes from charge to charge and melt to melt, the indication of this moment became of primary importance. The limits of optimal temperature and blowing time are so narrow that instruments for measuring and control become indispensable.

In the acid process the length of the blowing time can be assessed correctly by noting that the end is indicated by the presence of luminous manganese fumes in the flame, Fig. 16.13. The characteristic wave-length is 4033 A.U.

The Thomas process (basic) flame, however, does not permit of any such simple method. Naeser and Krächter (*202*) have extended their investigations through the whole of the visible and far into the infra-red region of the flame spectrum. In the beginning of the blow there is little energy radiated from the converter flame which, at that time,

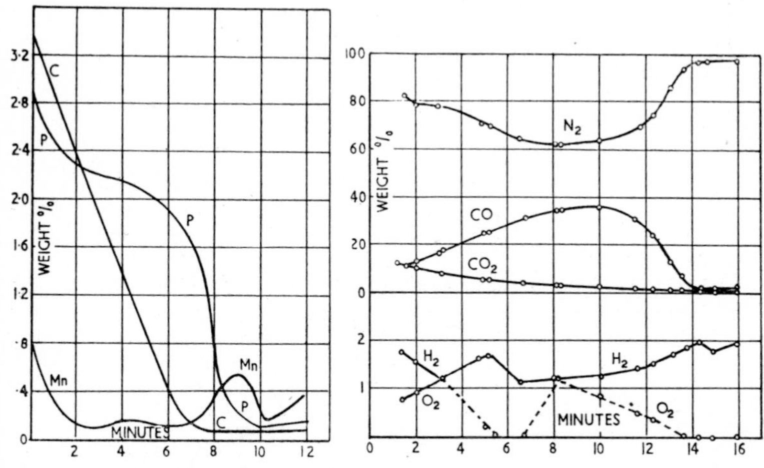

Fig. 16.13. Characteristic of Thomas charge rich in phosphorus. Note the manganese hump

Fig. 16.14. Relation of converter gases to blowing time

consists mostly of nitrogen, Fig. 16.14. It is not before carbon monoxide, carbon dioxide, and water vapour are present in the flame that the transmission of energy sets in. The emission bands are shown in Fig. 16.15. It is of the greatest interest to know that nearly all of the radiation lies in the infra-red region and that only towards the end has the luminous spectrum a greater share in the emission spectrum. This share, however, does not exceed about one fifth of the total radiation. The authors have used a selenium photo-e.m.f. cell, Fig. 16.16, and have found that it responds to infra-red radiation contrary to the general opinion. The flame spectrum of a Thomas converter is shown in Fig. 16.17. It is the luminous radiation which is indicative of the end of the blowing process. The range to be covered is up to about 6·5 microns if an isolated band at 15 microns is neglected. The photosensitor " par excellence " for work in this region would be the bismuth sulphide photo-e.m.f. cell as developed by Fink and Mackey (Chap. 4) if it ever becomes a practical instrument, or other types of I-R sensitive photosensitors.

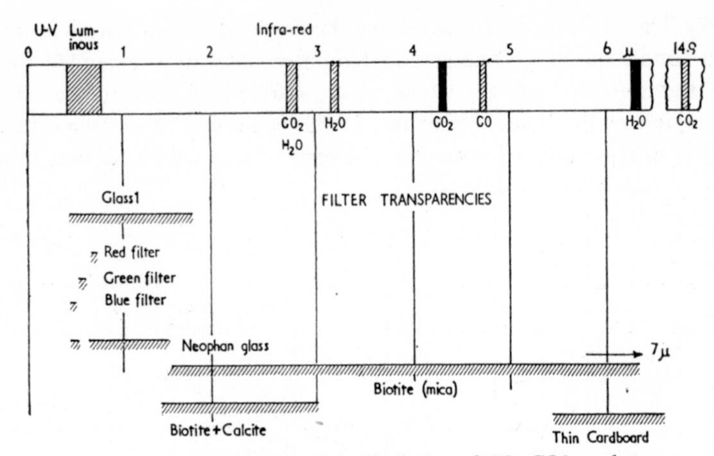

Fig. 16.15. Filter transparencies. Radiation of CO, CO2, and steam.

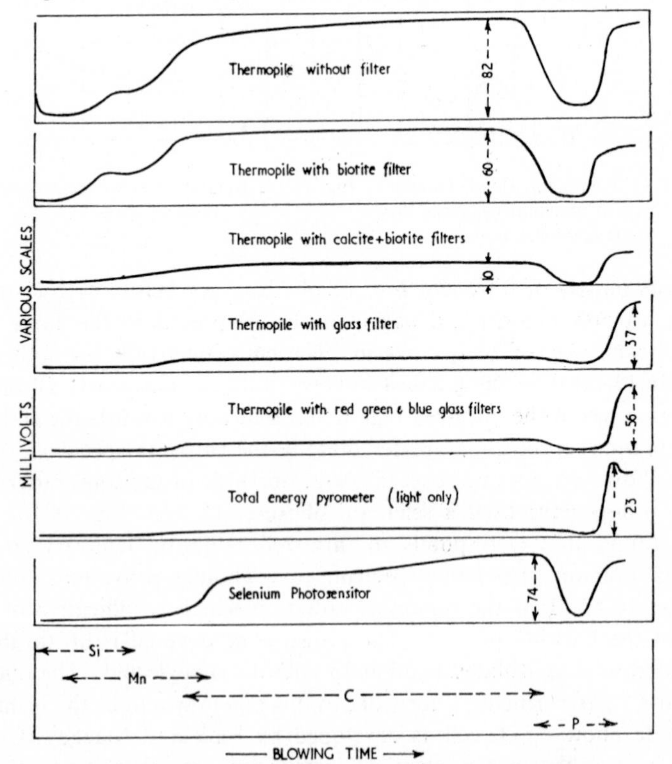

Fig. 16.16. Energy of radiation measured during blowing time. Measurements made with a variety of radiometers.

In an interesting paper (*869*) the emissivity (*1477*) of molten stainless steels is shown to change with the type of added contents of various materials. G. N. Goller states that " with increasing Cr, Mn, Ti, or Nb contents the emissivity increases, while a decrease in emissivity

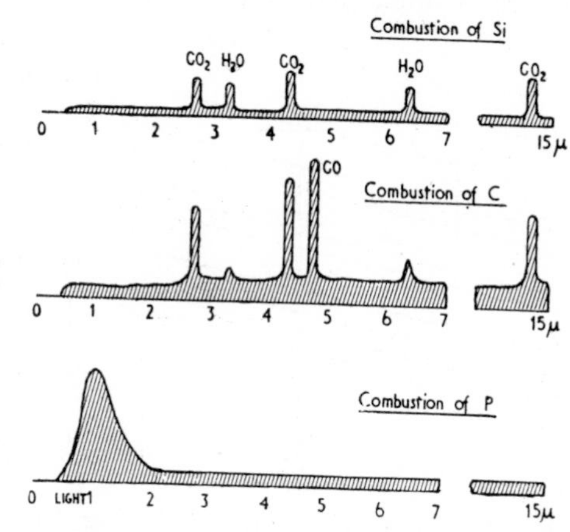

Fig. 16.17. Probable distribution of energy in a Thomas flame

occurs with increasing Ni, Si, S, or Se + P contents. No appreciable effect was noted for C or Mo". A content of:

15% Cr	increases the emissivity from	0·50 to 0·65
4 to 8% Mn	,, ,, ,, ,,	0·59 to 0·67
2% Si	reduces ,, ,, ,,	0·59 to 0·41
35% Ni	,, ,, ,, ,,	0·68 to 0·55

all at 2900° F. (1600° C.).

The emissivity (*348*), by definition the measure of the degree to which a body radiates compared to a Planckian radiator, is calculated

$$E_\lambda = \exp\{c_2/\lambda(1/T_t - 1/T_a)\}$$

where E_λ emissivity,

T_t true temperature (° K.) as indicated by a thermo-couple,

T_a apparent temperature (° K.) as read on an optical pyrometer,

λ effective wavelength of the filter in the optical pyrometer, viz., $\lambda = 6500$ A.U.,

c_2 second radiation constant = 14384 [μ deg.] (*51*).

Fig. 16.18 shows a family of emissivity curves at temperatures ranging from 2750 to 3000° F., i.e., from 1500 to 1650° C., for ten different types of steel. The emissivity characteristics of hot metals with special reference to the infra-red are discussed, and curves given, by Price and Lowerby (*873*).

In work involving photo-electric pyrometers care must be taken not only to select a stable photosensitor amongst many of its own type as

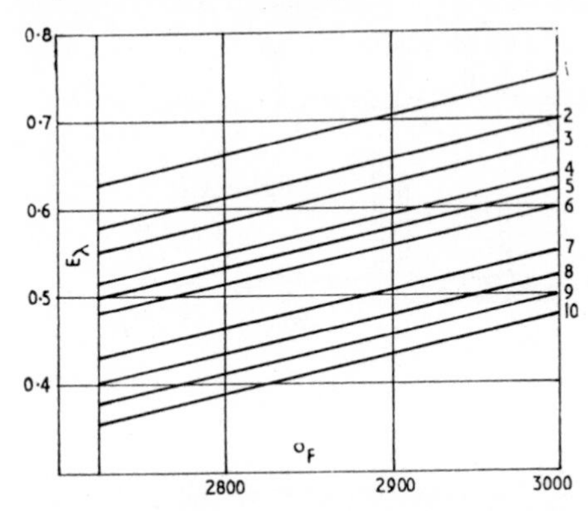

Fig. 16.18. Emissivity of different types of steel at temperatures between 1500 and 1650 °C.

1. (27Cr) 18—10 Nb + Ti
2. 16 Cr
3. 12 Cr
4. 18 — 12 — 3 Mo
5. 18-9 27-20
6. 5 Cr
7. 18-9 Sulphur
8. Carbon Steel
9. Cr Sulphur
10. 18 — 9 Se

shown by Hall (*148*) and Land (*147*), but, and this is of even more importance, to chose the correct type of photosensitor according to the temperature range to be observed. As shown by Larsen and Shenk

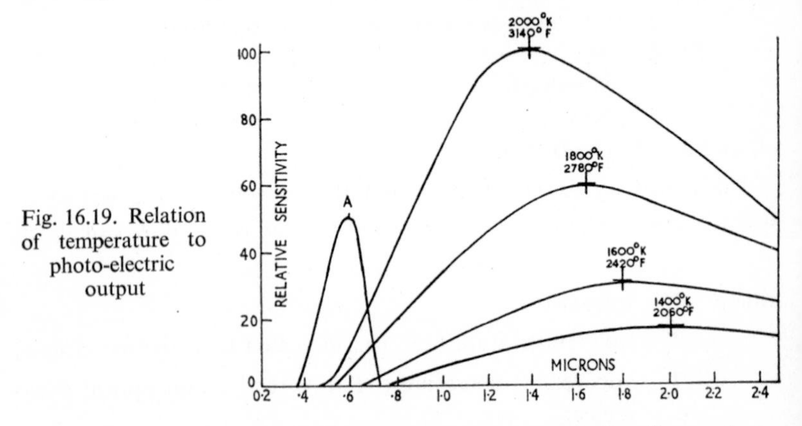

Fig. 16.19. Relation of temperature to photo-electric output

(*849*) the temperature v. photo-electric output variation for a photosensitor depends on the relative change in the common area covered by both the sensitivity curve of the photosensitor and the radiation intensity curve for any one particular temperature. The lower the temperature the smaller will be the common area and the more in the infra-red it will be situated, Fig. 16.19. Approximately the common area varies with the tenth power of the absolute temperature. A comparison of Figs. 16.19 (*849*) and 16.20 (*852*) shows how important is the spectral sensitivity of the photosensitor, when considered in the light of the above principle. The common area is much bigger in Fig. 16.4 than in Fig. 16.19.

A Table (*874*) listing the temperatures of tempering colours may be helpful in connection with the substance of this chapter.

TABLE 16.8

Temperatures of Tempering Colours

Tint of Oxide on Surface of Steel	Temperature ° C.	° F.
Dark blue	316	600
Blue	293	560
Bright blue	288	550
Purple	277	530
Purple, beginning to show brown	266	510
Brown	254	490
Golden yellow	243	470
Straw	230	446
Pale yellow	221	430

The radiation in the region from 8000 to 10,000 A.U. from hot, non-luminous gases has been measured down to 1000° C. and discussed by Mecke and Kempter (*875*).

The precision control of high temperatures has so been perfected that a furnace, set at 600° C., maintained a constant temperature to within 3° C. without adjustment over a two-months' period: the deviation during two hours was ± 0·05° C. Full details are given in the original paper by Waring and Robison (*876*).

The widest application of high-temperature measurement is in the metallurgical field. Controls of a kind hitherto unknown or impossible by the nature of the object or process are easily and in an elegant manner accomplished by means of photo-electric equipment. The outputs of different furnaces, serving one mill, can be controlled to ascertain an even temperature of each billet arriving at the mill, Fig. 16.20. A photo-electric pyrometer can be used to indicate the temperature inside cast-iron pipes which are manufactured by a centrifugal-casting machine. When the solidification temperature is reached the spinning of the machine is stopped (*877*).

The ratio of the radiation in two wavelength bands (blue-red or green-red) is a measure of the radiating body's surface temperature. If the emissivity of the body is constant with wavelength, etc., the ratio is independent of these quantities.

Fig. 16.20. Photo-electric pyrometer mounted above rolling mill—shown by arrow (*British Thomson Houston Co.*)

In optical pyrometry the effective wavelength varies with temperature. This is not so in pseudo-monochromatic photo-electric systems. The optical bandwidth of the systems is best for blue, green, and red filters ($<0.075\ \mu$) and less satisfactory for yellow and orange ($>0.100\ \mu$). The effective wavelengths are 4570, 5200, 5630, 5830, 6270 Å. The statistical dispersion is almost constant for all colours. Particular attention must be paid to the relationship of the blue-red radiations for high temperatures, and to the green-red radiations for low temperatures. Although photo-electric pyrometry is somewhat less accurate than optical pyrometry, its advantage is that the readings need not be taken by experienced men as only galvanometer deflexions are read. For details reference should be made to the original paper (*2615*).

Another instrument uses the ratio of the two wavelength bands and is, therefore, independent of the emissivity of the hot body (*vide supra*).

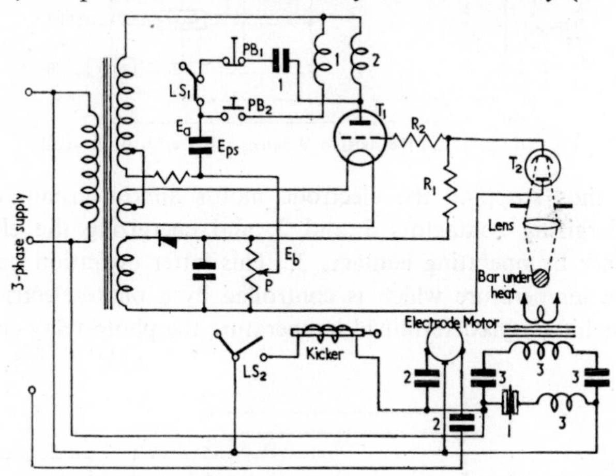

Fig. 16.21. Circuit of photosensitor-controlled rivet heater

A PbS photosensitor is used in the circuit and full details of the amplifier are given in the original paper (*2616*).

For the measurement of hot steel and other purposes of pyrometry a photo-electric instrument has been developed (*2617*) that embodies an interrupter in the optical path to avoid the inconveniences attending D.C. amplification.

Bibliography References : (*501, 532, 537, 546, 577, 1053, 1118, 1155, 1188, 1199, 1538, 1752, 1757, 1763, 1844, 1921, 1922, 1934, 1935, 1998, 2111, 2169, 2178, 2249, 2401, pp. 115, 116*).

16.4. Photo-electric Control of Rivet-Heater Machine

Vedder and Evans (*852*) have described a photosensitor controlled rivet-heater machine. Fig. 16.21 and the following brief description of the operation of the machine are taken from the original paper.

The depressing of the push button PB_2 closes the normally open contactors 1 and 2 ; this movement energizes the electrode motor through contacts 2, forcibly opening the electrodes against spring pressure. When the electrodes have fully opened up a rivet falls between, and is gripped by the electrodes, current being switched on at the same moment. A part of the mechanical gear fitted to the electrode shaft is arranged to break the circuit of the normally closed limit switch

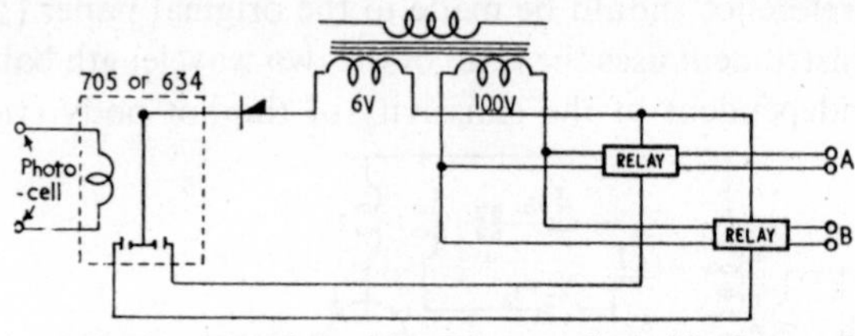

Fig. 16.22. Use of sensitive Weston relay with photo-cell

LS – 1, thus stopping the electrode motor almost instantaneously by de-energizing contactors 1 and 2, and energizing the electrode transformer by operating contacts 3. This latter operation heats the rivet to a temperature which is controlled by a photo-electric relay. Upon reaching a predetermined temperature the photo-relay energizes

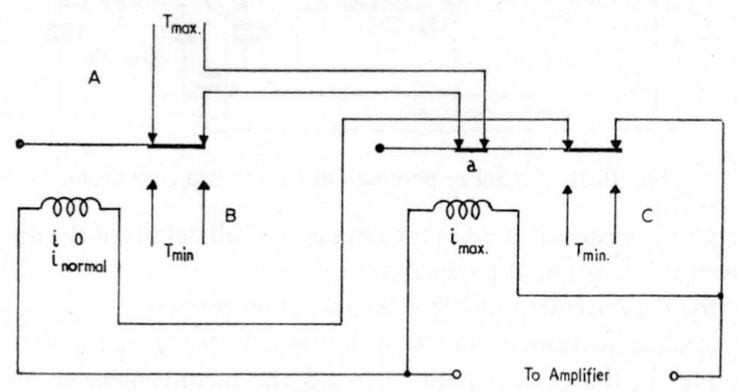

Fig. 16.23. Thermostatic control system using two relays

contacts 1 and 2 which operation opens contactor 3, thereby cutting off the transformer and closing the electrode motor circuit. In this way the entire operation is recycled.

Bibliography Reference : (*2014*)

16.5. Thermostatic Control System

In low temperature work a suitably graduated thermometer is used as discussed previously. The following method is particularly suited to thermostatically controlling the temperature of hot air or hot liquids. The graduation of the thermometer gives the range within which a constant temperature to a fair degree of accuracy may be maintained. The output of the photo-e.m.f. cell, Fig. 16.22, is fed into a high sensitivity relay which controls the power relay ; this in turn controls the heater of the enclosed air or water volume.

Another method uses a twin-pinhole tubular diaphragm, Fig. 16.3a, and two relays as shown in Fig. 16.23. The relations between temperature T, relay current i, conditions of light rays L_1 and L_2, respectively, and of the total intensity I striking the photosensitor at any time, are listed in Table 16.9.

TABLE 16.9

T	L_1	L_2	I	i	Circuits made	Circuits open
normal	passing through	cut off	normal	normal	B	A, C
too low	passing through	passing through	maximum	maximum	C	A, a, B
too high	cut off	cut off	nil	nil	A	B, C

The circuit of a galvanometer-controlled photo-electric device measuring the heat transfer coefficients of various materials is also

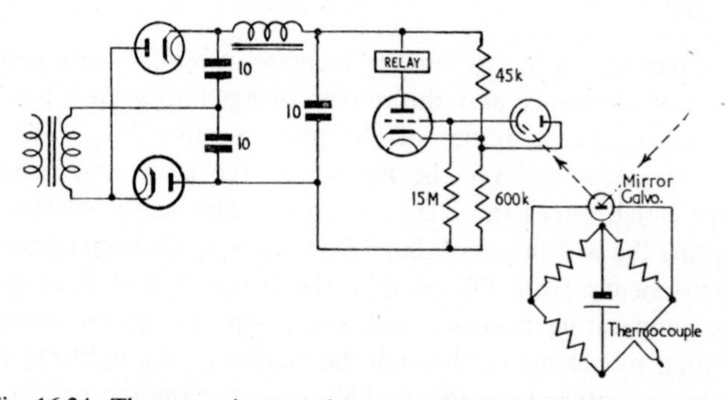

Fig. 16.24. Thermostatic control system using bridge and galvanometer

applicable to a thermostatic control system. The thermo-couple lies in one branch of a Wheatstone bridge. The movements of the galvanometer mirror are viewed by a photosensitor (*878*), Fig. 16.24.

A circuit used for thermostating a molten lead bath at 400° C. uses a bridge with a resistance thermometer and two photosensitors (*879*),

Fig. 16.25. A complete cycle begins by manually closing the self-locking switch S_3. As the temperature rises the resistance of the thermometer R_1 increases and the Wheatstone bridge approaches balance. The mirror of the galvanometer G causes the light-ray from the lamp L to strike the photosensitor PC_1; this closes the relay switch S_1

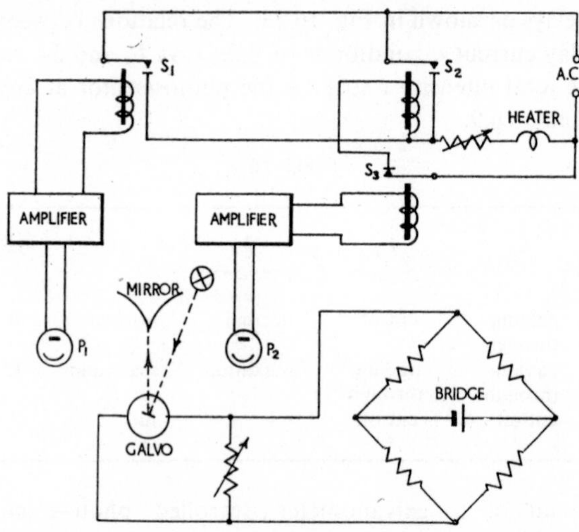

Fig. 16.25. Measurement of h.f. energy by photo-cell

which is parallel to S_2. A further increase in temperature causes the bridge to over-balance and the mirror swings into such a position as to de-energize the amplifier of the photosensitor PC_1. The photosensitor PC_2 now receives the light from the lamp and actuates its amplifier which opens the relay switch S_2. This action also opens S_3 by breaking the coil circuit of that relay. Since S_1 has been opened when the mirror swung from PC_1 to PC_2, the heater H is now switched off and the temperature begins to fall whereupon the mirror swings back to PC_1 and, by closing S_1 through the incidence of a light-ray on PC_1, the heater is switched on again. The resistance thermometer is of the usual wire-wound type.

Another temperature measuring system can be used instead although it is of a somewhat unorthodox type. This " electronic thermometer " was described by Weiller and Blatz (*880*) and consists of a pair of evenly spaced electrodes immersed in an organic liquid of high resistivity and extremely high temperature coefficient of resistance.

The apparent resistance of a bulb ranges from 10^5 to 10^6 ohms at room temperature. It is possible to adjust its sensitivity for a range of $\pm$ 0·01° F.

From the above examples it will be noticed that the two main groups of photo-electric equipment for use in temperature control employ two totally different principles, viz., (1) the direct observation of the hot body by photosensitors measuring the radiant energy emitted from that body ; and (2) the measurement of the temperature of the hot object by any type of heat indicator and observing these indications by means of photosensitors.

A very important application of photo-electric observation of hot bodies has been made to the routine testing of incandescent filaments under actual conditions of operation, e.g., exposed to severe shock. The study of vibrations of thin white-hot wires is essential in the testing of car lamps, railway lamps, rough-service lamps in general, aeroplane and ship lamps, etc. A convenient method for measuring both amplitude and frequency of vibrating hot bodies has been described by Meserve (*881*).

Bibliography Reference : (*2227*)

16.6. Measurement of High-Frequency Energy

The principle of observing the degree of incandescence of a body by means of a photosensitor has been used in measuring high frequency currents. Instead of directly measuring a current at many millions of cycles per second by means of an orthodox ammeter which, with regard to the high frequency of the current, would become a very cumbersome instrument difficult to design, the high frequency energy is caused to pass through a thin wire in a vacuum. This wire will become heated proportional to the intensity of the high frequency current. A photosensitor is arranged to observe the varying incandescence of the wire which is proportionally related to the high frequency current flowing through it. Since the amount of radiation emitted at dominant wavelength from that wire is proportional to the fifth power of the absolute temperature, this transmutation instrument is extremely sensitive and accurate (*882*). A similar system was used earlier, for the measurement of the high frequency output of a diathermy generator (*1280*).

A practical circuit and method for operating a r–f wattmeter was developed by W. Maron (*883*). A 60-watt lamp is fed by the r–f receiving circuit and viewed by a photosensitor, preferably a photo-e.m.f.

cell, which is bypassed for the r–f by three capacitors, Fig. 16.26. The leads to the microammeter must be short and shielded. The output

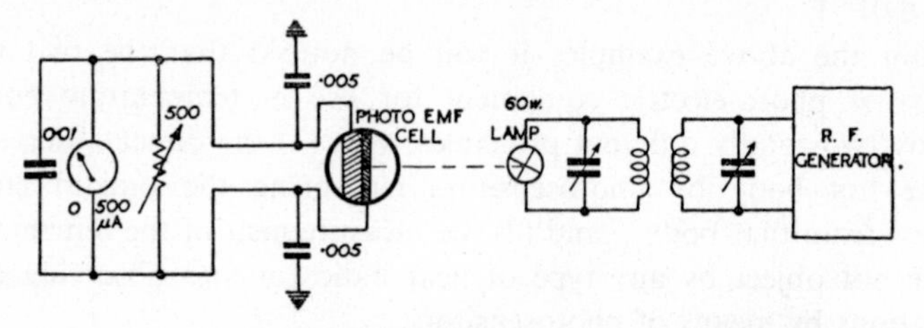

Fig. 16.26. Practical circuit for operating the r-f wattmeter.

of the unit is calibrated and remains constant for each individual lamp and distance between photosensitor and light source.

Bibliography References : (*406, 1178, 1841, 1919, 1937, 1945*)

CHAPTER 17

MINING

As early as 1931, when industrial applications of photo-electric gear had something adventurous about them, the mining industry had already installed two photo-electric relays. A. H. Hubbell describes the applications, i.e., the one signalling the hoistman whenever the cage goes down, the other being used to control the speed of a sintering machine at an ore-sintering plant, thus assuring a bed of even depth (*956*). In 1934 a thorough examination of the potentialities of

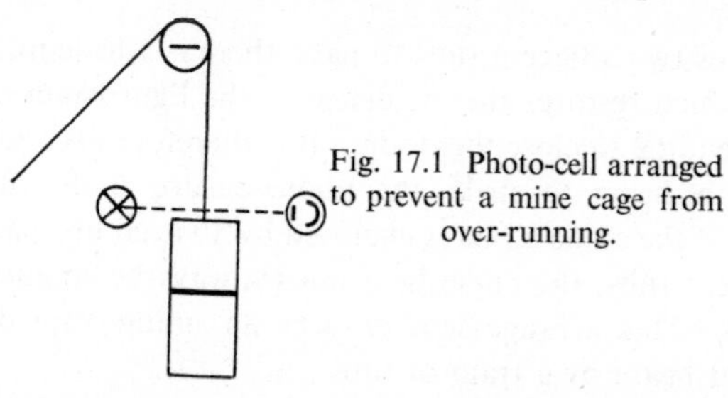

Fig. 17.1 Photo-cell arranged to prevent a mine cage from over-running.

photosensitors in the mining industry was published by Richardson (*989*). Many of the suggestions are still waiting to be carried out in practice.

Among the more usual applications may be classified the counting of tubs, prevention of cage overwinding, Fig. 17.1, smoke detection (cf. Chap. 15), detection of firedamp, etc.

Bibliography References : (*1378, 1381*)

17.1. Mine Door Opener

When a train of tubs is travelling from one section of the mine to another the sections being separated by doors which are permanently closed to prevent the spreading of fires or explosions, it is relatively simple for a photo-electric relay to be arranged to operate these doors. One precautionary measure has to be observed when designing mine door openers. Since the train will consist of many tubs which are spaced from one another by a distance about half the length of a single tub—and since the photo-electric mechanism of the door opener acts on the interruption of the light beam, it is obvious that every tub intersecting the light ray for only a very short period of time, will cause the opening mechanism to operate only for a brief moment and the doors to be opened only a few inches accordingly, Fig. 17.2, because during the

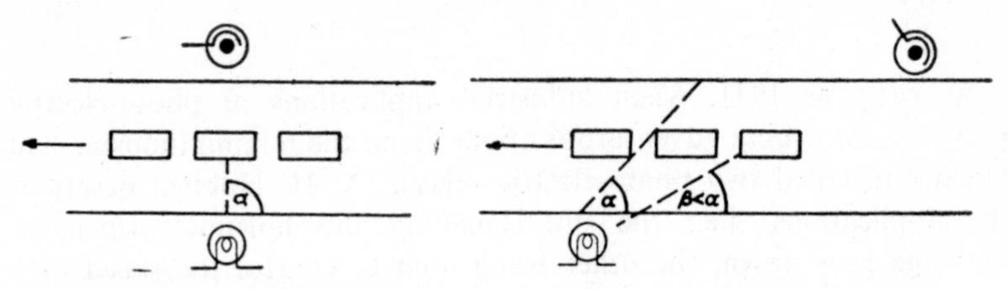

Fig. 17.2 Incorrect placing of the cell gives intermittent action

Fig. 17.3 Photo-electric opener for mine doors: correct arrangement

time it takes two adjacent tubs to pass, there is a little interval between the tubs which restores the incidence of the light beam on the photosensitor, tending to close the doors. It is therefore necessary to arrange for the light-beam to strike the photosensitor under an angle beta, Fig. 17.3. If the angle alpha is enclosed by a visual line passing between two adjacent tubs, the angle beta must always be smaller than alpha. (*990*, *991*). This arrangement ensures an uninterrupted obscuration of the light beam by a train of tubs.

17.2. Emptying Tubs

Loaded trucks, cars, tubs, etc., can be emptied automatically by a rotary dumping device. It is all-important that the emptied vehicles be completely clear of the rotated section of the rotary track before it is operated again. The dump must not rotate as long as one beam of light is prevented by the vehicle from striking the photo-relay. The latter is wired for negative action (*992*). To prevent mishaps by accidental screening of the photo-relay, two photosensitors are so arranged that the tub or truck must intercept both light beams simultaneously if the dumping device is to rotate. Two photo-relays in series or parallel will prevent any action if only one member of the control gear is eclipsed (Fig. 17.4).

Any such or similar arrangements can also be controlled by the Aniseikon (Chap. 10), or by limit switches (Chap. 21). In Fig. 17.5 a specially adapted limit switch relay is shown. Part of the light-sensitive cathode is covered by a stop the size of which is larger than the image of a man would be if picked up by the optical system of the device, but this stop is smaller than the image of a van or truck or tub which, when on the dumping device, is projected on the cathode. The scale of the measuring instrument (microammeter) is marked at a given value

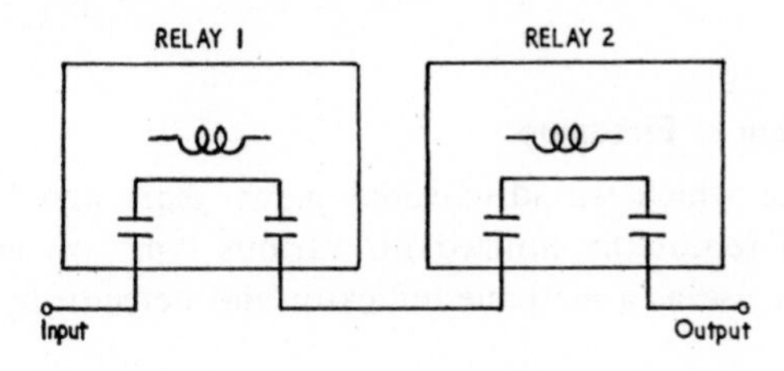

Fig. 17.4 Power contacts of two relays connected in series, giving an output only when both relays are energized simultaneously

by either having a hole drilled through it or by employing some other method of limiting the movement of the pointer as outlined in Chap. 21. The image of a man, being projected on to that part of the cathode which is covered by the stop, will not affect the electronic circuit. The image of a truck, however, will do so as it is larger than the obscuration

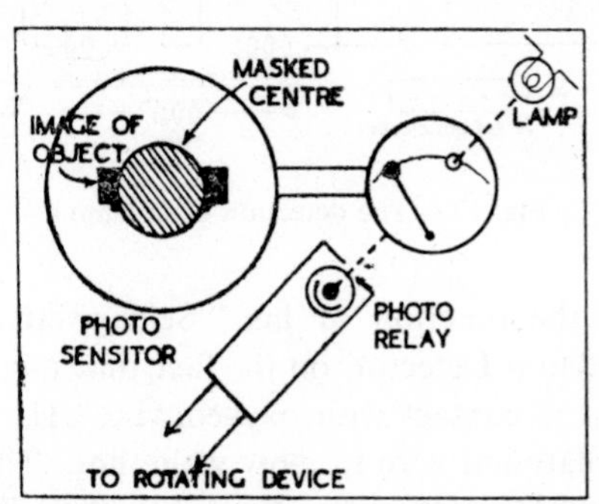

Fig. 17.5 Arrangement of mine tub emptying device

which, in turn, will cause the pointer of the limit switch to move up to or beyond the given value, thus actuating a power relay which energizes the rotating device.

17.3. Stripping Shovels

Large stripping shovels working in open-pit mines must be so positioned that the lower frame is close to level. The mechanical shovel is supported on four large and heavy tractors. Between each tractor and the basis of the machine, a hydraulic levelling jack is built-in and controlled by photo-electric gear which, once the operator has started the levelling action by pressing a button, takes only thirty seconds to level the 1500 ton machine to an error of less than half a degree (*877*).

17.4. Detection of Firedamp

A principle which was discovered many years ago by Werner v. Siemens and repeatedly utilized for various types of indicators, was suggested for use as a methane indicator and detector by Martienssen

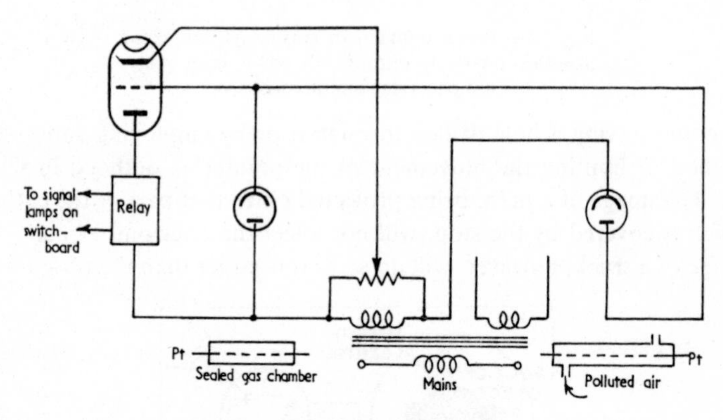

Fig. 17.6 The detection of firedamp.

(*784*) who based the function of his " Schlagwetteranzeiger Wetter-licht ", i.e., Firedamp Detector, on the fact that methane, on exploding when brought in contact with oxygen, viz., $CH_4 + 2O_2 = CO_2 + 2H_2O$, causes a platinum wire to glow white hot. This platinum wire, which is palladized for better operation (*781*, *782*, *783*), has been pre-heated by an electric current to about 250° C. at which temperature it just begins to glow visibly. Martienssen's indicator can easily be converted into a photo-electric methane detector when a two-cell circuit, as first developed by A. E. Hull (*229*) is employed together with a sealed standard cell containing a sample of pure air. As the emissive power of the filament is proportional to the fifth power of the absolute temperature a very sensitive instrument is produced, Fig. 17.6. The detector, if made portable, is self-contained with built-in batteries.

Other indicating reactions, either of the chemical or physical type can be worked out for different gases and used with the same or other equipment. In Table 17.1 some useful data are compiled.

TABLE 17.1

Explosive Limits

Gas or Vapour	Lower Limit %	Upper Limit %
Carbon bisulphide	1·1	—
Benzol	1·5	8·0
Petrol vapour	1·7	6·0
Hydrogen	4·1	76·0
Methane	5·0	15·4
Town gas	5·3	31·0

An addition of blackdamp to firedamp narrows the limits to 5·4 and 10·0%, respectively, With more than 35% blackdamp, i.e., less than 13·6% oxygen in the mine air there is no explosion (*785*).

A recent investigation by W. Davies (*789*) was made into the catalytic action of platinum wires in a methane atmosphere with a view to establish the relationship between temperature, amount of methane, and activation of the platinum wire.

A new wire of platinum or any element of the platinum group (rhenium, osmium, iridium, platinum) must be activated by heating it to a temperature of 1400° C. for three to five minutes in an atmosphere containing about 1% of methane. Carbon dioxide and water vapour have no effect on activated platinum, but sulphur and its compounds are a catalytic poison.

The minimum wire temperature at which catalytic combustion of methane in air is initiated is shown in Fig. 17.7. The graphs are of great importance for it is shown that surface combustion on activated platinum wire starts at about 650° C. while non-active wire must be heated to 1400° C. before initiating surface combustion. It is also shown that much higher temperatures are reached with the same heater input which is a consequence of the surface combustion. Examination of Fig. 16.4 gives a clear picture of how the radiant energy emitted by the incandescent platinum wire increases rapidly with increasing temperature, a fact which is also borne out well in Tables 16.5 and 16.6. The melting point of platinum is 1755° C. (*790, 791, 792, 793*).

A thermal conductivity type gas analyzer based on the principle of change in resistivity was described by C. A. Hansen, Jr. (*794*).

Bibliography References : (*470, 1320, 1334, 1339, 1340, 1341, 1733, 1766, 1842*)

17.5. Smoke Detection

The same mechanical arrangement as described for the detection of firedamp can be used if tests for smoke are made. Any sensitive

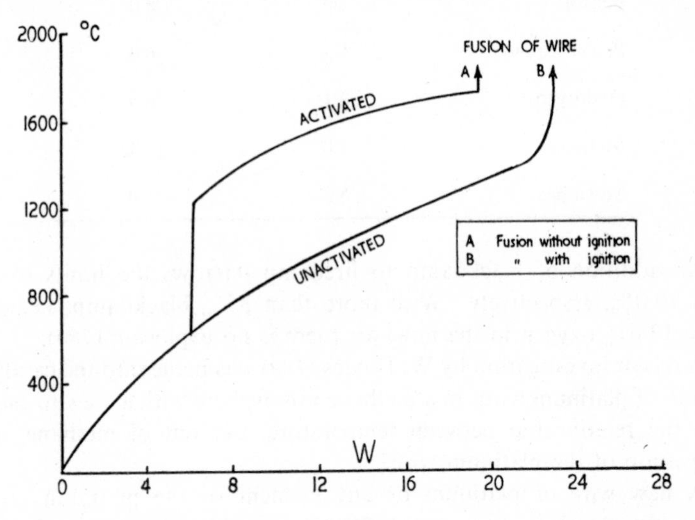

Fig. 17.7 Wire temperature and catalytic combustion of methane in air.

circuit, for instance one of those discussed in Chap. 15, can be employed. The mechanical arrangements for the firedamp detector can be used in the construction of a combined smoke-and-firedamp detector. One platinum filament is mounted in the air duct of the detector and the other filament in a sealed cell. The smoke detector is so arranged that the mine air is tested first for smoke and then for firedamp, Fig. 17.8. When smoke is present in the mine air the electronic relay *S* will operate. The smoke detector is not affected by the presence of methane in air. When firedamp is also detected in the air sample, the electronic relay *FD* will operate. The latter will not be tripped if smoke passes between the platinum filament and the photosensitors if a very simple precaution is taken. The operation of the firedamp detector *FD* is based on the phenomenon that the platinum filament emits energy of a certain wavelength λ in pure air and another wavelength or range of wavelengths λ′ in a polluted atmosphere, the change

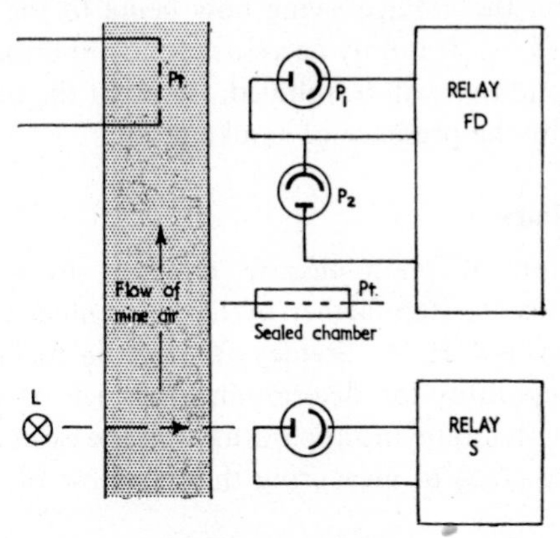

Fig. 17.8 Smoke and firedamp detector.

being due to an increase in temperature, i.e., to an intensification of the emitted energy. If smoke contaminates the air the opposite action will take place. The radiation will not be increased, but an illumination dimmer than normal will cause the electronic relay *FD* to swing to

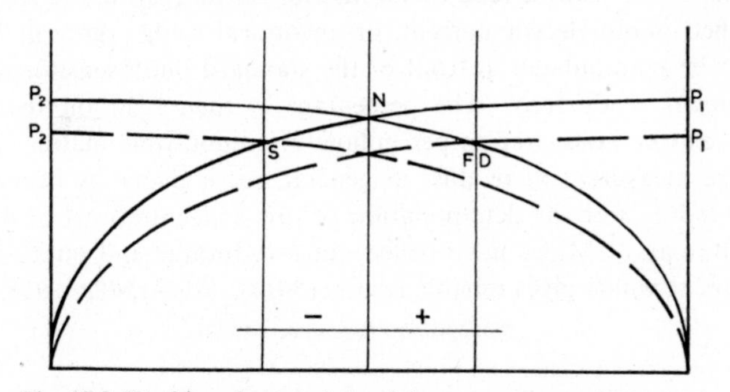

Fig. 17.9 Working characteristic of the arrangement of Fig. 17.8.

the opposite side. This is expressed in Fig. 17.9 by marking the intersection of the characteristics of the two photosensitors P_1 and P_2, respectively. The point for normally balanced photosensitors is *N*. An increase in incident energy on P_1, resulting from the presence of methane in air, intersects the characteristic of the other cell at *FD*.

This voltage swing, marked +, is ulitized in ringing an alarm. When smoke diminishes the amount of light falling on P_1, this will be equivalent to the photosensitor P_2 receiving an illumination which has been relatively increased by the same amount. This is expressed by point S in the diagram, the voltage swing now being to the other side and, therefore, marked −. It is only necessary to avoid utilizing this voltage swing and the condition will be fulfilled, viz., that the firedamp detector be not affected by the presence of smoke in air.

17.6. Dust in Mines

The application of photo-electric methods to measurements in mines was advanced a step farther by D. G. Skinner (*1445*, *1452*) and by J. I. Graham and H. A. Stanley (*1456*), the former working out methods and apparatus for determining the size of particles photo-electrically, the latter applying apparatus as in the estimation of noxious gases in industry (*752*) to measuring the dustiness of mine air photo-electrically.

In a lecture before the North Staffordshire Institute of Mining Engineers, J. G. Bromilow (*1458*, *1459*) has given the fundamentals of a colorimetric method for the estimation of the combustible content of mine road dust. If photo-electric principles are being applied the balanced two-cell circuit is indispensable. The percentage of combustible matter can be read on an instrument measuring the natural or amplified photo-electric current, or an optical wedge (grey or brown) can so be manipulated in front of the standard photosensitor that the instrument reads zero. The percentage is then read on the wedge which can be graduated in percentage of combustible matter content. For the measurement of dust in general, see a paper by Barnett and Free (*1650*). For the determination of low concentrations of dust the U.S. Bureau of Mines has worked out a technique and photo-electric equipment which gives reliable results (*2614*). Also (*2622*, *2623*, *2625*).

Bibliography Reference : (*500*)

CHAPTER 18

INSPECTION OF MASS-PRODUCED ARTICLES

If bottlenecks on the production line are to be avoided the inspection of mass-produced articles requires the upkeep, throughout the whole process of inspection, not only of at least the same speed as has been dominant in the process of production but also of a very high standard of accuracy and precision, usually of the order of 10^{-4} inch. The object to be inspected must be so mounted and moved that all of its surface passes within the field of view of the scanning head. In some cases it will be of advantage to move the scanner as well as the object. The high intensity light source is either a high-pressure mercury discharge lamp, a sodium lamp, or a tungsten-arc (Pointolite) lamp, depending on the conditions of the surface and type of the photosensitor used in the scanning head. The illumination system usually comprises a condenser and a lens of high curvature producing a small spot of very high brilliancy on the surface of the object. Precautions must be taken to prevent the focused light from causing thermal injury to the surface or uncontrollable thermal expansions by using either a heat-absorbing filter or moving the spot over the surface as quick as the inspection will permit.

18.1. Flaws, Impurities

An efficient method of inspecting a surface for cracks, flaws, impurities, etc., was developed in the Department of Engineering Research of the University of Michigan (*993*). Improved systems were described later by Powers and others (*994*, *995*, *996*).

The scanner consists of two photosensitors forming a balanced circuit. This is necessary not only for countering the fluctuations in the intensity of the light source due to small variations in the mains voltage, but also—and mostly—because the colour or shade may vary from object to object. The circuit can only be thrown out of balance by flaws or impurities or other irregularities in the surface of the specimen appearing in the field of view of the one photosensitor but not of the other. The optical system of the scanner is a microscope (vide Chap. 11) of suitable magnification which, in connexion with the sensitivity of the amplifier, accounts for the degree of accuracy. In almost all cases a microscope of the type used in mineralogical or metallurgical work, having a magnification of up to × 200, will serve the purpose. The magnification here depends on the proper working distance, i.e., the distance of the front lens of the microscopic objective from the surface under inspection. Table 18.1 gives the magnifications of the Greenough Microscope.*

TABLE 18.1

Working Distance and Magnification

Working Distance mm.	Object glass Focal length mm.	Eyepiece Magnification			Diameter of Field of view mm.		
		×6 42 mm.	×10 25 mm.	×15 17 mm.	×6	×10	×15
17	16	70	120	200	1·0	0·9	0·6
30	32	35	60	100	2·5	2·0	1·5
50	49	20	32	56	6·3	5·5	4·0
80	59	10	16	28	9·0	7·0	5·5

The field of view should be of the same order of magnitude as that of the smallest objectionable defect. The diaphragm is in the upper focal plane of the eye lens, thus protecting the photosensitor from any reflected stray light that otherwise might reach it. Photo-electric cells of the end type, (Fig. 4.20), must be used and should be situated in envelopes to suit the tube of the microscope. The standard diameter of eyepieces is 23 mm.

Bibliography References : (*2082, 2235, 2247, 2292*).

18.2. Rejector

The rejector unit is a mechanical relay (magnet or solenoid operated) actuated by the amplifier or by the integrator. The rejector, or thrustor,

* Quoted from the Catalogue of Messrs. R. & J. Beck, Ltd., London.

(Fig. 24.7), is controlled by the amplifier when the arrangement is for one defect to cause rejection. If, however, more than one defect, for instance three defects per yard of wire, are permissible, an integrator is connected between the amplifier and the rejector. An integrator suitable for all speeds occurring in industrial routine testing has been described by Lord and Livingston (*896*, *997*), Fig. 18.1.

The integrator must be combined with a suitable device for resetting it to zero when (1) the object has been rejected, (2) a certain quantity

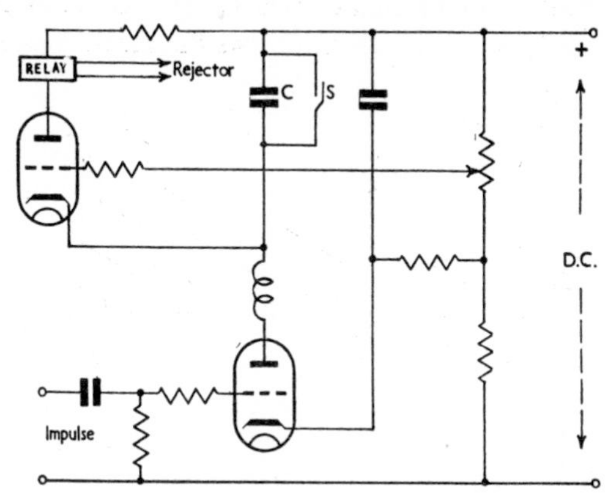

Fig. 18.1 Integrator circuit for multiple defect rejection.

(length, number, etc.) has been inspected without any rejects. In the above given instance of three deviations from standard thickness per yard of wire or thread the integrator must be reset to zero after each yard in order to prevent the accumulation of errors belonging to a previously inspected length of material. The resetting to zero is done by the measuring equipment ; this can be done by closing the press-button *S* temporarily and only for a short moment sufficient to discharge the capacitor *C*.

The integrator will energize the rejector coil when the voltage across the capacitor *C* equals the sum of the critical grid voltage of the output valve plus the voltage determined by the potentiometer. The potentiometer is the means of changing the number of impulses (i.e., the permissible number of deviations from the standard) allowed to be stored in the circuit before the rejector is actuated.

The rejector for individual objects may consist of a trap-door, a chute, or other similar device aiming at the quickest removal of the rejected object. Paper or textile web, sheet or strip metal, filamental material (fibres, wire), and all materials produced in continuous lengths and any width are not removed when faulty, but marked as such (*1407*). In that case the rejector bears a pad at its end which touches down very swiftly and marks the faulty material with a coloured stamp, or a spraygun is actuated thus, marking the spot.

18.3. Filamental Materials

In some cases the complicated optical system can be dispensed with and a simple equipment used which throws the much enlarged shadow

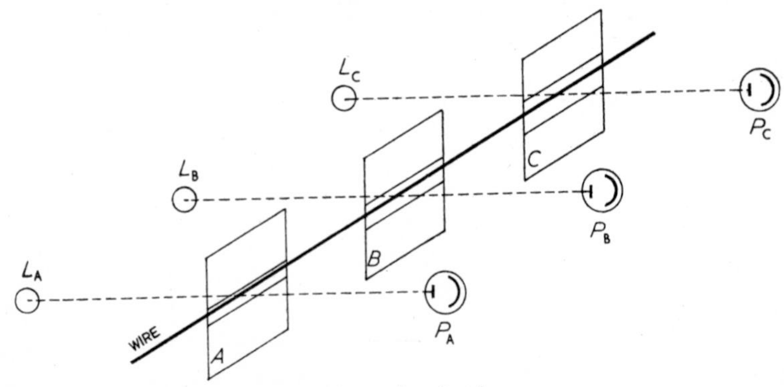

Fig. 18.2 Photo-electric wire gauge.

image of the wire or yarn on to the cathode of the photosensitor or on the slit of a diaphragm which is placed in front of the cell. Suitable action is taken by the photo-relay when the size of the image changes. When of correct size the image partly covers the cathode, the obscuration becoming smaller with decreasing and, up to total, with increasing thickness of the wire as discussed in Chap. 11. A similar method has been used by the British Research Association for the Woollen and Worsted Industries (at Torridon, Headingley, Leeds) to measure the uniformity of yarn (*998*) (cf. next section). A more complete device has been described by Nunan (*949*). (cf. Chap. 11). The instrument automatically tests and records the strength of yarn and stops operating when breaks occur, thus permitting the examination of the rupture.

Another arrangement is schematically shown in Fig. 18.2 using three photosensitors arranged in a line parallel to the reeling wire. The relative dimensions of the three slits in Fig. 18.2 are exaggerated in order to emphasize the object of arranging three slits *A*, *B*, and *C*.

The slit *B* represents standard thickness. Diaphragm *A* has a smaller, diaphragm *C* a wider slit (lower and upper limits, respectively). The following arrangement is made:

Slits eclipsed totally	Slits eclipsed partially	Diameter	Photosensitors* receiving light	Relay action
none	A, B, C	much too small	P_A, P_B, P_C	stops motor
A	B, C	too small	P_A, P_B	signals " lower limit "
A, B	C	correct	P_C	none
A, B, C	none	too large	none	signals " upper limit "

* Action of photosensitors :
P_A positive
P_B positive
P_C negative

Under these circumstances a wiring circuit may be arranged : to stop the motor when the diameter has decreased below the predetermined permissible lower limit ; to give one signal when the deviation is on the high side, and another signal when on the low side, but within the limits of tolerance ; and no action to be taken when the diameter is correct, Fig. 18.3. The addition of another unit and relay make it possible to stop the motor if the wire suddenly breaks, or turns out thicker than allowed by the " upper limit "-mask. Relays R_A and R_C may be used to operate a corrective mechanism in addition to giving alarm signals. Differences of 0·001 mm. (0·00004 inch) can be measured by such systems if the light source is sufficiently constant (cf. Chap. 7) and the wire not allowed to vibrate in front of the photosensitor (*999*). Enamel-coated fine wires can be inspected for " beady " coatings by the same method (cf. Chap. 11).

Bibliography Reference : (*2293*)

18.4. Statistical Quality Control

Irving I. Saxl (*1000*) has developed a method and a photo-electric device with which it is possible to determine probability curves (*1255*) by photo-electric integration of light impulses. The instrument measures automatically the relative times of exposure of a photosensitor placed in the path of a moving light beam : on illumination the photosensitor energizes a relay which operates an integrating counter. In the original paper the relay closes contacts for an electrical stop-watch. Accordingly, this clock runs only when the beam of light is projected upon the cell.

In a modification of this circuit a time base and an electronic integrating counter may be introduced, (cf. Chap. 23), with the effect that now

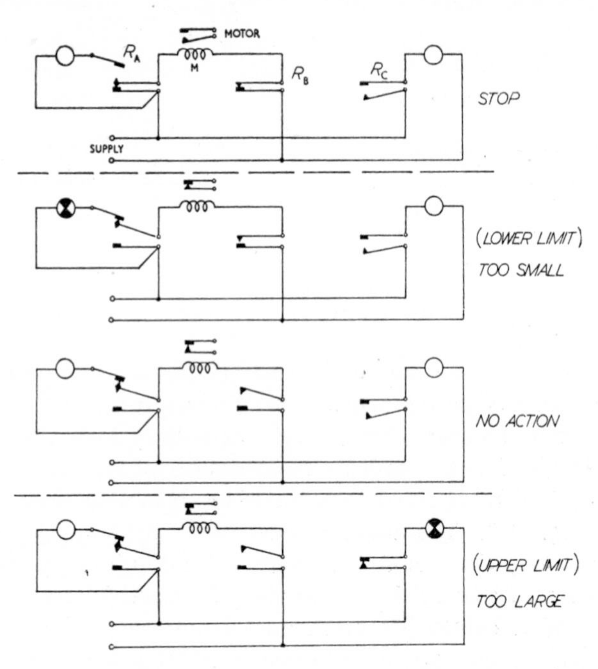

Fig. 18.3 Relay arrangements for the gauge of Fig. 18.2.

the counter can easily cope with impulses as short as 1 millisecond or less and give the exact number of pulses or, what amounts to the same result, the total exposure time of the photosensitor, Fig. 18.4. With a 50 c/s. supply the number of holes and the duration of the pulses on the input circuit of the counter are related as follows :

1 hole	0·02 sec.
2 holes	0·01 sec.
4 holes	0·005 sec.
20 holes	0·001 sec.

Frequency distribution curves are obtained and may be used in the analysis of filamentous material. The instrument has been used in the quantitative evaluation of the evenness quality for rayon, acetate, cotton, silk and woollen yarns (cf. section 18.4).

Bibliography References : (*494*, *1375*)

18.5. Aniseikonic Inspection

The task of inspecting relatively large areas moving along fast on a conveyor belt or in a machine raises appreciable difficulties for the designer of a scanning head, and means other than the usual type

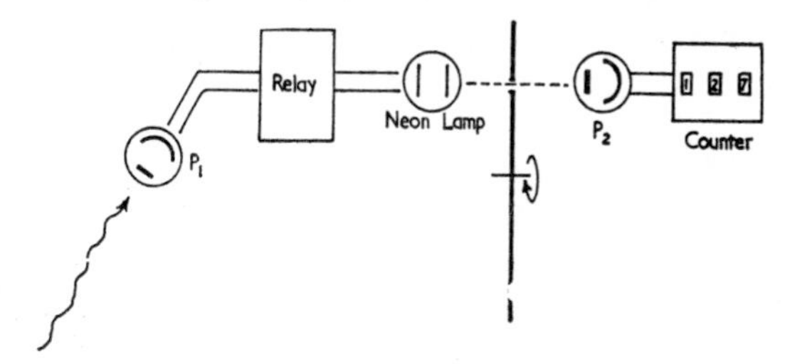

Fig. 18.4 Integration of light pulses to give time intervals.

scanner with micro- or teleoptical equipment must be used if the inspecting device is to cope with the area as well as with the speed at which the material is moving. In such cases the Aniseikon (*85*), fitted with good lenses, should be used (cf. Chap. 10). The lenses, if necessary, may be of the wide angle type. It is, however, not desirable to exceed an angle of 85 to 90°, because the difference in illumination between the edge and the centre would increase unfavourably. For inspection purposes rectangular photo-e.m.f. cells of as big a size as available will give the best service. As a general rule the diagonal of the rectangle should be equal or nearly equal to the focal length of the optical system. The ratio of the focal lengths of the binocular may conveniently be chosen to be between 1 : 1·25 and 1 : 1·50.

Bibliography Reference : (*2144*)

18.6. Illustrative List of Applications

The Aniseikon is readily applicable to a number of industrial problems as, for instance :

Detection of cracks and flaws in material being manufactured in continuous sheets, rolls, rods, tubes, as, for instance, sheet metal, rubber, plastics ;

Detection of stains in paper, fabric, tinned steel strips, moving at the usual speed in the making, re-rolling, or printing machines, through tubs, etc. ;

Detection of objects or persons in a prohibited area or room ; whether the persons or objects are stationary or moving ; whether they were hidden in the prohibited area or entered it later ;

Protection of objects, rooms, open spaces.

The output relay can so be arranged that it counts or marks the objectionable items, gives warnings, or scraps the faulty material.

Bibliography References : (*1739*, *1750*, *1768*, *1839*, *1913*, *1916*, *1984*, *1990*, *1992*, *2214*, *2216*).

18.7. Inspection and Filling of Bottles

There are a number of different systems, most of them covered by Patents, which are adjustable or directly applicable to the inspection and filling of glass bottles (*1413*). A remarkable utilization of the flaws

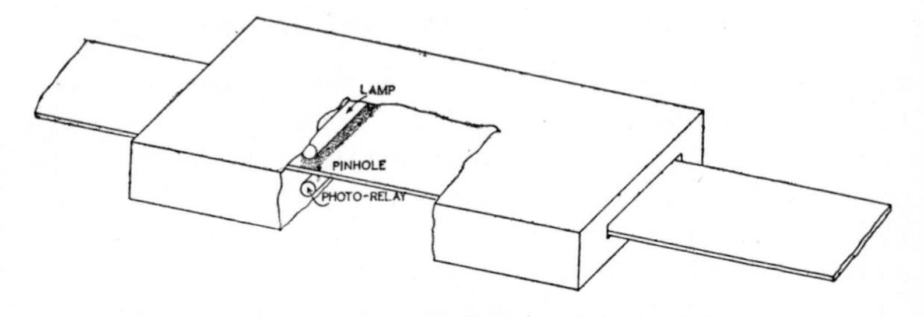

Fig. 18.5 Continuous inspection for pinholes in sheet steel

in the sealing edge of a bottle was developed by the General Electric Co. who caused a light pencil to be reflected from the sealing edge of the spinning bottle (*959*, *960*). The amplifier coupled to the photosensitor is sensitive only to modulated light. If the glass is without imperfection the impact of light on the photo-cell will be steady and there will be no output from the amplifier. The moment a chipped, cracked, or flawed bottle is inspected the light rays will be reflected in all directions from the edge of the spinning bottle, each flaw acting as a reflector. A series of light impulses, i.e., flickering light, will reach the photo-cell and the generated output by it is used to operate a rejector.

Bibliography References : (*1705*, *1743*, *1875*)

18.8. Inspection for Holes and Pinholes

In some cases the presence, and in others the absence, of holes in a mass-produced article is essential (*2459*). Instances of typical applications were given in the former case by R. Powers who inspects oil holes

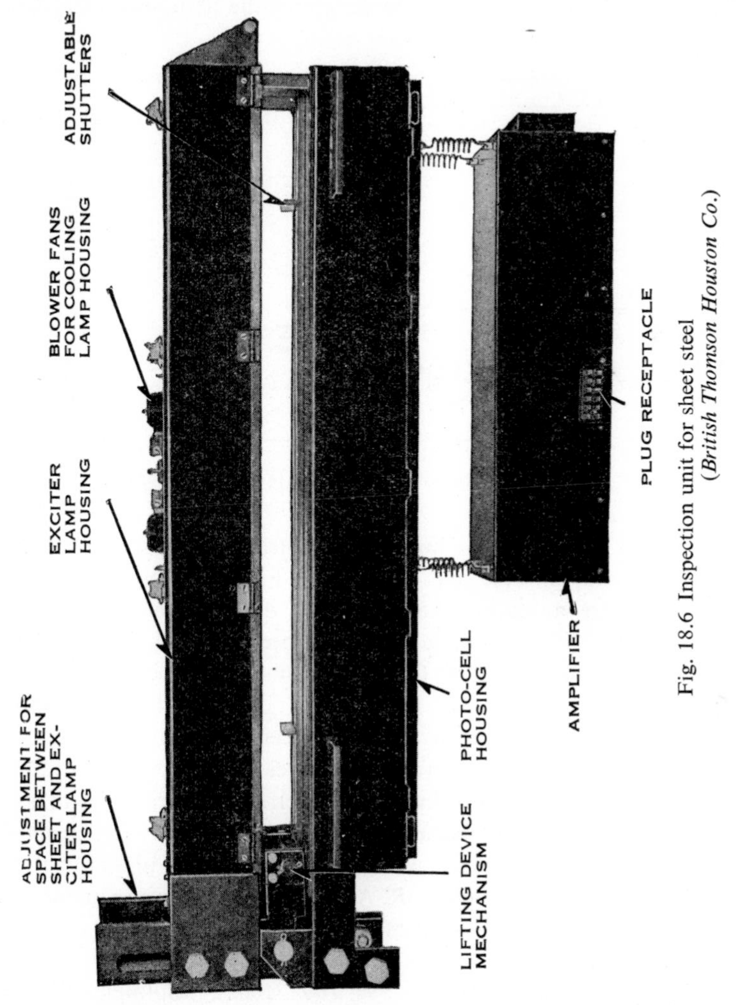

Fig. 18.6 Inspection unit for sheet steel (*British Thomson Houston Co.*)

and shackle bolts by means of photosensitors (*952*), the latter by G. Walsh in the case of inspection for pin-holes in collapsible tubes for toothpaste (*289*), in strip steel to be made into tins for canned food (*1407*), etc. Strip steel is inspected at speeds up to 1500 ft.p.m.

For continuous inspection for pinholes in strip steel (*1433*), paper, etc., an arrangement of the type represented in Fig. 18.5, is used. A cylindrical photosensitor and a tubular lamp, or any singular or multiple arrangement, (Fig. 18.6,) of these two elements in cases where the width of the strip is larger than the length of the photo-cell or tubular

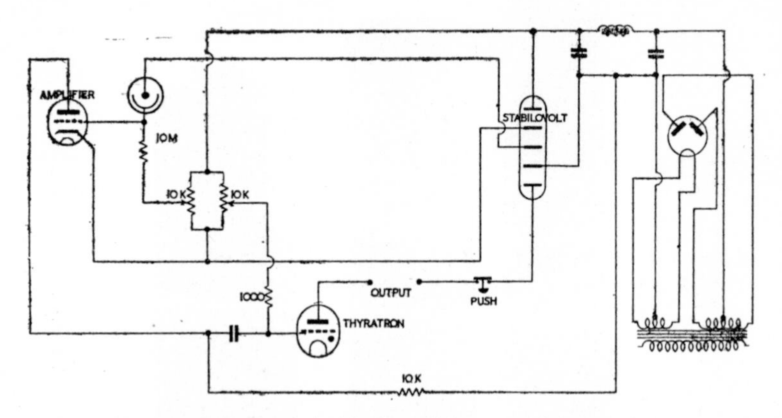

Fig. 18.7 Circuit used with the unit for operating a marker.

lamp, are so arranged in a box that the strip to be inspected moves between the lamp and the cell. The circuit, Fig. 18.7, employs a thyratron to operate a marker, i.e., any type of gear which marks the exact position of the pinhole that had been located. A glow-gap divider provides constant D.C. for the photo-electric circuit. The potentiometers P_1 and P_2, respectively, control the operational characteristic of the thyratron and photo-cell, respectively (*955*).

The automobile industry was one of the earliest of the heavy industries to profit from the introduction of electronic controls. Thanks to the energetic activities of an automobile engineer many problems of high-precision mass inspection were solved by means of photosensitors. In a series of papers and reports, R. A. Powers gives many an interesting and valuable method of how to tackle these problems which are in no way characteristic of the car industry alone, but are met in any branch of engineering (*14, 860, 994, 995, 996, 1001, 1002*). Photo-electric cells have been used in the inspection of oil holes in shackle bolts (*1003*), and in the inspection of piston rings (*1004, 1425*). This latter apparatus (*1005*), made by the Sheffield Corporation, Dayton, Ohio, is a worthy representative of photo-electric gear as applied to problems of high speed, high precision production and inspection. The apparatus automatically checks for trueness of periphery within a tolerance of 10^{-4} inch and inspects the width of gap of any specific size of piston ring. The instrument can be adapted to various nominal sizes and gaps of varying width, each complete cycle of inspection taking less than five

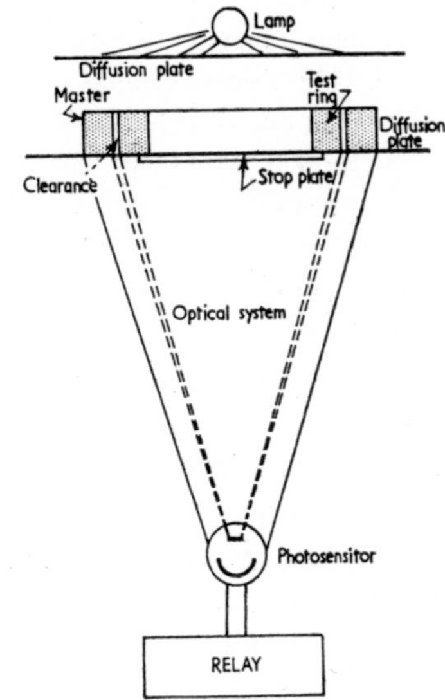

Fig. 18.8 Photo-electric inspection of piston rings

seconds. The piston ring to be checked is inserted and rotated once inside a master ring of correct dimensions. Any clearance between the test specimen and the master ring, respectively, transmits light which strikes a photosensitor, Fig. 18.8. This incidence of light is made to operate a red " reject " signal. If the periphery is within the allowed tolerance a green light is switched on at the end of one complete rotation of the test piece. Another light ray inspects the width of the gap and gives a yellow signal if undersized, and actuates the same red " reject " signal if oversized.

Bibliography References : (*565*, *574*, *1184*, *1941*, *2019*, *2048*, *2199*)

18.9. Determining the Wear of Engines

Photosensitors supervise not only the correctness of the combustion cycle of internal combustion engines (cf. Chap. 11) and test the quality of the fuel (*1420*, *1421*, *1422*, *1423*), but also check for the relative amount of wear of all those parts which are in contact with the lubricant. These tests can be carried out without interfering with the continuous operation of the engine or car motor and, by making the observations at regular intervals of time or mileage, give a true picture of the wear and follow closely the actual conditions. A method has been developed by Rescorla *et al.* (*1006*) whereby the iron content in the ash of the crank-case oil, when subjected to certain tests, and determined by a photo-electric colorimeter, is a sure indication of the amount of wear. The figure, quoted in the original paper, is 0·00025 cm. (0·0001 inch) cylinder wear per 10,000 miles of car engine operation. The chemical method described by Rescorla *et al.* readily detects the wear caused by a 10-mile run, i.e., 10^{-7} inch wear. (Another method for detecting engine wear uses radioactive iron). The electronic circuit is extremely simple (*1007*) and permits of it being used in laboratory as well as workshop tests.

Bibliography Reference : (*1974*)

18.10. Determination of Particle Size

The determination of particle size in powders is of great importance not only in metallurgical research but also in the production of inorganic phosphors, cement, finest sand, dust, inorganic powders of any description, etc. There are four methods at the command of the investigator, viz., microscopic (*1009*) ; air elutriation (separation) ; liquid elutriation ; gravitational fractionation. The first-named is the favourite method employed for investigations into the characteristics of dust (coal or stone dust) in mines (*1008, p. 5*). An improved gravitational fractionation method on a turbidimetric basis has been described be Kalischer (*1010*, *1429*) and is outstanding in that it attains a very high accuracy and reproducibility of the results. The time taken for a specimen to fall through the settling tube is ten minutes. This method has not been tried with low density materials. Putting an electrostatic charge on the particles might improve and widen the scope of the method. For details the reader is referred to the discussion of the above quoted paper, and to a publication by D. G. Skinner, (cf. Chap. 17) (*1445*, *1452*).

Bibliography References : (*1057*, *1447*, *1556*, *1966*, *2391*)

18.11. Inspecting Bomb Fuzes

During the war many unusual problems were solved by photo-electric methods and instruments. One of these problems was the testing of bomb fuzes (*1011*). An air blast whirls the vane of the fuze and releases the safety device. As this flies off it permits a beam of light to strike a photosensitor which closes the valve and stops the timer of the wind valve.

Another problem was presented by the need for readily inspecting filled shells and grenades, in particular grenade fuzes *in situ* (*3*). Each

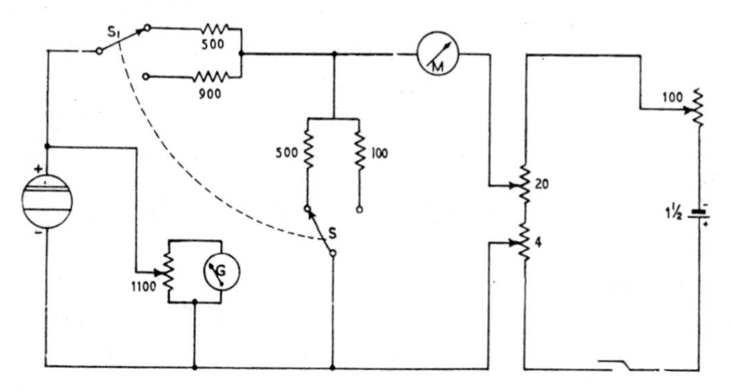

Fig. 18.9 Circuit of hazemeter (Diliberti and Kallas).

grenade fuze contains two charges of different powders (*4*). The task was to inspect automatically the grenade fuzes for light powder charges or displaced fuzes. This was done by passing the fuzes on a conveyor belt through the beam of a 100,000 volt X-ray tube.* The X-ray image of the fuze was visible on a fluorescent screen and was inspected by a photo-relay. So long as the fluorescent glow remains constant, nothing happens : however, should a faulty grenade pass through the X-ray beam the photo-cell will detect the change in the fluorescence and give a signal or mark the faulty grenade. The speed of inspection was 4000 grenades an hour.

These and other instances of individual application are quoted here both for the interest a particular device may arouse and for the methodological value of the solution.

18.12. Hazemeter

The use of transparent plastics in aircraft noses necessitated the development of a method and instrument with which to measure the haze caused by atmospheric and/or mechanical abrasion. The arrangement shown in Fig. 18.9 is that described by Diliberti and Kallas

* The electronic control of X-ray exposure time is described by Euler *et al.* (*739*).

(*1012*). It provides a method for obtaining the equivalent of a zero external resistance and thereby gives a linear cell current-to-illumination relationship. The selector-switch *S-S* multiplies the range by either 2 or 10 times. The instruments used in the original setup are :

photo-e.m.f. cell :	Weston type I or III plus Viscor filter ;
galvanometer G. :	General Electric type 32C 224 G 3 ; (0·45 microamp. per division ; crit. resistance 1100 ohms) ;
instrument M :	Weston D.C. microammeter, Model 622, ranges 0-10-50-100-500-1000 microamps.

A glossmeter was described by R. S. Hunter (*624*), (cf. Chap. 19.5.).

18.13. Food Sorting System

The inspection of eggs (*388*) (cf. Chap. 13.21) for freshness ; tomatoes for colour (*2643*); apples, oranges, grapefruits for colour and quality (*1623*) as well as size (cf. Chap. 21.6); beans for colour and size (*1605*), are only a few instances.

Bibliography References : (*1172, 1732, 1741, 1803, 1909, 2401, p. 118*)

18.14. Gauging

A suggestion, first made in the *Siemens Veröffentlichungen* (*1613*) in 1939, was developed by the Autotron Corporation, Danville, Ill. The instrument uses the movements of a razor-like flag target or attached to a metal stylus in order to control the amount of light which is permitted to fall on a photosensitor. In the original (Siemens) arrangement the instrument was used to gauge the thickness of the test specimen. The razor edge, when moving up or down according to the variations in the thickness of the specimen, narrowed or widened the beam between complete obstruction and free passage, thereby varying the intensity of illumination on the photosensitor. The Autotron arrangement is an extension of the above principle in that two photosensitors are employed. The shadow of the target must remain within a given area if the specimen is to pass as correct. The critical area is formed by two slits, each one in front of the cathode of a photosensitor. The distance of these two slits marks the tolerances, and is variable by means of a micrometer. The magnified image of the target, making contact with the test object, is viewed by an optical equipment which projects this image on to the critical area. An accuracy of 10^{-4} in. is attained and rates of more than 3000 inspections per hour are by no means a maximum.

Bibliography References : (*1189*, *1217*, *1730*, *1771*, *1803*, *1804*, *1932*, *2012*)

18.15. Measuring Vibrations

An arrangement which permits of controlling the evenness of a flat surface, or the thickness of an object without resorting to mechanical contacts, is as follows: A beam of light, after passing through a fine grating (which must be coarse enough so as to avoid diffraction) is focused onto the test surface whence it is reflected and, after having passed through an identical grating, strikes a photosensitor. The last-mentioned grating is so arranged that it can be moved into the right position, i.e., so that those rays of light which have passed through the transparent slits in the first grating also pass through the slits of the second grating (*2441*). Any uneveness, vibration, variation in thickness, etc., will now cause the rays of light to vary their position relative to the second grating, and these rays will move up and down, thus resulting in an A.C. output of the photosensitor which after amplification can be utilized to mark the trouble area, or stop production, give alarm signals, etc. This arrangement is, for instance, an effective means of investigating rotating shafts for smooth running as any vibratory motion or " knocks " will cause an immediate response in the electronic circuit. Reciprocating movements of machine parts can also be checked (*1613*). (Cf. Chap. 11.2).

CHAPTER 19

COLORIMETRY

19.1. Conditions and Standards

The measurements here described are almost exclusively of the colorimetric type, i.e., based on the measurement of colour, light, or any other optical characteristic (*2415*). The photo-electric colorimeter employs a suitable photosensitor, mostly a photo-e.m.f. cell to measure intensity, spectral distribution, etc.

The applicability of photosensitors to colorimetric work was first discussed in a paper by H. E. Ives (*819*) and their limitations in three-filter colorimetry were given by J. A. vanden Akker (*820*). The conditions to be fulfilled by photo-electric colorimeters are detailed by K. S. Gibson (*1480*) and suggestions as to the best design of suitable and sufficiently accurate instruments have been made by various authors (*543*, *1481*, *1482*, *1483*, *1484*, *1485*). The fundamental requirements are discussed in British Standard 667 : 1945 and, for the United States, in the National Bureau of Standards Letter Circular LC 545 (1939). A wealth of information is contained in the Reports of the Committee on Colorimetry (*254*, *321*, *517*, *1549*, *1559*, *1551*).

Bibliography References : (*517*, *1082*, *1097*, *1102*, *1154*, *1342*)

19.2. Photo-electric Photometry

For the comparison of two light intensities, circuits have been designed for an accuracy of 0·1 %. Usually the arrangement is set up on a photometric bench, the lamp to be calibrated is moved nearer to, or farther from, the respective photosensitor and the correct distance is read when the instrument, for instance, a centre-zero microammeter, is balanced. According to the inverse square law the intensity Φ of the test lamp is given by $\Phi_{test.} = \Phi_{std.} (D_{std.}/D_{test.})^2$. At balance, $\Phi_{test.} = \Phi_{std.} \times K^2$ where $1 > (K = D_{std.}/D_{test.}) > 1$. The scale of the micro-ammeter can be directly marked in relative intensities. The direct voltage for the circuit is supplied by a rectifier (*333*) using a voltage regulator.

A recording colour analyser was described by A. C. Hardy (*335*). This type of instrument is preferable to colorimeters as it operates and records automatically and is independent of the individual visual characteristics of the observer.

For details on photo-electric tristimulus colorimetry the National Bureau of Standards Circular 429 should be consulted (*332*). The filters for tristimulus work are compounds, Table 19.1, the thickness of each component being a function of the actual melt.

TABLE 19.1

Filters for Tristimulus Work

Filter	Components	Corning Glass No.
Amber	yellow	326
	green	978
Green	blue-green	428
	yellow	330
Blue	blue	554
	yellow	038

The spectral transmission of these filters is compiled in Table 19.2 (*331*, *336*). For data on Wratten filters see "Wratten Light Filters" (Kodak Ltd., 1953).

H. J. Eppig (*1453*) gives details on German trichromatic colour measurements conducted during the war. Three photometers were used. One photosensitor must have a spectral sensitivity the same as that of the average human eye (CIE $\bar{y}$ curve); the other has a red, and the third a blue filter. The latter two photosensitors and their respective filters must have a spectral response identical with, or closely resembling to, the standard CIE $\bar{x}$ curve (red) and $\bar{z}$ curve (blue), respectively. The accuracy with which the standard CIE trichromatic coefficients can be calculated depends on the degree of approximation of the spectral sensitivities of the three photosensitors and their respective filters to the standard CIE ($\bar{x}$, $\bar{y}$, $\bar{z}$) curves.

The Physikalisch-Technische Reichsanstalt, Berlin, has developed a suitable photometer, Fig. 19.1. The two photosensitors employing filters are connected to a differential galvanometer or differential micro-ammeter, indicating 100% colour 1 and 100% colour 2 at the respective ends of the scale. The third photosensitor operates another micro-ammeter, indicating total luminous energy.

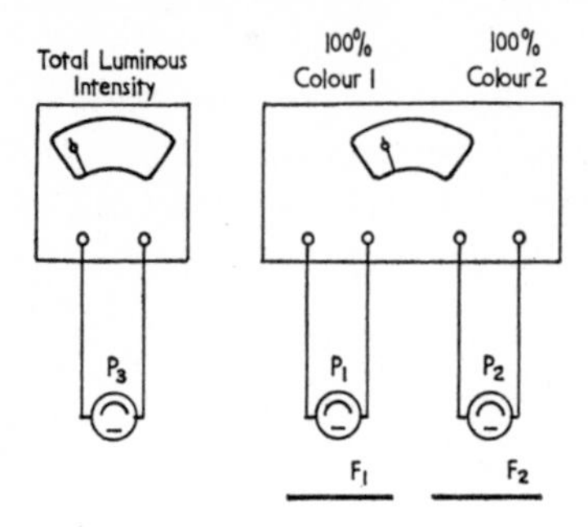

Fig. 19.1 Differential photometer for colour measurement. (*P-T Reichanstalt, Berlin*)

TABLE 19.2

Spectral Transmission of Filters used in Tristimulus Colorimetry

Wavelength A.U.	Spectral Transmission of		
	Amber Filter	Green Filter	Blue Filter
3800		0·010	
4000		0·011	
4200		0·012	0·298
4400		0·017	0·478
4600		0·035	0·445
4800		0·077	0·195
5000	0·010	0·138	0·045
5200	0·038	0·209	0·003
5400	0·095	0·249	
5600	0·164	0·243	
5800	0·224	0·193	
6000	0·238	0·135	
6200	0·206	0·086	
6400	0·153	0·053	
6600	0·099	0·032	
6800	0·057	0·020	
7000	0·030	0·014	0·003
7200	0·016	0·010	0·004
7400	0·008	0·008	0·004

Tristimulus coefficients in colour determination are discussed by P. Moon (*1491*). The colorimetric specifications of Wratten filters are discussed by MacAdam (*1476*).

Photo-electric methods in the measurement of the absorption and scattering of solar radiation by sea-water have been used by Darby *et al.* (*2457*, *2458*), Hulburt, and others.

The general arrangement of a photo-electric colorimeter is very simple (*1626, p. 834*). The light source L usually is a medium-power projection lamp to allow for high absorption in narrow-band monochromatic filters. A collimator C, Fig. 19.2, projects a beam of parallel light on to the photosensitor PC_1. In the path of the beam is a filter or

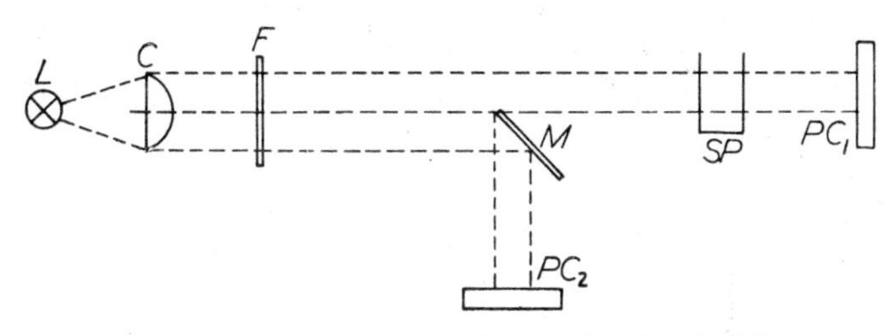

Fig. 19.2 General arrangment of photo-electric colorimeter.

combination of filters F, a small mirror M, and a fixture to hold the specimen Sp. The mirror splits the light beam in two, one part being deflected to a comparison photosensitor PC_2, the other going through the specimen to the measuring photo-cell PC_1. The most suitable photo-electric circuit is the one developed by B. A. Brice (*195*). Another circuit was designed by Fairchild and Parsegian (*328*). The monochromatic filters should transmit as small a region as possible (cf. Chap. 9). A photo-e.m.f. cell is well suited to operate the galvanometer. The lamp, optical system, mirror, specimen holder, and measuring photosensitor must be well aligned. The mains voltage must be kept constant (cf. Chap. 5) and free from fluctuations, or the spectral distribution in the light ray would not be constant. If the resistance of the slide wire and the series internal resistances of the photo-e.m.f. cells are small in comparison with the parrallel internal resistances of the photo-e.m.f. cells, the slide wire reading will indicate the transmittance or reflectance of the light beam by a test specimen.

Fig. 19.3 gives the circuit of a portable self-contained instrument for matching measurements of colour, candle-power, turbidity, and other photometric quantities. This circuit, designed in the laboratories of RCA, is based on the function of the two cells as explained in Fig. 5.10. The circuit is very sensitive.

A test-tube colorimeter, the main applications of which will be found in chemistry, biology, pharmacology, etc., was devised by E. J. King (*1263*). For details of construction and operation the original paper should be consulted. The photosensitor is an EEL photo-e.m.f. cell (22 × 40 mm.). In more recent models of this direct reading photo-electric colorimeter a shutter is used for controlling the amount of light admitted to the photosensitor. This shutter is controlled by a

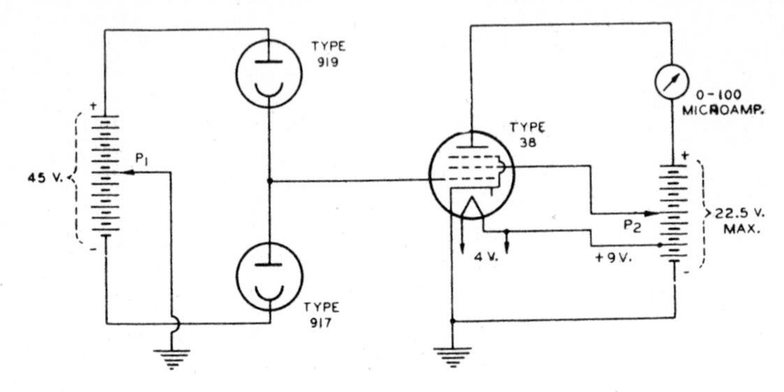

Fig. 19.3 Portable instrument for colour matching: circuit (*RCA Laboratories*)

handwheel working on a screw, forty threads to the inch, which allows for fine adjustment as well as calibration.

D. L. Drabkin (*340*) gives a detailed description of a photo-electric ultra-violet spectrophotometer. The design of a precision colorimeter has been published in great detail by Withrow *et al.* (*341*). The general layout used is a balanced series-opposing or differential circuit, using resistor decades as balancing elements. The optical equipment is identical for both standard and test specimen and is arranged symmetrical to the light source.

A Wheatstone bridge colorimeter is described by Underhill (*342, pp. 219, 239*). One photosensitor receives illumination from the standard specimen, thereby making three of the bridge's four resistors constant. The fourth resistor, i.e., the photosensitor receiving its illumination from the test specimen, is variable. The galvanometer can be calibrated in terms of the quantity under investigation. A Wheatstone bridge nephelometer is described by Pianto and Quercia (*2500*).

In measuring the colour of textiles a simple method is employed, The specimen is mounted on a disk fitted to the shaft of a fractional horsepower motor. The light of the lamp is concentrated on to the specimen by means of a lens or a reflector, and filter if necessary. The light reflected by the specimen is measured by the photosensitor and a suitable measuring instrument. The fabric is made to rotate which eliminates both irregularities in, or different types of, the weaving pattern and the sheen or lustre effect (*400*). First the standard specimen is mounted and the diaphragm so adjusted that the instrument reads 100. Any readings taken with the test specimen mounted on the disk will then be in terms of percentage of the standard. Sheen effects are overcome by using highly diffused light. Neither directed nor mixed diffused light must be used with glossy fabrics.

A simple photometer was described by E. D. Wilson (*344*), the arrangement being based on the generation of a photo-electric A.C. as discussed in Chap. 6, Fig. 6.19c. The standard lamp is fixed and the test lamp is made movable on an optical bench type sliding carriage. Since the photosensitor used by Wilson was of the unidirectional type it became necessary to rotate the photosensitor, making it view the test lamp and the standard lamp alternately. The graphite-on-graphite commutator was the only obstacle to making this photometer an industrial tool. With the advent of the non-directional photo-electric cell (cf. Chap. 4.26), or the non-directional titanium light-sensitive resistor (cf. Chap. 4.52) the photosensitor may now be stationary, which makes it a sturdy workshop photometer. The optical bench may be calibrated in units of candle-power.

A new type recording photometer was developed by B. Lange (*1453*).

A spectrophotometer using the FP-54 (cf. Chap. 31.4) is discussed by West (*1626, p. 788*), and a logarithmic photometer by M. H. Sweet (*1653*).

The microphotometer, now in general use, was first described by Furth (*2629*) and a photosensitor bridge circuit (*2630*) by Glasser. The question of noise in light sensitive semi-conductors has been discussed by Görlich (*2631*). A microspectrophotometer (*2634*), a rapid and sensitive spectrophotometer (*2635*), an integrating flame photometer (*2636*), three crystal scintillation spectrometers (*2637*, *2638*), a recording microphotometer (*2639*), and a photoelectric control circuit for the ion source of a pressure type electrostatic generator (*2640*) are but a few instances of the large variety of instruments in this class.

Bibliography References: (*403, 405, 411, 425, 436, 439, 464, 471, 482, 499, 505, 513, 515, 538, 543, 596, 597, 1055, 1072, 1091, 1092, 1143, 1160, 1203, 1204, 1209, 1227, 1344, 1363, 1369, 1384, 1387, 1507, 1508, 1526, 1528, 1544, 1549, 1551, 1574, 1664, 1726, 1728, 1734, 1735, 1744, 1746, 1747, 1748, 1751, 1753, 1758, 1769, 1772, 1783, 1788, 1791, 1800, 1802, 1820, 1837, 1843, 2029, 2030, 2031, 2040, 2041, 2056, 2066, 2090, 2099, 2100, 2105, 2118, 2184, 2188, 2238, 2269, 2273, 2294, 2344, 2352, 2401, pp. 115, 116*).

19.3. Densitometer

A reflexion densitometer, was described by Mohler and Taylor (*329*). The slit, on which the specimen rests, is 0·5 × 0·125 inch. The reflecting factor R_t of the test specimen is calculated by employing the substitution method, viz., $R_t = R_s d_t / d_s$, where R_s is the known reflexion factor of the standard specimen, and d_t and d_s are the respective deflections on the galvanometer *G*.

M. H. Sweet has designed a direct-reading colour densitometer using a nine-stage multiplier photo-electric cell (*330*). A push-pull photo-electric densitometer was constructed by Loofbourow (*402*). L. Raitière described a microdensitometer (*1688*).

An electronic differential nephelometer using a balanced photosensitor circuit will produce 1 volt potential difference for 0·002 Lm difference in illumination. The instrument is of excellent service in bacteriological and microbiological work (*2633*).

Bibliography References : (*407, 442, 463, 491, 1120, 1126, 1166, 1186, 1200, 1736, 1759, 1814, 1826, 1834, 2287, 2370, 2401, p. 115*). *2628, 2632.*

19.4. Reflectometer

The EEL reflectometer, which has been developed in conjunction with the Paint Research Station, uses an annular photo-e.m.f. cell through the orifice of which the light is directed. The 6-volt 6-watt lamp is mounted in a well ventilated housing on the base of which there is a heat filter to prevent excessive heat transmission to the photosensitor. Beneath this protective filter is mounted a rotatable disk containing a number (normally six) of circular holes, one of which is left clear, while the others contain colour filters. Beneath the filter disk are interchangeably placed such optical accessories as to permit a concentrated or diffused illumination. This entire structure is mounted on top of the photosensitor, a photo-e.m.f. cell.

A multi-purpose photo-electric reflectometer has been described by Hunter (*331*).

Details of an instrument particularly designed for use in the paper industry have been published by Michelson (*339*) who also points out that light of a wavelength of 4500 A.U. is best suited for classifying various types of paper.

Bibliography References : (*503, 589, 1506, 2292, 2627*)

19.5. Glossmeter

If the lustre or sheen of a textile material is to be measured the arrangement described on p. 498 can be used, the beam of light now being well concentrated. An achromatic filter (cf. Chap. 9.27) must be used in order to reduce the effect of colour (*400*).

For the measurement of the relative smoothness of machine-finished surfaces the glossmeter developed by Hunter (*624*) will prove of great value.

Bibliography References : (*489, 1242*)

19.6. Compensating Microphotometer

This instrument is used in measuring densities, transparencies, etc., by means of an adapted microscope whose eyepiece has been replaced by a low-volt 6- to 12-watt lamp (*394*). Light is admitted to a photo-e.m.f. cell through the film and a slit in the stage to another photo-e.m.f. cell through the V-shaped aperture of the diaphragm. The two photosensitors are connected in opposition and a differential galvanometer G indicates equality of photo-currents by taking the zero-position. The V-shaped aperture measures 1×5 mm. and may be calibrated in units to suit any particular measurements. The galvanometer used by Spiegler had a sensitivity of 1650 mm./μA at 1 m.

A photo-cell compensator for the measurement of thermal radiation was described by Hübner (*2498, 2501*).

Bibliography Reference : (*533*)

19.7. Ratiometer

The circuit of Fig. 19.4 allows for the measurement of one quantity (illumination, transparency, reflectivity, turbidity, density, etc.) in

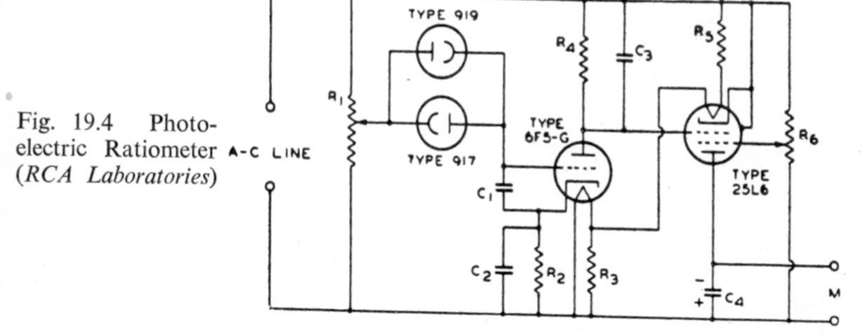

Fig. 19.4 Photo-electric Ratiometer (*RCA Laboratories*)

ratios (fractions, multiples, percentage) of another standardized quantity of equal quality. The operation of the circuits is as follows: capacitor C is charged in one direction during one half-cycle through one photo-electric cell, and in the opposite direction during the next half-cycle through the other photosensitor. Equal illumination on both cells results in the direct voltage across the capacitor being zero. A differential illumination sets up a direct voltage across the capacitor, the magnitude of the voltage change being a function and a direct measure of the ratio of the measured quantities. The meter can be calibrated in per cent.

Bibliography Reference : (*507*)

19.8. Light Intensity Indicator

A high sensitivity indicator, sensitive to changes in illumination in the order of fractions of 1% was devised by Shepard (*345*). A high-impedance pentode acts as a load impedance for the high-impedance photosensitor. In the anode circuit of the power output pentode a microammeter (range 0 to 100 μA) can be calibrated in light intensity units. Variable range and sensitivity of the circuit is introduced by arranging for points P_1, P_2, P_3 to be connected to the sliding contacts of three potentiometers, respectively, each having a resistance of 20,000 ohms. The voltage swing is determined from a diagram showing the anode voltage-anode current curve of the photosensitor in juxtaposition to the respective curve of the high-impedance pentode (cf. Fig. 5.10).

A circuit which has made possible the reproducible measurement of an intensity of 0·1 Lumen with an error smaller than 10^{-5} Lumen has been described by B. Chance (*1488*, *1489*). With this light regulator it is possible to measure the disappearance of colour from a 0·0005% solution of methylene blue within 0·02 second.

Bibliography References : (*504*, *539*, *1731*, *1796*)

19.9. Colour Temperature Meter

The colour temperature of incandescent lamps can be measured by a photo-electric device which uses a balanced circuit with a cathode-ray tuning indicator as an output indicator : no electronic amplification is necessary (*355*), Fig. 19.5. The two photosensitors cover two widely different spectral regions, viz., the blue end and the red end of the luminous spectrum, respectively. It is therefore necessary to calibrate the instrument and to use it only for measuring lamps which belong to the type of the standard. The instrument can, however, be calibrated for more than one type standard.

Since the ratio of the short-wave energies to the long-wave energies (blue to red) emitted by incandescent bodies increases continuously as

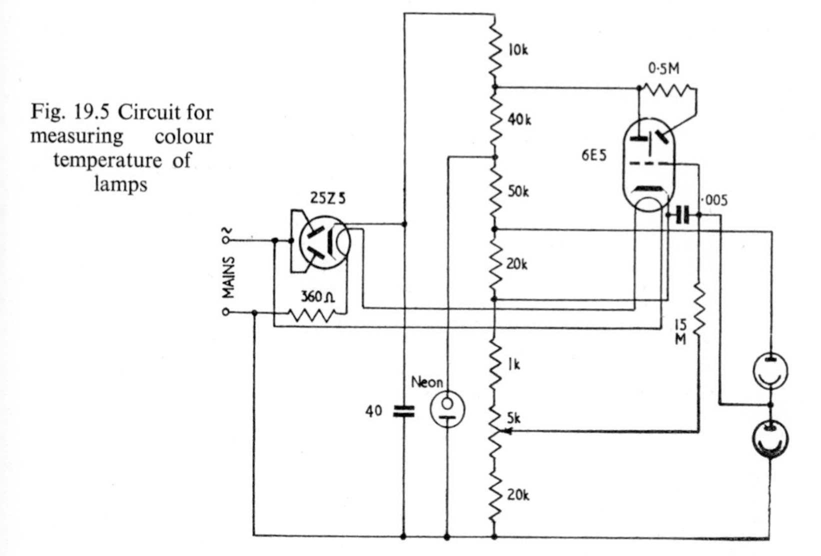

Fig. 19.5 Circuit for measuring colour temperature of lamps

the colour temperature is increased (*864*), the output of the photo-sensitors will increase proportionally with the rising colour temperature. The instrument measures directly colour temperatures within the range of 2300 to 3200° K.

TABLE 19.3

Number $N = B.10^r$ of Photons/cm²/sec/μ Emitted in the Blue and Red Region of the Spectrum, respectively, at Various Colour Temperatures (864)

Wavelength A.U.	Colour Temperature 1000° K.		1500° K.		2000° K.		2500° K.		3000° K.		3500° K.	
	B	r	B	r	B	r	B	r	B	r	B	r
blue 4500	6·4	10	2·6	15	5·4	17	1·3	19	1·1	20	5·0	20
red 6500	2·7	14	4·2	17	1·7	19	1·5	20	6·7	20	1·9	21
Ratio B/R	2·4	−4	0·6	−2	3·2	−2	0·9	−1	0·16	0	2·6	−1

Bibliography References : (*546, 1103, 1545*)

19.10. Methods Abroad

Summaries of methods and instruments used abroad are given :
for Russia by Sukhikh and Vsesoynez (*337*),
for Germany by A. Knutze (*338*).

19.11. Measuring Smoke Density and Colour

In his report on Photometric Procedures used in Research and Production of German Pyrotechnic Ammunition, H. J. Eppig (*1453*) describes how the density and colour of smoke from flares and signals

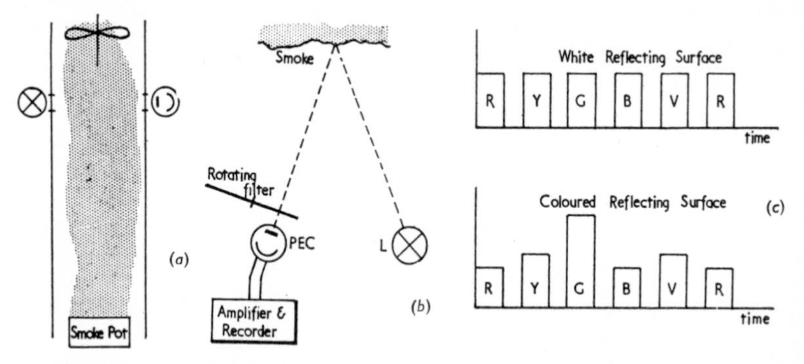

Fig. 19.6 Arrangement for measuring the colour and density of smoke.

was tested, Fig. 19.6a. A constant-speed fan draws a column of smoke through a stack. The smoke density is then $D = \log_{10}(1/T)$ where T is the transparency. A light source and a photosensitor are arranged as discussed in Chap. 15, p. 434.

The colour of smoke is investigated by using the smoke column as a reflecting medium. A beam of white light is projected on to the smoke and reflected through a rotatable filter on to a photosensitor, the latter driving an electronic amplifier and photographic recorder Fig. 19.6b. The filter disk contains five individual filters, viz., red, green, yellow, blue and violet. Each colour filter remains in position for three seconds, one second being allowed for the change over. The photographic records are of the block diagram type. The record of a non-selective, i.e., white, surface is shown in Fig. 19.6c.

A photo-electric dustmeter was described by Barnett and Free (*1650*).

A number of photo-electric instruments to measure the concentration of dust in air has been described in the literature, for instance (*2614*. *2645*, *2646*, *2647*), and is used industrially.

Bibliography References : (*1530*, *1532*, *1547*)

CHAPTER 20

*STEP-CONTROL OF A PRODUCTIVE PROCESS

20.1. Definition

Continuous control of a process is not always either necessary or desirable. A control by degrees or by steps, allowing for a given tolerance either side of the " correct " or zero mark, will often meet the case. Instances are : the inspection of pins for correct diameter

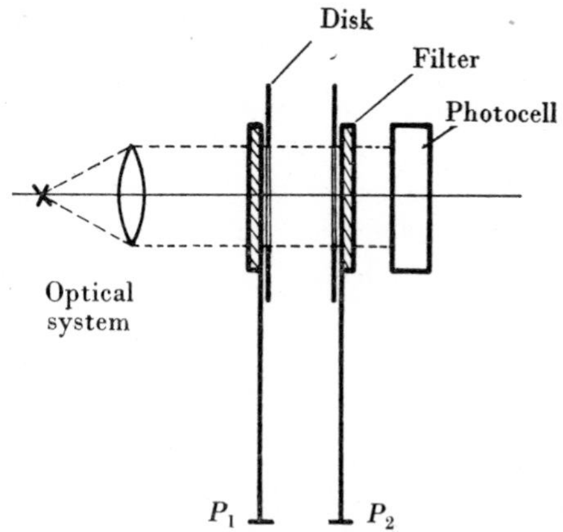

Fig. 20.1. Usual arrangement for step-control. P_1, P_2, pointers of measuring instruments

and length within permissible tolerances $\pm T$; the control of synchronism in electric networks, within given limits $\pm P$ of phase, $\pm F$ of frequency, and $\pm V$ of voltage ; the sorting of coloured objects according to hue and shade ; colour or turbidity and temperature of liquids ; thickness and colour of paper or any other web ; smoke density, carbon dioxide, and fuel movement, and/or fan operation ; etc.

The underlying principle of step-control is the synchronization of two or more measurements, distinctly different and independent of one another, and allowing the same, or different, sets of quantitative

* Reprinted from the *J. Scientific Instruments* (*1464*)

tolerances. The usual arrangement is that shown in Fig. 20.1. The pointer of the instrument is fitted with a tiny U-shaped clip to take a series of three or (very rarely) more achromatic (grey) filters. These filters measure about 5 × 5 to 7 × 7 mm. and are made of thin transparent plastic material. The " correct " or zero position is marked by an aperture in the front disk of the meter. A light source with its optical equipment, the hole (or the holes) in the instrument (or instruments), and a photo-cell are alined and the achromatic filters so arranged that the the darkest filter takes the central position, corresponding to " correct ", the lighter shades grouping either side of it (Fig. 20.2).

Bibliography Reference : (*2341*)

20.2. Filters

The densities of the filters are graded in the way set out in the following sections dealing with the theory of step-control. Although it does not matter whether the darkest filter is in the centre or at the sides of the arrangement, from the instrument builders' point of view it will be better to have the maximum-density filter in the centre, because then only one filter on either side will give four steps altogether, viz. filters No. 1, 2, 3, and " no filter " which can be interpreted by the

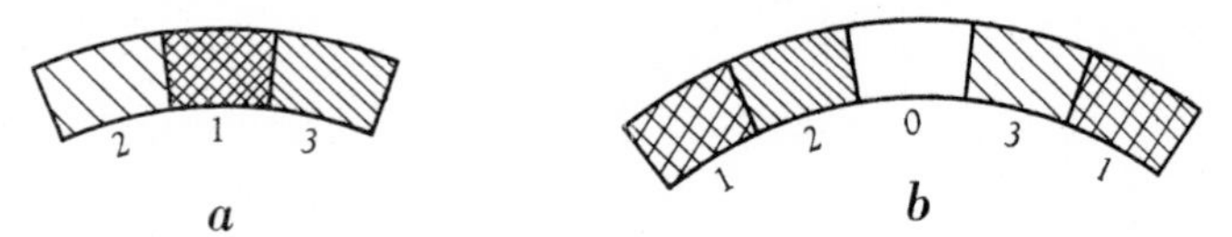

Fig. 20.2. 0, clear transparent filter, or no filter at all. 1, opaque, black filter. 2, light grey filter. 3, medium grey filter

photo-relay as " waste ", meaning that the dimensions of the test specimen are beyond the set tolerances, (Fig. 20.2a), whereas the reverse arrangement (Fig. 20.2b) necessitates the spreading of the darkest filter on either side to at least half-scale length, making the whole system too heavy for high sensitivity instruments.

The total density of two or more filters in the path of a light ray is the sum of all individual densities. For a first approach to this problem it may be postulated that two sets of four filters each are used, the " no filter " position being marked " zero ", and that all possible combinations have to result in an arithmetical progression with a given difference between any two adjacent members of the series, and that no duplication of values is allowed.

If all possible combinations of two sets of two filters per set are considered, it becomes obvious that the two sets must not be identical

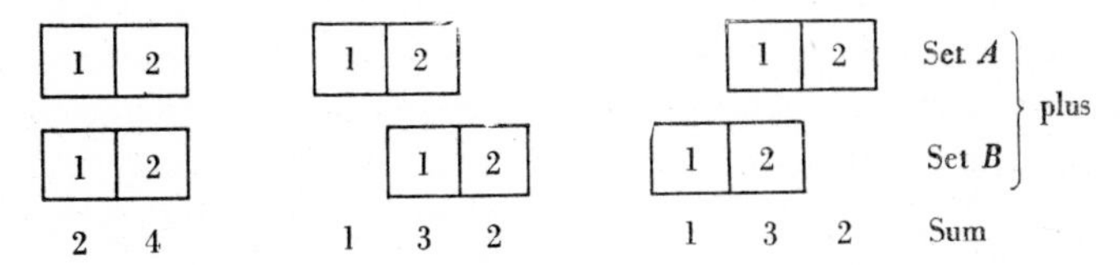

Fig. 20.3. The top row represents the values of one set A of filters, the bottom row those of another B set. The figures in the squares represent the individual values of the filters as shown in Fig. 20.2. The figures below the squares are the sum of the respective figures within the squares.

if duplications are to be avoided (Fig. 20.3). The figures in the squares represent the respective densities of the individual filters, the figures at the bottom being the total number of filters in any of the positions. The frequency of occurrence can be seen from Table 20.1.

TABLE 20.1

Frequency of Occurrence of Filters

Value	Frequency of duplication
1	2
2	3
3	2
4	1

Such a result does not, of course coincide with the above stipulation of " no duplication " which means that the frequency of each value must be 1. The problem must, therefore, be approached from another angle.

20.3. The Definant

The definant is the mathematical expression of a kind of additive variation of several elements, the result being an arithmetical progression showing a certain predetermined continuity and certain predetermined individual values.

The basis of the definant consists of any number n of elements, each element differing from its immediately adjacent neighbours by a value Δ. If e be the first element the basis consists of the elements

$$e, \quad e + \Delta, \quad e + 2\,\Delta, \quad .., \quad e + (n - 1)\,\Delta. \tag{1}$$

After the basis there are one, two, or more rows of a similar structure. In the first row the elements are a multiple of the elements of the basis, the characteristic multiplier k for the first row being $k = n$, thus

$$en, \quad (e + \Delta)n, \quad (e + 2\,\Delta)n, \quad .., \quad [e + (n - 1)\,\Delta]\,n. \tag{2}$$

For the second row the multiplier $k = n^2$, viz.

$$en^2, \quad (e + \Delta)n^2, \quad (e + 2\,\Delta)n^2, \quad ...., \quad [e + (n - 1)\,\Delta]\,n^2. \tag{3}$$

Thus, the qth row contains the elements of the basis, equation (1), each element being multiplied by a factor

$$k_q = n^q. \tag{4}$$

The total number of all additive variations is

$$N = n^r, \tag{5}$$

where r is the total number of rows including the basis.

The scheme for the actual carrying out of all additive variations is shown in Table 20.2 for the case when $n = 3$, $r = 3$.

TABLE 20.2

Scheme for carrying out all Additive Variations

A	B	C
L	M	N
X	Y	Z
$A+L+X$	$B+L+X$	$C+L+X$
$A+L+Y$	$B+L+Y$	$C+L+Y$
$A+L+Z$	$B+L+Z$	$C+L+Z$
$A+M+X$	$B+M+X$	$C+M+X$
$A+M+Y$	$B+M+Y$	$C+M+Y$
$A+M+Z$	$B+M+Z$	$C+M+Z$
$A+N+X$	$B+N+X$	$C+N+X$
$A+N+Y$	$B+N+Y$	$C+N+Y$
$A+N+Z$	$B+N+Z$	$C+N+Z$

A numerical instance will show how the definant works. Suppose 2, 3 and 4 to be the basis, the definant consisting of two rows altogether (one basis and one row). Therefore the number of elements is $n = 3$, $\Delta = 1$, $e = 2$, $k = 3$, $r = 2$. The total of all variations will be $N = 3 \times 3 = 9$. The first row, then, reads 6 9 12. The definant is

2	3	4	2+ 6= 8	3+ 6= 9	4+ 6=10
6	9	12	2+ 9=11	3+ 9=12	4+ 9=13
			2+12=14	3+12=15	4+12=16

The result is the arithmetical series 8 9 10 11 12 13 14 15 16.

20.4. Constructing the Definant

It is necessary to propound this theoretical section in order to view the solution of the problem of constructing the definant from the result, i.e., to find the elements when the arithmetical progression is given. This is the task with which the practical engineer will be confronted. The total number N of members of the series represents the number of relays which it is desirable to control by the number r of measuring instruments, each having a set of n filters, representing n steps of density.

A definant has the following elements :

$$\begin{array}{lllll} e & e+\Delta & e+2\Delta & .. & [e+(n-1)\Delta] \\ en & (e+\Delta)n & (e+2\Delta)n & .. & [e+(n-1)\Delta]\,n \\ \cdots & \cdots & \cdots & \cdots & \cdots \\ en^{r-1} & (e+\Delta)n^{r-1} & (e+2\Delta)n^{r-1} & .. & [e+(n-1)\Delta]n^{r-1}. \end{array}$$

The result shows that E_1 is the lowest, and E_{nr} the highest member. N is the total number of all members in the progression :

$$E_1 = e + en + en^2 + .. + en^{r-1},$$

$$E_{nr} = [e + (n-1)\Delta] + [e + (n-1)\Delta]n + [e + (n-1)\Delta]\,n^2 + .. + [e + (n-1)\Delta]n^{r-1},$$

or

$$E_1 = e\,(1 + n + n^2 + .. + n^{r-1}) = e\,\frac{n^r - 1}{n - 1}, \tag{6}$$

$$E_{nr} = [e + (n-1)\Delta]\;(1 + n + n^2 + .. + n^{r-1}) = [e + (n-1)]\,\Delta\,\frac{n^r - 1}{n - 1}. \tag{7}$$

After splitting E_{nr} into a sum of two products, viz.

$$E_{nr} = e\,\frac{n^r - 1}{n - 1} + (n-1)\,\Delta\,\frac{n^r - 1}{n - 1}$$

and writing E_1, equation (6), for the first member of the sum

$$E_{nr} = E_1 + \Delta(n^r - 1).$$

From this
$$n^r = \frac{E_{nr} - E_1}{\Delta} + 1$$

and
$$n = \left[\frac{E_{nr} - E_1}{\Delta} + 1\right]^{1/r}. \tag{8}$$

Since r is known, n can be calculated immediately. The same result will be obtained by deriving n from its relation $N = n^r$, viz. $n = N^{1/r}$, or, more conveniently,
$$\log n = \frac{1}{r} \log N. \tag{9}$$

The first element of the basis will be obtained from equation (6), viz.
$$e = E_1 (n - 1)/(n^r - 1).$$

With e, n, r and Δ known, the definant is given without ambiguity.

An example will make the method clear. Two instruments r are used in controlling a certain process or given qualities, each instrument having n steps. Which is the ratio the densities of the filters must have in order to yield photo-electric currents of such a gradation that no duplication of individual values can occur and that the densities of the filters form an arithmetical progression?

The highest member E_{nr} of that series will be determined by the relations
$$E_{nr} = D_{\text{max.}} = \log (1/T_{\text{min.}}) \text{ and } IT_{\text{min.}} = I_{T\text{min.}} \propto i_{\text{min.}};$$
the lowest member E_1 is correspondingly
$$E_1 = D_{\text{min.}} = \log (1/T_{\text{max.}}) \text{ and } IT_{\text{max.}} = I_{T\text{max.}} \propto i_{\text{max.}};$$
where D is the density, T the transmittance, I the incident intensity of illumination, I_T the transmitted intensity of illumination and i the photo-electric current. The total number of density steps, i.e., the number of relays to be controlled, is N, therefore $\log n = 1/r \log N$.

With the following given:

- r, number of measuring instruments,
- n, number of filters per instrument,
- N, number of relays to be controlled,
- E_1, lowest density, corresponding to the maximum photo-electric current, and
- E_{nr}, highest density, corresponding to the minimum photo-electric current,

the lowest element e of the basis is determined from

$$e = E_1 \frac{n-1}{n^r - 1} = E_1 \frac{n-1}{N-1},$$

and the difference Δ (from equation (8))

$$\Delta = \frac{E_{nr} - E_1}{N-1}.$$

After having ascertained the arithmetical progression of the densities, the respective transmittances of the filters are collated. From the illumination-photo-current diagram of the light-sensitive element to be employed the currents, resulting from the interaction of the filters, can be computed. This will determine the design of the relay coils, for instance :

$$r = 2, \quad n = 3, \quad N = 9, \quad E_1 = 0{\cdot}4, \quad E_{nr} = 1{\cdot}2.$$

From this results

$$e = 0{\cdot}1 \quad \text{and} \quad \Delta = 0{\cdot}1.$$

TABLE 20.3

Determination of Photo-electric Current

The progression of densities	0·4	0·5	0·6	0·7	0·8	0·9	1·0	1·1	1·2
Transmittance T	0·4	0·32	0·25	0·20	0·16	0·125	0·1	0·08	0·0625
Transmitted intensities I_r	40	32	25	20	16	12·5	10	8	6·25
Photo-electric current	100	80	62·5	50	40	31·25	25	20	15·725
		$4i$			$2i$			i	

Note.—The incident intensity I of illumination has been taken to be 100 units. The ratio I_T/i has been taken to be 1 : 2·5 over the linear range of the curve.

The one set of filters has the densities	0·1	0·2	0·3
and the other set	0·3	0·6	0·9

20.5. Practical Application

This section outlines the design of a step-control equipment using two measuring instruments and two different degrees of tolerance. Generally, the arrangement of the instruments will be that of Fig. 20.4 and of the filters that of Fig. 20.5.

The basic operations relative to the position of a particular filter in front of the aperture in the instrument are given in Table 20.4.

The electrical arrangement is shown in Fig. 20.6 The points *YY* mark the input of the controlling energy. Each relay consists of the coil *L*, a parallel resistor *R*, relay contacts *a*, *b*, *c*, and load contacts

TABLE 20.4

Basic Operations

Filter	Action	Test object	Tolerance
1. Black	None	Passed (into bin No. 1)	Correct value
2. Shade I	Relay 1 energized	Passed (into bin No. 2)	Minus
3. Shade II	Relay 2 energized; relay 1 disconnected	Passed (into bin No. 3)	Plus
4. Clear	Relay 3 energized; relays 1, 2 disconnected	Rejected (into bin No. 4)	Rejected

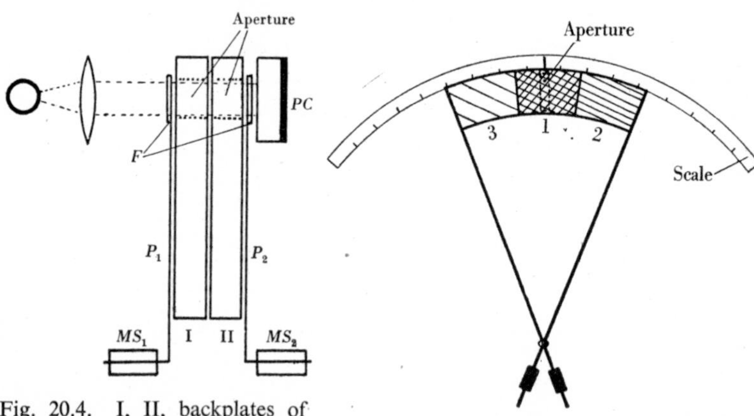

Fig. 20.4. I, II, backplates of measuring instruments. MS_1, MS_2, measuring systems of two instruments. *F*, filter sets mounted on the pointers P_1, P_2, *PC*, photo-cell

Fig. 20.5. Alternative way of mounting and balancing a set of the tiny filters. Visual indication may be maintained as shown

d, *e*. All relay coils are in parallel. In this instance there may be four relays which are so stepped as to be actuated by 1, 2, 3, 4, or any other sequence of units of current. Since the arrangement provides protection from overload in that all relays, designed for smaller currents than the instantaneous current, are switched off by the action of contact *a*, provision had also to be made to keep the load constant. This is achieved by switching in the resistances *R* of all those relays whose coil has been disconnected for safety reasons. Relay No. 4,

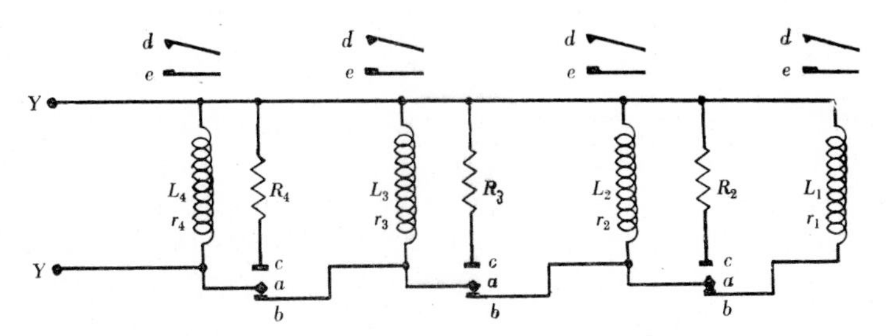

Fig. 20.6. Electrical arrangements for step-control. Sets of relay coils *L* and parallel resistors *R* are connected in parallel to the input *YY*. The resistors are so dimensioned that

$$R_2 = r_1, \quad R_3 = (r_1 r_2)/(r_1 + r_2),$$
$$R_4 = (r_1 r_2 r_3)/(r_1 r_2 + r_2 r_3 + r_3 r_1),$$

where *r* is the resistance of relay coil. *d*, *e*, load contacts, *a*, *b*, *c*, relay switching contacts

therefore, has in parallel to its coil a resistor whose resistance is to replace all coil resistances in circuit before coil No. 4, i.e., in this instance,

$$1/R_4 = 1/r_1 + 1/r_2 + 1/r_3,$$

where *r* is the resistance of the respective coil *L*, Contacts *d*, *e* are the load contacts controlling the output circuits.

A twin instrument with four steps (black, two different shades, clear) to each instrument will be governed by the general definant

0	1	2	3
0	4	8	12

where

Zero	(0)	means Reject
Shades	(1, 2, 4, 8)	means Tolerances
Black	(3, 12)	means Pass

The arithmetic progression will consist of 16 members, viz.

0 1 2 3 4 5 6 7 8 9 10 11 12 13 14 15.

If arranged in the proper sequence the definant now reads

0	1	2	3
0	4	8	12

0	4	8	12
1	5	9	13
2	6	10	14
3	7	11	15

it being obvious that the members of the progression reading the same as the members of the definant, viz., 0 1 2 3 4 8 12, are sums of two members, one of them being zero. Since it was stipulated that " zero " means " rejection ", the members 0 1 2 3 4 8 12 also stand for rejection. Similarly, all sums having three or twelve, respectively as one member and any of the tolerances as the other member; or all combinations of the two tolerances, stand for " passed with tolerance ". Only fifteen, which is the sum of three (correct) and twelve (correct), stands for " passed correct ". The progression reads now

0	4	8	12
1	5	9	13
2	6	10	14
3	7	11	15

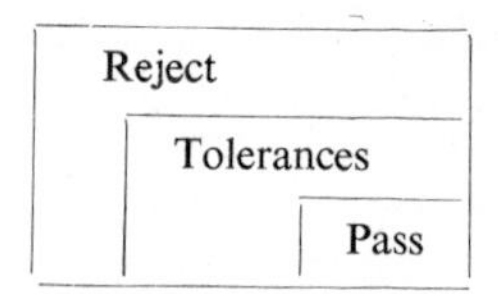

Bibliography Reference : (*2316*)

20.6. Simplifications

A simplification is attainable by reducing the number of tolerances from two to one, which results in a definant of much simpler construction, viz.,

0	1	2
0	3	6

0	3	6
1	4	7
2	5	8

Reject
Tolerances
Pass

This means that the electric circuit, having fifteen relays in the first instance, now has but eight. If a distinction into " pass " and " reject " only is to be made, identical filter sets are the simplest and most convenient arrangement. The definant, then, reads :

0	1	2
0	1	2
Reject	Tolerances	Pass

0	1	2
1	2	3
2	3	4

Reject
Pass

Since the central figure 2 is the sum of 1 plus 1, both being tolerances, it might be better, from a production point of view, to reject also any objects which would be passed on the strength of two tolerances only This gives the above diagram, meaning that only relays picking up at 1, 2, 3 and 4 units of current, respectively, must be in circuit. Another simplification will result in the circuit of Fig. 20.7 if the one coil is designed for picking up at between 1 and 2, and the other at between 3 and 4 units of current, respectively. Two and four units will be the upper limit of each of them.

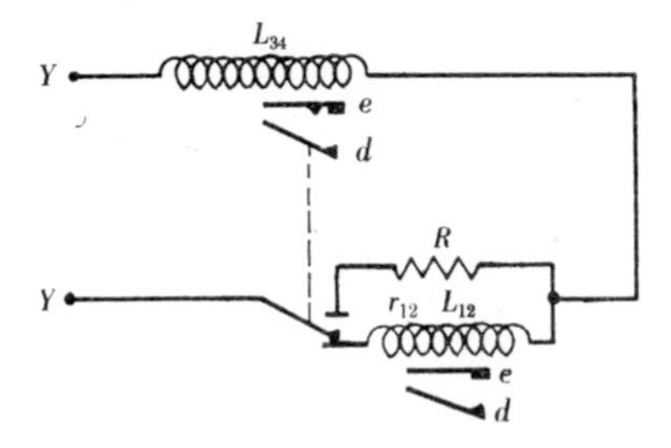

Fig. 20.7. Circuit with further simplification. L_{12}, relay coil operating at 1 or 2 units of current. L_{34}, relay coil operating at 3 or 4 units of current. $R=r_{12}$, where r is the resistance of relay coil.

The step-control arrangement can also be utilized in switching an indicator board and in assisting semi-skilled people. In this case the relays are not included in the load circuits, but actuate the respective windows of the indicator board or the glow-lamps or other light sources behind the windows. The text on the window, becoming visible only when the lamp behind it is switched on by the relay, gives short instructions of what action to take. If this indicator were used with a generator synchronizing panel, these indications might perhaps read :

Voltage :	correct
Frequency :	correct
Phase :	leading.

CHAPTER 21

LIMIT SWITCHES

21.1. Definition

Limit switches are high sensitivity precision measuring instruments whose pointers, after reaching a predetermined point on the scale, affect a power circuit which actuates any type of control. The delicate structure of the measuring system makes the use of mechanical, i.e., direct-contact-making pointers, levers, etc., prohibitive, The photoelectric relay offers the best solution in all those cases where the movement and slow approach of an instrument pointer to, and its eventual arrival at, a given scale value must be watched.

The basic idea is to mark by optical means one or two different limits, in the latter case also designated as " upper " and " lower " limit, respectively. There is no objection in principle to mark more than two points on the instrument scale. At these points an optical lever (cf. Chap. 7), i.e., a beam of radiant energy, is intercepted whenever the pointer reaches either of the limits. The light beam is transmitted through a number of slits or holes in the measuring instrument, a method that is responsible for the somewhat colloquial term " hole-in-the-meter " instrument (*1670*) ; or reflexion is employed in controlling the light beam by means of the instrument pointer.

Bibliography References : (*2076*, *2095*, *2120*, *2134*, *2147*, *2190*, *2203*, *2237*, *2257*, *2266*, *2342*).

21.2 Transmission Method

The basic construction is shown in Fig. 21.1 which, at the same time, demonstrates the incipient difficulties of the transmission method. The light source must be fixed either in front of the hole (*1013*), or it can be fixed on the pointer of some sturdy instrument or industrial scales, for instance. Both solutions of the problem are far from being satisfactory.

Bibliography References : (*2124*, *2145*, *2161*, *2230*)

21.3. Reflexion Method

These and all other intrinsic difficulties of "hole-in-the-meter" switches are eliminated by applying the principle of reflexion. In this method neither is the photosensitor continuously illuminated nor are any structural elements attached to the pointer, nor is there a need for

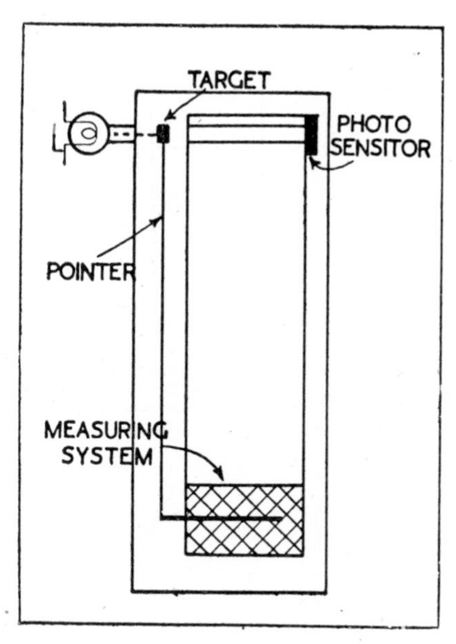

Fig. 21.1. Basic construction of a limit switch employing the transmission method

any holes to be made in the scale on the dial of the instrument. The unit shown in Fig. 21.2 is a self-contained photo-electric limit switch to be used with any type of instrument having a moving pointer. This unit can be clamped to a shoulder running across the back of the instrument and fixed at any desired value of the scale. This system allows the range and limits of the controlling action to be chosen and altered at random within the full range of the instrument without the need of damaging it by a series of holes being bored into the dial.

This switch (*1443*) can be used as a wide-range as well as a narrow-range limit switch as is necessary, for instance, in thermostating chemical or metallurgical baths. The limit switch consists of two parts, viz., the measuring instrument proper with its pointer and case suitably adapted and the photo-electric limit switch which can be moved along the slotted shoulder and fixed at any point of the latter. The back of the pointer is silvered or in another way prepared for reflecting incident light. The back cover of the instrument is made from transparent material, part of the front cover being opaque to light. One compartment of the limit switch contains the light source and simple optical

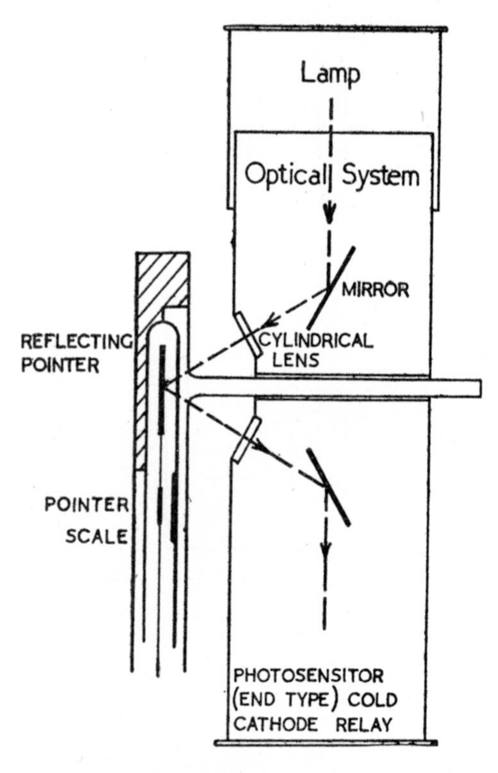

Fig. 21.2. Construction of a limit switch employing the reflexion method

equipment, the other compartment the photosensitor and a cold-cathode valve. The cylindrical lenses are used to narrow and concentrate the light beam and to give it a rectangular cross-section. No light can reach the photo-cell if the pointer is in any other than the " limit " position, and extraneous light is made ineffective by the opaque front-cover. When the pointer swings into the correct position the light beam is reflected back into the other compartment of the switch and strikes the photosensitor. In Fig. 21.3b, the path of the light pencil is shown when the pointer is off the mark. Fig. 21.3a, gives the complete path with the pointer dead on any of the set limits. The advantages of this system are : the action is positive ; the photosensitor

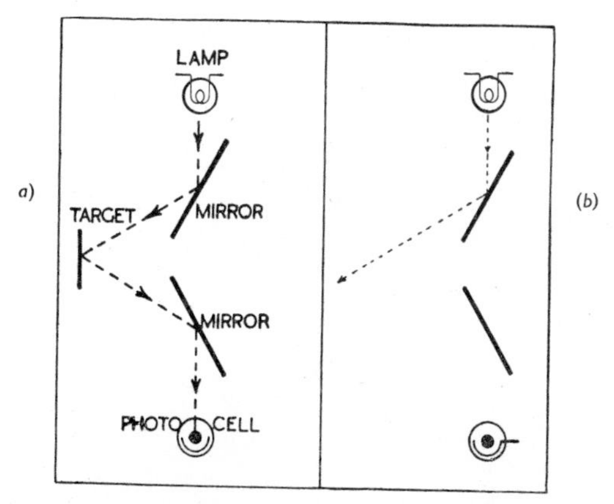

Fig. 21.3. Light pencil paths of limit switch when pointer is (a) on the target, and (b) off the target

is only illuminated when a limit value is reached ; the pointer carries no load whatever ; the limit ranges are easily variable within the range of the instrument ; no damage is done to the measuring instrument by providing slits, holes, etc.

Another arrangement uses two small mirrors M_1 and M_2 which can be set to any desired value. According to the position of the pointer target either one or other of two light beams will be cut off. This action operates the photo-relays.

An instance of how to control a heavy machine tool by a photo-electric limit switch is given in Fig. 21.4. It was desired automatically to stop the feed of the wheel when the work being ground had reached the correct size. An indicating micrometer (minimeter) is mounted close to the work and a lever of the instrument rests against it. The instrument is so designed that the pointer always comes to a certain mark when the work is correct to size : this mark is a narrow slit. A photosensitor is mounted on one side of it and a light source on the other. If the moving pointer obscures the light beam the relay stops the feed to the grinding wheel. An accuracy of $\pm$ 0·0001 inch per inch diameter (0·01 %) can be attained by an unskilled labourer.

The arrangement of the " Precimax " photo-electric grinder control is discussed in the *Automobile Engineer* (*1693*).

Bibliography References : (*1873, 2341*)

21.4. Weighing

Automatic weighing of different quantities makes use of a method described by A. H. Lamb (*1014*). A metal dial has as many holes as

Fig. 21.4. A heavy machine tool controlled by a photo-electric limit switch

there are different loads to be weighed out. The operator puts the selector on the number indicating the weight he wishes to weigh automatically. The photo-e.m.f. cells are connected in parallel and circuited to give positive action. As the lamp, corresponding to weight, e.g., 1 cwt., is switched on the container or bunker opens and the material flows or falls into the receptacle. The pointer of the scales moves along the holes in the dial. When the hole corresponding to a correct weight of one cwt. is covered by the target of the pointer the illumination on the photo-e.m.f. cell is reduced to zero, the photo-relay operates and switches on the motor which, in turn, closes the doors of the bunker.

Other arrangements employ variations of the principle set out above (*801, 1015*).

Bibliography References: (*1830, 2143, 2177, 2265*)

21.5. Barrelling

Liquids are conveniently and speedily barrelled by using a platform-balance and a photo-electric-type limit switch. A high degree of accuracy can be attained by arranging for another limit switch to be situated so that the pointer must pass this precontrol limit switch before it reaches the main limit switch. The pre-control switch can then be used to reduce the flow of the liquid for the last two or three seconds before the exact weight is reached.

21.6. Sizing of Spherical Objects

Steel balls for ball bearings, oranges, or any kind of spherical object can automatically be sized by simple photo-electric equipment. As many instruments must be provided as different sizes it is desired to grade.

The image of the object is projected on to a translucent screen (opal sheet glass). Another optical system picks up this silhouette and projects it on to a photosensitor. The diaphragm in front of this cell has an aperture of a definite shape and size, for instance a circle of diameter d in the case of spherical objects. If the size of the ball is such that the projected image completely covers the aperture, thus entirely obscuring the photosensitor, the tray (on which the object is centred by means of a depression) will open and release the ball into the proper bin. A counter can be actuated every time a tray releases an object.

When, for instance, four different sizes of circular shape are to be sorted the general layout will be as follows. The aperture in the diaphragm appertaining to tray No. 1 must be of maximum size d. The average object will not enable the optical system to produce a large enough silhouette to cover completely the aperture, but will admit some light to the photo-relay, thus preventing it from being tripped. The object is conveyed to tray No. 2 by any suitable mechanical means. The No. 2 diaphragm has a smaller diameter d'. The process of inspection is repeated and if the image is still too small the object will be passed on to the third tray. If the photosensitor should now be obscured the relay will open the trap and the object will be dropped into bin No. 3 and graded accordingly. The circuit of the photo-relay will be wired for negative action as the condition " no light " is supposed to trip the mechanical relay.

Bibliography References : (*1838*, *1999*, *2191*, *2270*, *2401*, *p. 118*)

21.7. Galvanometer Methods

There are many cases of sizing, grading, sorting, measuring, etc., where the quantities involved do not directly permit of being expressed in terms of " incident light ". A galvanometer arrangement must then be set up to indicate the quantity measured and a light pencil be utilized as a means of operating via a photo-relay any combination of mechanical equipment (*1016*).

Bibliography Reference : (*533*)

21.8. Synchronizing A.C. Generators

Alternating current generators must not be switched in parallel unless they coincide in voltage, frequency, and phase, respectively. A combination of measuring instruments, preferably of the differential

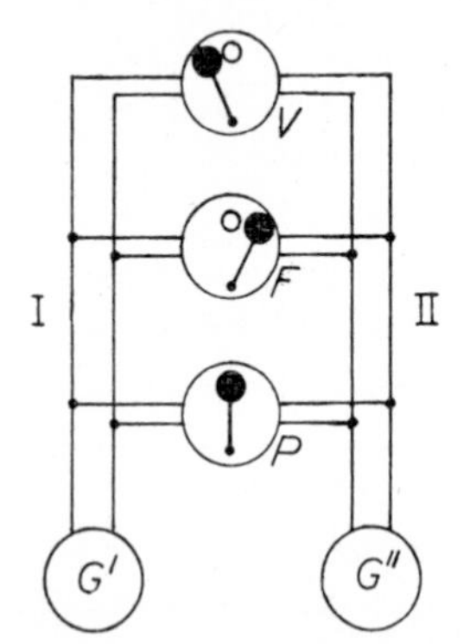

Fig. 21.5. Use of limit switch for control of A.C. Generators

type, afford a simple means of maintaining control of this condition. Two generators G' and G'', Fig. 21.5, work into two networks I and II, respectively, The measuring instruments are of the hole-in-the-meter or any suitable limit switch type. If a limit switch, as shown in Fig. 21.2, is chosen synchronism will be indicated by all three photo-sensitors receiving an impulse from the incident light rays. As such a coincidence may be only a momentary one, the photosensitors energize time-delay relays which close the contactor only if synchronism has been maintained during a predetermined period.

21.9. Neon Limit Switch

The neon filled (resonance) "tuning indicator" can be adapted to act as an inertialess limit switch. The length of the glow is a function of the voltage across (or current in) the tube. The tube can be painted black with the exception of a narrow longitudinal slit through which the glowing column is observed to move up and down like the column in a thermometer. A photo-relay watches the luminous discharge column reach a given predetermined height and is then energized by the incident radiation.

21.10. Control of Movement

To this group belong installations that are instanced by the Kincardine Bridge (*397, p. 142*) (alinement of the swing span) ; levelling equipment operating large elevators, etc. Another utilization of the limit switch principle is the control of the movement of travelling coal bins which distribute fuel to a sectional hopper (*1041*).

Bibliography References : (*1176, 2352, 2376, 2379, 2382, 2383*)

CHAPTER 22

LEVEL INDICATORS

Among the many and varied types of level indicators, photo-electric systems take the first place because the ray of luminous or non-luminous radiation which is used as an optical feeler or lever in no way contaminates, or can be damaged by, the material. Photo-electric methods are usually still applicable to problems where other level indicators fail.

22.1. Solid Level Indication

The sand for the sand boxes of railway engines (*1026*) is dried by steam coils wound over drums in which the sand is kept in steady

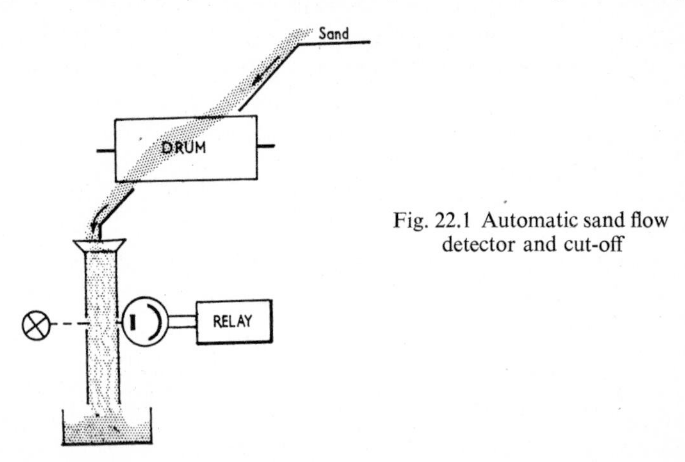

Fig. 22.1 Automatic sand flow detector and cut-off

motion. The sand flows by gravity into the drum ; when this container becomes full, the surplus sand flows over and into a pipe into which a window is inserted on each side, Fig. 22.1. As the surplus sand falls down the pipe the light ray is intercepted and the photo-sensitor of the relay R is obscured. This causes the relay to stop the flow of sand into the drum and empties the latter into the store bin.

The same principle can be employed in controlling the flow of any powder (powdered solid fuel ; cement ; flour, etc.) or in maintaining it at a constant level. The best method of attaining a positive indication is to insert a short length of tubing through which the powder is forced to fall by gravity. The photo-relay must then be circuited to operate on incident light.

Bibliography References : (*1793*, *1846*, *2183*)

22.2. Liquid Level Indication

Levels of liquids can be indicated by various methods, the more important ones being shown in Fig. 22.2. With transparent liquids

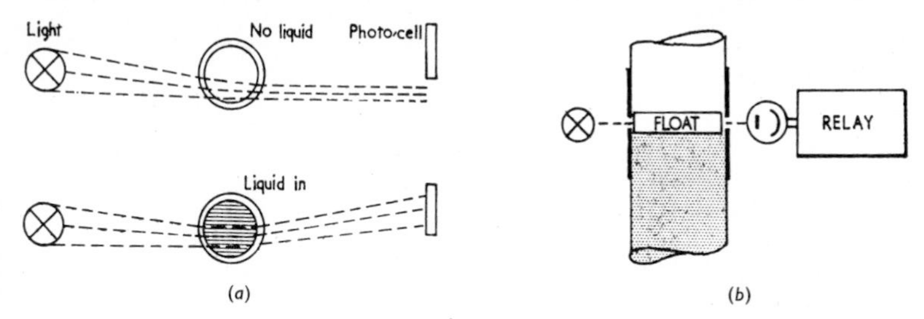

Fig. 22.2 Two methods of indicating liquid level: (a) by refraction, (b) by float

indication and/or control by refraction or obscuration by means of a float is usual. For opaque or turbid media the simple on-off arrangement may be used as either a maximum height or minimum height control.

The complete circuit of a liquid level control apparatus (*1027*) consists of a photo-relay operating a solenoid valve which controls the flow of the liquid.

McNickle developed another method (*951*) employing a rotameter, Fig. 22.3, or rate-of-flow indicator. Two light beams are thrown across the measuring tube in which the position of a float is indicative of the rate of flow. This float is enclosed by two light beams. Any displacement of the float causes a disturbance in the balanced electronic circuit which actuates a control valve. The float can be maintained in a predetermined position (equivalent to a predetermined rate of flow) within $\pm 0{\cdot}25$ mm. (cf. Chap. 11). The rotameter is also applicable to measuring the rate of flow of gases.

A photo-electric level indicator which will prove sufficiently accurate for boiler house practice and other similar uses, for instance, water works, sewerage, etc., consists of a number of photo-e.m.f. cells all of which are connected in parallel (*79, p. 395*).

An electronic flowmeter for remote recording (*281*) was developed by Weinberger. He utilizes the effect of a Venturi tube indicating the differential pressure by means of a U-shaped tube filled with mercury. The change of level

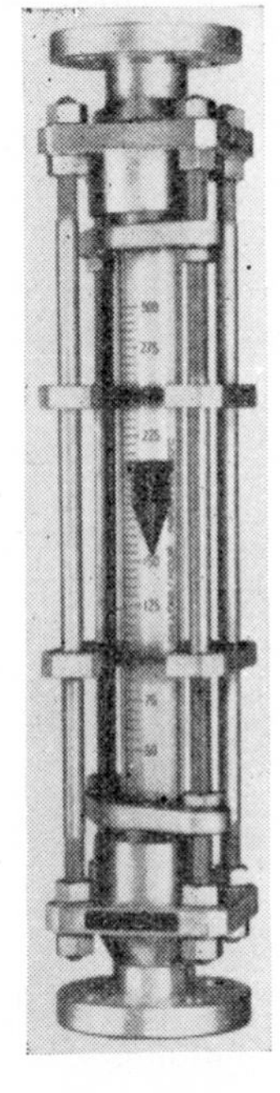

Fig. 22.3 Rate-of-flow indicator

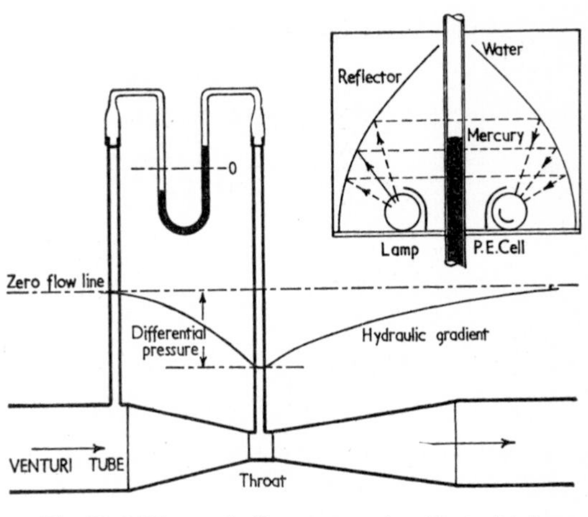

Fig. 22.4 Electronic flowmeter using Venturi tube (from *Electronics*)

(*H*) is proportional to the quantity of liquid flowing through the Venturi tube, Fig. 22.4. Weinberger has devised a special measuring device the particular feature of which is that all rays of light reaching the manometer are of the same length. The optical device is described in Chap. 6.

Bibliography References : (*1738, 1824, 2176, 2401, p. 115*)

CHAPTER 23

COUNTING DEVICES

Counting devices (*1681*) may be operated in a variety of ways according to the set-up of which they are a part. In many cases the interruption of a single light beam energizes the photo-electric counter irrespective of the type of object that causes this interruption. At other times this circuit, by a simple trick, can be made to discriminate between objects of various colours, or various transparencies, reflectivities, etc. Then again, it is necessary to count full containers and empty ones separately and give the sum of each count ; or to register on different cyclometers objects of different sizes.

These relatively simple counting devices will count objects moving in either direction, i.e., towards or away from the counter. In cases where this is not admissible, unidirectional counting comes into its rights. Such a device is so constructed as to count objects moving in one direction only, for instance towards the counter, but to neglect the registering of objects moving away from it. A unidirectional counting system will be resorted to when, for instance, two conveyor belts or chains, moving close together in opposite directions, make it impossible for the counter to be installed in such a way as to view one conveyor only. It will, then, count only the objects on the nearby conveyor, but take no notice of the other transport line.

A still more complicated device is the differentiating counter which is a combination of two unidirectional counters. By registering objects moving towards a given point of the production line as well as those moving away from this point, the differentiator indicates on a cyclometer movement of special construction the instantaneous number of objects in that particular place at any time.

Lastly, there is the integrating counter, an apparatus that counts electronically at a speed which forbids the use of mechanical or electromagnetic counters whose upper limit of registration (resolution) is about 600 counts per minute.

Where the usual methods of high speed counting are impracticable as, for instance, is the case with objects of very small size or light weight and a resolution of about 200/sec. is required the shadow counting method has proved successful. A short beam of light is focused through an aperture of a guide, a steel tube, for instance, which is so placed that the objects to be counted fall through it by force of gravity. The focus of the optical arrangement is so adapted that the objects to be counted fall right through it. The falling object's image is projected on to a white background which is scanned by the photocell. Thus it is possible to count clear drops of liquids, razor blades, closely spaced sheets of paper or metal, etc.

Bibliography Reference : (*1533*)

23.1. Non-directional Counters—Opaque Objects

A light beam is interrupted by the opaque object, Fig. 23.1. The electronic circuit is connected for " reverse action ", resulting in an

Fig. 23.1. Counting opaque objects on a moving belt.

increased anode current when the illumination is reduced . A hot or cold cathode valve can be used. An A.C.-supplied, D.C.-operated counter using a dry disk rectifier and a gaseous cold-cathode triode has been designed by Atkinson (*892*). The circuit is based on the principle of the relaxation oscillator. When the light beam is interrupted the resistance of the photosensitor increases. The grid voltage rises and, when exceeding the triggering potential of the cold cathode valve, causes it to fire. The relay coil becomes energized and closes a pair of contacts with the result that the load resistance of the photosensitor is reduced. This prevents slowly-moving objects from being counted. If the switch connects the counter coil to the circuit an electromagnetic counter will count at the maximum rate of about 15,000 objects per hour. If thrown into the other position an external circuit can be connected and tripped by the counting impulses.

Bibliography References: (*488, 490, 1215, 1220, 1229, 1300, 1358, 1363, 1570, 1806, 2073, 2078*).

23.2. Non-directional Counters—Transparent Objects

The optical principle has been discussed elsewhere in this book (cf. Chaps. 6 and 14). If the objects are all coloured alike any simple

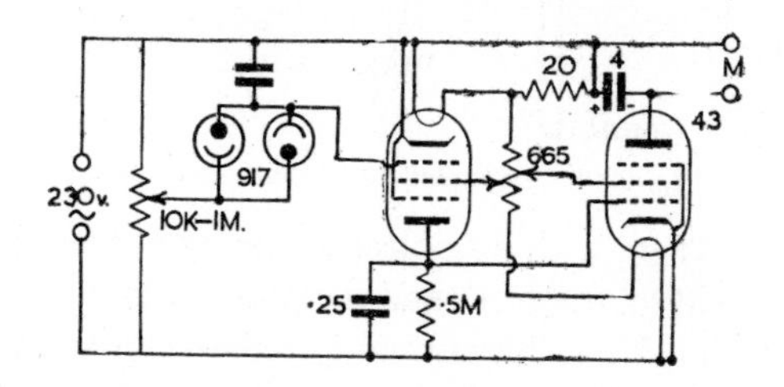

Fig. 23.2. Two-cell circuit for objects of different colours

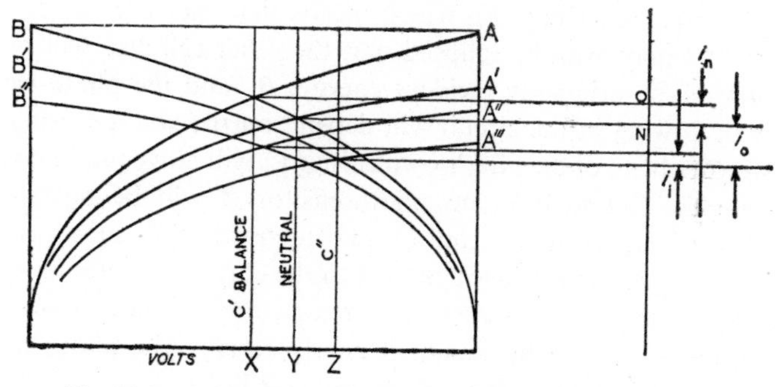

Fig. 23.3. Graph illustrating operation of circuit of Fig. 23.2

relay circuit can be used for energizing a cyclometer. If white light is not sufficiently attenuated by the passage of the transparent object through the beam to ensure safe operation of the photo-relay, light of a colour complementary to that of the object must be used.

Things are slightly more complicated when the objects are of two different colours, each colour to be counted separately. A two-cell circuit must be employed, for instance the one shown in Fig. 23.2. The working principle is outlined in Fig. 23.3. The graphs A, B are the respective cell characteristics (cf. Chap. 5), intersection X marking equal illumination on both photosensitors. The other graphs represent the characteristics of cell A at illuminations lower than necessary for balance. If the colours of the two groups of objects are C' and C'', respectively, the filter F, Fig. 23.4, must be of either C' or C'' colour.

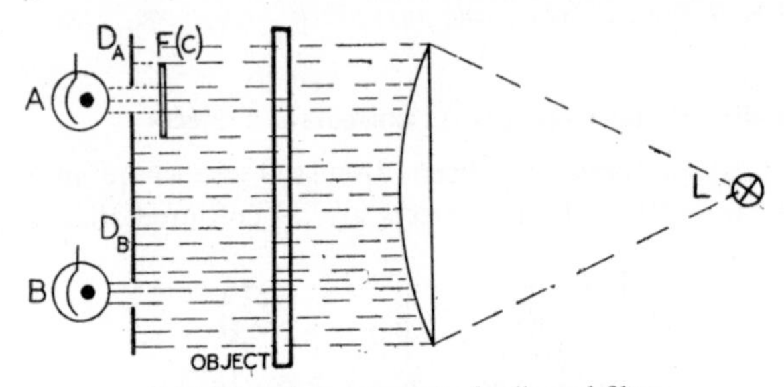

Fig. 23.4. Arrangement of cells and filter

Assume it is C'. Then, with no object in the light beam the illumination will correspond to graph A', and the photo-current i_n is dependent on the voltage swing XY. This current i_n is characteristic of the neutral position. If an object of C'' colour moves into the beam the illumination on cell A will be greatly reduced, for instance to A'''. If $C' = C_0$ and $C'' = C_{180}$ (cf. Chap. 8), which means that they are complementaries, cell A may even be eclipsed, but the other cell also will receive only part of the originally incident energy, B', and the photo-electric current i_0, flowing in the circuit will depend on the voltage swing YZ.

Lastly, an object of the filter's own colour C' will move into the beam. This time the illumination on photosensitor A will be but slightly reduced, for instance to A'', and on photosensitor B to such a magnitude B'' (the reduction being regulated to the correct amount by means of the diaphragm D_B) that curve B is reduced to B'', thus making the illumination on both cells equal, or nearly equal. The photo-electric current i_1 is a function of the voltage swing ZX.

The position Y is taken as a starting or neutral point, and the position on the scale of the meter marked " zero " accordingly, although this " zero " is not identical with the zero mark on the instrument indicating " no current ". The adjustment of the electronic part of the counter must not tend to produce equal illumination on both photosensitors but, by interposing the filter F and adjusting the respective diaphragms D_A and D_B, to cause a certain current i_n (characteristic of position Y) to flow in the meter. If an object with the same colour as, and then with the complementary colour of, the filter is introduced into the beam, the currents i_1 and i_0 respectively will be indicated. Adjustments of the optical as well as of the electronic part should tend to space i_1 half-way between the neutral position and i_0. The coils of two electromagnetic counters will then be connected in series and placed in the anode circuit either in series with, or instead of, the measuring instrument, Fig. 23.5. The characteristic coil data are listed in Table 23.1.

TABLE 23.1

Character Coil Data

Current	Relay *A*	Relay *B*
Operating current	i_1	i_1*
Holding current	i_n	—
Releasing current	i_o*	i_n

* The asterisk indicates the condition under which the unit disk in the counter is advanced one step.

Relay *B* is counting the objects of the same colour as the filter *F*, and relay *A* the objects of the other (complementary) colour.

In Table 23.2 some recommendations as to the optimal equipment are compiled.

TABLE 23.2

Recommended Assemblies for Counting Transparent Objects

Colour of Transparent Object	Light Source Type of Lamp	Colour of Filter	Type of Photosensitor
Violet	Mercury vapour or Panchromatic	Leafgreen	S_{-1} surface. Selenium-on-iron.
Ultramarine Blue	Sodium vapour	Yellow	S_{-1} surface. Selenium-on-iron.
Green	Neon or Panchromatic	Red	S_{-1} surface. Selenium-on-iron.
Yellow	Panchromatic	Blue	S_{-4} surface. Hydrogen sensitized (thick film type) Potassium.
Red	Mercury vapour or Panchromatic	Seagreen	S_{-1} surface. Copper oxide-on-copper.

Bibliography Reference: (*416*)

23.3 Counting according to Size of Object

The simple method of non-directional counting is easily adapted to a system that discriminates, and counts separately, objects of various

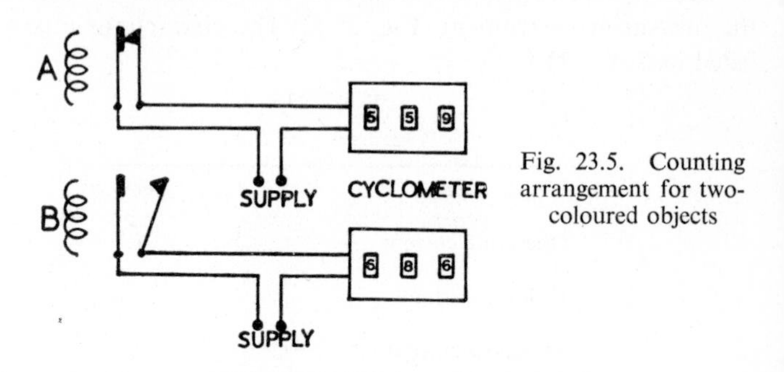

Fig. 23.5. Counting arrangement for two-coloured objects

sizes. It is assumed that the various objects, for instance boxes, parcels, crates, etc., are fed on to the conveyor regardless of any set order. It is then for the counting device to make the important discrimination.

In one system a two-cell balanced circuit is employed. Fig. 23.6 demonstrates a conveyor belt carrying different types of boxes. *AB*

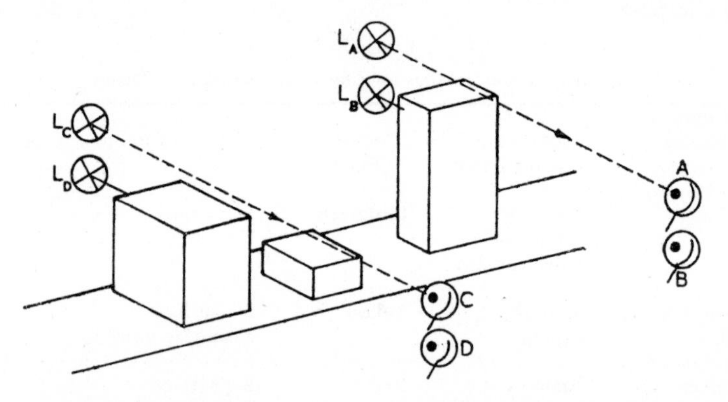

Fig. 23.6. Arrangement for counting objects of different heights

are the photosensitors of one, *CD* of another counter. The photosensitors are mounted at such heights above the level of the conveyor as corresponds to the dimensions of the parcels to be counted by that particular counter. The two cells of each circuit are mounted one below the other. Care must be taken to allow the one light beam to reach the top cell even if the passing object, which is to be counted by this set, intercepts the lower light beam and prevents it from reaching the cell. Every set of two photosensitors counts only one type of object, the set *AB*, for instance, registering the large parcels while the set *CD* will count the small ones. Any object eclipsing only one photosensitor of the balanced two-cell circuit will upest the balance and cause the cyclometer to count 1. If, in the course of moving along on the belt, the tall object reaches the spot where the set *CD* is waiting for the small objects to be counted, the tall objects will obscure both cells *C* and *D* at the same moment which results in keeping the two-cell circuit in balance. A counter will, therefore, register no objects that eclipse either none or both photosensitors simultaneously. A count is made when the lower cell is obscured, the top cell remaining illuminated.

Bibliography References : (*1895, 1969, 2401, p. 118*)

23.4. Multiple Counting

This system allows the separate counting of as many different sizes as photosensitors are installed. The goods are conveyed on a belt regardless of size, Fig. 23.7. At any given position of the run a curtain

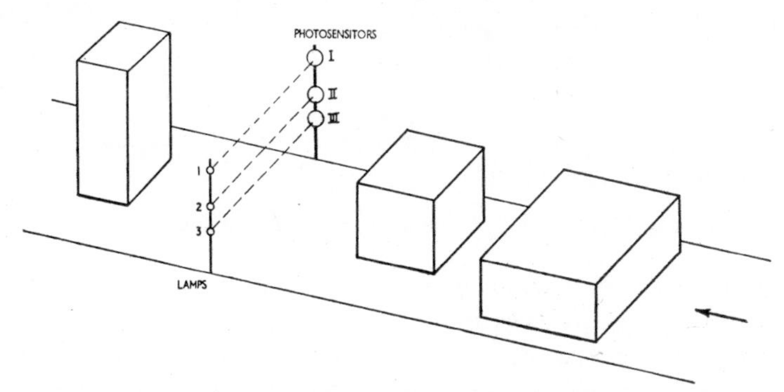

Fig. 23.7. Multiple counting of different objects with several cells

of individual rays, luminous or non-luminous, is so arranged in a vertical plane that each beam is kept separate and crosses the whole width of the conveyor. In passing through the curtain of beams, object *A* cuts all rays simultaneously. According to the circuit, Fig. 23.8, only the counter marked *a* will be actuated and in doing so all the other counters have been made inoperative. When all three photosensitors *I, II, III,* have been obscured, all three relay coils *a′*, *b′*, *c′*, are energized, all contacts *PQ* are closed and all contacts *QR* open.

The circuit of the battery E_a is now: E_a-Q_a-P_a-a-E_a; the circuit is closed and registers 1. The circuit of battery E_b is: E_b-b-R_a-. . ., and of battery E_c : E_c-Q_c-R_c-. . . , the latter two batteries being in

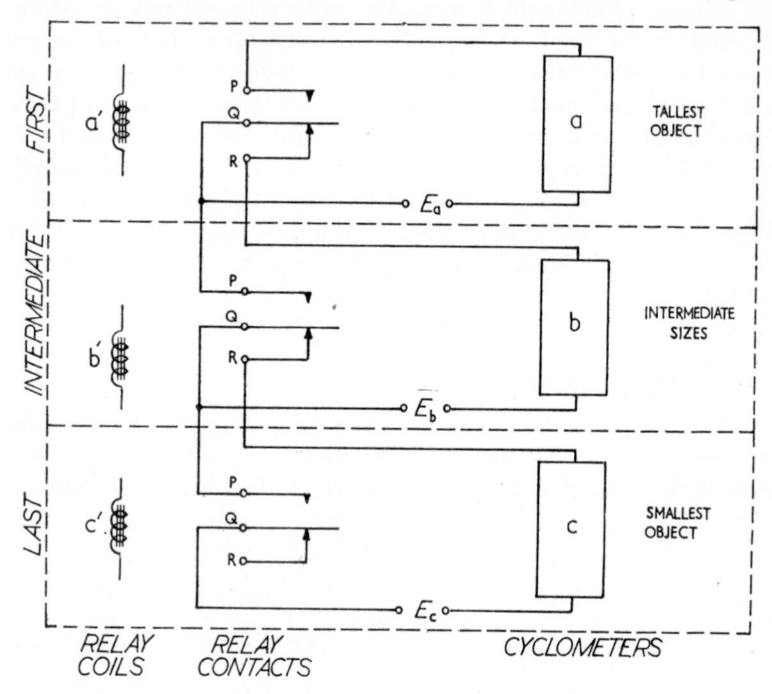

Fig. 23.8. Relay and counter arrangement for Fig. 23.7

an open circuit. This results in a being the only counter in a complete and closed or operative circuit.

If now an object passes the curtain obscuring all cells but I, then all relay coils but a' will be energized and all relay contacts Q will close circuit P except contact Q_a which makes contact with R_a. The battery circuits are now as follows :

E_a-a-P_a- . . . (open, not registering) ;
E_b-b-R_a-Q_a-P_b-Q_b-E_b (closed, counting 1) ;
E_c-c-R_b- . . . (open, not registering).

The same principle applies to any size for which a light source and corresponding photosensitor have been provided. Between the "first" and "last" circuit, i.e., between the counters for the tallest and smallest object, respectively, any number of " intermediate " circuits can be interposed to count any number of " intermediate " sizes. The " first " and the " last " circuit differ in the electrical wiring from that of the " intermediate " circuits which are all identical. The relays are all of the same type, viz., SPDT.

23.5. Controlled Counting

The arrangement in Fig. 23.9a provides for separately counting empty and full bins or tubs, respectively (*397, p. 82*). The containers move along on a pocket or cabin conveyor. A switch *S* is closed by a projection *C* as each bin moves past, the switch being closed for a certain length of time depending on the length of the cam. The closing of *S* causes the counter *E* to register if the bin was empty, i.e., if no object eclipsed the photosensitor *PC*, Fig. 23.9b. If, however, an object

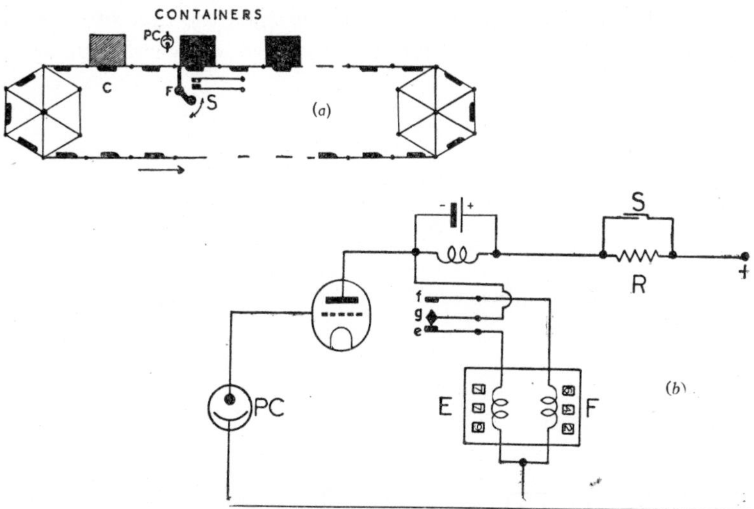

Fig. 23.9. (a) separate counting of full and empty bins (b) counting circuit

is in the bin just above *S*, the light beam will be intercepted. The photosensitor, now eclipsed, will send a photo-current through the relay coil. This breaks contacts *ge* and makes contacts *fg*, causing the counter *F* to register. The length of the cam and the position of the cell must be so arranged to cause an object in a bin to obscure the photosensitor before the cam closes switch *S* and to open this switch before light is admitted again to the photosensitor. The resistor *R* reduces the current through the relay coil below the holding current so that the contact arm *g* stays released although a small current flows through the coil.

If the conveyor moves fast or has many small compartments, the mechanical switch S may easily be exchanged for a photo-electric switch using another light source and photosensitor. The cam is now so shaped as to form a suitable target shielding the light ray from the photosensitor controlling the relay switch.

Other arrangements are suggested in Fig. 23.10a, b. The light beam from the lamp L is reflected on to a photosensitor by utilizing the glossy surface of an object. If no object is on the conveyor, reflexion takes place at a lower plane, viz., the plane of the belt and is therefore, out of focus with the aperture A in the diaphragm. Either another aperture at A' and another photosensitor may be provided to count full and empty bins separately, or the cam may be made always to register an empty bin unless the light beam, reflected on to the photo-relay by an object in the bin next to be counted, has switched over for the (full bins) counter to be in the circuit when the cam supplies the counting impulse. In Fig. 23.10b, the case is shown where a change in

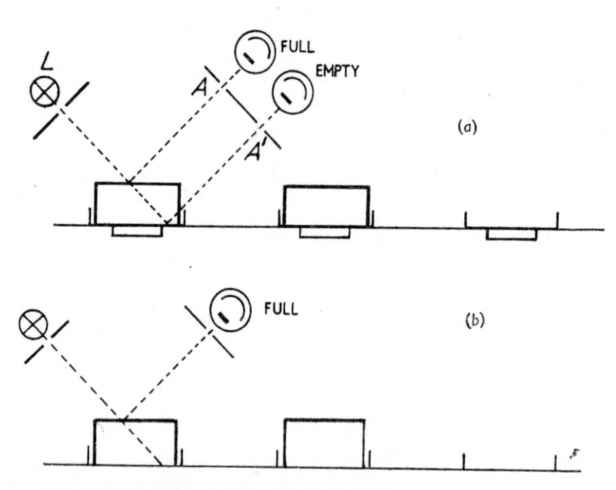

Fig. 23.10. (a) Counting full and empty bins by two cells
(b) counting by variation in light from the bins

reflexion is enhanced by making the conveyor a dull grey or black or any dark colour having a very low reflexion coefficient. When an object passes, light will be reflected into the photo-relay. If the bin is empty the conveyor absorbs most of the light and none, or practically none, reaches the photosensitor. Use can also be made of colours and colour filters as described in detail elsewhere (cf. Chaps. 8 and 14).

23.6. Unidirectional Counting

The basic idea in unidirectional counting is the definition of direction in which moving objects are to be counted. This is simplest done by stating a certain spatial sequence in which two (or more) light rays

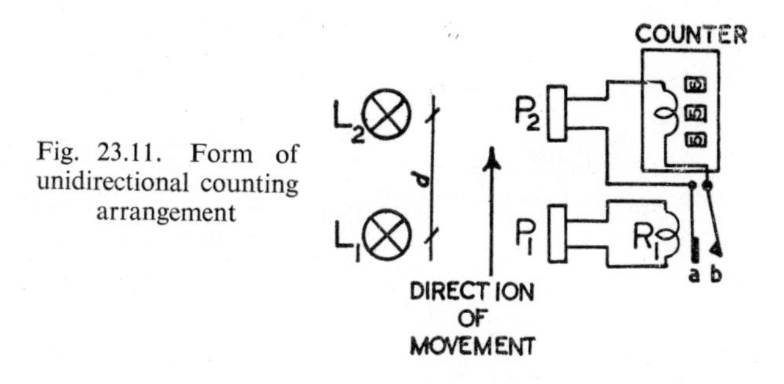

Fig. 23.11. Form of unidirectional counting arrangement

must be intercepted by one and the same object in order to result in a count. Objects moving in the reverse or any other direction do not fulfil that particular condition and, therefore, are not counted. Fig. 23.11 gives the design of a very simple one-way counting circuit. The objects are counted when they move in such a way as to cut off the light beam first from L_1 and then from L_2. The distance d between the two light beams must be greater than the largest dimension of the object. The two photosensitors are not eclipsed at once and then the photosensitor P_1 will be obscured while the object is passing. This closes contacts *a*, *b* of the relay *R* which, in this case, must be of the delaying type so as to keep the contacts *a*, *b* closed until the object arrives at the other photosensitor P_2 which, on being eclipsed, causes the electromagnetic cyclometer to register one count. The time of the delay must be at least $t = d/v$, where v is the velocity with which the object moves.

An object moving in the opposite direction can not be counted since the counter circuit is open when the light beam from L_2 is intercepted by the object and has been restored again when it reaches the beam from L_1.

Similar circuits (*397, p. 84*) have been designed and a modification has been suggested by K. Henney (*79, p. 353*) whose design demands that both photosensitors must be eclipsed at once, d being equal to, or smaller than, d' (*870*).

Bibliography References : (*2024, 2064, 2065, 2075, 2089, 2104, 2277*)

23.7. Selective Counting

If from a variety of goods on a conveyor only one type is to be selected, the object having a certain dimension d' which none of the other goods have, the simple circuit of Fig. 23.12 will select these objects. A count is made when both photosensitors are eclipsed at

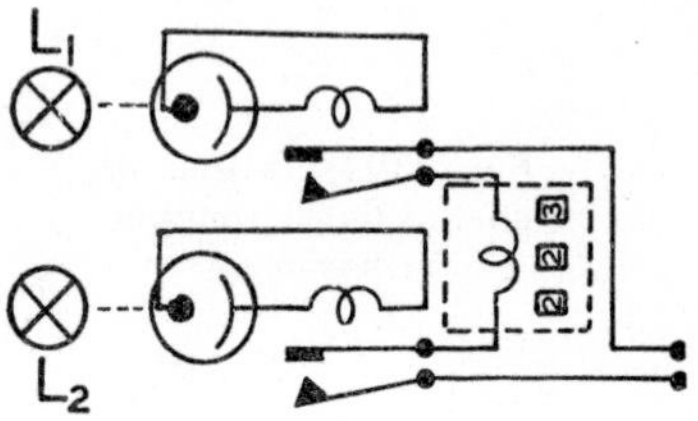

Fig. 23.12. Selective counting: both cells eclipsed at once

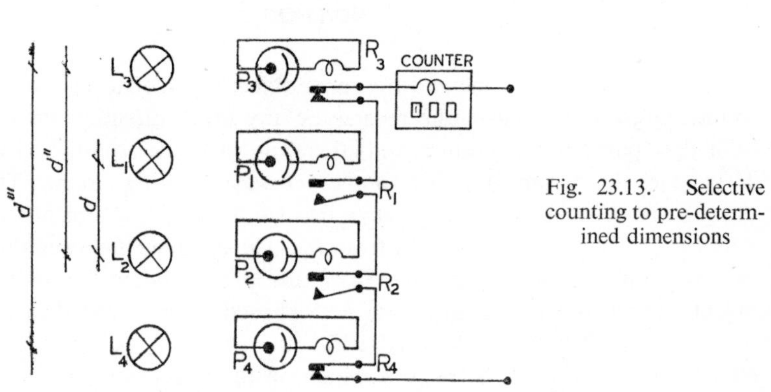

Fig. 23.13. Selective counting to pre-determined dimensions

once, closing the relays simultaneously. The distance d of the two photosensitors is, of course, equal to d'. If there are amongst the goods, objects of a dimension $d''>d$, then the arrangement of Fig. 23.13 must be applied. Since a larger object would also eclipse P_1 and P_2 simultaneously, causing the counter to register when it should not, four photosensitors must be so arranged that the passing object obscures P_3 first, then P_1 and P_2 simultaneously, and P_4 last. The condition for the various distances is set out as :

$$d = d' < d''' < d'' > d''''$$

An object moving into the barrage of the four light beams is :

(1) counted, if $d \leqq d' < d'''$;
(2) not counted, if $d > d'$;
(3) not counted, if $d''' < d'' > d''''$.

If the object is larger than the one to be counted ($d'' > d'$) the light beam of L_3 (relay R_3 open) will be kept cut off until the rays from L_4 (relay R_4 open) are also intercepted. The counter circuit is kept open regardless of the position of contacts R_1 and R_2. This circuit can also be used to control the points of a conveyor belt or chain (cf. Chap. 24),

Bibliography Reference : (*1895*)

23.8. Differentiating Counter

This arrangement of one-way-only counters enables the cyclometer to indicate the instantaneous number of objects (or people) in a department or place, when the number of objects moving into or out of this place is neither constant but fluctuating, nor the one identical with the other but continuously changing. Two (unidirectional) counters are set up to count each movement separately, Fig. 23.14, i.e. the one counting the incoming objects Q' and the other the outgoing ones, Q''.

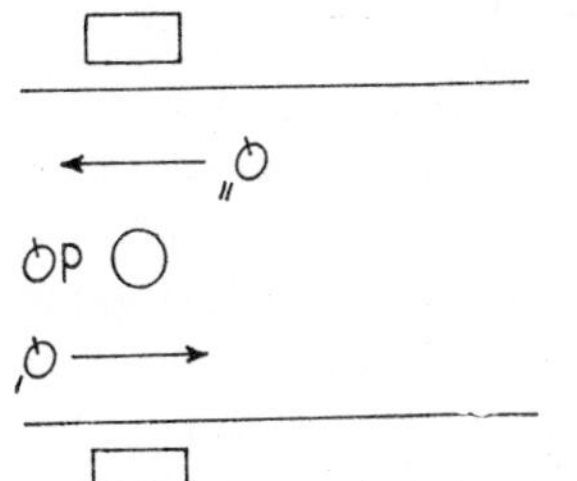

Fig. 23.14. Differentiating counting arrangement

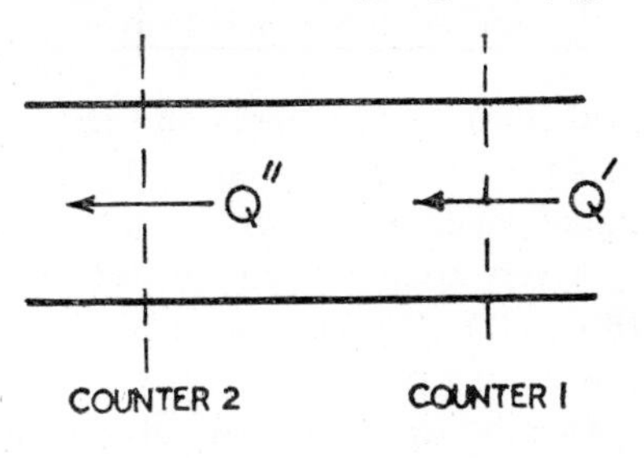

Fig. 23.15. Another arrangement of differentiating counter

The cyclometer is constructed to allow for positive, i.e., additive, movements as well as negative, i.e. subtractive movements, the instantaneous figure $dQ = Q' - Q''$ being the net amount of objects in that place. The cyclometer will show $\pm dQ$. Another arrangement of the counting equipment is shown in Fig. 23.15.

23.9. Integrating Counter

These counters are electronic devices which, when applied to industrial problems, work on the principle of a capacitor receiving a partial charge every time an object passes the photosensitor (*1675*). The accumulation of a certain number of these charges causes the capacitor to discharge after m partial charges through the coil of a mechanical counter. The reading on the cyclometer must then be multiplied by this constant m in order to give the value of the true count. The principle of such counters has been developed by Wynn-Williams (*893*, *894*, *895*) who cascades a number of units, Fig. 23.16. All valves V_1 are connected in parallel and so are all valves V_2. The counter is connected between B and C of the last unit. Each unit consists of two

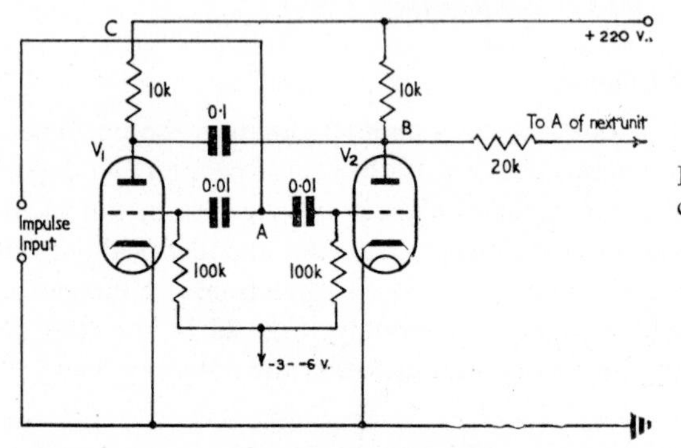

Fig. 23.16. Basic circuit of integrating counter (*Wynn Williams*)

grid-controlled rectifiers and reduces the rate of counting by a factor of 2 per unit. Such a circuit counts 1000 or more objects per second, a figure which will hardly be met in industrial processes.

A very adaptable circuit has been designed by Lord and Livingston (*896*, *897*). Objects can be counted at the rate of 120 per second or as low as two per minute.

One of the first four-valve counter decades using double-triodes was described by J. T. Potter (*898*, *899*). Its function is based on the principle that two pulses generated in one circuit trigger the next circuit. This readily suggests a binary (as opposed to the decimal) system of calculation, having as basis the four numbers 1–2–4–8. Being different from other binary circuits whose next step is 16, the Potter circuit interrupts the binary count at 10 and resets the electronic circuit to zero, at the same time stepping up the next higher decade by one unit. This type of counter decade operates at rates as high as 10^6 impulses per second or as low as desired and any number of decades can be cascaded in order to count large quantities. The two-decade counter comprises two electronic decades. The multiplication factor m of each is ten: this makes the factor of the whole instrument a hundred. Units from zero to ninety-nine are counted electronically and indicated on two banks of neon lamps, Fig. 23.17. An electromagnetic relay is actuated once for every one hundred impulses counted electronically. A neon lamp is connected with the second half of each stage and used as an indicator for electronically counting units and tens below one hundred. When the counting is terminated, the electro-mechanical counter will read that first figures of the count and the electronic counter, viz., the neon lamps, will give the final two places.

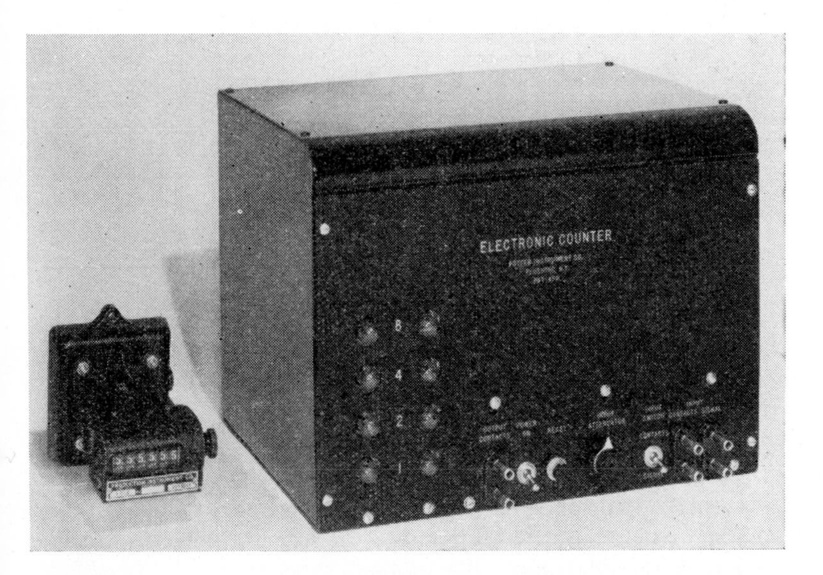

Fig. 23.17. Electronic counter with neon indicators. (*Potter Instrument Co.*)

The four stages of a decade are connected in series. Each count is registered, as it occurs, on the appropriate neon lamps on the front panel, Fig. 23.17 The count is read from the combination of lamps that remain lighted at the termination of a count until the unit is reset. Representation of the ten places of any one decade, here of the units, progresses thus :

Lamps lighted	Figure registered
none	zero
1	one
2	two
2 & 1	three
4	four
4 & 1	five
4 & 2	six
4 & 2 & 1	seven
8	eight
8 & 1	nine

The electronic counter is reset to zero by a momentary pressure upon the reset push-button.

Another decimal counter is described by West (*1654*) and a new valve, the Dekatron, introduces a new era in electronic decimal counters (*2502*).

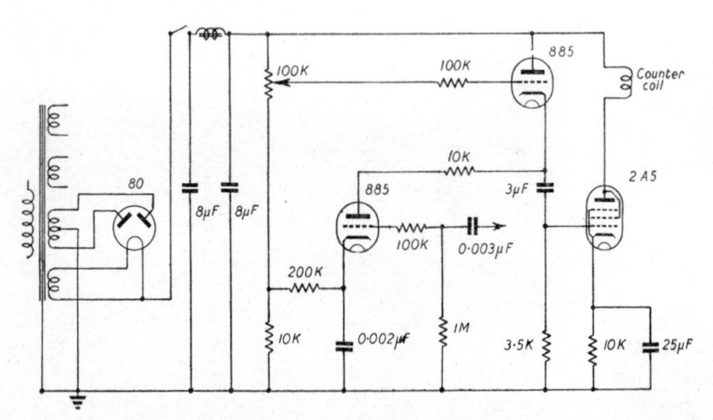

Fig. 23.18. Basic integrating counting circuit for biological work

Another " scale-of-eight " counter was devised by J. Giarratana (*900*) and counts up to 4000 impulses per second. For circuit details the reader should consult the original paper.

A vacuum-valve counting circuit, using pentodes, is described by H. J. Reich (*901*). Details of a triode vacuum valve scale-of-two counter and the complete scale-of-sixteen circuit are given by Lifschutz and Lawson (*902*) ; the circuit counts 120,000 impulses per second. Another scale-of-two counter for industrial use with a resolution of 10,000 per minute was described by Mäder (*895*).

A portable recording counter which originally was designed for the measurement of weak sources of gamma-radiation can easily be adapted for operation by impulses from photo-electric cells (*903*, *904*).

A scale-of-two counter, similar to the Wynn-Williams circuit, but operating with cold-cathode gasfilled valves, was used by Ingram (*367*). The simple circuit of Atkinson (*892*) uses only one grid-controlled cold-cathode valve in a straightforward circuit. The maximum count is four to five per second.

Another integrating circuit, originally designed for biological work (counting the action potential spikes of nerves), counts between 600 and 1000 impulses per second and reduces this figure to any which suits the electromagnetic counter. With the circuit constants as in Fig. 23.18 the ratio is 300 : 1 (*905*).

A modified Wynn-Williams scale-of-eight counter was developed by Shepherd and Haxby (*906*) using type 885 thyratrons which have an exceedingly small de-ionization time. The time-constants are so arranged that the *RC* of the anode (extinguishing) circuit is greater

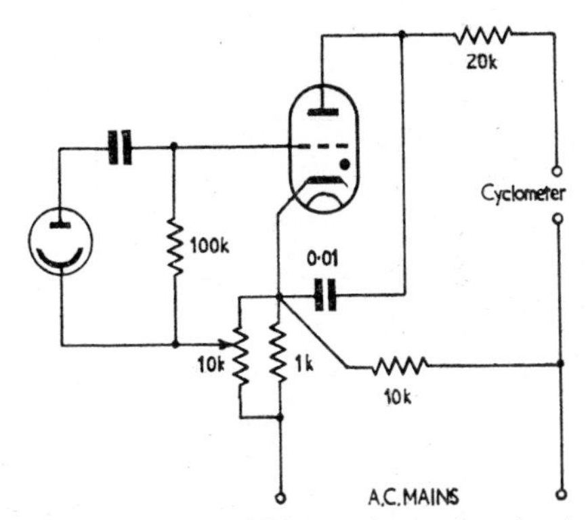

Fig. 23.19. Simple high-speed counting circuit

than the time constant of the grid (firing) circuit. This condition guarantees the constancy and stability of the circuit. If the firing pulse could exist longer than the extinguishing pulse the circuit would tend to hunt the pulse back and forth. The time-constants are of the order of 10^{-4} sec.

A direct-reading counting rate meter for random pulses was described in a paper by Gingrich, Evans, and Edgerton (*907*). Although designed for use with Geiger-Müller counters, the circuit is easily adapted for use with photosensitors. An improved counting rate meter is described by Evans and Alder. (*908*).

Bibliography References : (*441*, *443*, *456*, *459*, *466*, *486*, *501*, *570*, *1075*, *1081*, *1087*, *1181*, *1304*, *1546*, *2394*).

23.10. Simple High-Speed Circuits

Non-integrating counters have been designed on a number of different principles, and two circuits are shown. Figure 23.19 is a circuit for counts up to 50 per second. The instrument can be used as a quick-acting relay as well (*345*). The light impulses must occur on the positive half-cycle and care must be taken to keep the instantaneous polarities of the transformer as shown. Fig. 23.20 is a circuit responding to rapid variations in light. For maximum sensitivity the circuit must be adjusted so that the potential of the 43 grid varies over a range whose upper limit is slightly more negative than zero bias.

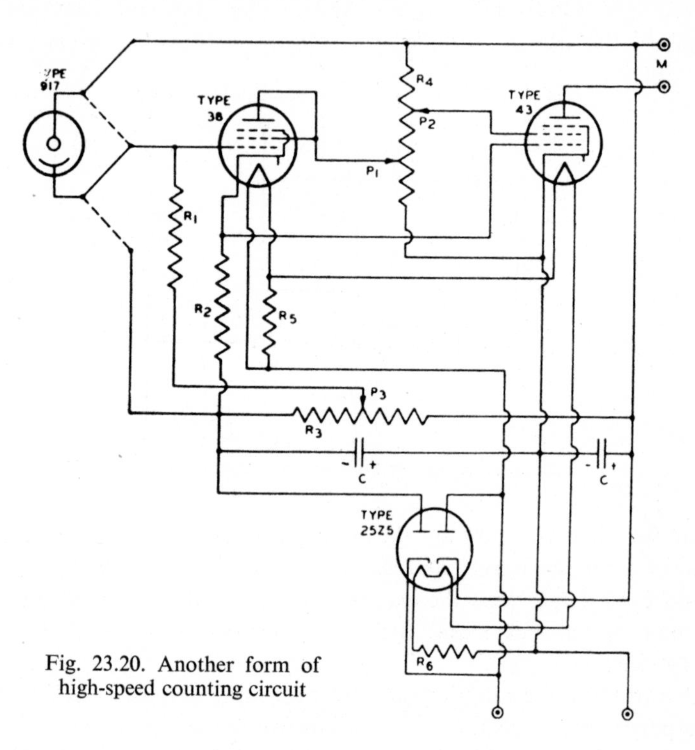

Fig. 23.20. Another form of high-speed counting circuit

For positive action (solid lines; also cf. Chap. 5), the adjustment can be made as follows : Set the potentiometer P_3 at the positive end of R_3 ; potentiometers P_1 and P_2 at the positive end of R_4, and the illumination on the photosensitor at the maximum value it will have in the actual use of the circuit. Then move P_1 towards the negative end of R_4 until the drop across R_2 due to cathode current of the 38 brings the 43 to zero bias. When the movement of P_1 begins to affect the meter reading, the 43 is approximately at zero bias and P_1 has the correct setting. Maximum output current is attained by adjusting the screen voltage of the 43 by means of setting P_2 ; the maximum output current must be just large enough to keep the electromagnetic relay closed. Lastly, P_3 is moved toward the negative end of R_3 to the

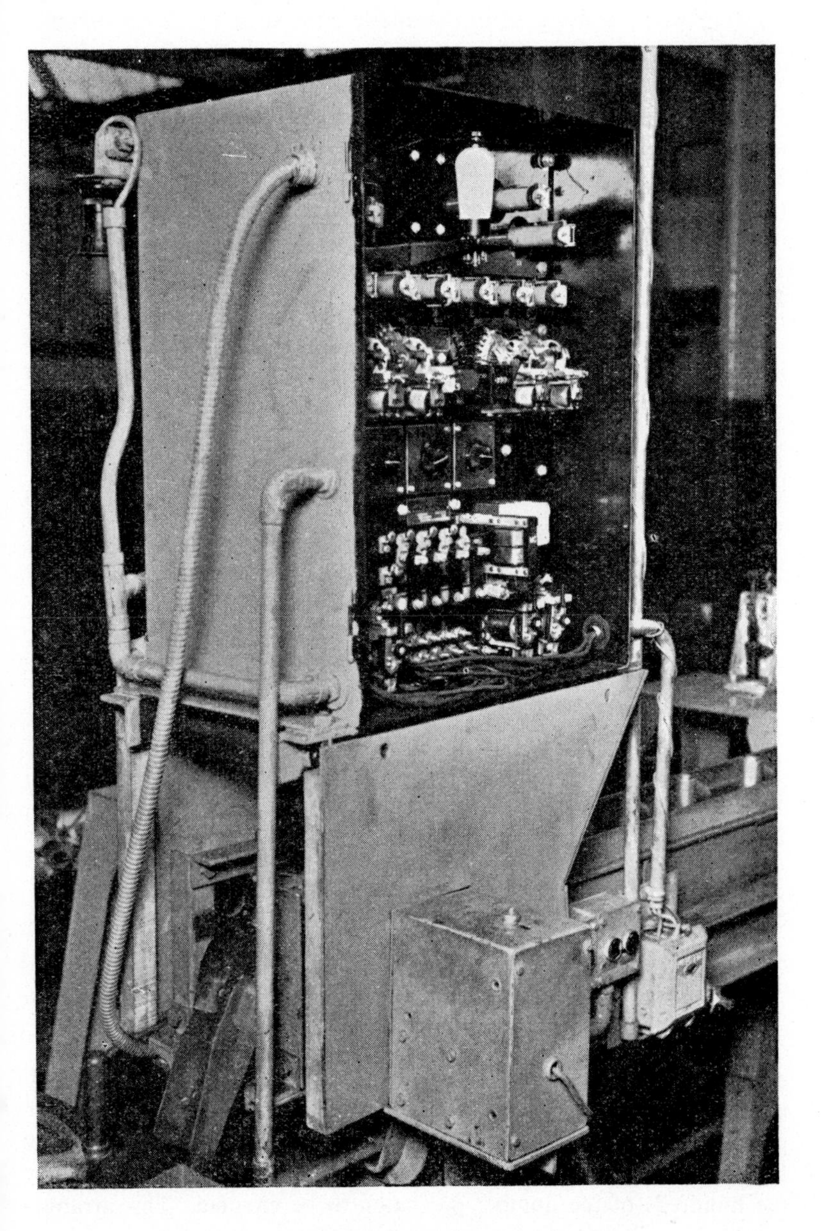

Fig. 23.21. Commercial form of pre-selective counter (*British Thomson-Houston Co.*)

position where a decrease in the anode current of the 25A6 becomes noticeable.

For negative action (dotted lines) the procedure is the same except that the adjustment is made with the illumination on the photosensitor at its minimum value.

Other high-speed counters were described by Lane (*909*), by Rymer (*910*), Livingston and Lord (*1287*), and others.

Bibliography References : (*496*, *1171*, *1173*, *2281*)

23.11. Preselective Lot Counter

There are many counting applications where an operation or process is to be controlled, or a signal given, or a servo-circuit energized, after

Fig. 23.22. Counter for two independent channels. (*Potter Instrument Co.*)

a predetermined number of counts. A ten-point rotary selector switch is associated with each counter unit. Three hand-setting switches are provided in the Preselective Lot Counter equipment as illustrated by Fig. 23.21, viz., one for the units, the other for the tens, and the third for the hundreds of the number per batch to be counted. This arrangement allows for a maximum number of 999 items to be counted per batch. The counter is self resetting after each complete count.

Integrating counters also can be made predetermined as is instanced in the case of the electronic counter described by Potter (*898*, *1700*). The principle is explained by assuming that, for instance, neon lamps four and two (having as sum 6) are switched on by resetting the counter inversely. The output will then operate when four (i.e., ten minus the above six) impulses have passed through the counter.

Another Potter instrument employs four counter decades which are arranged to give two independent predetermining channels in which any number from zero to 10,000 may be initially set up by simply manipulating rotary switches mounted on the front panel, Fig. 23.22. During the operation of the equipment each channel is alternatively preset to the desired predetermined number. This function is accomplished automatically and occurs in less than one millisecond. Input frequencies may be in excess of 250 c/s. The output electromagnetic relay is energized at the end of one complete electronic count.

Bibliography Reference : (*1887*)

23.12. Conditional Counting

In many inspection processes the permitted tolerance will be expressed as the number of faults or rejects per thousand items or per 100 ft. inspected length of paper web, or sheet steel, yarn, wire, etc.

The general method underlying the design of Conditional Counters is based on the principle that two distinctly different counts are made by two sets of counters, viz., the one counting the number of faults and the other counting the number of units within which a given tolerance is permitted.

The *modus operandi* is set out below, viz. :

" Faults " Counter	" Units " Counter
(1)	(1)
Automatically reset by the resetting action of the " Units " counter.	Automatically reset after every so many units, e.g., 1000 pieces, or 100 ft. or 10 seconds, etc.
(2)	
If the tolerated number of faults is reached before the " Units " counter has counted the required total number of reference units, a relay is operated which energizes the load circuit (signal ; thrustor, etc.)	

A faulty batch will be marked as such by the action described under (2). If the batch is within tolerance limits after the " Units " counter has reached the predetermined count (1000 items ; 100 ft. ; or 10 seconds, in the above instances), the " Faults " counter will cancel any accumulated counts and automatically be reset to zero, ready for the next count (1).

23.13. Rotation Counter

Counters can be used in a variety of ways, for instance, counting rotations. If either a small mirror is cemented to the shaft, or a strip

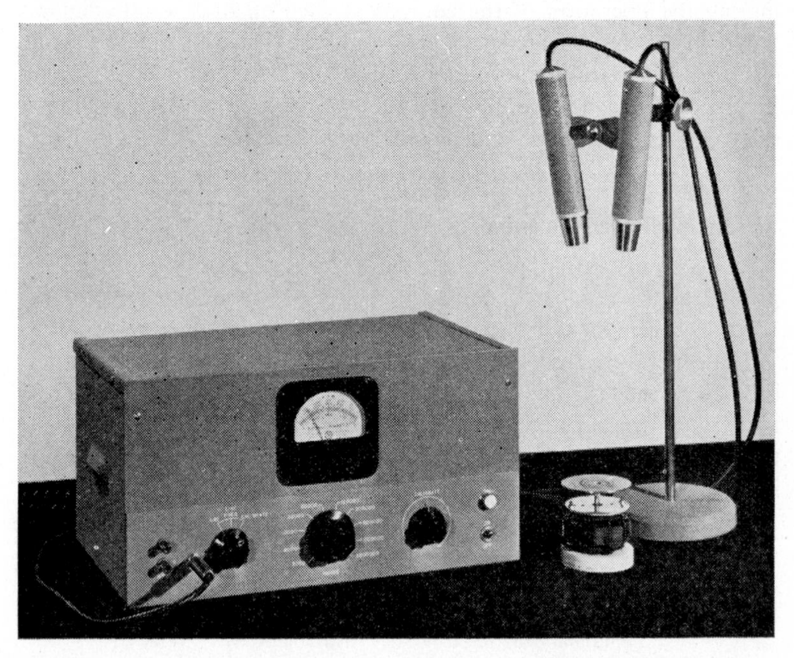

Fig. 23.23. Electronic tachometer. (*Hewlett-Packard Co.*)

of black paper wound round it so as to leave free a space of $\frac{1}{2}$ inch or 1 inch width between the ends of the strip (this part of the shaft now acting as a reflector) the number of rotations of this shaft can be counted without having to make mechanical contact with the moving machinery. The photosensitor must be capacitance-coupled to the amplifier (*911*, *912*).

Photo-electric rotation counters are the only practical means of registering the decrease in the number of rotations that an armature makes after the driving power has been cut off. Other systems would distort the count since their driving power would have to be taken from the energy of the armature.

The electronic preselective counter can be adapted to count accurately the number of rotations per minute when the observer is unable to count. A four-decade counter (counting up to 10,000) is so preset as to stop counting after 3000 impulses (for 50 c/s networks ; 3600 impulses for 60 c/s networks) have passed through it. This counter provides the exact timing of the measuring period. The timing counter is so connected to another four- (if necessary five-) decade counter of the same type that this latter, the rotation counter proper, starts counting the number of impulses received by the photo-electric cell and stops counting when the stop pulse from the timing counter is received after 3000 or 3600 timing impulses, respectively.

An electronic tachometer was described by Downie (*913*). Fig. 23.23 shows the Hewlett-Packard electronic tachometer Model 505-A : this is a device for measuring speed of moving parts which cannot be measured by ordinary methods. It provides a continuous record of the instantaneous speed which can be transformed into a permanent record by connecting a recorder to the output of the instrument. The complete tachometer consists of the tachometer head and an electronic frequency meter. The tachometer head contains a photosensitor pick-up in combination with a light source. A suitable means provides alternate reflecting and absorbing surfaces for the moving part whose speed is to be measured. The interrupted light is picked up by the photosensitor and the number of these impulses per second is measured by means of the frequency meter. The reading of this (one milliampere D.C.) meter is proportional to the number of pulses per second and hence proportional to the signal frequency applied to the photosensitor. The speed calibration is independent of the valve characteristics, voltages and size of output signal. The input voltage covers a range from 0·2 to 200 volts. The accuracy of the instrument is $\pm 2\%$ of the full scale value. The instrument is capable of measuring speeds of from 5 r.p.s. to 50,000 r.p.s. Another instrument was designed by the General Radio Co. to measure the r.p.s. of an ultra high speed centrifuge. The photosensitor picks up the light ray which, as described above, is reflected from the rotating shaft and interrupted by a black target previously put on the shaft. The output of the photo-electric amplifier is fed to a frequency meter (*1676, p. 225*).

Bibliography References : (*507, 2133, 2222, 2228*)

23.14. Scintillation Counters

The counting of fast charged particles was first introduced in 1903 by W. Crookes. He collected alpha particles on a screen of zinc sulphide, the impact of each particle manifesting itself as a momentary flash or scintillation on the fluorescent screen. This instrument was called a spinthariscope.

The Geiger-Müller counter is the modern equipment for counting nuclear particles and radiation. The low resolving time of the G-M counter (50 to 100 μs) and its low conversion efficiency are serious drawbacks in many instances. Moreover, these counters have a very poor efficiency (about 1 %) for gamma radiation, but are highly efficient (close on 100%) in counting beta particles.

The development of photomultipliers (*2595*) has opened up a new avenue of approach. A much improved method known as scintillation counting makes use of the phenomenon which produces light flashes in a suitable material that has absorbed nuclear radiation. Scintillation counters have a resolving time of less than 1 μs and the energy conversion efficiency is better by several orders of magnitude, particularly for gamma rays. The principle of a scintillation counter has been anticipated to a certain degree by an arrangement of H. M. Smith (*729*) who deposited a X-ray sensitive phosphor (ZnS : Ag or $CaWO_4$) on a photomultiplier (cf. Chap. 13.20). A scintillation counter consists principally of a transparent crystal of suitable material which is fixed to the cathode of a photomultiplier or whose scintillations (light flashes) are conducted by light guides (cf. Chap. 6.29) from the crystal to the photomultiplier, whose output is passed through a chain of electronic instruments to the final count rate meter. Transparent phosphor crystals may be zinc sulphide ZnS (*2553*), calcium tungstate $CaWO_4$, thallium activated sodium iodide NaI : Tl (0·5%), double bonded carbon organic crystals, for instance anthracene $C_{14}H_{10}$, naphthalene $C_{10}H_8$, phenanthrene $C_{14}H_{10}$ (an isomer of anthracene), and other aromatic hydrocarbons. The fundamental aspects of the fluorescence produced in organic crystals by ionizing radiations are discussed by Birks (*2539*). The gamma quanta are absorbed in the phosphor and produce fast secondary electrons which, in turn, produce scintillations. The flash time, i.e., the life of a single scintillation, may be as short as 10^{-10} sec. The resolution of short time intervals with scintillation counters is discussed in a paper by Benedetti and Richings (*2540*) who find a resolution in the order of 10^{-4} μs.

Transparent crystals of various chemical composition have been produced by a number of processes, the best known of which is named after his inventor Kyropoulos (e.g. *2541*). Details of phosphors and methods of preparation are discussed by Coltman and Marshall. Crystals are used which produce a fluorescence spectrum either in the ultra-violet region or in the luminous region. The former group is instanced by synthetic white sapphire Al_2O_3, pentamethyl benzene $C_{11}H_{16}$, strontium fluoride SrF_2, barium fluoride BaF_2, glass B_2O_3, and calcium fluoride CaF_2, which is used for the detection of alpha, beta, and gamma radiation whereas the others respond to excitation by alpha particles only. Glass powder is, usually, immersed in a counting liquid, e.g., terphenyltoluene (for counting thermal neutrons) (*2525*). Thallium activated sodium iodide, which is stored and used immersed in liquid paraffin to prevent liquefaction, is employed in the counting of alpha, gamma, or X-radiation. This crystal has a very high stopping power* and a short afterglow (*2543*) of 0·25 μs. The other group is represented by anthracene, phenanthrene, etc., the fluorescence lines of which are in the blue end of the spectrum. Anthracene responds to excitation by alpha particles, electrons, protons below 3·7 Mev, and deuterons.

The principal arrangement of a scintillation counter is shown in Fig. 23.24. The pulse height discriminator is of great importance due

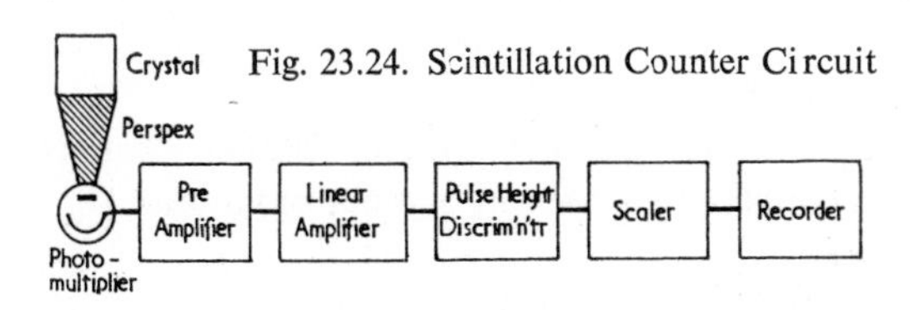

Fig. 23.24. Scintillation Counter Circuit

to background noise which is generated in the photomultiplier at a rate that greatly depends on ambient temperature:

number of electrons/sec.	ambient temperature
some 10,000	room temperature 15°C.
some 100	solid CO_2 −78°C.
some 1	liquid air −183°C.

*The relative stopping power of a substance is the weight per unit area (mg/cm²) which is equivalent to 1 cm of air (1·22 mg/cm² at 15°C., 760 mm Hg) for the stopping of alpha particles (*2544*).

The voltage amplitude V of the output pulse which is to operate the discriminator (*2545*) is

$$V = \frac{3{\cdot}2 \times 10^{-15}\Gamma}{y \times C}$$

and the total electrical charge Q produced at the output stage of the photomultiplier, is

$$Q = \frac{N \times 1 \times e}{n \times y \times \Gamma}$$

where N . . . number of light quanta produced by each alpha particle
n . . . number of light quanta reaching the photo-cathode
y . . . number of light quanta producing one electron (quantum yield)
e . . . charge of each electron ($e = 1{\cdot}60203 \times 10^{-19}$ coulomb).
Γ . . . gain of photomultiplier
C . . . capacitance of output circuit (farad).

Attainable values are:

$N = 2{\cdot}10^5$ (NaI : T1 will produce 20,000 photons of light in converting 1 Mev of gamma radiation)
$n = 0{\cdot}1$
$y = 10$ to 20
$\Gamma = 10^6$ to 10
$C = (10$ to $30) . 10^{-12}$ F $(=10$ to 30 pF)

The background of the photomultiplier can be minimized either by reducing the ambient temperature (*2443*, *2479*) or by using an electronic circuit which is known as coincidence counter, Fig. 23.25. With that circuit which always operates with the photomultipliers at room temperature, scintillations can be detected that are so small as to release only one electron. Coincidence technique enables the detection of a single proton emission in KI : T1 crystals (*2547*). In a coincidence counter the first few stages of the photomultiplier work at a lower voltage than the final stages. Depending on the application either of the two techniques will yield optimum results. The emission of anthracene and other substances harmonizes well with the position of the peak sensitivity of the photocathode, namely,

naphthalene	3450 Å,	3850 Å	
anthracene	4440 Å		
phenanthrene	4100 Å,	4300 Å,	4500 Å.

The overlapping of the fluorescence bands of certain transparent synthetic media and of the absorption bands of certain crystals make it

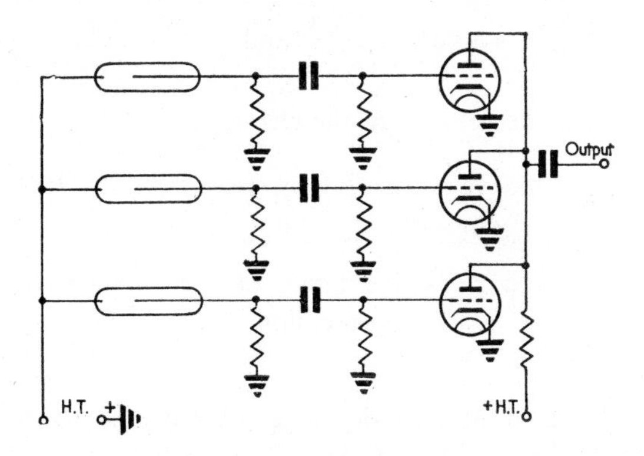

Fig. 23.25. Coincidence counter

possible for these crystals to be dissolved in the media, thus forming a radiation receptor of any given shape and size and of highly efficient energy transfer. Anthracene $C_{14}H_{10}$ and stilbene $C_{14}H_{12}$ should be dissolved in polystyrene, but not in methyl methacrylate (Perspex) (*2548*).

There are no other transparent materials the fluorescence emission wavelength of which falls beyond the sensitivity range of the S_4 type cathode used in photomultipliers. These substances are not likely to be used because that would entail a S_1 type photocathode which, however, is not favoured in multipliers due to the sensitivity of the cathode to dark space radiation (cf. 4.53).

The luminescence in a transparent material caused by electrons passing through it is known as the Čerenkov (Cherenkov) phenomenon.

Čerenkov found that transparent media in a very pure state emit a faint blue fluorescence when absorbing gamma radiation. This fluorescence is not influenced by a change in concentration or by the addition of a quenching agent. Such a change is characteristic of the fluorescence excited by light. The fluorescence due to the Čerenkov phenomenon is emitted in cone form, Fig. 23.26 and the characteristic value of this phenomenon (phase velocity of light in the transparent medium) is

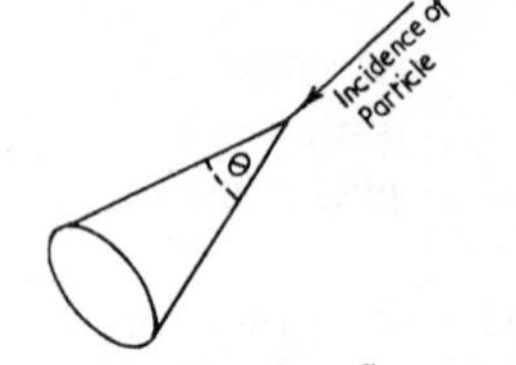

Fig. 23.26. Cerenkov fluorescence

$$\cos \Theta = \frac{1}{\beta n}$$

$$\text{where } \beta = \sqrt{\frac{v}{c}} \text{ and}$$

v . . . the velocity of the electron,

c . . . the velocity of light ($c = 2.99776 \cdot 10^{10}$ cm/sec)

n . . . the refractive index of the transparent medium.

There are also a number of liquids exhibiting this phenomenon, for instance, p-terphenyl $C_6H_5 \cdot C_6H_4 \cdot C_6H_5$ in benzene (10 g/litre) and $\alpha\,\alpha'$ dinaphthyl (*2549*).

For the counting of radiation arriving over a large area as, for instance, in cosmic ray research, an integrating sphere is the best collector of light from scintillations produced in different parts of the crystal. The surface of the sphere is highly deflecting and diffusing. This is achieved by a coat of magnesium oxide MgO_2. The photocathode of the multiplier projects into this sphere and the efficiency at the periphery is 90% as against 100% in the centre of the collector sphere (*2550*). A photomultiplier with an omnidirectional cathode structure should be used in conjunction with a collector sphere.

Portable scintillation spectrometers for prospecting have been built and show an improvement by a factor of between 20 and 100 as against similar meters using G-M tubes (*2581*).

It was only to be expected that G-M tubes would be developed which are almost photocells. Geiger-Müller tubes have a photosensitive metal cathode in a quartz envelope and are sensitive to radiation in the 2000–3000 Å range. These " scintillation G-M tubes " carry a ring of phosphor on the tube making the angle of detection a full 360°. This is truly an omnidirectional device and rather cheaper than photomultipliers, which are unidirectional.

Scintillation counters for the detection of alpha particles are discussed by Sherr (*2554*), of thermal (slow) neutrons by Draper (*2555*), of X-rays by Ter-Pogossian *et al.* (*2556*) and (*2557*). The scintillation counter as a proportional device has been described by Hoyt (*2558*), and its applications in radioactive measurements by a number of authors, e.g., Anger (*2559*) and Schardt *et al.* (*2560*).

Bibliography References: (*2561, 2562, 2563, 2564, 2565, 2566*)

Chapter 24

SYNCHRONIZERS

24.1. Transport Conveyors

An interesting combination of selsyn motors and photosensitors achieving complete synchronization of two conveyors was described by Snyder (*1020*) and Henney (*79, p. 388*).

In the case of two conveyors running parallel and in the same direction a simple method can be employed to safeguard synchronism between the two. The light source is mounted on the conveyor A, for instance, and the photo-relay travels with the conveyor B, Fig. 24.1.

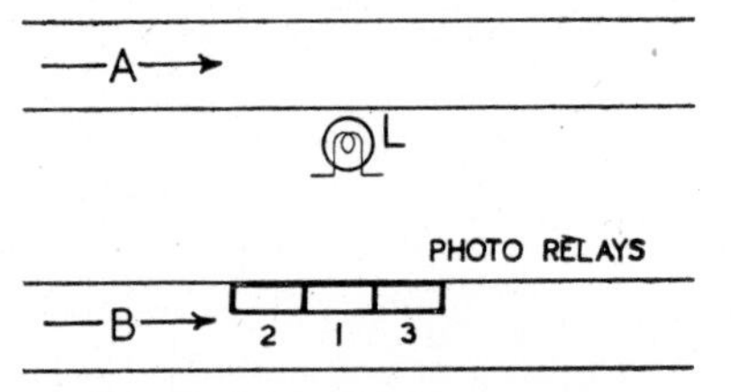

Fig. 24.1. Simple method of ensuring synchronization between two conveyors

Table 24.1

Conveyor	Speed	Relative Motion	Speed	Relative Motion	Speed	Relative Motion
A	$V_A = V_B$	0	$V_A > V_B$	leading	$V_A < V_B$	lagging
B	$V_B = V_A$	0	$V_B < V_A$	lagging	$V_B > V_A$	leading

Bibliography References : (*1176, 1740, 1756*)

The relative speed of B with respect to A is zero when both are in synchronism, Table 24.1. Therefore, light from the lamp L will strike the photo-relay PR_1 and no correcting action will be taken. When the photo-relay leads, the light ray will strike PR_2 and corresponding action will ensue. When the photo-relay lags, light will be incident on PR_3 and reverse action will ensure that the correct speed is attained.

24.2. Routeing

The transport of a number of containers from one shop in the factory to other shops and the dispersal at certain points of the route to the various departments is known as routeing. Any number of side conveyors can be branched off the main conveyor the points being controlled by photo-electric gear.

How the photosensitors are made to discriminate between the containers destined for Departments A, B, C, etc., is in general terms explained by referring to Fig. 24.2. One or any number of targets, often called " flags ", is so placed on a frame on the rim of the container as

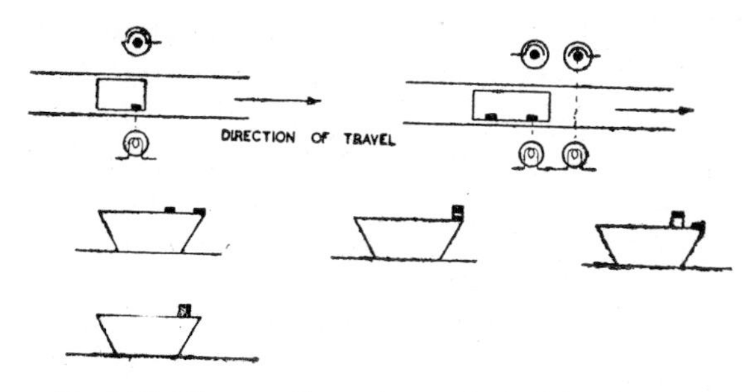

Fig. 24.2. Diagram illustrating method of departmental discrimination employed in routeing

to intercept one, or a number of, light beams projected on or across the track of the conveyor. The points where the side conveyors branch off are characterized by the number of light rays to be intercepted by the " flags ", and by the method of interception.

(1) If one light ray is used, two points can be operated by making the one responsive to light thrown across the track of the conveyor (photo-relay and light source on opposite sides of the track) and the other responsive to reflected light (photo-relay and light source on the same side of the track), the target acting as reflector.

(2) Two light rays may be thrown across or reflected back, the principle common to both systems being the condition that the mechanical relay actuating the points must be energized only when

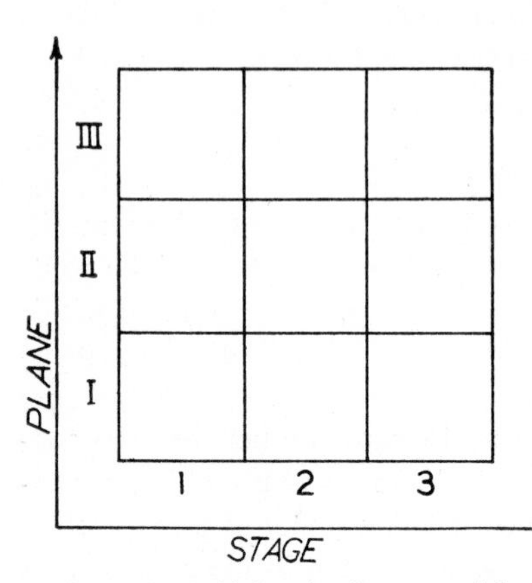

Fig. 24.3. Grid for plotting potential routeing positions

both photosensitors are stimulated simultaneously. This safeguards point *b* against being operated by a container carrying a single "flag".

Four different points can be operated by a combination of two "flags" and photo-relays in different planes for horizontal, vertical and two-dimensional arrangements.

(3) With three "flags" arranged in three different planes a total of 27 points can be operated as is shown below. For any particular arrangement a grid, Fig. 24.3, will prove of assistance in marking out all potential positions. Place flag F_1 in square *I*-1, flag F_2 in square *I*-2, and arrange flag F_3 first in *I*-3, then in *II*-3, and lastly in *III*-3. Then move F_2 to *II*-2 and rearrange F_3, etc. The only condition for the electromagnetic relays is that either the photosensitor or the coils of the electromagnetic relays are connected in parallel or all the load contacts in series with the circuit of the point-operating mechanism (thrustor). This calls for all photosensitors to be eclipsed at the same time.

(4) Another potential arrangement can be worked out where use is made of the laws governing complementary colours. The light sources are monochromatic luminous radiators. The " flags " are transparent colour filters, some of them of the same colour (C_0) as the light source at a particular point, others of the complementary colour (C_{180}). If two light sources, the C_0 and the other C_{180} are arranged at different points then all containers bearing a filter of colour C_0 will be branched off at the point having a light source of colour C_0, but will pass those points having a light source C_{180}, and vice-versa.

(5) The number of combinations can be increased by mixing the various methods, for instance by mixing the reflecting system with the one throwing the light across the conveyor.

Fig. 24.4 shows a photo-electric routeing equipment (*1021*) using two " flags " in a horizontal arrangement, the light rays being thrown across the conveyor.

Two uni-directional counters can be used for discriminating the direction of moving objects and to switch points along the route.

Fig. 24.4. Section of conveyor showing photoelectric routeing equipment (*Courtesy of British Thomson-Houston Ltd., Rugby*)

24.3. Control of Speed of Travel

Although an early installation (*1022*), the principle underlying this application is so simple and it has worked effectively for many years at a large West American mine, that it might well find a place in this chapter.

As the " feed " drops on to the sinter bed it falls against a " shoe " which hangs from a rod which spans the machine horizontally above the pallets. The shoe is thus deflected more or less, the amount of deflection depending on the height and width of the pile. As the shoe moves the horizontal rod from which it hangs and to which it is rigidly attached rotates, while a pinion on its end actuates another smaller pinion on an adjacent shaft on the opposite end of which is mounted a rocker.

In one end of this rocker is a hole, which, as the arm rocks, permits a beam of light to pass at intervals from a lamp to the photo-electric cell. Every time the beam is intercepted an electromagnetic switch is actuated. This switch is hooked up between the second and fourth contactor of the controller motor of the propelling pallet. The second contactor would give a speed of four feet per minute and the fourth contactor a speed of eight feet per minute. Thus the device permits a speed range of four to eight feet per minute. This speed is therefore indirectly governed by the amount fed on the 24-inch conveyor. The device will not let the feed pile up but, if it tends to do so, it makes the bed run faster (*1023*).

24.4. Register Control

In other applications the principle described under the heading of Register Control (Chap. 11) can be used with advantage in controlling and correcting the speed of the conveyor or the action of another mechanism. Flour-filling machines not only transport the empty paper bags or cardboard boxes on to the scales but also automatically operate the filling mechanism. This mechanism is so coupled to the movement of the flour bag on the conveyor that the moving into position of the bag operates the chute release. If both were well timed yet operated independently it might soon happen that a small time-delay in one or other movement would throw the two actions out of synchronism, with the result that the flour would be spilled. The " Register Control " system couples the two movements, the bag taking the place of the printed mark, and a correct, 100% effective operation is guaranteed.

24.5. Synchronizing a Stroboscopic Light Source

A method which was developed in the laboratories of Ferranti Ltd. to synchronize the flashes of light in a stroboscopic lamp (Ferranti

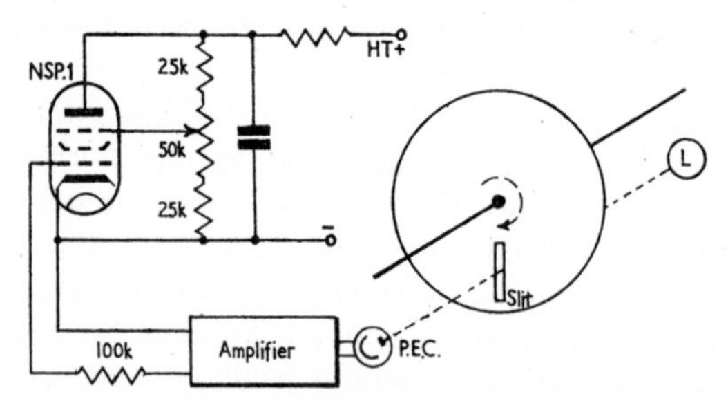

Fig. 24.5. Method of synchronizing light flashes from a stroboscopic lamp

Neostron lamp) with the speed of rotation of a disk, without it being permissible to use a direct contact-making system, utilizes the coupling property of a light ray-photosensitor system. A slot was cut in the disk and allowed to intersect a light beam striking a photosensitor and the A.C. output of the photo-relay was fed into the control grid circuit of the Neostron lamp (*1256*), Fig. 24.5.

Chapter 25

DOOR OPENERS

The photo-electric operation of doors must not be looked upon as an unnecessary refinement. As already mentioned (Chap. 2) the door opening equipment means a genuine reduction in direct costs (*11*, *12*), speeds up the job, and prevents the workmen from loosing time while attending to heavy or locked doors.

In works canteens, restaurants, and other much-frequented places where meals are served ; in goods yards, electroplating departments, mines, etc., doors can be operated by photosensitors much more conveniently and efficiently than by any other means. In hospitals a " phantom doorman " watches the connexion between the doctor's scrub room and the operating theatre, see Fig. 25.1. This opens the door for the doctor who now can keep his hands perfectly clean and sterilized (*1089*).

The doors of annealing ovens, soaking pits, furnaces, etc., are opened by light from the crane-man's cabin (*212, p. 235*).

Garage doors are usually operated by one of the following methods. The photosensitor is so mounted near the door that the light of the head lamp, when projected on to a certain area the size of a foot square, energizes the photo-cell and opens the door. Another method has been developed by the Tiffin Electro-Mechanical Corporation (*1030*). A metal box, containing a magnetic needle carrying a mirror, is mounted close to the track where a car must pass close to it. When at rest the little mirror reflects a light beam on to a photosensitor. If a car passes, its mass of iron changes the magnetic flux and the needle swings out of its rest position thereby unbalancing the electric circuit. This unbalancing is made use of in actuating a signal.

Yet another method uses either two separate horizontal or vertical beams of light for the opening and closing of garage doors, Fig. 25.2. The one light beam is inside the garage and, when interrupted by an outgoing vehicle, is made to open the garage door. The other light beam is outside the building and, when intercepted by the vehicle, closes the door again. Automatic car washers operate on the same principle (*1030*, *1031*).

Fig. 25.1. Automatic door giving access from surgeon's scrubroom to operating theatre

(*Courtesy of Stanley Works, New Britain, Conn.*)

In mines, ventilation doors must be operated by the driver of a horse-drawn tub which necessitates the driver leaving his horses first to open and then to close the doors as he drives through. The photo-electric door-opener saves these unnecessary delaying actions.

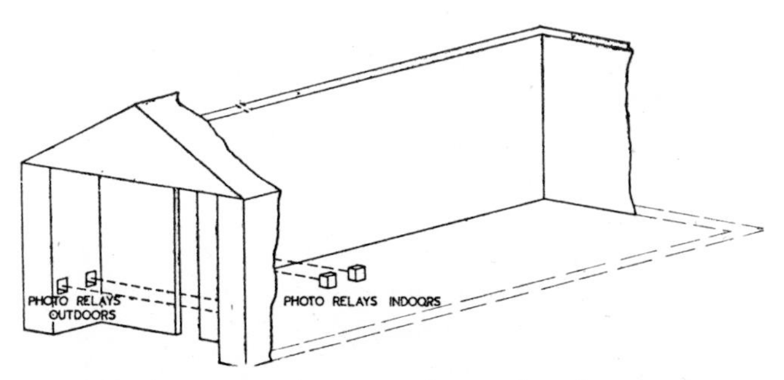

Fig. 25.2. Arrangement for automatic operation of garage doors

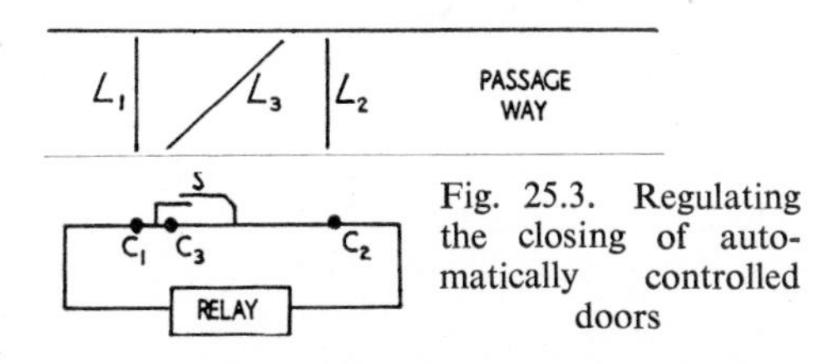

Fig. 25.3. Regulating the closing of automatically controlled doors

Fig. 25.4. An automatic door operated by diagonal ray control
(Courtesy of Stanley Works, New Britain, Conn.)

A solution to the problem of how to prevent a fully-automatically controlled door from closing behind a passing man or vehicle as soon as the broken light beam has been restored was given by developing the scheme shown in Fig. 25.3. The light beam L_3 across the passage way prevents the doors from closing if an object remains in one of the main beams. The closing door leaf closes the switch S by mechanical action, this short-circuits cell C_3. Interruption of either L_1 or L_2 reduces the output of the series arrangement of the three photo-sensitors $C_1C_2C_3$ to such an extent that the relay operates (*79, p. 349*). In this instance the current characteristic of the series-connected cells is used. The darkening of any number of cells adds so much resistance to the circuit that a large change will occur in the load circuit.

The mechanical arrangement of sliding or hinged doors is simple and easily devised. Turnstile doors deserve more consideration. Good descriptions have been given by Walker and Lance (*397, p. 98*), Gullik-sen and Vedder (*998, p. 83*), in *Electronics* (*1032*), and elsewhere. In a construction of the International Steel Company a photosensitor limits the rotation of the door to periods when there is traffic flow. Both

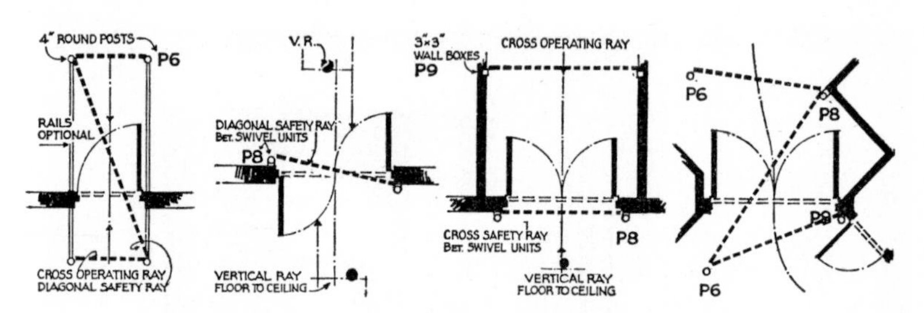

Fig. 25.5. Layouts of various photo-electric door openers

sides of the turnstile door are guarded by light rays which, on being interrupted by a would-be user of the door, automatically set it in motion. The arrangement is so made that persons may move faster or slower than the door rotates, and it is kept in rotation for another six to ten seconds for persons entering or leaving the door before it stops. A 0·25 h.p. A.C. motor drives the door with about 9 r.p.m.

The installations erected by the Stanley Works have proved the variability and adaptability of that type of photo-electric equipment. How it stands up to wear and tear is perhaps best illustrated by the doors having operated about 40,000 times daily for fifteen years. One of these doors is shown in Fig. 25.4.

The power medium mostly used is compressed air with copper pipes having a diameter of between *1* and *3* inch. Fig 25.5 demonstrates that all types of doors can be handled by door opening equipment, viz., single doors, double doors, in-and-out double doors (i.e., doors the one

Fig. 25.6. Photo-electrically controlled doors for incoming and outgoing traffic
(*Courtesy of Stanley Works, New Britain, Conn.*)

leaf of which is swinging towards and the other away from the approaching vehicle or man), single sliding doors, double sliding doors, bi-folding and double bi-folding doors, Fig. 25.6 shows another example of photo-electrically controlled doors for incoming and outgoing traffic.

Bibliography References : (*1174, 1196, 1896, 2284*)

CHAPTER 26

TIMING DEVICES

Timing devices in daily workshop practice differ from those employed in laboratory work in that the required accuracy is less in industrial practice. In nearly all cases the period of the A.C. mains supply will be the upper limit of accuracy. This makes it 1/50 sec. in Europe and 1/60 sec. in America.

26.1. Photo-electric Timer

A device was described by Carlson (*1017*), the accuracy of which is based on the constancy of the A.C. mains frequency. A number of disks, usually three, are driven by a synchronous clock motor, Fig. 26.1. One disk rotates once a second, another once a minute, the third

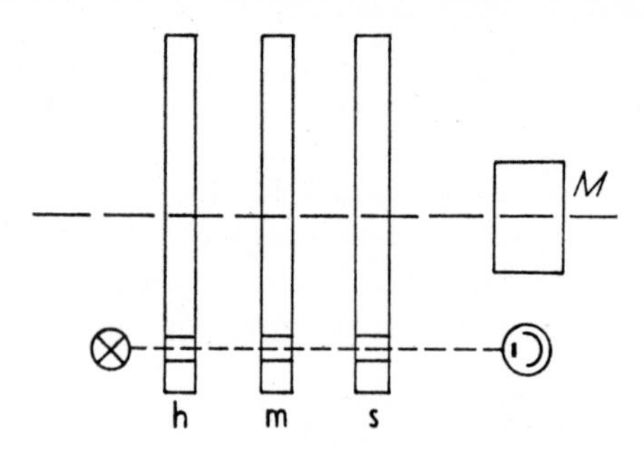

Fig. 26.1. Diagram showing arrangment of photo-electric timer

once an hour. The disks bear apertures which, by means of adjustable collars, can be so aligned that a ray from the light source is admitted to the photosensitor at any desired time. The apertures are wedge-shaped and subtend an angle of 6°. The circuit of the timer is very simple ; for positive action, i.e., acting in the presence of light, the circuit in Fig. 27.8 can be chosen ; for negative action the one in Fig. 27.9 will be satisfactory.

Bibliography References : (*1981*, *2025*, *2270*, *2280*, *2405*, *2641*)

26.2. Time-Interval Meter

A photo-electric time-interval meter operating from 1 ms. to 1 sec. was designed by Berry (*1018*). This instrument can be made to measure the time interval :

(1) between two light impulses ;
(2) between a light impulse and an electrical impulse or contact ;
(3) between two electrical impulses or contacts.

Another method was suggested by R. J. Wey (*1019*) who operates a stop-watch by means of a photo-relay.

Bibliography References : (*1205, 1218, 1386, 1573, 2022, 2641*)

CHAPTER 27

RELAYS

Two types of relay can be used in photo-electric equipment: the electromagnetic type and the electronic type, e.g., thyratrons, and ionotrons.

27.1. Electromagnetic Relays

The considerations governing the design of electromagnetic relays following electronic amplifiers have been discussed by various authors (*25*, *96*, *220*, *929*, *930*, *931*, *1602*). Conditions for optimal co-operation of electronic amplifier and electromagnetic relay are given in Table 4.1. Electronic amplifiers are of widely varying design each suiting the particular characteristics of the circuit (*2416*, *2417*).

Time delay of the order of fractions of a second is achieved through the use of copper slugs ; according to whether the copper slug is fitted to the heel* or head of the relay coil, Fig. 27.1, the releasing or attracting action will be delayed. The length of the copper slug controls the duration of the time delay. By their inductive effect the slugs tend to retard any change in the magnetic flux. Longer delays, from seconds to minutes, are achieved by various mechanical (air dash pot), thermal (bimetal), or power driven (motor) means.

Electromagnetic relays can be fitted with any type and number of contact springs to fulfil any operation. Sometimes mercury contacts are used, but for heavier currents only types should be used which are safe against trailing and back-splash as such phenomena lead to explosions.

Mechanical or electrical latch-in or lock-in relays can be reset either by manual, mechanical, or electrical operation. Sequence relays are ratchet-operated devices opening the contacts at one impulse and closing the contacts only when another impulse arrives. The contacts always remain in their latest position until the coil is de-energized and again energized. Closing times of less than 1 millisecond at sensitivities as good as 500 μW are now realizable (*1251*).

Bibliography References : (*2068*, *2074*, *2077*, *2331*)

* The heel end of the core is the end remote from the armature.

27.2. High-Sensitivity Electromagnetic Relays

These relays are built and operated on the principle of a permanent-magnet moving-coil type instrument. Operation is effected by electric energies of 1 mV or 2 μA which makes these relays suitable for direct

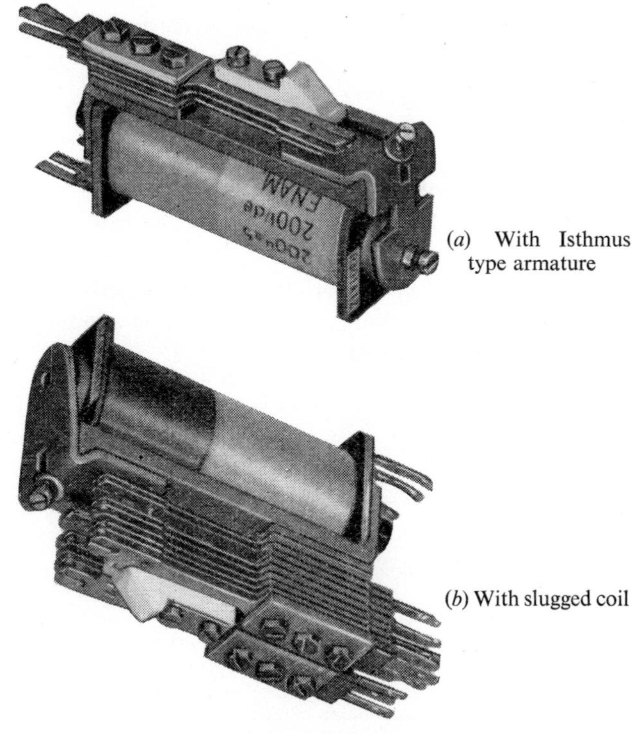

(*a*) With Isthmus type armature

(*b*) With slugged coil

Fig. 27.1. Typical electromagnetic 3000 type relays
(*Courtesy of Automatic Telephone Electric & Co. Ltd.*)

operation from photosensitors without necessitating electronic amplification. High-sensitivity relays have an inherent time delay of about 5 ms. or less.

27.3. Contacts

The load contacts can be protected against the detrimental effect of inductive loads by connecting a capacitor or a neon discharge tube or a thermistor parallel to the load. The speed of operation is very high. The only requirement is that sufficient inductive voltage be developed to cause the load to fire the neon tube (*932*).

27.4. Contactors

If heavier loads are to be controlled than relay contacts can possibly handle, a power relay or contactor must be used. The larger type contactor entails a rather considerable inherent time delay. Heavy relays and contactors should be mounted separately as the shock produced by the operation of the heavy gear can prove detrimental to the safe operation of high-sensitivity gear and electronic equipment. For specified cases shockproof relays can be obtained.

Bibliography Reference : (*2317*)

27.5. Precautionary Measures

Chattering contacts are usually met in A.C. or half-wave rectified circuits. Different types of load may cause serious disturbances, arcing with consequent burning or even welding together of the contacts, insulation by oxide films, etc. The more common preventive measures are compiled in Table 27.1.

TABLE 27.1

Precautionary Measures

Load	Preventive Measures
resistive (general)	none.
resistive (tungsten fil.)	contact-rating must consider the starting current which is about ten times its normal value.
inductive (coils, motors)	neon lamp parallel to coil ; resistor and capacitor in series, both parallel to coil ; silicon-carbide disk (thermistor) across contacts.
capacitive	restrictive resistor in series with load.
very small	arc not sufficient to break up oxide film : dummy resistive load in parallel with main load ; contacts made of precious or non-oxidizing metal.
very heavy	sufficiently dimensioned contacts of precious metal, tungsten, molybdenum, etc. ; large contact pressure ; no bouncing ; contacts for heavy loads must not be subdivided in a group of smaller contacts all in parallel.

27.6. Electromagnetic Valve for Liquids

An electromagnetic valve for the control of liquids is shown in Fig. 27.2. It was devised by Ralph H. Plumlee (RCA Laboratories) (*937*) to control the flow of water from a storage tank to the boiling flasks.

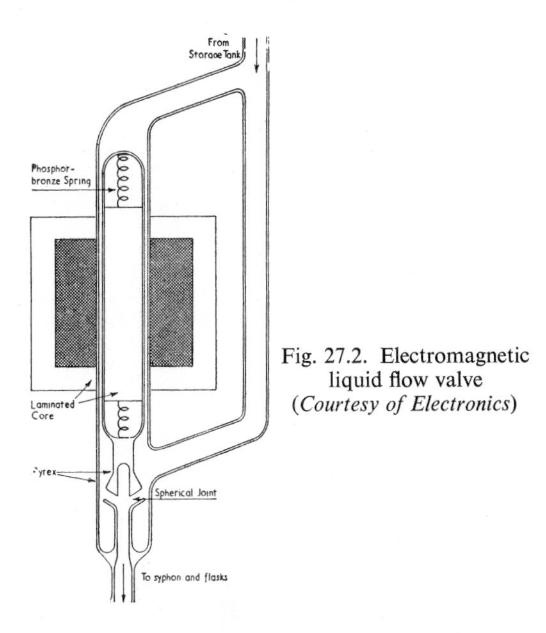

Fig. 27.2. Electromagnetic liquid flow valve (*Courtesy of Electronics*)

The plunger is lifted and the valve opened when the solenoid is energized. The weight of the laminated iron core and glass stem is sufficient to close the valve.

27.7. Vacuum Thermal Delay Switches

In the Ediswan type DLS10 delay switch a small filament is mounted adjacent to a thin strip of thermostatic bi-metal. On application of 4 volts the filament is heated and closes the load contacts after a time delay which is controllable by the value of the filament current. A similar switch is the VSL631, made by Standard Telephone & Cables, Ltd., for a filament voltage of 6·3V.

The Sunvic Hotwire Vacuum Switch works on a different principle. A time delay up to 30 seconds can be achieved. A load of 10 kW can be switched by a heater (filament) load of only 5 watts.

Bibliography Reference : (*2337*)

27.8. Electronic Time Delay Relays

Thyratrons, ionotrons, and vacuum valves, respectively are used in the construction of electronic delay switches. The few references given here are illustrative examples.

(*79, p. 488* : tetrode thyratrons ; *398, p. 44* : cold-cathode valve /ionotron/ ; *934* : triode thyratron ; *935* : vacuum triode.)

Bibliography Reference : (*465*)

27.9. Electronic Relays

By far the greatest variety in the family of electronic relays is represented by thermionic relays, cold-cathode relays (ionotrons) being not yet in general use.

Bibliography References : (*480, 483, 1198, 1518, 1522, 1531, 1721, 1725, 1892, 2083, 2084, 2085, 2087, 2097, 2107, 2114, 2141, 2142, 2154, 2158, 2166, 2173, 2201, 2204, 2218, 2308, 2309, 2312, 2314, 2315, 2318, 2326, 2327, 2329, 2330, 2335, 2336, 2339, 2340, 2345*).

27.10. Thyratrons

The thyratron is a hot-cathode, gas or vapour filled valve with one or more grids to control the starting of the anode current. Examples of these valves are shown in Figs. 27.3 and 27.4. The atmosphere in the

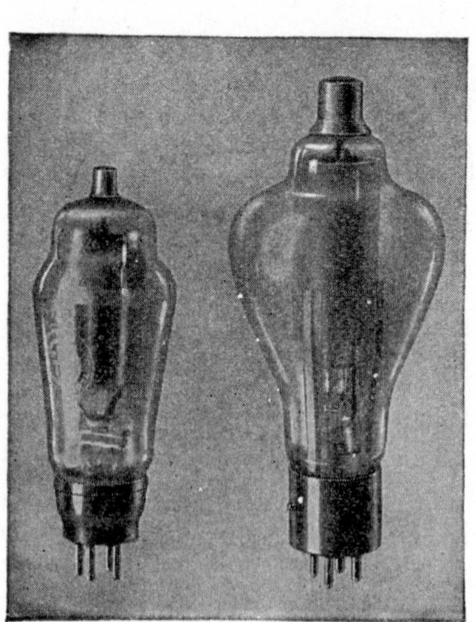

Fig. 27.3. Typical thyratrons

(*Courtesy of British Thomson-Houston Ltd., Rugby*)

thyratron is either argon gas or mercury vapour or a mixture of both. In a D.C. circuit the thyratron has the lock-in feature of the electromagnetic relay, i.e., once the current flow through the valve is started by the grid circuit and the grid loses its control. The anode current can be stopped by completely breaking the anode circuit or by lowering the anode voltage to such an extent that the discharge is extinguished. There is no lock-in feature in A.C. circuits. The current flow ionizes the

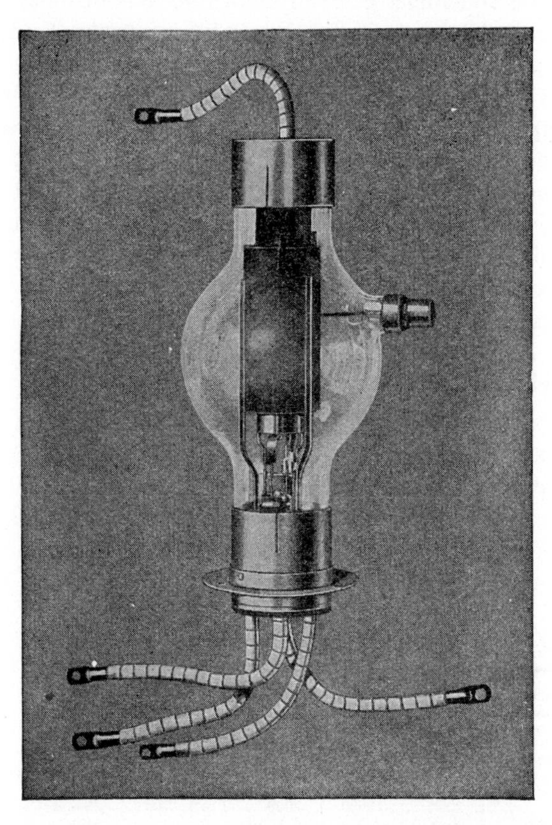

Fig. 27.4. " Shield grid " thyratron, designed to reduce grid current to a minimum
(*Courtesy of British Thomson-Houston Ltd., Rugby*)

gas particles, thus rendering the gas conducting; it takes the gas about one milli-second to de-ionize. If the anode voltage is interrupted and then restored within a period smaller than the de-ionization time the valve immediately refires. The grid, in these cases, loses control. A thyratron, therefore, cannot be operated safely in circuits working with modulated light of a frequency approaching the reciprocal of the de-ionization time.

Bibliography Reference : (*2162*)

27.11. Ionotrons

Ionotrons have a cold cathode and, usually, one (control) grid. They are gasfilled (neon or argon) valves, with a low gas pressure. The control grid is sometimes made of fine gauze or sometimes consists of two coplanar plates or any other suitable geometrical arrangement. The main gap voltage is in the region of from 100 to 300 volts, the control gap voltage being approximately half, or more, of it. Maximum current output at present is of the order of 20 to 30 mA. Peak currents are in the order of 100 mA. When the valve has fired, the control grid loses the control of the discharge and the current is practically independent of the voltage ; resistors to limit this current must be incorporated in the circuit. Ionotrons have a rather high de-ionization time, some of them as much as in the order of 100 milli-seconds.

Bibliography References : (*1667, 2079, 2160, 2260, 2263, 2346*)

27.12. Shield-Grid Electronic Relays

Thyratrons as well as ionotrons can have more than one grid. Examples are the hot-cathode gas-filled tetrode type 2D21, and the cold-cathode gas-filled tetrode type CK 1089 (*936*). In photo-electric circuits the four-electrode thyratron can be operated directly from the photosensitor (Fig. 27.5). The values of the resistors and the connexions of the photosensitor-resistor network are shown in Table 27.2.

TABLE 27.2

Action of circuit	Type of cell	Resistors					Connexions
		R_1	R_2	R_3	R_4	R_5	
positive	vacuous	0	40000 (1 W)	2000 (1 W)	1 to 10 MΩ	to be so chosen as to keep relay current within rated value.	C-H ; D-E ; F-A ; E-K.
positive	gas-filled	20000 (½ W)	18000 (½ W)	2000 (1 W)	1 to 10 MΩ		
negative	vacuous	0	10000 (4 W)	200 (1 W)	1 to 10 MΩ		D-G ; C-E ; F-B ; E-K.
negative	gas-filled	6000 (2 W)	4000 (1 W)	200 (1 W)	1 to 10 MΩ	R_5 plus coil resistance > 1500 ohms.	

The values of the resistors are in ohms unless stated otherwise

Multigrid valves provide an effective means of interdependent circuit control. If it is desired to control a circuit by, for instance, two independent quantities in such a way as to make their effect on the control element depend on either of them, a two-grid valve (tetrode) can be used with one grid for each quantity. The firing of the valve is prevented by applying a blocking voltage to either grid. If the control element is to be actuated by the coincidence of a certain temperature (signal 1)

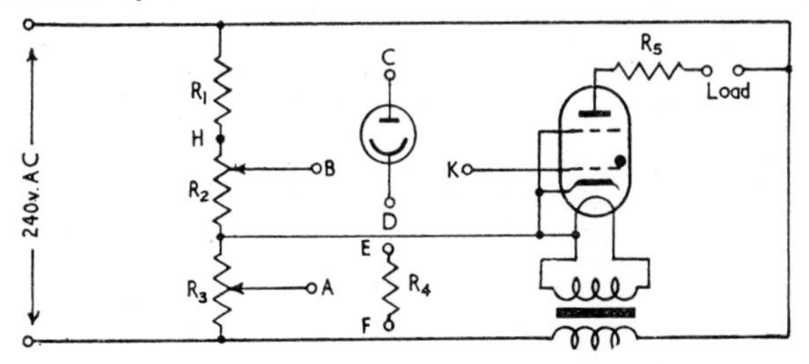

Fig. 27.5. Circuit for four-electrode thyratron operated directly from photosensitor.

and a certain density or colour (signal 2), the valve must not operate unless both blocking potentials are removed. That is done by any type of instrument measuring the two controlling quantities.

Care must be taken always to connect the innermost grid (control grid) to the circuit having the higher impedance.

An interesting circuit (*623*) connects a photosensitor to two four-electrode thyratrons so that the polarity of the grid of the first thyratron changes in the opposite direction from the polarity of the grid of the second thyratron, Fig. 27.6. An increase in illumination will make the

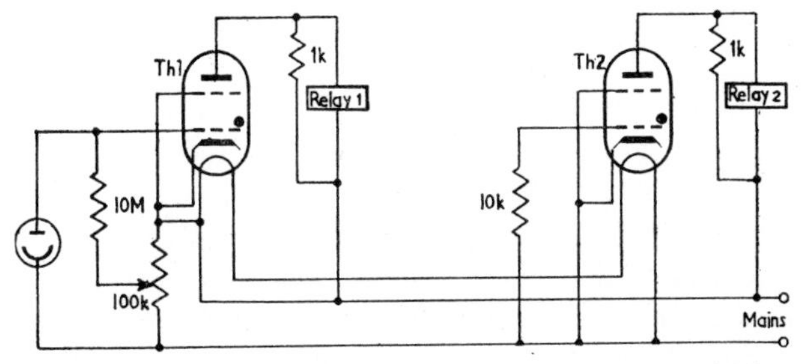

Fig. 27.6. Circuit connecting photosensitor and two four-electrode thyratrons

grid of the thyratron Th_1 more positive and that of the thyratron Th_2 more negative and vice-versa.

Circuits using four-electrode ionotrons (*936*) have been described. The basic circuit of an ionotron-tetrode is given in Fig. 27.7 (a), featuring the Westinghouse air-cooled KU-618, and Fig. 27.7 (b) indicates the control characteristics to be expected with two values of grid resistance.

27.13. Relays

A high-sensitivity low-speed relay can be employed where the changes in light do not last for less than 100 milliseconds; the change in light intensity can be very minute.

A quick-acting quick-releasing relay of positive action was described by Shepard (*345*) and is shown in Fig. 23.19 (Chap. 23). The duration

Fig. 27.7.
Ionotron-tetrode (Westinghouse KU-618)

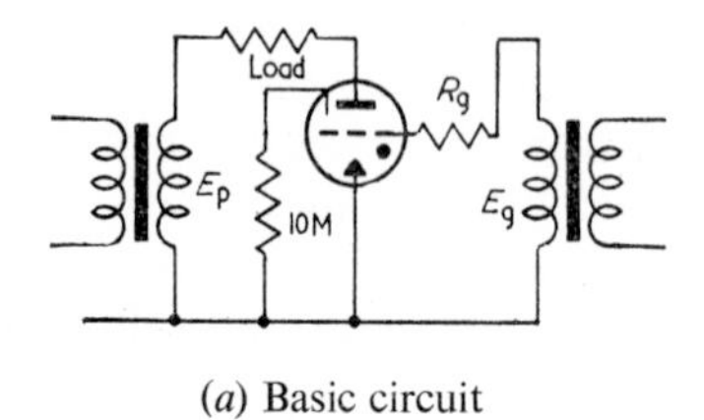

(*a*) Basic circuit

(*b*) Characteristics

of the output current is equal to the duration of the input light impulse, i.e., only a fraction of a cycle (<20 ms). While it may prove difficult to find an equally quick-acting electromagnetic relay to cope with the output impulses of that circuit, any reasonably constructed relay can be operated by the quick-acting slow-releasing relay, Fig. 27.8. This is an adaptation of the previously discussed diagram in that the resistor-capacitor combination in the control grid of the pentode is here so connected as to result in an output current the duration of which extend over a period of several cycles (> 20 ms).

Relays using high-vacuum thermionic valves instead of thyratrons (no lock-in feature) are instanced in Fig. 27.9 (*345*). It is a two-stage A.C.-operated pentode relay of simple but very reliable and sturdy operation. Its output current is 30 mA max. A different version is given by K. Henney (*19, p. 389*).

Another circuit using triodes and a rectified A.C. supply was developed by Kegamaster (*998*). The photosensitor is resistor-capacitor

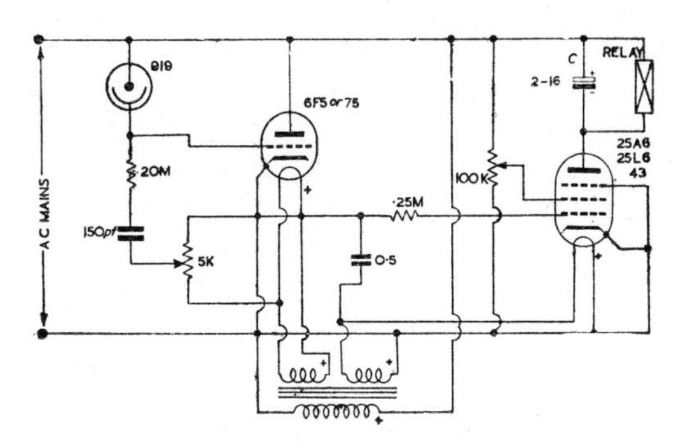

Fig. 27.8. Quick acting, slow releasing relay

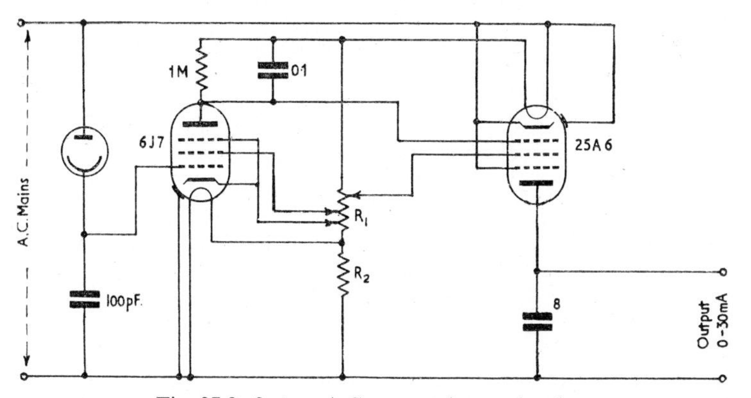

Fig. 27.9. 2-stage A.C. operated pentode relay

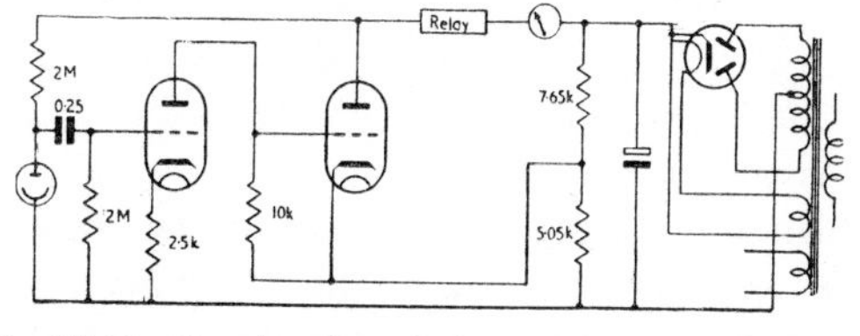

Fig. 27.10. Circuit using triodes and rectified A.C. supply

coupled to the amplifier, Fig. 27.10. The electro-magnetic relay has a pick-up current of 35 mA max. and a drop-out current of 20 mA max. Such a relay can carry mercury contacts for a 50 Amp. (non-inductive) load at 550 V.

In a circuit for relays as well as for counters two different types of thyratrons are used (*999*). The two valves V_1 and V_2 are usually of the " trigger " type, i.e., the discharge can be started, but not controlled by the grid ; the third valve V_3 is a Mazda T31, in which the discharge can be started and stopped by proper grid control.

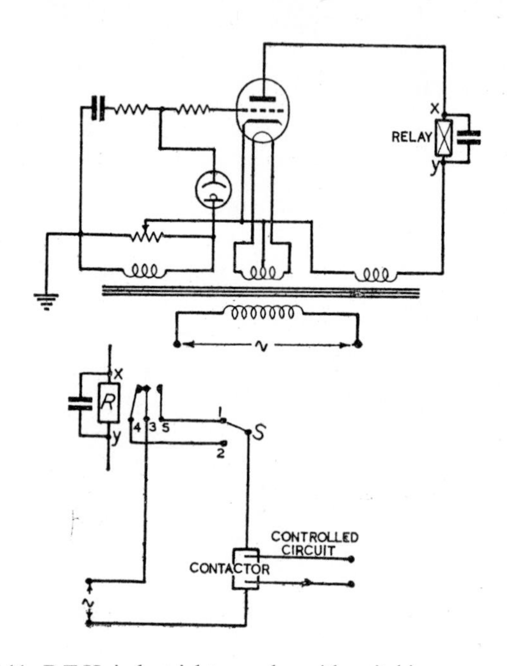

Fig. 27.11. B.T.H. industrial type relay with switching arrangment

A vacuum-valve relay using a beam tetrode can be operated by any medium that changes its resistance under certain conditions (*940*). The circuit is designed to either make or break the load contacts by simply interchanging two resistors.

A BTH industrial type relay has an interesting switching arrangement, Fig. 27.11, with sensitivity control and the possibility of closing the load circuit alternatively on picking-up or releasing the sensitive relay in the anode circuit.

Other circuits are quoted by K. Henney (*79, p. 472*).

Bibliography Reference : (*1382*)

CHAPTER 28

RECORDERS

28.1. Electronic Recorders

The basic feature of electronic recorders and their main advantage over other type recorders is the fact that the measuring system is independent of the recording system in that no mechanical or electrical

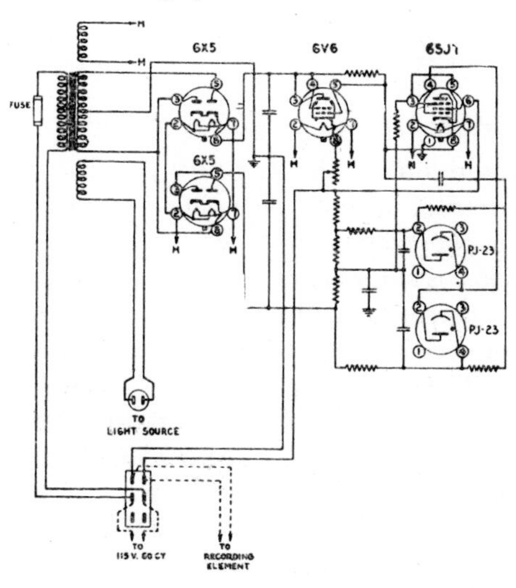

Fig. 28.1. Power unit circuit of G.E.C. electronic recorder
(*Courtesy of Gen. Electr. Rev.*)

coupling method or contact is employed. The measuring system transmits its output to the recording system by means of electronic circuits. In electronic recorders the measuring system can be of very high sensitivity and yet it is possible to employ powerful recorders.

The power unit of a recorder as made by the General Electric Co. (*1034*) is shown in Fig. 28.1. The electric circuit is so arranged as to rotate the recording element away from the photosensitor receiving the major amount of light. The speed of response is five cycles per second.

The circuit of another useful pen recorder which may be used for frequencies as low as one per second and as high as 200 per sec., the response being linear from 0·5 c/s to 6 kc/s, was developed by D. Robinson (*1035*).

Other methods and circuits are described by Müller, Garman and Droz (*961, p. 155*). The principle of an instrument for recording pressure as measured by a manometer (*1033*) can be also applied to heat-recording instruments.

A method for modulating photoelectric recordings uses a modulation frequency of between 50 and 8000 c/s. Between 1000 and $3 \cdot 10^{10}$ ohm the response between the light flux and the amplitude of the records is almost linear. This method has been applied to photometering autoradiographs (*2642*).

Bibliography References : (*460, 549, 563, 566, 569, 2033, 2098, 2401, p. 114*)

28.2. Recording Methods

Besides the pen recorder using ordinary type paper, photographic, chemical, and electrical methods of producing permanent records are well known. The photographic method, although very useful in some special applications, is still only rarely used in industry. The development and fixation processing of the record is a serious drawback.

The number of chemical methods is legion. Solutions for chemical recording are described by Fagan (*1036*).

Electrical recording was a rather unsatisfactory method because of the processing necessary in some cases before, in others after the records have been made. The Western Union Telegraph Company has introduced a novel dry recording paper which is known under the Trade name " Teledeltos " (U.S. Pat. 2251742). The paper is marketed in England by Standard Telephones & Cables, Ltd. This paper is an electrically conducting sheet of aluminium-grey lustre, coated with material which presents a permanent change in colour at any point where an electric current passes through the paper. Neither the coating nor the record is affected by light or atmospheric conditions. No processing whatever is required and printing may be placed upon Teledeltos paper as easily as upon any other paper. With proper paper speeds distinct marks representing 10^{-4} sec. can be recorded. The marking potential, which may be either A.C. or D.C., is applied to the coated side of the paper by means of a stylus.

The voltage and current requirements are dependent on the grade of Teledeltos used and on the speed at which the stylus moves over the paper. For recording instrument charts, Grade " L " (low resistance) is more suitable than grade " H " (high resistance). It is recommended that the supply voltage be in excess of the open circuit voltages indicated in Table 28.1. If an amplifier is used best results are obtained when the output transformer provides an approximate impedance match to the paper.

TABLE 28.1

Teledeltos Grade " L "

Stylus speed in./min.	Current mA	Voltage drop V	Open Circuit V
0·1	10	20	45
1·4	10–15	25	50
140·0	10–25	35–50	55
700·0	15–30	70–100	110
1400	15–30	80–115	200
1750	15–30	100–130	215
2800	15–30	100–140	220

Recording potentiometers were described by C. Walsh (*953*), V. L. Parsegian (*1439*, *1431*), and others.

Bibliography References : (*425*, *1797*, *1815*, *1970*, *1989*, *2020*, *2042*)

CHAPTER 29

INSTALLATION, MAINTENANCE AND SERVICING

All electronic as well as photo-electric equipment is built to withstand the rather rough conditions of handling and use in workshop and factory. There is nothing which when treated unreasonably could not be damaged or destroyed. Given reasonable care electronic equipment will last as long and give as good and reliable a service as any other control instrument.

29.1. Temperature, Dust, Electrical Leakage

In industrial applications most of the trouble during operation will be caused by leakage currents or vibrations. The former are due to atmospheric conditions, manufacturing processes, dust and dirt ; the latter are caused by moving machinery.

When designing the photosensitor housing, care should be taken to allow for sufficient ventilation in order to keep the ambient temperature within the limits. Louvres, vent-holes, and forced-air inlets should be so arranged that dust and dirt are not precipitated on any components inside the housing ; components must not act as baffles. If, in spite of preventive measures taken, grease and dirt accumulate on parts of the photo-electric equipment, thereby reducing the primarily high insulation to a value which, particularly with small photo-currents, would mask the effect of any fluctuations of the incident radiation, cleaning with a cloth damped in alcohol or carbon tetrachloride* or dichloroethylene or any other grease solvent must take place at regular intervals.

In damp atmospheres the forming of moisture films can be inhibited by applying a thin layer of a non-hygroscopic wax, for instance ceresin, to all those parts between which leakage currents or creep current might establish themselves.

Bibliography References : (*455*, *2226*)

* The application of carbon tetrachloride is likely to cause rust.

29.2. Anti-vibration Mountings

It is not always possible to mount the photo-relay so distant from machinery that the vibrations have been attenuated to such an extent as to be no danger to the life of valves or lamps or to the accuracy of the equipment. The use of shock-absorbing pads of cork, rubber, etc., is only rarely commendable.

A safe method of avoiding mechanical and sonic vibrations causing trouble in photo-electric apparatus has been introduced by Finn H. Gulliksen (*1291*). The novel feature is that the cathodes of all photo-sensitors are securely earthed together with the relevant parts of the amplifier. In his first claim, Gulliksen, quotes " a plurality of photo-sensitive devices . . . amplifying means including an electric discharge valve having a control electrode . . . means including a capacitor for coupling the anodes of said photo-electric devices to said control electrode, and means for connecting the cathodes of said photo-sensitive devices to ground."

29.3. Installation

The general rules are few and largely matters of common-sense. They may be summarized as under:

(1) read and follow manufacturers' instructions ;
(2) provide for good ventilation ;
(3) keep ambient temperatures within specified limits ;
(4) avoid vibration ;
(5) make leads as short as possible ;
(6) keep insulation resistance of all wiring at highest order ;
(7) provide good earth connexions ;
(8) wire leads in conduit and keep it well earthed ;
(9) avoid accumulation of moisture in conduit, housing, etc. ;
(10) use shielded cable ;
(11) keep the photosensitor as close as possible to its amplifier ;
(12) have the entire equipment easily accessible for adjusting and servicing.

Bibliography References : (*485, 2186*)

29.4. Maintenance

(1) Keep the entire equipment cool, clean, and check regularly ventilation and cooling equipment ;

(2) check rated voltages, currents ; make sure they keep constant ;

(3) inspect connexions for looseness, corrosion, breakage ;

(4) keep contacts clean and inspect for correct spring pressure, arcing, sticking, chattering ;

(5) beware of extraneous sources of radiation ;

(6) have a diagram of the circuits attached to each piece of equipment ;

(7) keep a plan of the layout of all electronic devices.

E. B. McDowell (*941*) and W. D. Cockrell (*1434*) have published a set of charts dealing with problems of maintenance and servicing. General rules are discussed in a paper by H. L. Palmer (*1044*) and W. D. Cockrell (*942*).

Bibliography References : (*485, 1385, 1666, 2321*)

29.5. Servicing

(1) Keep a stock of spare parts ; mainly of valves, capacitors, contacts ;

(2) check valves every 3000 hours, i.e., once a year on a one-shift-a-day basis ;

(3) avoid voltages in excess of rated values ; the life of valves and radiant emitters depends on this ;

(4) clean all optical parts of the equipment according to local atmospheric conditions ;

(5) avoid surface leakage which is caused by unclean or damp surfaces : dust, grit, metallic dust, etc., must be avoided or cleared away frequently ;

(6) inspect for alignment of all optical parts ; check for vibrations ;

(7) inspect for proper mechanical conditions ; no loose terminals, cables, connexions, springs, contacts ;

(8) temperature of air stream or of water cooling system should be inspected regularly ; filters cleaned or replaced.

Maintenance and Servicing Chart

The general diagram of an industrial photo-electric control is shown in block form in Fig. 29.1.

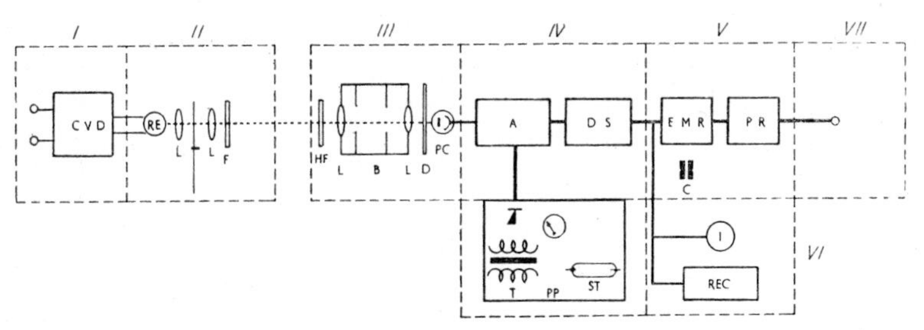

Fig. 29.1. Block diagram of representative industrial photo-electric control

In Chart I a number of troubles, their origin and cause are listed, and a remedy is suggested in each case. Reference is made in the first column of the chart to the block diagrams of Fig. 29.1.

CHART I

MAINTENANCE AND SERVICING

Origin of Trouble	Trouble	Cause	Remedy
RE (II)	(1) emitted radiation fluctuates		
	(*a*) continuously,	(*a*) CVD (I) faulty;	(*a*) repair or replace CV-transformer.
	(*b*) erratically;	(*b*) loose contacts; bad fit of cap in holder; extraneous vibrations;	
		(α) mechanic vibrations; (β) sonic vibrations.	(α) isolate (II) from vibrating machinery or structures (β) soundproof (II).
MOD (II)	(1) incorrect frequency	(1) driving device	(1) (*a*) correct r.p.m. of driving motor; (*b*) correct length of vibrating reed; (*c*) correct frequency generator;
	(2) incorrect shape of impulse;	(2) shape of apertures in disk and stencil;	(2) redesign shape of apertures.
L (II, III)	(1) the optical system yields no focus; (DIII)	(1) (*a*) incorrect focal length	(1) (*a*) replace lenses;
		(*b*) lens holders not adjustable;	(*b*) provide lens holders which can be adjusted and fixed when in correct position;

	(*c*) baffle B is incorrectly designed; its lenses (L III) are not parallel;	
(2) too little radiation incident on PS (III);	(2) (*a*) output of RE (II) too small;	(2)
	(*b*) apertures in MOD (II) too small;	
	(*c*) LL (II) dirty;	(*c*) clean with soft cloth or silk damped in alcohol;
	(*d*) F (II) too thick;	
	(*e*) apertures of B(III) too small;	
	(*f*) aperture of D (III) too small;	
	(*g*) cathode of PS (III) not in alignment or in incorrect position;	(*g*) adjust position of PS so that cathode receives maximum amount of radiation;
	(*h*) window of PS (III) too small.	(*h*) replace by correct type PS.
(3) no radiation strikes PS (III) although RE (II) operates correctly	(3) (*a*) MOD (II) or a foreign body obstructs the path of the rays;	(3)

CHART I — *continued*

Origin of Trouble	Trouble	Cause	Remedy
L (II, III) —*cont.*	(3) no radiation strikes PS (III) although RE (II) operates correctly	(*b*) optical system very dirty	(*b*) clean with soft cloth or silk damped in alcohol
		(*c*) optical components not aligned with RE (II) and PS (III)	
PS (III)	(1) response too low;	(1) (*a*) range of energy spectrum of RE (II) does not approach to, or coincide with, the spectral range of PS (III)	(1) (*a*) replace either RE or PS by more suitable type;
		(*b*) wrong type PS (III);	(*b*) replace by type having higher sensitivity (μA/Lm);
		(*c*) anode voltage too low;	(*c*) correct voltage; be careful of maximum voltage;
		(*d*) anode voltage too high, PS damaged by glow discharge;	(*d*) replace by new PS;
		(*e*) photo-electric circuit too insensitive for incident radiation	(*e*) redesign circuit, or use correct type PS;
		(*f*) irradiation of PS too small;	(*f*) increase output of RE.

	(2) ambient temperature above admissible maximum temperature;	(2) insufficient ventilation;	(2) (*a*) natural ventilation (holes, louvres, chimneys);
			(*b*) forced draught;
			(*c*) water cooling of (III);
			(*d*) use PS designed for 100° C. max. amb. temperature.
			(*e*) insert HF (III); careful of spectral changes involved.
A (IV)	(1) amplification insufficient;	(1) (*a*) wrong design (PS-output is A.C.; amplifier designed for D.C. input or vice-versa);	(1) (*a*) redesign (II) or (IV);
		(*b*) electronic valves deficient;	(*b*) check on heater voltage and current, anode voltage, insulation, contacts; remedy or replace valve when anode current begins to fall off;
		(*c*) PP supply operates incorrectly;	(*c*) as above;
	(2) thyratron does not fire;	(2) (*a*) valve deficient;	(2) (*a*) as above
		(*b*) ambient temperature too low;	(*b*) increase ambient temperature by reducing ventilation in (IV) or by installing a small heater close to the thyratron, or by applying thermal insulation (lagging) of (A);

CHART I—*continued*

Origin of Trouble	Trouble	Cause	Remedy
A (IV)—*cont.*	(3) thyration arcs back	(3) ambient temperature too high	(3) increase ventilation of (A);
	(4) reduced life;	(4) (*a*) electric circuit constants in excess of rated valve values;	(4) (*a*) apply correct filament voltage and anode voltage;
		(*b*) vibrations;	(*b*) shock-proof mounting of (A); fix lead-in wires and cables;
		(*c*) faulty operation of (thyratron) cathode protective timer, or absence of timer, or wrong type rectifier valve.	(*c*) check function of timer; install timing device; use correct type rectifier valve (its filament must take more time to heat up than the thyratron filament).
DS (IV)	(1) incorrect timing;	(1) incorrect delay;	(1) (*a*) adjust pressure on bimetallic strip;
			(*b*) adjust heater voltage of thermo-electric switch;
			(*c*) adjust mechanism of delaying gear;
PP (IV)	(1) T supplies incorrect voltage	(1) mains voltage differs from rated transformer input voltage;	(1) connect mains to correct tappings;
	(2) R gets hot;	(2) R output inconsistent with load;	(2) replace R;

	(3) E.F. passes ripples;	(3) incorrect design;	
	(4) St	(4) voltage not stabilized.	(4) replace by correct type St.
EMR (V)	(1) does not operate when intensity of radiant energy changes;	(1) (*a*) coil circuit open;	(1) (*a*) repair circuit; replace coil;
		(*b*) radiant energy does not reach PS (III);	(*b*) as under L (II, III), (3).
		(*c*) radiant energy reaches PS, but photo-electric current is not, or insufficiently amplified;	(*c*) as under A (IV);
		(*d*) poor insulation;	(*d*) check for moisture accumulation on components of photo-electric circuit; minimum leakage resistance should be of the order of 2500 megohms.
	(2) operates erratically;	(2) (*a*) loose contacts or connexions;	
		(*b*) moving extraneous radiation reaches PS;	(2) (*b*) look out for: hot object (infra-red radiation); lamps (bench lamps, car lamps, lamp of inspector); fix hood on optical system of PS.
		(*c*) supply voltage fluctuates excessively;	(*c*) install St (IV) or CVD (I);
		(*d*) erratic vibrations and shock cause RE (II) to move;	(*d*) as under RE (II);

CHART I—*continued*

Origin of Trouble	Trouble	Cause	Remedy
EMR (V)—*cont.*	(3) chatters;	(3) (*a*) EF (IV) faulty;	(3) (*a*) replace capacitor or neon lamp across rectified voltage;
		(*b*) C (V) open;	(*b*) replace C (V);
		(*c*) earthed mains connected to wrong terminal of photo-electric circuit.	(*c*) correct connexions; install 1 : 1 transformer in mains supply for isolating the circuits and earth proper terminal of relay.
EMR (V) PR (V)	(1) contacts stick, do not open;	(1) (*a*) excessive load, contacts fused;	(1) (*a*) reduce load and replace contacts; if load reduction impossible, install heavy duty contacts; do not connect contacts in parallel to reduce load;
		(*b*) armature movement hindered by mechanical obstruction;	(*b*) look out for objects obstructing the movement
			(*c*) correct bend or position of armature stop to allow for sufficient clearance;
	(2) contacts do not close;	(2) (*a*) armature movement incorrect	(2) (*a*) increase tension of contact spring; reduce clearance between contact spring and armature.

Appendix

WAVELENGTH SCALE

The wavelength scale shown in Chart II ranges from 1000 to 14,000 A. The luminous region (3820 to 7660 A) is divided in seven, eight, or ten portions called " colours ". The limits of these portions vary greatly according to author and investigation. In this chart, " natural " limits are used in preference to more arbitrarily selected liminal wavelengths. (*42; 162; 171; 172: 173; 174; 175; 176; 177; 178: 179*). The author suggests a generally acceptable definition of the colours, the limits being physical constants and physiological standards or, rather, standardized means:

violet:	3820 (physiological standard, also Fraunhofer L line) to 4358 (Hg line)
blue:	4358 to 4861 (Fraunhofer F line)
blue-green:	4861 to 5130 (physiol. std., i.e. max. of scotopic vision)
green:	5130 to 5461 (Hg line)
green-yellow:	5461 to 5550 (physiol. std., i.e., max. of photopic vision)
yellow:	5550 to 5890 (Fraunhofer D line)
orange:	5890 to 6402 (Ne line)
red:	6402 to 7660 (physiological standard, also Fraunhofer A line).

The Fraunhofer lines are quoted for reference:

A	7661	B	6867	C	6563	D	5890	E	5270
F	4862	G	4308	H	3968	K	3934	L	3820
M	3720	N	3580	O	3440	Z	8228		

Commission International d'Éclairage (C.I.E.) (International Commission on Illumination; I.C.I.) standard illuminants are:

A colour temperature 2848°K; dominant wavelength 10150 A.
B colour temperature 4800°K; dominant wavelength 6025 A.
C colour temperature 6500°K; dominant wavelength 4450 A.

The dominant wavelengths of the three C.I.E. standard illuminants as well as of the Planckian radiator (Black Body) at certain absolute temperatures (°K), as quoted under the heading of Dominant Wavelength, have been calculated from Wien's law λ dom = 28976200/T. The spectral distribution of a 5-watt neon glow lamp is near enough the same as that of a hot cathode neon flood light lamp. The argon lamp is the small 5-watt, A.C. mains supply cold cathode glow discharge type. The wavelength of maximum radiant output of tungsten filament lamps is marked against the wattage of the lamps, the high wattage lamps being rated at 230 V the 36 W being a 12 V car head lamp operating at between 2900 and 3100°K (colour temperature). INFRA-RED marks the maximum output of the industrial I-R lamp as used in infra-red paint baking, etc. Filters are marked as in the chart, the overall transmission range having been used as a characteristic. Luminescent materials are represented as follows:

Inorganic: (the element after the colon is the activator)

A	calcium tungstate: lead
B	calcium sulphide: bismuth
C	magnesium tungstate
D	calcium sulphide: copper
E	zinc sulphide: copper
F	strontium sulphide: copper
G	strontium sulphide: manganese
H	zinc ortho-silicate: manganese
J	zinc sulphide: manganese
K	cadmium silicate: manganese
L	calcium sulphide: manganese
M	cadmium borate: manganese
N	magnesium silicate
P	calcium sulphide: nickel $(< 10^{-5})$

Organic:

1	alpha-naphthol
2	fluorescein, acid sol.
3	fluorescein, alkaline sol.
4	erythrosin
5	rhodamin 6G; eosin G extra
6	rhodamine 3B
7	rhodamine B extra

Photographic emulsions:

1, 4	Ilford
N, L, M, Z, Q	Kodak

Photosensitors:

A	Uranium in Corex D envelope (Westinghouse)
B	Cu_2O phto-emf frontwall cell (Westinghouse)
C	Sodium, UNG7 (Osram)
D	Cu_2O photo-emf backwall cell (Westinghouse)
E	Cadmium, UDG7 (Osram)
F	Potassium hydride, KG7 (Osram)
G	Thallium sulphide photo-emf cell (Bell Labs.)
H	CsO-Ag in quartz envelope, QVA38 (Cintel)
K	Thallium sulphide light resistor (Case Res. Labs.).

CHART II *WAVELENGTH SCALE*

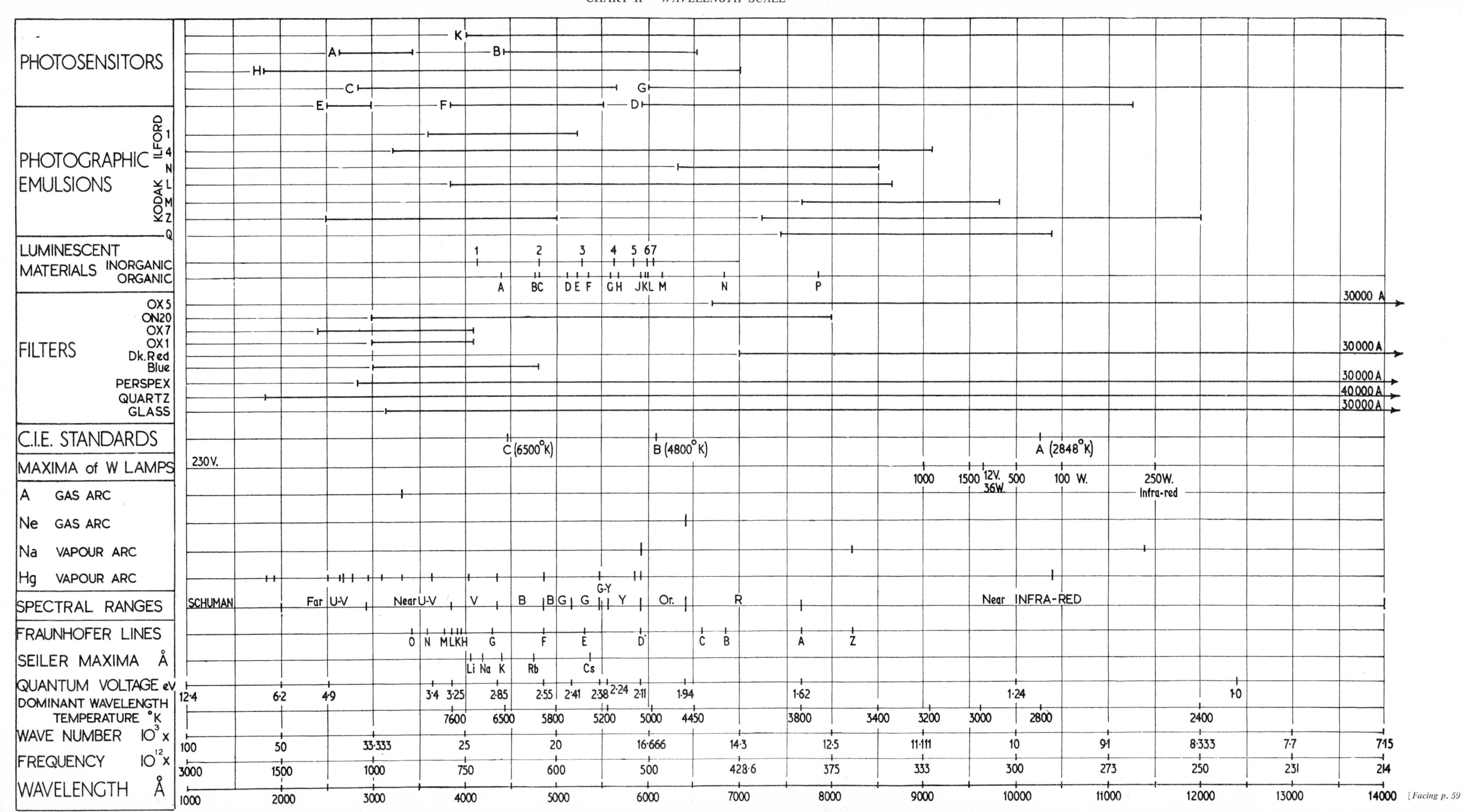

[Facing p. 59

BIBLIOGRAPHY

In this bibliography an attempt has been made to collect a number of relevant and important papers on the subject of this book and related matters, and to present them to the reader in such a way that it will be easy for him to use the references as a further approach to the practical applications of each subject dealt with in the various chapters. Only those Periodicals have been searched for publications which are easily accessible to the reader, either in his works library or in the public libraries on both sides of the Atlantic or, if they are not available publicly, may be borrowed on loan or exchange from any technical library.

As far as publications other than English and American are concerned the reader is asked to accept the author's apologies for not having been able to supply more than an occasional mention of French, Russian, or German publications between 1939–1945 which fact can be explained as one of the many unfortunate results of the war.

Besides the periodicals listed below, such compendia as
Industrial Arts Index,
Engineering Index,
Electronics Master Index, 2 vols.,
Review of Current Literature relating to the Paint, Varnish and Allied Industries,
Science Abstracts,
Chemical Abstracts,
British Chemical Abstracts,
Science Museum, Bibliographical Series,
Bolletino del Centro Volpi Di Elettrologica,
and various cumulative indices,
have also been scanned for information.

As a general rule, the period from 1936 to 1946 has been searched for references, but earlier publications have also been included when necessary.

The title of quoted publications is not always given, the subject matter becoming obvious from the meaning of the context where the reference is cited.

(*1*) EDELMANN, A., *Electronics* 1938; **11,** 3; 15
(*2*) *Electronic Engineering*, 1944; **17,** 198; 120
(*3*) *J. Franklin Inst.* 1944; **237,** 3; 202
(*4*) *Electronics* 1944; **17,** 12; 150
(*5*) KING, R. O. *Engineering* 1933; **6,** 136; 183
(*6*) WEILLER, P. G. *Electronics* 1945; **18,** 4; 96
(*7*) *Electronics* 1940; **13,** 10
(*8*) *Electronics* 1939; **12,** 9
(*9*) WISMER, A. R., *et al.*, *Power* 1945; **89,** 7; 68, (434)
(*10*) *Electronics* 1933; **6,** 1
(*11*) *Timely Ideas* 1941; July
(*12*) *Electronics* 1941; **14,** 10; 94
(*13*) JOHNSTONE, JOHN *Electronics* 1939; **12,** 2; 38
(*14*) POWERS, R. A. *Electronics* 1937; **10,** 7; 21
(*15*) *Electronics* 1945; **18,** 5; 190
(*16*) CATHCART, E. P., *The Human Factor in Industry*, 1928, p. 22
(*17*) HUTCHINS, B. L. and HARRISON, A., *A History of Factory Legislation*, 1911, pp. 21, 88
(*18*) *Annual Report of the Chief Inspector of Factories*, 1943, p. 20
(*19*) WYATT, S., *A Study of Variations in Output* (H.M.S.O.), 1944
(*20*) LUCKIESH, M. and MOSS, F. K., *The Science of Seeing*, 1937, p. 218
(*21*) LADD, G. T. and WOODWORTH, R. S., *Elements of Physiological Psychology*, 1911
(*22*) DOCKERAY, F. C. and ISAACS, S., *J. Comp. Psychol.*, 1921; **1**; 115

(23) MYERS, CH. S., *A Textbook of Experimental Psychology*, 1926, p. 126
(24) *Electronics*, 1945; **18,** 2; 53
(25) ZWORYKIN, V. K. and WILSON, E. D., *Photocells and Their Applications*, 1932
(26) LANGE, B., *Photoelements*, 1938.
(27) Technical Data on Weston Photronic Cells.
(28) IOFFE, A. F., *Vestnik Akad. Nauk., U.S.S.R.*, 1940; **10,** 10; 12
(29) SPURR, J. C. *Electronic Applications in Industry*, 1944
(30) *Electronics*, 1931; **3,** 10; 134
(31) U.S. Department of Commerce, *Biennial Census of Manufacturers* (1937 and 1939)
(32) WHITE, W. C., *Electronics*, 1945; **18,** 9; 92
(33) GEORGE, S., *Light, Principles and Experiments*, 1937
(34) WALLS, G. L., *The Reptilian Retina*, Pt. 1, *Proc. Ass. for Res. Ophthalmol.*, 1934; 10
(35) LUCKIESH, M., *Ultra-Violet Radiation*, 1923
(36) CLARK, W., *Photography by Infra-Red; Its Principles and Applications*, 1939 (Chapman and Hall)
(37) LAURENS, H., *The Physiological Effects of Radiant Energy*, 1933
(38) Corning Glass Works, *Glass Colour Filters*
(39) MACEDONIO, MELLONI, *Compt. Rend.*, 1842; 1823
(40) OVIO, J., *Anatomie et Physiologie de L'Oeil dans la série animale*, 1927
(41) SIVÉN, *Skandinavisches Archiv fuer Physiologie*, 1905; **17;** 306
(42) WALLS, G. L., *The Vertebrate Eye*, 1942
(43) SCHULTZE, M., *Arch. mikr. Anat.*, 1866; **2;** 175, and 1867; **3;** 215
(44) VERRIER, L., *Bull. Biol. de France et de Belgique*, 1935; suppl. 20; 1
(45) BOLL, F., *Arch. f. Physiologie*, 1877; **1**; 4
(46) KÜHNE, W., *Unters. physiol. Inst. Heidelberg*, 1877; **1;** 15
(47) EWALD, A., and KÜHNE, W., *Unters. physiol. Inst. Heidelberg*, 1878; **1;** 181
(48) WALD, G., *J. Gen. Physiol.*, 1938; **21;** 795
(49) *J.O.S.A.*, 1940; **30,** 12; 609
(50) *J.O.S.A.*, 1944; **34,** 7; 382
(51) BIRGE, R. T., *Rev. Mod. Phys.*, 1941; **13,** 4; 233
(52) KAYE, G. W. C. and LABY, T. H., *Physical and Chemical Constants and Some Mathematical Functions*, 1936
(53) HECHT, S., *J.O.S.A.*, 1942; **32,** 1; 42
(54) GIBSON, K. S. and TYNDALL, E. P. T., *Sci. Pap. Nat. Bur. Stand.*, 1923; 19 (S 475); 131
(55) GIBSON, K. S., *Proc. 6th Session; Intern. Com. Illum.*, Geneva, 1924; 232
(56) GIBSON, K. S., *J.O.S.A.*, 1940; **30,** 2; 51
(57) WEAVER, K. S., *J.O.S.A.*, 1937; **27,** 1; 36
(58) HECHT, S. and WILLIAMS, R. E., *J. Gen. Physiol.*, 1922-23; **5;** 1
(59) POLYAK, S. L., *The Retina*, 1941
(60) LAURENS, H., *Am. J. Physiol.*, 1924; **67;** 348
(61) GRANIT, R., *J. Physiol.*, 1934; **81;** 1
(62) BERGER, H., *Arch. Psychiatr. Nervenkrankheiten*; 1929; **87;** 527, *et sqq.*
(63) WALTER, W. G., *J. Neurology and Psychiatry*, 1938; **1** (new series); 4
(64) GÖTHLIN, G. F., *J.O.S.A.*, 1944; **34,** 4; 147
(65) HENSCHEN, S. E., *Hygeia* (Stockholm), 1929; **91;** 705
(66) FRY, G. A., *J.O.S.A.*, 1945; **35,** 3; 114
(67) HARTRIDGE, H., *Nature*, 1945; **155,** 3944; 657
(68) PÜTTER, A., *Arch. ges. Physiol.*, 1918; **171;** 201
(69) LAZAREFF, P., *Pflüg. Arch.*, 1926; **213;** 256
(70) HECHT, S., *J. Gen. Physiol.*, 1935; **18;** 767
(71) WALD, G., *Biol. Symposia*, 1942; **7;** 43
(72) MOON, P. and SPENCER, D. E., *J.O.S.A.*, 1945; **35,** 1; 43
(73) PINEGIN, N. I., *Compt. Rend., U.S.S.R.*, 1944; **43,** 4; 157
(74) PINEGIN, N. I. *Compt. Rend., U.S.S.R.*, 1941; **30,** 3
(75) HAGUE, H. J., *Electronics*, 1944; **17,** 4; 115
(76) HARTLINE, H. K., *J.O.S.A.*, 1940; **30;** 239
(77) NUTTING, P. G., *J.O.S.A.*, 1920; **4,** 2; 55

(78) LANGMUIR, J. and WESTENDORP, W. F., *Physics*, 1931; **1,** 5; 273
(79) HENNEY, K., *Electrontubes in Industry*, 1937
(80) BRYAM, G. M., *J.O.S.A.*, 1944; **34;** 571, 718
(81) MAKSUTOV, D. *Compt. Rend., U.S.S.R.*, 1944; **43,** 8; 338
(82) *Ind. Heating*, 1943; **10,** 3; 401
(83) MEES, C. E. K., *The Theory of the Photographic Process*, 1942
(84) MARTIN, L. C. and GAMBLE, W., *Colour and Methods of Colour Reproduction*, 1942
(85) SOMMER, W., *Electronic Engineering*, 1944; **17,** 200; 189
(86) BARTLEY, S. H., *Vision*, 1941
(87) WRIGHT, W. D., *The Perception of Light*, 1938
(88) SOMMER, W., *Electronic Engineering*, 1944; **17,** 202; 296
(89) MATTLER, J., *Compt. Rend.*, 1943; **217;** 143
(90) ROMAIN, B. P., *Rev. Sci. Instr.*, 1933; **4;** 83
(91) DUBAR, L., *Compt. Rend.*, 1931; **193;** 659
(92) FINK, C. G. and ADLER, E., *Trans. Electrochem. Soc.*, 1941; **79;** 377
(93) FINK, C. G. and MACKAY, J. S., *Trans. Electrochem. Soc.*, 1940; **77;** 299
(94) BERRAZ, G. and VIRASORO, E., *Anales inst. investigaciones cient. tecnol.*, 1943; **12/13;** 119. (Universidad nacional litoral, Santa Fé, Argentina)
(95) BARTLETT, C. H., *Rev. Sci. Instr.*, 1932; **3;** 543
(96) WILSON, E. D., *Rev. Sci. Instr.*, 1931; **2;** 797
(97) METCALF, G. F. and KING, A. J., *Electronics*, 1937; **10,** 12
(98) SMITH, W., *Nature*, Feb. 20, 1873; **7;** 303
(99) SMITH, W., *Soc. Tel. Eng. J.*, 1873; **2;** 31
(100) REICH, H. J., *Theory and Application of Electron Tubes*, 1944
(101) GÖRLICH, P., *J.O.S.A.*, 1941; **31,** 7; 504
(102) KOLLER, L. R. and TAYLOR, A. H., *J.O.S.A.*, 1935; **25;** 184
(103) RUTKOWSKY, W. I., *Measuring Technique* (Ismeritelbnay Technika, U.S.S.R.), 1941; **3,** 3; 14
(104) RUTKOWSKY, W. I., *Measuring Technique* (Ismeritelbnay Technika, U.S.S.R.), 1941; **3,** 4; 13
(105) DRESLER, A., *E.T.Z.*, 1933; **54;** 476
(106) BECQUEREL, E., *Compt. Rend.*, 1889; **9;** 561
(107) HERTZ, H., *Wied. Ann.*, 1887; **31;** 983
(108) HALLWACHS, W., *Ann. d. Phys.*, 1888; **33;** 301
(109) ELSTER, J. and GEITEL, H., *Ann. d. Phys.*, 1889; **38;** 40, 479
(110) FRITTS, A. E., *Am. J. Sci.*, 1883; ser. 3, 26; 465
(111) HALLWACHS, W., *Phys. Z.*, 1904; **5,** 489
(112) EINSTEIN, A., *The Quantum Law of Emission and Absorption*, 1905
(113) WEBER, A. H. and FRIEDRICH, L. W., *Phys. Rev.*, 1944; sec. ser.; 66; **9,** 10; 248
(114) GOLDMANN, A. and BRODSKY, J., *Ann. d. Phys.*, 1914; **44;** 849
(115) NIX, F. C. and TREPTOW, A. W., *J.O.S.A.*, 1939; **29,** 11; 457
(116) FINK, C. G. and ADLER, E., *Trans. Electrochem. Soc.*, 1941; **79;** 367
(117) ROULLEAU, J., *Compt. Rend.*, 1936; **202;** 470
(118) ZENOR, H. M., *Phys. Rev.*, 1936; **50;** 1050
(119) RICHARDSON, O. W., *The Emission of Electricity from Hot Bodies*, 1916
(120) FAN, H. Y., *Phys. Rev.*, 1945; **68,** 1 & 2; 43
(121) CAMPBELL, N. R. and RITCHIE, D., *Photoelectric Cells*, 1934
(122) MAXFIELD, F. A. and BENEDICT, R. R., *Theory of Gaseous Conduction and Electronics*, 1941
(123) FINK, D. G., *Engineering Electronics*, 1938
(124) TEVES, M. C., *Ph. T. Rev.*, 1937; **2,** 1; 13
(125) JAMIESON, M. F., SHEA, T. E. and PIERCE, P. H., *J. Soc. Mot. Pict. Eng.*, 1936; **27;** 365
(126) *Intern. Crit. Tables*, 1928; **6**; 53
(127) JAMISON, N. C. and CASHMAN, R. J., *Phys. Rev.*, 1936; **50,** ii, 7; 624
(128) DE VOE, CH. F., *Phys. Rev.*, 1936; **50,** ii, 5; 481
(129) SCHNEIDER, E. G., *Phys. Rev.*, 1938; **54;** 185
(130) BRUINING, H. and DEBOER, J. H., *Physica*, 1937; **4;** 473

(*131*) Rentschler, H. C. and Henry, D. E., *J.O.S.A.*, 1936; **26,** 1; 30
(*132*) Jones, R. B., *Phys. Rev.*, 1929; **34;** 227
(*133*) Hughes, A. L. and DuBridge, L. A., *Photoelectric Phenomena*, 1932
(*134*) Rentschler, H. C. and Henry, D. E., *Trans. Electrochem. Soc.*, 1945; **87;** preprint 14
(*135*) Seiler, E. F., *Astrophys. J.*, 1920; **52,** 3; 129
(*136*) Fleischer and Goldschmidt, *Phys. Z.*, 1928; **29;** 691
(*137*) Fleischer and Goldschmidt, *J.O.S.A.*, 1931; **21,** 9; 554
(*138*) Wrobel, H. T., *G.E. Rev.*, 1942; **45,** 10; 585
(*139*) Perrin, J., *Compt. Rend.*, 1908; **147;** 594
(*140*) Koller, L. R., *Physics of Electron Tubes*, 1934
(*141*) Skelett, A. M., *Bell Lab. Rec.*, 1938; **16;** 321
(*142*) Fourmarier, M. P., *Compt. Rend.*, 1932; **194;** 86
(*143*) Anderson, J. S., *A Discussion at a Joint Meeting of the Physical and Optical Societies*, June 4, 5, 1930
(*144*) Sommer, A., *Electronic Engineering*, 1945; **17,** 207; 504
(*145*) Preston, J. S., *J.I.E.E.*, 1936; **79,** 478; 424
(*146*) Wilson, E. D., *Electronics*, 1939; **12,** 1; 15
(*147*) Hall, J. A., *Iron and Steel Inst. J.*, 1944; **149;** 547
(*148*) Land, T., *Iron and Steel Inst. J.*, 1944; **149;** 481
(*149*) Preston, J. S., *Nature*, 1944; **153,** 3892; 680
(*150*) Poole, H. H., *Nature*, 1944; **154,** 3904; 274
(*151*) Poole, H. H. and Atkins, W. R. G., *Sci. Proc. Roy. Dub. Soc.* 1941; **22;** 393
(*152*) Houstoun, R. A., *Phil. Mag.*, 1941; **31,** vii, 209; 498
(*153*) Cavassilas, D., *Compt. Rend.*, 1941; **213;** 346
(*154*) Bergmann, L., *Phys. Z.*, 1932; **33;** 513
(*155*) Zworykin, V. K., Morton, G. A. and Malter, L., *Proc. I.R.E.*, 1936; **24;** 351
(*156*) Reich, H. J., *Principles of Electron Tubes*, 1941
(*157*) Rajchman, J. A. and Snyder, R. L., *Electronics*, 1940; **13,** 12; 20
(*158*) James, R. B. and Glover, A. M., *R.C.A. Rev.*, 1941; **6,** 1; 43
(*159*) Farnsworth, Ph. T., *J. Franklin Inst.*, 1934; **218;** 411
(*160*) Farnsworth, Ph. T., *Electronics*, 1934; **7,** 8; 242
(*161*) Larson, C. C. and Salinger, H., *Rev. Sci. Instr.*, 1940; **11,** 7; 226
(*162*) Farnsworth, Ph. T., *Electronics*, 1940; **13,** 5; 54
(*163*) Winans, R. C. and Pierce, J. R., *Rev. Sci. Instr.*, 1941; **12,** 5; 269
(*164*) Pierce, J. R., *Bell Lab. Rec.*, 1938; **16;** 305
(*165*) Zworykin, V. K., and Rajchman, J. A., *Proc. I.R.E.*, 1939; **27;** 558
(*166*) Teves, M. C., *Ph. T. Rev.*, 1940; **5;** 261
(*167*) Harris, J. H. O., *Electronics*, 1944; **17,** 9; 100
(*168*) Rann, W. H., *J. Sci. Instr.*, 1939; **16,** 8; 241
(*169*) Afanas'eva, A. V., *Uchenje Zapiski, Moskov Ordena Lenina Gosudarst. Univ. M.V. Lomonosova*, 1944; **74;** 114
(*170*) Martin, L. C., *An Introduction to Applied Optics*, 1930
(*171*) Leverenz, H. W., *J.O.S.A.*, 1940; **30,** 7; 309
(*172*) Ostwald, W., *Colour Science* (English edit.) 2 vols., 1931, vol. 1
(*173*) Granville, W. C. and Jacobson, E., *J.O.S.A.*, 1944; **34,** 7; 382
(*174*) Glenn, J. J. and Killian, J. T., *J.O.S.A.*, 1940; **30,** 12; 609
(*175*) *Nat. Bur. Stand.*, LC 454
(*176*) Priest, I. G., *J.O.S.A.*, 1920; **4;** 388
(*177*) Hardy, A. C., *Handbook of Colorimetry*, 1936
(*178*) Abney, W. W., *Researches in Colour Vision*, 1913
(*179*) Taylor, A. H., *J.O.S.A.*, 1942; **32,** 11; 651
(*180*) Taylor, L. S. and Tucker, K. L., *Nat. Bur. Stand.*, 1932; **3;** RP 475
(*181*) Lynch, A. C. and Tillman, J. R. *Electronic Engineering*, 1943; **16,** 189; 250
(*182*) *Television and Shortwave World*, 1937; **6;** 343
(*183*) Sommer, A., *Electronic Engineering*, 1945; **17,** 207; 526

(*184*) Prilezhaeva, S. S., *J. Techn. Phys., U.S.S.R.*, 1939; **9;** 1439
(*185*) Massa, E. A. and Pike, E. W., *U.S. Pat.* 2244720; *B. Pat.* 546764
(*186*) Timofev, P. V. and Nalimov, V. V., *J. Techn. Phys., U.S.S.R.*, 1936; **6;** 47
(*187*) Gleichmann, D. S. and Ssoroka, M. J., *Automatika i Telemechanika, U.S.S.R.*, 1941; **6,** 3; 49
(*188*) Ives, H. E. and Briggs, H. B., *J.O.S.A.*, 1937; **27,** 11; 395
(*189*) Ives, H. E. and Briggs, H. B., *J.O.S.A.*, 1937; **27,** 5; 181
(*190*) Chevallier, A. and Dubouhoz, P., *Compt. Rend.*, 1932; **194;** 452
(*191*) Case, T. W., *Phys. Rev.*, 1921; **17;** 398
(*192*) Newbury, K. and Lemery, F., *J.O.S.A.*, 1931; **21,** 5; 276
(*193*) Young, T. F. and Pierce, W. C., *J.O.S.A.*, 1931; **21,** 9; 497
(*194*) Smith, A. W., Newhouse, H. and Drake, P., *Rev. Sci. Instr.*, 1936; **7,** 11; 433
(*195*) Brice, B. A., *Rev. Sci. Instr.*, 1937; **8;** 279
(*196*) Berraz, G. and Virasoro, E., *Anales inst. investigaciones cient. tecnol.*, 1940-41; **10-11;** 17
(*197*) Eckart, F. and Schmidt, A., *Z. Phys.*, 1941; **118;** 199
(*198*) Körber, E., *U.S. Pat.* 2317776
(*199*) Hewlett, C. W., *U.S. Pat.* 2296670
(*200*) Fink, C. G. and Adler, E., *U.S. Pat.* 2293248
(*201*) Nix, F. C. and Treptow, A. W., *J.O.S.A.*, 1940; **30,** 2; 91
(*202*) Naeser, G. and Krächter, H., *Stahl und Eisen*, 1942; **62,** 17; 341
(*203*) Hewitt, G. W., *U.S. Pat.* 2104483
(*204*) Radiovisor Parent Ltd., *B. Pat.* 284942
(*205*) Thirring, H., *U.S. Pat.* 1703798; 1790850
(*206*) Metcalf, G. F. and King, A. J., *Electronics*, 1931; **3,** 12; 234
(*207*) Case, W. T., *Phys. Rev.*, 1920; **15,** ii, 4; 289
(*208*) Coblentz, W. W., *Nat. Bur. Stand., Scient. Pap.*, 1920; 380
(*209*) Schroter, F. and Michelssen, F. in: *J. S. Anderson, A Discussion at a Joint Meeting of the Physical and Optical Societies*, June 4, 5, 1930; p. 211
(*210*) Electronics, 1931; **3,** 8
(*211*) Committee on Colorimetry; *J.O.S.A.*, 1944; **34,** 4; 200
(*212*) Morecroft, J. H., *Electron Tubes and Their Applications*, 1933
(*213*) Volta, A., *Phil. Trans.*, 1793; **73;** 10, 27
(*214*) Gudden, B., *Lichtelektrische Erscheinungen*, 1928
(*215*) Fink, C. G. and Alpern, D. K., *Trans. Electrochem. Soc.*, 1930; **58;** 133
(*216*) *U.S. Pat.* 2298030
(*217*) Metcalf, G. F., *Proc. I.R.E.*, 1929; **17;** 2064
(*218*) *Electronics*, 1940; **13,** 8; 13
(*219*) Lamb, A. B., *Electronics*, 1940; **13,** 12; 35
(*220*) Furst, U. R., *Electronics*, 1944; **17,** 12; 134. 1945; **18,** 1; 136. 1945; **18,** 2; 135. 1945; **18,** 4; 438
(*221*) Boettner, E. A. and Brewington, G. P., *J.O.S.A.*, 1944; **34,** 1; 6
(*222*) Livingston, O. W. and Maser, H. T., *Electronics*, 1934; **7,** 4; 114
(*223*) Light, G. S., *Electronic Engineering*, 1945; **17,** 206; 454
(*224*) Zepler, E. E., *The Technique of Radio Design*, 1943
(*225*) Thomas, H. A., *Electronics*, 1944; **17,** 9; 142
(*226*) Nottingham, W. B., *J. Franklin Inst.*, 1931; 271
(*227*) Cockrell, W. D., *Electronics*, 1944; **17,** 6; 124
(*228*) Chin, P. T., *Electronics*, 1945; **18,** 4; 138. 1945, **18;** 5.
(*229*) Hull, A. W., *G.E. Rev.*, 1929; **32,** 4; 213 .1929; **32,** 7; 390.
(*230*) Knowles, D. D., *El. Journal*, 1928; **26;** 176
(*231*) Gilbert, R. W., *Rev. Sci. Instr.*, 1936; **7,** 1; 41
(*232*) Raymond, H. H., *Electronics*, 1933; **6,** 2
(*233*) Wood, L. A., *Rev. Sci. Instr.*, 1936; **7,** 3; 157
(*234*) Muller, R. H. and Spector, A., *J.O.S.A.*, 1936; **26;** 305
(*235*) Lamb, A. H., *U.S. Pat.* 2096902
(*236*) Goodwin, W. N., *U.S. Pat.* 2032010
(*237*) Wilcox, L. V., *Ind. Eng. Chem., Anal. Ed.*, 1934; **5,** 3; 167

(238) MULLER, R. H., *Ind. Eng. Chem., Anal. Ed.*, 1939; **11,** 1; 1 (260 references)
(239) LANGE, B., *Z. Techn. Phys.*, 1932; **13;** 600
(240) RIGHI, A., *Rend. Accad. Bologna*, 1902; **6;** 188
(241) PEARSON, S. O. and ANSON, H. S., *Proc. Phys. Soc. Lond.*, 1922; **34,** 175; 104
(242) GEFFCKEN, H. and RICHTER, H., *Z. Techn. Phys.*, 1924; **5;** 511
(243) LENIHAN, J. M. A., *Electronic Engineering*, 1944; **16,** 193; 408
(244) SASHOFF, S. P. and Roberts, W. K., *Electronics*, 1940; **13,** 9; 40
(245) VAN DEN BOSCH, F. J. G., *Electronic Engineering*, 1945; **17,** 206; 474
(246) HUNT, F. V. and HICKMAN, R. W., *Rev. Sci. Instr.*, 1939; **10,** 1; 6
(247) *Electronics*, 1939; **12,** 3; 48
(248) *Electronics*, 1943; **16,** 9; 160
(249) *R.C.A. Application Note No. 96*
(250) *Kodak Wratten Filters* (Handbook)
(251) *Ilford Filters* (Handbook)
(252) Corning Glass Works, *Filter Handbook*
(253) BRUDER SCHOTT UND GEN., *Jenaer Filter Gläser* (American edition (the Fisher-Schurman Corp.)
(254) Report of the Committee on Colorimetry, *J.O.S.A.*, 1944; **34,** 4; 183
(255) JACOBS, D. H., *Fundamentals of Optical Engineering*, 1943
(256) STOKES, G. G., *Phil. Trans.*, 1852; **142;** 463
(257) BOUGUER, M., *Essai d'Optique sur la Gradation de la Lumière*, Paris, 1729
(258) *Electrical World*, 1914; **63,** 26; 1504
(259) MOREY, G. W., *The Properties of Glass*, 1938
(260) *Discovery*, 1943; **4,** new series, 1; 4
(261) KOLLMORGEN, F., *Trans. I.E.S.*, 1916; **11;** 220
(262) *The Manufacture of Optical Glass*, 1921. Ordnance Dept. Document No. 2037, p. 76 (U.S.A.)
(263) RAYLEIGH, LORD, *Scientific Papers* 1900; **4;** 546
(264) NICOLL, F. H., *R.C.A. Rev.* 1942; **6;** 287
(265) JONES, F. L. and HOMER, H. J., *J.O.S.A.* 1941; **31,** 1; 34
(266) STRONG, J., *J.O.S.A.* 1936; **26,** 1; 73
(267) CARTWRIGHT, C. H., *J.O.S.A.* 1940; **30,** 3; 110
(268) *Electronics*, 1945; **18,** 1; 164
(269) JOSTEN, G. W., *Ind. Eng. Chem.*, Anal. Ed., 1938; **10,** 3; 165
(270) JOSTEN, G. W., *U.S. Pat.* 1953716
(271) PERRY, J. W., *Proc. Phys. Soc. Lond.*, 1943; **55;** 291
(272) I.C.I. (Plastics Division) Ltd., *Techn. Bull.* No. 7
(273) EDSER, E., *Light*, 1931
(274) MELCHIOR CENTENO V, *J.O.S.A.*, 1941; **31,** 3; 244
(275) PFUND, A. H., *J.O.S.A.*, 1939; **29,** 7; 291
(276) DRUDE, P., *Theory of Optics*, 1922
(277) *Electronics*, 1944; **17,** 12; 98
(278) *British Patents* 428836; 505836; 510007
(279) SOWERBY, J. McG. and WALTON, W. H., *J. Sci. Instr.*, 1945; **22,** 4; 71 (Correction: *J. Sci. Instr.*, 1946; **23,** 6; 134)
(280) JOLLEY, L. B. W., WALDRAM, J. M. and WILSON, G. H., *The Theory and Design of Illuminating Engineering Equipment*; 1930
(281) WEINBERGER, J. M., *Electronics*, 1940; **13,** 1; 30
(282) THIKOV, G. A., *Compt. rend. (Doklady) U.S.S.R.*, 1944; **44,** 6; 238
(283) DRESLER, A., *Licht*, 1914; **11;** 139
(284) GÖRLICH, P. and SAUER, H., *Zschr. f. Instrumentenkunde*, 1936; **56;** 423
(285) KOECHEL, W. P., *Electronics*, 1932; **4,** 12; 372
(286) MCILVAINE, H. A. *Electronics*, 1933; **6,** 8; 224
(287) ASADA, T. and HAGITA, K., *J.I.E.E.* (Japan), 1931; **51**; 8
(288) REICH, H. J., *Rev. Sci. Instr.*, 1938; **9;** 222
(289) WALSH, CRAIGH, *Electronics*, 1940; **13,** 10; 16
(290) DUNTLEY, S. Q., *J.O.S.A.*, 1942; **32,** 2; 61
(291) DUNTLEY, S. Q., *J.O.S.A.*, 1943; **33,** 5; 252
(292) MCNICKLE, R. C., *Electronics*, 1944; **17,** 9; 110
(293) *Electronics*, 1940; **13,** 12; 4

(*294*) FIES, J., *Electrical World*, 1933; **102;** 396
(*295*) MATHEWS, B. H. C., *J. Sci. Instr.*, 1939; **16,** 4; 124
(*296*) MUNSELL, A. H., *A Colour Notation*, 1936
(*297*) The Munsell Colour System, A Symposium, *J.O.S.A.*, 1940; **30,** 12; 573
(*298*) NEWHALL, S. M., NICKERSON, D. and JUDD, D. B., *J.O.S.A.*, 1943; **33,** 7; 385
(*299*) Symposium on the Ostwald Colour System, *J.O.S.A.*, 1944; **34,** 7; 353
(*300*) OSTWALD, W., *Die Harmonie der Farben*, 1918
(*301*) KRUGER, F. A. O., *Vergleichstabelle der Farbtafeln des Repertoire de Couleurs de la Société Française des Chrisanthemistes und der Colour Standards and Nomenclature of 1930*
(*302*) JACOBSEN, E. G., *Colour Harmony Manual*, 1942
(*303*) BOND, M. E. and NICKERSON, D., *J.O.S.A.*, 1942; **32,** 12; 709
(*304*) TYLER, J. E. and HARDY, A. C., *J.O.S.A.*, 1940; **30,** 12; 587
(*305*) HELMHOLTZ, H. *Physiological Optics*, 1929 (English Edition), vol 2; p. 107
(*306*) SINDEN, R. H., *J.O.S.A.*, 1932; **7;** 1132
(*307*) *British Standard Specification* 381/1930; cf. also *Revised Edition* 381/1943
(*308*) *The British Colour Council Dictionary of Colour Standards 1934; Schedule*, 543
(*309*) LEVERENZ, H. W., *J.O.S.A.*, 1940; **30,** 7; 309
(*310*) JUDD, D. B., *J.O.S.A.*, 1940; **30,** 1; 2
(*311*) JUDD, D. B., *J.O.S.A.*, 1940; **30,** 7; 296
(*312*) American Soc. for Testing Materials, D 672-42 T
(*313*) DUNTLEY, S. Q., *J.O.S.A.*, 1942; **32,** 2; 61
(*314*) HERZBERGER, M., *J.O.S.A.*, 1942; **32,** 2; 70
(*315*) KETCHAM, H., *Automobile Engineer*, 1940; **30,** 1; 29
(*316*) LUCKIESH, M., *J. Franklin Inst.*, 1917; **184;** 80
(*317*) Electric Lamp Manufacturers' Association (ELMA) *Handbook No. 8B*
(*318*) MOON, P., *J.O.S.A.*, 1942; **32,** 4; 238, 243
(*319*) GUREVICH, M. M., *Compt. rend.* (*Doklady*) *U.S.S.R.*, 1944; **45,** 4; 149
(*320*) MOON, P. and SPENCER, D. E., *J.O.S.A.*, 1943; **33,** 5; 260
(*321*) Report of the Committee on Colorimetry, *J.O.S.A.*, 1944; **34,** 5; 245
(*322*) GRADNER, H. A., *Proc. Scient. Section, Nat. Paint, Varnish and Lacquer Assoc., Incorp*, 1943; Jan. 1; Circ. 636
(*323*) BLACKMORE, P. O., *Ind. Finishing*, 1942; September
(*324*) *Analar Standards for Laboratory Chemicals*, 1937 (The British Drug Houses, Ltd.)
(*325*) FAUCETT, P. H., *Paint, Oil and Chemical Review*, 1944, July 27
(*326*) SCHOFIELD, F., *Proc. Scient. Section, Nat. Paint, Varnish and Lacquer Assoc., Incorp.*, 1943; Jan. 1; Circ. 638
(*327*) HANT, L. P., *Proc. Scient. Section, Nat. Paint, Varnish and Lacquer Assoc., Incorp.*, 1943; Jan. 1; Circ. 637
(*328*) FAIRCHILD, C. O. and PARSEGIAN, V. L., *Rev. Sci. Instr.*, 1938; **9,** 12; 422
(*329*) MOHLER, M. and TAYLOR, D. A., *J.O.S.A.*, 1936; **26,** 10; 386
(*330*) SWEET, M. H., *Electronics*, 1945; **18,** 3; 102
(*331*) HUNTER, R. S., *J.O.S.A.*, 1940; **30,** 11; 536
(*332*) HUNTER, R. S., *Nat. Bur. Stand., Circular C 429*; 1942
(*333*) FINK, D. G., *Electronics*, 1934; **7,** 6; 190
(*334*) SWEET, M. H., *J.O.S.A.*, 1943; **33,** 4; 194
(*335*) HARDY, A. C., *J.O.S.A.*, 1929; **19,** 2; 96
(*336*) HUNTER, R. S., *J. Research, Nat. Bur. Stand.*, 1940; **25;** 581 (RP 1345)
(*337*) SUKHIKH, V. A. and VSESOYNEZ, T., *Konferentsii Anal. Khim.*, 1943; **2;** 253
(*338*) KUNTZE, A., *Messtechnik* (Dusseldorf), 1943; **19,** 5; 91
(*339*) MICHELSON, J. L., *G.E. Rev.*, 1935; **38;** 194
(*340*) DRABKIN, D. L., *J.O.S.A.*, 1945; **35,** 2; 163
(*341*) WITHROW, R. B., SHREWSBURY, C. L. and HRAYBILL, H. R., *Ind. Eng. Chem., Anal. Edit.*, 1936; **8,** 3; 214
(*342*) UNDERHILL, CH. R., *Electronics at Work*, 1933
(*343*) HILLIARD, J. K., *Electronics*, 1944; **17,** 3; 180
(*344*) WILSON, E. D., *J.O.S.A.*, 1939; **29,** 1; 35
(*345*) SHEPARD, F. H., Jun., *RCA Rev.*, 1937; **2,** 2; 149
(*346*) SCULLY, J. F., *Electronics*, 1945; **18,** 10; 168

(*347*) *Brit. Stand. Specif.* 205/1943; part 6; section 8
(*348*) WORTHING, A. G., *J. Appl. Physics*, 1940; **11;** 421
(*349*) JUDD, D. B., *J.O.S.A.*, 1936; **26,** 11; 409
(Correction: *J.O.S.A.*, 1937; **27,** 2; 74)
(*350*) AMICK, CH. L., *Fluorescent Lighting Manual*, 1942
(*351*) FORSYTHE, W. E., *J.O.S.A.*, 1923; **7;** 1115
(*352*) JUDD, D. B., *J.O.S.A.*, 1933; **23;** 360
(*353*) DAVIS, R. and GIBSON, K. S., *Nat. Bur. Stand., Misc. Public. No. 114;* Jan. 1931
(*345*) SMITH, T. and GUILD, J., *Opt. Soc. London*, 1931-2; **33;** 41
(*335*) SWEET, M. H., *J.O.S.A.*, 1940; **30,** 11; 568
(*356*) LUCKIESH, M., *Artificial Sunlight*, 1930
(*357*) *Brit. Stand. Specif.* 793/1938; part 2; section 4; also Appendix A
(*358*) MACBETH, N., *Trans. Illum. Eng. Soc.*, 1928; **23,** 3; 302
(*359*) NIX, F. C., *Rev. Modern Physics*, 1932; **4;** 723
(*360*) MAJORANA, Q., *Phys. Zschr.*, 1932; **33;** 947
(*361*) ETZRODT, A., *Phys. Zschr.*, 1935; **36;** 433
(*362*) GUDDEN, B., *Phys. Zschr.*, 1931; **32;** 825
(*363*) GUDDEN, B., *Ergebnisse der Exakten Naturwissenschaften*, 1934; **13**
(*364*) PINEGIN, N. I., *Compt. rend.* (*Doklady*), U.S.S.R., 1944; **45,** 2; 58
(*365*) BRUINING, H., *Ph. T. Rev.*, 1938; **3,** 3; 80
(*366*) HOUSTOUN, R. A. and HOWATSON, A. F., *Phil. Mag.*, 1945; **36,** vii, 255; 279
(*367*) INGRAM, S. B., *Electrical Engineering*, 1939; **58,** 7; 342
(*368*) KUPFER, J. B., BRACKETT, F. S. and EICHER, M., *Rev. Sci. Instr.*, 1941; **12,** 2; 87
(*369*) PORTER, B. H., *Rev. Sci. Instr.*, 1936; **7,** 3; 101
(*370*) PORTER, B. H., *Rev. Sci. Instr.*, 1942; **13,** 3; 129
(*371*) BARR, E. S. and SCOTT, L. B., *Rev. Sci. Instr.*, 1942; **13,** 12; 533
(*372*) ROBERTSON, A. F., *Rev. Sci. Instr.*, 1941; **12,** 3; 142
(*373*) HEIDELBERG, Q. S., and RENSE, W. A., *Rev. Sci. Instr.*, 1940; **11,** 9; 386
(*374*) WILSON, R. G., *Rev. Sci. Instr.*, 1942; **13,** 7; 300
(*375*) SANDSTRÖM, A. E., *Phil. Mag.*, 1939; **28,** vii, 191; 642
(*376*) DE MENT, J., *Phil. Mag.*, 1943; **34,** vii, 230; 212
(*377*) SHERRATT, G. G. and GRIFFITHS, E., *Phil. Mag.*, 1939; **27,** vii, 180; 68
(*378*) GÖRLICH, P., *Phil. Mag.*, 1938; **25,** vii, 167; 256
(*379*) TEICHMANN, H., *Phil. Mag.*, 1938; **25,** vii, 167; 269
(*380*) MORRISON, C. A., *Rev. Sci. Instr.*, 1941; **12,** 3; 156
(*381*) SHAXBY, J. H., *Phil. Mag.*, 1943; **34,** vii, 232; 289
(*382*) MEAGHER, R. E. and BENTLEY, E. P., *Rev. Sci. Instr.*, 1939; **10,** 11; 336
(*383*) RUSSELL, J., *Rev. Sci. Instr.*, 1937; **8,** 12; 495
(*384*) ROGERS, R. and WILLIG, J. F., *Rev. Sci. Instr.*, 1939; **10,** 5; 150
(*385*) JUPE, J. H., *Electronics*, 1939; **12,** 4; 44
(*386*) KRUITHOF, A. A., *Ph. T. Rev.*, 1939; **4,** 2; 48
(*387*) DE GROOT, W., *Ph. T. Rev.*, 1938; **3,** 5; 125
(*388*) VAN WIJK, A., *Ph. T. Rev.*, 1938; **3,** 1; 5
(*389*) CATH, P. G., *Ph. T. Rev.*, 1937; **2,** 9; 270
(*390*) BLODGETT, K. B., *Science*, 1939; **89,** 1; 60
(*391*) BLODGETT, K. B., *Phys. Rev.*, 1939; **55,** 2; 391
(*392*) ALGER, P. L., *G.E. Rev.*, 1940; **43,** 2; 60
(*393*) PFUND, A. H., *J.O.S.A.*, 1935; **25,** 11; 351
(*394*) SPIEGLER, G., *J. Sci. Instr.*, 1945; **22,** 6; 116
(*395*) SANDSTRÖM, A. E., *Phil. Mag.*, 1938; **26,** vii, 178; 906
(*396*) *G.E. Rev.*, 1940; **43,** 6; 263
(*397*) WALKER, R. C. and LANCE, T. M. C., *Photo-electric Cells*, 1935
(*398*) GULLIKSEN, F. H. and VEDDER, E. H., *Industrial Electronics*, 1935
(*399*) WAINER, EUGENE, *U.S. Pat.* 2331444
(*400*) *Electronics*, 1934; **7,** 6; 187
(*401*) *J.A.I.E.E.*, 1927; 563
(*402*) LOOFBOUROW, J. R., *J.O.S.A.*, 1939; **29,** 12; 535

(*403*) YOE, J. H. and CRUMPLER, T. B., "Colorimeter", *Ind. Eng. Chem.*, Anal Ed., 1935; **7,** 4; 281

(*404*) MULLER, R. H., "Photo-electric colorimetry in macro- and microanalysis", *Ind. Eng. Chem., Anal. ed.*, 1935; **7,** 4; 223

(*405*) ZINZADZE, Ch., "Photo-electric photometer for use in colorimetry", *Ind. Eng. Chem., Anal. ed.*, 1935; **7,** 4; 280

(*406*) WALSH, W. L. and MILAS, N. A., "Simple photo-electric thermoregulators", *Ind. Eng. Chem., Anal. Ed.*, 1935; **7,** 2; 122

(*407*) BARTHOLOMEW, E. T. and RABY, E. C., "Photo-electric turbidimeter for determining HCN in solutions", *Ind. Eng. Chem., Anal. ed.*, 1935; **7,** 1; 68

(*408*) EDDY, C. W. and DE EDS FLOYD, "Photo-electric method for the determination of phosphorus", *Ind. Eng. Chem., Anal ed.*, 1937; **9,** 1; 12

(*409*) GOODLOE, P., "Photo electric determination of added phosphorus in oil", *Ind. Eng. Chem., Anal. Ed.*, 1937; **9,** 11; 527

(*410*) KEANE, J. C. and BRICE, B. A., "Photo-electric grading of white sugars and their solutions by reflectancy and transparency measurements", *Ind. Eng. Chem., Anal. Ed.*, 1937; **9,** 6; 258

(*411*) BARTON, C. J. and YOE, J. H., "Photo-electric spectrophotometer of null type", *Ind. Eng. Chem., Anal. Ed.*, 1940; **12,** 3; 166

(*412*) PARKER, A. E. and OSER, B. L., "Photo-electric photometer for vitamin A estimation", *Ind. Eng. Chem., Anal. Ed.*, 1941; **13,** 4; 260

(*413*) DEMAREST, B., "Photo-electric photometer for vitamin A measurement", *Ind. Eng. Chem., Anal. Ed.*, 1941; **13,** 6; 374

(*414*) HATFIELD, W. D. and PHILLIPS, G. E., "Photo-electric photometer for water and sewage colorimetric determinations", *Ind. Eng. Chem., Anal. Ed.*, 1941; **13,** 6; 430

(*415*) HANSON, V. F., "An ultra-violet photometer for the quantitative measurement of traces of solvent vapours in air", *Ind. Eng. Chem., Anal. Ed.*, 1941; **13,** 2; 119

(*416*) JOSTEN, G. W., "Counting drops with the photo-electric relay (478 drops per minute)", *Ind. Eng. Chem., Anal. Ed.*, 1938; **10,** 7; 353

(*417*) FORSEE, W. T., Jr., "Photo-electric determination of sugars in plant materials by colorimetric methods", *Ind. Eng. Chem., Anal Ed.*, 1938; **10,** 8; 411

(*418*) ROWLAND, G. P., Jr., "Photo-electric colorimetry. An optical study of permanganate ion and of the chromium-diphenyl carbazide system", *Ind. Eng. Chem., Anal. Ed.*, 1939; **11,** 8; 442

(*419*) BRICKER, L. G. and PROCTOR, K. L., "Application of colorimetry to the analysis of corrosion resistant steel. The determination of lead is a rapid method and the precision is greater than in any other procedure investigated", *Ind. Eng. Chem., Anal. Ed.*, 1945; **17,** 8; 511

(*420*) WEINBERG, S., PROCTOR, K. L., MILNER, O., Same as preceding item. "Determination of boron"), *Ind. Eng. Chem., Anal. Ed.*, 1945; **17,** 7; 419

(*421*) PARTRIDGE, R. F., "Colorimetric detection of copper in aluminium alloys", *Ind. Eng. Chem., Anal. Ed.*, 1945; **17,** 7; 422

(*422*) BAILES, E. L. and PAYNE, M. G., "Colorimetric method of determination of DDT", *Ind. Eng. Chem., Anal. Ed.*, 1945; **17,** 7; 438

(*423*) CADE, G. N., "Photometric determination of fluosilic acid in hydrofluoric acid", *Ind. Eng. Chem., Anal. Ed.*, 1945; **17,** 6; 372

(*424*) BROWN, E. H. and CLINE, J. E., "Continuous photometric determination of bivalent copper in ammoniacal solutions", *Ind. Eng. Chem., Anal. Ed.*, 1945; **17,** 5; 284

(*425*) STANSBY, M. E. and DASSOW, J. A., "Recording the colour of opaque objects, in particular of fish fillets", *Ind. Eng. Chem., Anal. Ed.*, 1942; **14,** 1; 13

(*426*) BOUCHET, CH. and LAFONT, R., "Emploi du nitrate de sodium dans la construction des polariseurs á champ normal", Compt. Rend. 1945; **221,** 7; 75

(*427*) DILLER, J. M., DEAN, J. C., DE GRAY, R. J. and WILSON, J. W., Jr., " A colour index of photo-electric colour of products from petroleum ", *Ind. Eng. Chem., Anal. Ed.*, 1943; **15,** 6; 367
(*428*) SNELL, F. D. and SNELL, C. T., *Colorimetric Methods of Analysis*, 1936, 2 vols. (Section on photo-electric colorimeters: vol .1; pp. 57. 100 references for different types of work).
(*429*) HARRIS, L. and SIEGEL, B. M., " A simplified photometer for determining nitrogen dioxide concentrations. Luminous radiation and photo-e.m.f. cells are used ". *Ind. Eng. Chem.*, Anal Ed., 1942; **14,** 3; 258
(*430*) PICHLER, A. A. B. and SIGGIA, S., " Endpoint of microtitrations with colour indicators using the coloriscopic capillary ", *Ind. Eng. Chem., Anal. Ed.*, 1942; **14,** 10; 828
(*431*) CLARK, G. L. and GROSS, S. T., " Technique and applications of industrial microradiography ", *Ind. Eng. Chem., Anal. Ed.*, 1942; **14,** 8; 676
(*432*) SAMMET, C. F., " Photo-electric colorimeter for the determination of turpentine ", *Ind. Eng. Chem., Anal. Ed.*, 1916; **8;** 519
(*433*) PETERS, B. G., " Photo-electric colorimeter for the determination of sewage ", *J. Helminthology*, 1929; **7;** 201
(*434*) BAWTREE, A. E., " Photo-electric colorimeter for the determination of sugar ", *Intern. Sugar J.*, 1920; **22;** 556
(*435*) PATERSON, W.—B.P. 314155 (1928) and PEET, G. D.—U.S. Pat. 1976672 (1934), " Photo-electric colorimeter for the determination of chlorine "
(*436*) SCHWARTZ, M. C. and MORRIS, L. W., " Studies in filter photometry ", *Ind. Eng. Chem., Anal. Ed.*, 1943; **15,** 1; 20
(*437*) OSBORN, R. H., ELLIOTT, J. H., MARTIN, A. F., " Photo-electric titration apparatus for dark resins ", *Ind. Eng. Chem., Anal. Ed.*, 1943; **15,** 10; 642
(*438*) SCHULTZ, J. and GOLDBERG, M. A., " Photometric routine estimation of traces of lead by dithizone. Endpoint of titration reached in 15 min., accuracy 1% ", *Ind. Eng. Chem., Anal. Ed.*, 1943; **15,** 2; 155
(*439*) HAMILTON, R. H., " Photo-electric photometry. An analysis of errors at high and at low absorption ", *Ind. Eng. Chem., Anal. E.*, 1944; **16,** 2; 123
(*440*) SMALLER, B. and HALL, J. F., Jr., " Carbon monoxide determination in air ", *Ind. Eng. Chem., Anal. Ed.*, 1944; **16,** 1; 64
(*441*) DE VAULT, D., " Vacuum tube scaling circuit ", *Rev. Sci. Instr.*, 1941; **12,** 2; 83, and 1943; **14,** 1; 23
(*442*) SILVERMAN, S., " Photo-electric turbidimeter; simple, very rugged; for use with very clear liquids; intensity measurements of fluorescent solutions ", *Rev. Sci. Instr.*, 1941; **12,** 2; 77
(*443*) BAY, Z., " Electron multiplier as an electron counting device ", *Rev. Sci. Instr.*, 1941; **12,** 3; 127
(*444*) ALLEN, J. S., " X-ray photon efficiency of a multiplier tube ", *Rev. Sci. Instr.*, 1941; **12,** 10; 484
(*445*) KUPFER. J. B. H., BRACKETT, F. S., EICHER, M., " Integrating ultra-violet photo-electric meter ", *Rev. Sci. Instr.*, 1941; **12,** 2; 87
(*446*) THOMAS, L. B., " A monochromatic source of Hg resonance radiation ", *Rev. Sci. Instr.*, 1941; **12,** 6; 309
(*447*) CRIST, P. W., " An improved optical lever ", *Rev. Sci. Instr.* 1941; **12,** 4; 214
(*448*) NOTTINGHAM, W. B., " Starting characteristics of a ' trigger ' tube with a radioactive cathode controlled by currents $<10^{-11}$ amp.", *Rev. Sci. Instr.*, 1940; **11,** 1; 2
(*449*) NEHLER, H. V. and PICKERING, W. H., " Two voltage regulators ", *Rev. Sci. Instr.*, 1939; **10,** 2; 53
(*450*) COLLINS, S. C. and BLAISDELL, B. E., " Illumination of mercury menisci ", *Rev. Sci. Instr.*, 1936; **7,** 5; 213
(*451*) ZELENY, JOHN, " Illumination of mercury menisci ", *Rev. Sci. Instr.*, 1936; **7,** 7; 289

(*452*) HARNWELL, G. P., "Thin windows for photo-electric cells", *Rev. Sci. Instr.*, 1936; **7,** 5; 216
(*453*) ROCHA, P. S. and GROSS, B., "Alternating-current voltage stabilizer", *Rev. Sci. Instr.*, 1936; **7,** 7; 290
(*454*) HAZEN, H. L., JAEGER, J. J. and BROWN, G. S., "Automatic curve follower", *Rev. Sci. Instr.*, 1936; **7,** 9; 353
(*455*) HOU, C. H., "Surface conductivity of ceresin-coated quartz", *Rev. Sci. Instr.*, 1938; **9,** 3; 90
(*456*) KERST, D. W., "High resolving power tenfold thyratron counter for 2,000 impulses per second", *Rev. Sci. Instr.*, 1938; **9,** 4; 131
(*457*) BAKER, E. B. and BOLTZ, H. A., "Photo-electric current limiting device for insulation measurements", *Rev. Sci. Instr.* 1938; **9,** 6; 196
(*458*) ASHWORTH, J. A. and MONSON, J. C., "Voltage stabilizer circuit using valves", *Rev. Sci. Instr.*, 1937; **8,** 4; 127
(*459*) STEVENSON, E. C. and GETTING, I. A., "Vacuum tube circuit for scaling down counting rates", *Rev. Sci. Instr.*, 1937; **8,** 11; 414
(*460*) KNORR, H. V. and ALBERS, V. M., "A new recording microphotometer", *Rev. Sci. Instr.*, 1937; **8,** 6; 183
(*461*) GABUS, G. H. and POOL, M. L., "A portable phototube unit using a RCA 954 valve. The amplifier is built of standard radio equipment", *Rev. Sci. Instr.*, 1937; **8,** 6; 196
(*462*) BYLER, W. H., "Measurement of the brightness of luminous paint with photo-e.m.f. cells used as photoconductors", *Rev. Sci. Instr.*, 1937; **8,** 1; 16
(*463*) KREBS, R. P., FERKINS, P., TYTELL, A. A., KERSTEN, H., "A turbidity comparator", *Rev. Sci. Instr.*, 1942; **13,** 5; 229.
(*464*) CHANCE, B., "Photo-electric colorimeter for rapid reactions", *Rev. Sci. Instr.*, 1942; **13,** 4; 158
(*465*) KREBS, R. P. and KERSTEN, H., "Time delay relay", *Rev. Sci. Instr.*, 1942; **13,** 2; 83
(*466*) REICH, H. J. "New vacuum valve counting circuits", *Rev. Sci. Instr.*, 1938; **9,** 7; 222
(*467*) BRONK, D. W., "Photo-electric colorimeter for blood analysis", *Rev. Sci. Instr.*, 1945; **16,** 6; 148
(*468*) HOUSTOUN, R. A., "The formula of the selenium barrier-layer cell", *Phil. Mag.*, 1942; **33,** vii, 218; 226
(Correction: *Phil. Mag.*, 1942; **33,** vii, 224; 699)
(*469*) ARCHER, C. T., "Variation of the thermal conductivity of carbon dioxide with temperature", *Phil. Mag.*, 1935; **19.** vii, 133; 901
(*470*) DAVIES, W., "Catalytic combustion of methane", *Phil. Mag.*, 1936; **21,** vii, 141; 513
(*471*) BOUTRY, G. A. and GILLOD, P., "A photo-emissive cell specially designed for high precision measurements", *Phil. Mag.*, 1939; **28,** vii, 187; 163
(*472*) BEALE, E. S. L. and STANSFIELD, R., "High speed engine indicators", *Engineer*, 1937; **163;** 4233
(*473*) BROOKES-SMITH, C. H. W. and ELLIS, J. A., "Electromagnetic pick-up", *J. Sci. Instr.*, 1939; **16,** 12; 361
(*474*) SCHROEDER, H. J., "Cathode-ray engine pressure measuring equipment; piezo-electric pick-up", *RCA Rev.*, 1937; **2;** 202
(*475*) *J. Sci. Instr.*, 1939; **16,** 1; 30
(*476*) *J. Sci. Instr.*, 1939; **16,** 2; 97
(*477*) ROBERTSON, A. F., "Engine pressure pick-up", *Rev. Sci. Instr.*, 1941; **12,** 3; 142
(*478*) ROES, L. C., "Engine pressure pick-up", *Rev. Sci. Instr.*, 1940; **11,** 6; 183
(*479*) BLISS, W. H., "Light modulator; chopper", *Radio Facsimile* (*RCA*), vol 1; p. 252
(*480*) CLOTHIER, W. K., "A 'hard' valve electronic relay switch", *J. Sci. Instr.*, 1939; **16,** 9; 285
(*481*) SCHMITT, O. H. "A thermionic trigger", *J. Sci. Instr.*, 1938; **15,** 1; 24

(*482*) Preston, J. S., " A portable photo-electric illumination meter ", *J. Sci. Instr.*, 1938; **15**, 3; 102
(*483*) Grace, A., " Photorelays ", *J. Sci. Instr.*, 1938; **15**, 4; 128
(*484*) Pressey, B. G. " A thyratron impulse generator; 4 to 200 impulses per second ", *J. Sci. Instr.*, 1938; **15**, 5; 163
(*485*) Ockelford, C. W., " A method of maintaining transparency in glass observation windows ", *J. Sci. Instr.*, 1938; **15**, 6; 190
(*486*) Uffelman, F. L., " A thyratron counter; 20,000 impulses per second ", *J. Sci. Instr.*, 1938; **15**, 7; 222
(*487*) Wheatcroft, E. L. E., " A direct voltage amplifier ", *J. Sci. Instr.*, 1938; **15**, 10; 333
(*488*) Madsen, C. B., " A counter circuit for d.c. mains ", *J. Sci. Instr.*, 1938; **15**, 11; 373
(*489*) " Comparative Gloss Meter ", *J. Sci. Instr.*, 1937; **14**, 1; 32
(*490*) Fertel, G. E. F., " Simple counting circuit ", *J. Sci. Instr.*, 1937; **14**, 4; 142
(*491*) " Transparency comparator ", *J. Sci. Instr.*, 1937; **14**, 4; 143
(*492*) Hill, S. G., " A photo-electric smoke penetrometer ", *J. Sci. Instr.*, 1937; **14**, 9; 296
(*493*) Baxter, A. " The reflexion and absorption of light by partially transparent films of aluminium and silver ", *J. Sci. Instr.*, 1937; **14**, 9; 303
(*494*) Richardson, E. G., " A photo-electric apparatus for delineating the size frequency curve of clays or dusts ", *J. Sci. Instr.*, 1936; **13**, 7; 229
(*495*) " Viscor correction filter ", *J. Sci. Instr.*, 1936; **13**, 10; 338
(*496*) " A mechanical counter of improved resolving power; 3,000 counts per minute, and more ", *J. Sci. Instr.*, 1936; **13**, 11; 367
(*497*) Barnard, G. P., " A portable photo-electric daylight factor meter ", *J. Sci. Instr.*, 1936; **13**, 12; 392
(*498*) Brookes, F. J. C., " Measurement of the Light Centre Length of electric lamps ", *J. Sci. Instr.*, 1936; **13**, 12; 414
(*499*) Sowerby, J. McG., " A photo-electric photometer for measuring the light scattered by the surface of a transparent material ", *J. Sci. Instr.*, 1944; **21**, 3; 42
(*500*) Goodall, K. L., " Physics and protection against dust ", *J. Sci. Instr.*, 1942; **19**, 3; 33
(*501*) Maddock, A. J., " Some useful circuits employing thyratrons and ignitrons ", *J. Sci. Instr.*, 1943; **20**, 3; 37
(*502*) Poole, J. H. J., and Gilmour, J. C., " A sensitive relay operated by fluid flow ", *J. Sci. Instr.*, 1943; **20**, 3; 49
(*503*) May, K. R., " Apparatus for coating surfaces with magnesium oxide ", *J. Sci. Instr.*, 1940; **17**, 9; 231
(*504*) Preston, J. S., " Photo-electric measurement of the average intensity of fluctuating light sources ", *J. Sci. Instr.*, 1941; **18**, 4; 57
(*505*) Poulter, A. C., " Simple photo-electric brightness meter ", *J. Sci. Instr.*, 1941; **18**, 8; 166
(*506*) Gluckauf, E., " A photo-electric method of measuring directly the ratio of two illuminations ", *J. Sci. Instr.*, 1945; **22**, 2; 34
(*507*) Wilkie, M. J., " A speed indicator for high speed shafts ", *J. Sci. Instr.*, 1945; **22**, 2; 36
(*508*) Cox, A. and Martin, H. W., " The assessment of lenses ", *J. Sci. Instr.*, 1945; **22**, 1; 5
(*509*) Greenland, K. M., " Theory of surface treatment of lenses ", *Nature*, 1943; **152**; 290
(*510*) Jones, L. W., " Notes on resistance of selenium cells deposited in certain gases, viz. oxygen, carbon dioxide, etc.", *J.O.S.A.*, 1935; **25**, 1; 1
(*511*) Hein, C. C., " Quantum efficiency of certain light sensitive devices ", *J.O.S.A.*, 1935; **25**, 7; 203
(*512*) Holmes, R. M., " Photo-e.m.f. and currents in single crystals of selenium ", *J.O.S.A.*, 1935; **25**, 10; 326
(*513*) Muller, R. H. and Kinney, G. F., " Photo-electric colorimeter with logarithmic response ", *J.O.S.A.*, 1935; **25**, 10; 342

(*514*) DIEKE, G. H. and CROSSWHITE, H. M., " Direct intensity measurements of spectrum lines with multiplier photocells ", *J.O.S.A.*, 1945; **35,** 7; 471
(*515*) TEELE, R. P., " Photometer for luminescent materials ", *J.O.S.A.*, 1945; **35,** 6; 373
(*516*) WALD, G. " The spectral sensitivity of the human eye ", *J.O.S.A.*, 1945; **35,** 3; 187
(*517*) Committee on Colorimetry, " Colorimeters and colour-standards ", *J.O.S.A.*, 1945; **35,** 1; 1
(*518*) HERZBERGER, M., " Replacing a thin lens by a thick lens ", *J.O.S.A.*, 1944; **34,** 2; 114
(*519*) WALLS, G. L., " Factors in human visual resolution ", *J.O.S.A.*, 1943; **33,** 9; 487
(*520*) BEGGS, E. W., " Activating light sources for luminescent materials ", *J.O.S.A.*, 1943; **33,** 2; 61
(*521*) NICOLL, F. H. and WILLIAMS, F. E., " Properties of low reflexion films ", *J.O.S.A.*, 1943; **33,** 8; 434
(*522*) ANDERSON, W. T., Jr., " Ultra-violet irradiation by means of linear high pressure mercury lamps ", *J.O.S.A.*, 1942; **32,** 2; 121
(*523*) STUTZ, G. F. A., " Luminescent pigments and coatings ", *J.O.S.A.*, 1942; **32,** 10; 626
(*524*) BEESE, N. C. and MARDEN, J. W., " Fatigue effect in luminescent materials ", *J.O.S.A.*, 1942; **32,** 6; 317
(*525*) BANNING, M., " The far ultra-violet reflectivities of metallic films ", *J.O.S.A.*, 1942; **32,** 2; 98
(*526*) DUNTLEY, S. Q., " Optical properties of diffusing materials ", *J.O.S.A.*, 1942; **32,** 2; 61
(*527*) RANK, D. H., PFISTER, R. J. and COLEMAN, P. D., " Photo-electric detection and intensity measurement in Raman spectra, using a multiplier photocell of the 931-A type ", *J.O.S.A.*, 1942; **32,** 7; 390
(*528*) COLBERT, W. and KREIDL, N. J., " Unusual colours produced by uranium in glasses ", *J.O.S.A.*, 1945; **35,** 11; 731
(*529*) SCHNEIDER, E. G., " Absorption by air in the extreme ultra-violet ", J.O.S.A., 1940; **30,** 3; 128
(*530*) BENFORD, F. " Transmission factors of ultra-violet radiation through water ", *J.O.S.A.*, 1940; **30,** 3; 133
(*531*) MARDEN, J. W., BEESE, N. C. and MEISTER, G., " Operating temperatures of vapour lamps ", *J.O.S.A.*, 1940; **30,** 4; 184
(*532*) RUSSELL, H. W., LUCKS, C. F. and TURNBULL, L. G., " A new two-colour optical pyrometer on photo-electric principles ", *J.O.S.A.*, 1940; **30,** 6; 248
(*533*) HARRISON, G. R. and MOLNAR, J. P., " Photo-electric measurement of scale marks and spectrum lines. The measurements are taken automatically ", *J.O.S.A.*, 1940; **30,** 8; 343
(*534*) GRAHAM, R., " A variable focus lens and its uses ", *J.O.S.A.*, 1940; **30,** 11; 560
(*535*) PFUND, A. H., " Colours of mosaic powder films ", *J.O.S.A.*, 1939; **29,** 1; 10
(*536*) PFUND, A. H., " Screens for the near infra-red ", *J.O.S.A.*, 1939; **29,** 2; 56
(*537*) BENFORD, F., " Temperature corrections in optical pyrometry ", *J.O.S.A.*, 1939; **29,** 4; 162
(*538*) TAYLOR, A. H. " Ultra-violet meter ", *J.O.S.A.*, 1939; **29,** 5; 218
(*539*) KNIAZUK, M., " Null indicator for matching light intensities " *J.O.S.A.*, 1939; **29,** 6; 223
(*540*) PERKINS, T. B., " An automatic spectral sensitivity curve tracer ", *J.O.S.A.*, 1939; **29,** 6; 226
(*541*) BEESE, N. C., " The response of several fluorescent materials to short wavelength ultra-violet radiations ", *J.O.S.A.*, 1939; **29,** 7; 278
(*542*) JOHNSON, R. P., " Luminescence of sulphide and silicate phosphors ", *J.O.S.A.*, 1939; **29,** 9; 387

(*543*) BARNES, B. T. " A four-filter photo-electric colorimeter ", *J.O.S.A.*, 1939; **29,** 10; 448
(*544*) JOHNSON, E. A., MOCK, W. H. and HOPKINS, R. E., " Limiting sensitivity of the a.c. method of photocell-current amplification ", *J.O.S.A.*, 1939; **29,** 12; 506
(*545*) ALEXANDER, E. H., " Measuring continuously the width of moving webs or strips; applications in the paper, textile, and metal industry ", *G.E. Rev.*, 1941; **44,** 11; 615
(*546*) MALPICA, J. T. MIRELES, " Blocking layer cell colour temperature pyrometer ", *G.E. Rev.*, 1941; **44,** 8; 439
(*547*) " Weft straightening ", *G.E. Rev.*, 1942; **45,** 1; 28
(*548*) " Multicolour gravure printing control ", *G.E. Rev.*, 1942; **45,** 1; 30
(*549*) CLARK, H. L., " High Speed photo-electric recorder ", *G.E. Rev.*, 1942; **45,** 7; 384
(*550*) DALTON, B. J., " Electronic motor control ", *G.E. Rev.*, 1945; **48,** 5; 12
(*551*) BOUMA, P. J., " Characteristics of the eye ", *Ph. T. Rev.*, 1936; **1,** 4; 102
(*552*) BOUMA, P. J., " Visual acuity and speed of vision ", *Ph. T. Rev.*, 1936; **1,** 7; 215
(*553*) BOUMA, P. J., " The perception of colour ", *Ph. T. Rev.*, 1936; **1,** 9; 283
(*554*) GISOLF, J. H. and DEGROOT, W., " Fluorescence and phosphorescence ", *Ph. T. Rev.*, 1938; **3,** 8; 241
(*555*) UYTERHOEVEN, W. and ZECHER, G. " Low-pressure mercury discharge within a luminous tube ", *Ph. T. Rev.*, 1938; **3,** 9; 272
(*556*) HALBERTSMA, N. A. and ITTMANN, G. P., " Illumination by means of linear sources of light ", *Ph. T. Rev.*, 1939; **4,** 7; 181
(*557*) SCHOUWSTRA, F. and ZECHER, G., " Tubular luminescence lamp ", *Ph. T. Rev.*, 1939; **4,** 12; 338
(*558*) VAN DIJK, B., " Several problems of X-ray fluoroscopy ", *Ph. T. Rev.*, 1939; **4,** 4; 114
(*559*) HALBERTSMA, N. A., " Reflecting surfaces in the neighbourhood of linear sources of light ", *Ph. T. Rev.*, 1940; **5,** 1; 16
(*560*) BARR, W. and PEARSON, T. F., " Physical control methods in the steel industry ", *J. Sci. Instr.*, 1945; **22,** 1; 1
(*561*) TAYLOR, A. H. and KERR, G. P., " Distribution of energy in the visible spectrum of daylight ", *J.O.S.A.*, 1941; **31,** 1; 3
(*562*) LUCKIESH, M. and HOLLADAY, L. L., " Penetration of fog by light from sodium and tungsten lamps " *J.O.S.A.*, 1941; **31,** 8; 528
(*563*) " Double photo-electric recorder ", *G.E. Rev.*, 1938; **41,** 1; 20
(*564*) " Photo-electric car washing equipment ", *G.E. Rev.*, 1938; **41,** 6; 295
(*565*) " Continuous steel strip inspection for pin holes at speeds of 900 ft./min.), *G.E. Rev.*, 1938; **41,** 12; 559
(*566*) " Double photo-electric recorder ", *G.E. Rev.*, 1937; **40,** 5; 228
(*567*) " Photo-electric control for removing skew from cotton cloth ", *G.E. Rev.*, 1937; **40,** 6; 305
(*568*) MIGHELL, R. H., " The light sensitive cell, describing the G.E. selenium-on-iron cell ", *G.E. Rev.*, 1937; **40,** 8; 372
(*569*) CARSON, W. L., " Applications of the photo-electric recorder ", *G.E. Rev.*, 1936; **39,** 4; 189
(*570*) GISOLF, J. H., " The counting of electrons by means of a discharge tube ", *Physica*, 1937; **4,** 1; 69
(*571*) WILSON, E. D., " Comparison of photo-emissive and photovoltaic devices ", *Trans. Electrochem. Soc.*, 1936; **69;** 433
(*572*) FOGLE, M. E., " Applications of the photronic photocell to chemical processes ", *Trans. Electrochem. Soc.*, 1936; **69;** 443
(*573*) MULLER, R. H. and TEETERS, W. O., " Study of the sensitization of cuprous oxide barrier-layer photo-electric cell ", *Trans. Electrochem. Soc.*, 1936; **69;** 457
(*574*) CYMBOLISTE, M., " The formation and growth of pits (pinholes) in electro-deposited metals ", *Trans. Electrochem. Soc.* 1936; **70;** 379

(575) RENTSCHLER, H. C., " Photo-electric cells ", *Trans. Electrochem. Soc.*, 1937; **71;** 45
(576) CLARK, G. L. and ROACH, P. G., " An X-ray study of the structure of rectifying selenium films ", *Trans. Electrochem. Soc.*, 1941; **79;** 355
(577) FOGLE, M. E., " Temperature measurement and control with solid photo-electric cells ", *Trans. Electrochem. Soc.*, 1943; **83;** 77
(578) COETERIER, F. and TEVES, M. C., " An apparatus for the transformation of light of long wavelength into light of short wavelength ", *Physica*, 1937; *4*, 1; 33
(579) COETERIER, F. and TEVES, M. C., " An apparatus for the transformation of light of long wavelength into light of short wavelength ", *Physica*, 1933; **1**, 4; 297
(580) LANE, F. E., " Some aspects of special electron tubes; electron multipliers ", *J. Brit. I.R.E.*, 1945; **5,** new series, 2
(581) KUBETSKY, L. A., " Multiple amplifier ", *Proc. I.R.E.*, 1937; **25,** 4; 421
(582) COCKRELL, W. D., " Is industrial electronic technique different? ", *Proc. I.R.E.*, 1945; **33,** 4; 217
(583) HUMPHREY, H. C., " Electronic tin fusion ", *Proc. I.R.E.*, 1944; **32,** 2; 61
(584) THOMPSON, B. J., " Voltage-controlled electron multiplier " *Proc. I.R.E.*, 1941; **29,** 11; 583
(585) LUCKIESH, M. and MOSS, F. K., " Infra-red radiation and visual function ", *J.O.S.A.*, 1937; **27,** 2; 69
(586) KENT, C. V. and LAWSON, J., " A photo-electric method for the determination of the parameters of elliptically polarized light ", *J.O.S.A.*, 1937; **27,** 3; 117
(587) FROST, A. A., " A photometric comparison of absorption lines ", *J.O.S.A.*, 1937; **27,** 4; 147
(588) IVES, H. E. and BRIGGS, H. B., ' The optical constants of potassium ", *J.O.S.A.*, 1936; **26**, 8; 238
(589) HUNTER, R. S., Problems in the development of a multiple purpose reflectometer ", *J.O.S.A.*, 1937; **27,** 6; 225
(590) KUNZ, J., TYKOCINER, J. T. and GARNER, L. P., " Water vapour in the construction of more sensitive photo-electric cells of alkali metals ", *J.O.S.A.*, 1937; **27,** 10; 354
(591) SCHLAER, S., " Photo-electric transmission spectrophotometer for the measurement of photosensitive solutions ", *J.O.S.A.*, 1938; **28,** 1; 28
(592) ELVEGARD, E., LINDROTH, S. and LARSSON, E., " Drift effect in selenium photovoltaic cells ", *J.O.S.A.*, 1938; **28,** 2; 33
(593) ELVEGARD, E., LINDROTH, S., and LARSSON, E., " Resistance in selenium photovoltaic cells ", *J.O.S.A.*, 1938; **28,** 2; 36
(594) MACADAM, D. L., " Photometric relationship between complementary colours ", *J.O.S.A.*, 1938; **28,** 4; 103
(595) STAATS, E. M., " Design of monochromatic filters for the type H-3 mercury lamp ", *J.O.S.A.*, 1938; **28,** 4; 112
(596) ALBERS, V. M. and KNOLL, H. V., " Recording photo-electric spectroradiometer ", *J.O.S.A.*, 1938; **28,** 4; 121
(597) FORSYTHE, W. E., BARNES, B. T. and SHRIDER, A. L., " Photometry of coloured light sources ", *J.O.S.A.*, 1938; **28,** 7; 241
(598) IVES, H. E. and BRIGGS, H. B., " Correlation of optical properties and photo-electric emission in thin films of alkali metals ", *J.O.S.A.*, 1938; **28,** 9; 330
(599) CARR, E. P. and STUCKLEN, H., " Ultra-violet absorption of benzene ", *J. Chem. Phys.*, 1938; **6,** 2; 55
(600) COHN, W. M., " A spectral investigation of glucose glass ", *J. Chem. Phys.*, 1938; **6,** 2; 65
(601) FORSYTHE, W. E. and ADAMS, E. Q., *G.E. Rev.*, 1944; **47,** 10; 59
(602) Standard Handbook for Electrical Engineers
(603) FORSYTHE, W. E. and ADAMS, E. Q., *J.O.S.A.*, 1945; **35,** 2; 108
(604) BARNES, B. T. and FORSYTHE, W. E., *J.O.S.A.*, 1936; **26,** 8; 313

(*605*) Ives, H. E., *Proc. Roy. Soc. Lond.*, 1929; A122; 304
(*606*) Barnes, B. T. and Forsythe, W. E., *J.O.S.A.*, 1937; **27,** 2; 83
(*607*) Anderson, W. T., Jr. and Bird, L. F., *J.O.S.A.*, 1937; **27,** 3; 95
(*608*) Valasek, J., *Elements of Optics*, 1932; 233
(*609*) Eshbach, *Handbook of Engineering Fundamentals*, 1932
(*610*) Skogland, J. F., *Misc. Publ. Nat. Bur. Stand.*, 1929; 86
(*611*) Millar, P. S., *Electr. Eng.*, 1944; **63,** 4; 126
(*612*) Langmuir, I., *G.E. Rev.*, 1914; **17;** 294
(*613*) Gibson, K. S., *J.O.S.A.*, 1940; **30,** 2; 55
(*614*) Pringsheim, L. and Vogel, M., *Luminescence*, 1943
(*615*) Watts, H. E. G., *Electrical Rev.*, 1944; Sept. 25th; 445
(*616*) Dushman, S., *G.E. Rev.*, 1934; **37;** 262
(*617*) Buttolph, L. J., *J.O.S.A.*, 1939; **29,** 3; 124
(*618*) Bourne, H. K., *J. Sci. Instr.*, 1945; **22,** 6; 107
(*619*) Fonda, G. R., *J.O.S.A.*, 1935; **25,** 12; 412
(*620*) Harris and Jenkins, *G.E.C. Journal*, 1931; **2,** 8; 63
(*621*) Harris, N. L., *J. Sci. Instr.*, 1939; **16,** 6; 173
(*622*) Beggs, E. W., *J.O.S.A.*, 1943; **33,** 2; 61
(*623*) Smiley, G., *Electronics*, 1941; **14,** 1; 29
(*624*) Hunter, R. S., *J.O.S.A.*, 1946; **36,** 3; 178
(*625*) Forsythe, W. E., Barnes, B. T. and Easley, M. A., *J.O.S.A.*, 1931; **21,** 1; 30
(*626*) Taylor, A. H., *J.O.S.A.*, 1931; **21,** 1; 20
(*627*) Gibson, K. S., *J.O.S.A.*, 1940; **30,** 2; 51
(*628*) Dushman, S., *J.O.S.A.*, 1937; **27,** 1; 1
(*629*) *Electronics* 1944; **17,** 2; 118
(*630*) Haynes, *Illumin. Eng. Soc.*, 1941; **36;** 61
(*631*) Winans, J. G., *Rev. Sci. Instr.*, 1938; **9,** 6; 203
(*632*) Barker, A. K., *Electronics*, 1939; **12,** 9; 52
(*633*) Reich, H. J., *Rev. Sci. Instr.*, 1931; **2;** 164, 234
(*634*) Case, T. W., *Phys. Rev.* 921; **17;** 398
(*635*) Newbury, K. and Lamery, F., *J.O.S.A.*, 1931; **21,** 5; 276
(*636*) Stager, A., *Electronics*, 1937; **10,** 7; 29
(*637*) *Electronics*, 1931; **2,** 1; 467
(*638*) LaPierre, G. W. and Mansfield, A. P., *Electronics*, 1945; **18,** 11; 316
(*639*) Clothier, W. K., *J. Sci. Instr.*, 1939; **16,** 9; 285
(*640*) Köhler, J. W. L., *Ph. T. Rev.*, 1936; **1,** 5; 152
(*641*) Schulman, D., *Electronics*, 1945; **18,** 2; 177
(*642*) Hunt, V. F., *Rev. Sci. Instr.*, 1935; **6,** 2; 43
(*643*) Kline, J. F., *Electronics*, 1945; **18,** 6; 258
(*644*) Thomas, E. L., *Electronic Engineering*, 1945; **17,** 205; 409
(645) LeClair, W. E., *Electronics*, 1943; **16,** 5; 122
(*646*) Schouten, J. F., *Ph. T. Rev.*, 1939; **4,** 6; 167
(*647*) Schouten, J. F., *Proc. Kon. Ned. Akad. Wet.*, 1938; **41;** 1086
(*648*) Harris, L. and Scholp, L. C., *Rev. Sci. Instr.*, 1940; **11,** 1; 23
(*649*) Timmer, A. L. and van Assum, A. H., *Ph. T. Rev.*, 1936; **1,** 10; 307
(*650*) Gage, H. P., *J.O.S.A.*, 1937; **27,** 4; 159
(*651*) Yarsley, V. E., *Plastics Applied*, 1945
(*652*) Lougee, E. F., *Mod. Plastics*, 1944; **21,** 12; 90
(*653*) Johnston, B. K., *J. Sci. Instr.*, 1934; **11,** 11; 390
(*654*) Drummond, D. G., *Proc. Roy. Soc. Lond.*, 1936; A153; 318
(*655*) The Thermal Syndicate, Ltd., *About Vitreosil, A Reference Handbook*
(*656*) Murray, H. D. and Spencer, D. A., *Colour Filters*, 1939
(*657*) The Eastman Kodak Company, *Wratten Light Filters*
(*658*) Costey, R. S., *J.O.S.A.*, 1936; **26,** 7; 293
(*659*) Bayley, P. L., *J.O.S.A.*, 1937; **27,** 8; 303
(*660*) Hulburt, E. O., *J.O.S.A.*, 1935; **25,** 5; 125
(*661*) Koller, L. R., *G.E. Rev.*, 1936; **39,** 5; 232
(*662*) Dawson, L. H. and Hulburt, E. O., *J.O.S.A.*, 1937; **27,** 6; 199
(*663*) Pfund, A. H., *J.O.S.A.*, 1934; **24,** 6; 143

(664) Plummer, J. H., *J.O.S.A.*, 1936; **26,** 12; 434
(665) Christiansen, C., *Ann. Phys. & Chem.*, 1884; **23;** 298
(666) Christiansen, C., *Wied. Ann.*, 1885; **24;** 439
(667) MacAlister, E. D., *Smithsonian Misc. Publ., 3297*; 1935
(668) Forsythe, W. E., *The Measurement of Radiant Energy*, 1937
(669) Weigert, F. and Shidei, J., *Z. Phys. Chem.*, 1930; B9; 329
(670) Fragstein, K. v., *Ann. d. Phys.*, 1933; **17,** 5; 22
(671) Denmark, H. S. and Cady, W. M., *J.O.S.A.*, 1935; **25,** 10; 330
(672) Mees, C. E. K., *An Atlas of Absorption Spectra*, 1909
(673) Gibson, K. S., *J.O.S.A.*, 1935; **25,** 3; 131
(674) Gibson, K. S., *Nat. Bur. Stand. J. Res.*, 1935; **14;** 545; RP 785
(675) Barnes, R. B. and Bonner, L. G., *J.O.S.A.*, 1936; **26,** 11; 428
(676) Grabau, M., *J.O.S.A.*, 1937; **27,** 11; 420
(677) Grabau, M., *J. Appl. Phys.*, 1938; **9,** 4; 215
(678) Hyde, E. P., Forsythe, W. E. and Cady, F. E., *Astrophys. J.*, 1918; **48;** 65
(679) Gibson, K. S. and Tyndall, E. P. T., *Trans. Ill. Eng. Soc.*, 1924; **19,** 1; 176
(680) d'Angers, P. Pothiers, *Pharmacopea spagirica*, 1635, 3rd edit., vol. 2, last chapt. p. 264
(681) Becquerel, E., *La Lumière*,1867; **1;** 16
(682) Hirschlaff, E., *Fluorescence and Phosphorescence*, 1938
(683) Levy, L. and West, D. W., *Endeavour*, 1943; **2,** 5; 22
(684) Hardy, A. E., *Trans. Electrochem. Soc.*, 1945; 87 (preprint)
(685) Verneuil, A., *Comp. rend.*, 1886; **103;** 600
(686) Lenard, P. and Klatt, V., *Ann. d. Phys.*, 1904; **105;** 286
(687) Lenard, P., *Phosphorescence and Fluorescence*, 1938
(688) " Luminescence Survey ", *Electronics*, 1943; **16,** 5; 156
(689) De Ment, J. A., *Fluorescent Chemicals and their Applications*, 1942
(690) Leverenz, H. W., *Proc. I.R.E.*, 1944; **32,** 5; 256
(691) Tasker, H. S. and Dub, H., *Brit. Pat. 557841* (1943)
(692) Clark, G. L., *Applied X-rays*, 1940
(693) Hill, C. G. A., *Trans. I.E.E.*, 1945; **92,** III, 20; 299
(697) Leverenz, H. W., *RCA Rev.*, 1940; **5;** 131
(695) *Electronics*, 1943; **16,** 2
(696) Francesconi e Bargellini, *Accad. Lincei, Atti*, 1906; **15;** 184
(697) Thayer, R. N. and Barnes, B. T., *J.O.S.A.*, 1939; **29,** 4; 131
(698) Harris, D. T., *The technique of ultra-violet radiology*, 1932
(699) Sproull, W. T., *Electronics*, 1945; **18,** 6; 122
(700) Radley, J. A. and Grant, J., *Fluorescence Analysis in ultra-violet light*, 1939
(701) Dhar, N. R., *The Chemical action of light*, 1931
(702) Hanovia Ltd., *Rapid Testing by Fluorescence*
(703) *G.E. Rev.*, 1939; **42,** 1; 52
(704) Goodman, C., *Rev. Sci. Instr.*, 1938; **9,** 8; 233
(705) *Electronics*, 1945; **18,** 4; 176
(706) Woodson, T. T., *Rev. Sci. Instr.*, 1939; **10,** 10; 308
(707) Wood, R. W., *Physical Optics*, 1910
(708) Müller, K. and Pringsheim, P., *Naturwiss.*, 1930; **18;** 364
(709) Saville, W. *The Strowger Journal*, 1939; **5,** 1; 17
(710) Oldham, M. S. and Kunerth, W., *J.O.S.A.*, 1941; **31,** 2; 102
(711) *Scientific American*, 1943; **200,** 5; 168
(712) *Iron Age*, 1942; **150,** 56; Dec. 17
(713) *Iron Age*, 1942; **150,** 69; Nov. 26
(714) De Ment, J., *Petroleum Refiner*, 1943; **22;** 83
(715) Déribéré, M., *Les Applications pratiques de la Luminescence*, 1938
(716) Luckiesh, M. and Holladay, L. L., *G.E. Rev.*, 1944; **47,** 4; 45
(717) Morton, G. A., *J. Soc. Mot. Pict. Eng.*, 1936; **27;** 321
(718) Zworykin, V. K. and Morton, G. A., *J.O.S.A.*, 1936; **26,** 4; 181
(719) Zworykin, V. K., *Electronics*, 1936; **9;** 16
(720) Coeterier, F. and Teves, M. C., *Physica*, 1936; **3,** 9; 968
(721) Vedder, E. H., *Trans. A.S.M.E.*, 1944; **66,** 5; 261

(722) JOHNSON, R. P., *J.O.S.A.*, 1939; **29**, 9; 387
(723) *Brit. Pat. 295230*
(724) NICHOLS, E. L. and MERRITT, E., *Studies in Luminescence*, 1912
(725) LEWSCHIN, V. L., ANTONOW-ROMANOVSKY, V. V. and TUMERMAN, L. A., *Comp. Rend.* (U.S.S.R.), 1933; 276
(726) LEWSCHIN, V. L., ANTONOW-ROMANOVSKY, V. V. and TUMERMAN, L. A., *Phys. Z. d. Sowjet Union*, 1934; **5**; 811
(727) *G.P. 629800* (1936)
(728) *Electronics*, 1944; **17**, 9; 160
(729) SMITH, H. M., *G.E. Rev.*, 1945; **48**, 3; 13
(730) BLAU, M. and DREYFUS, B., *Rev. Sci. Instr.*, 1945; **16**, 9; 245
(731) WOLF, P. M. and RIEHL, N., *Ann. d. Phys.*, 1931; **11**; 108
(732) TAYLOR, J. and CLARKSON. W., *J. Sci. Instr.*, 1924; **1**; 173
(733) TAYLOR, A. H., *J.O.S.A.*, 1939; **29**, 5; 218
(734) LUCKIESH, M. and TAYLOR, A. H., *Rev. Sci. Instr.*, 1940; **11**, 3; 110
(735) ANDREWS, H. L., *Rev. Sci. Instr.*, 1945; **16**, 9; 253
(736) KOCH, W., *Nature*, 1944; **154**. 3903; 239
(737) KREBS, R. P. and KERSTEN, H. J., *Ind. Eng. Chem., Anal. Ed.*, 1943; **15**, 2; 132
(738) TEELE, R. P., *J.O.S.A.*, 1945; **35**, 6; 373
(739) EULER, F. J., Jr., KALSTEIN, J. E. and ZAVALES, C. T., *Electronics*, 1945; **18**, 1; 146
(740) MORGAN, O. M. and LANKLER, J. G., *Ind. Eng. Chem., Anal. Ed.*, 1942; **14**, 9; 725
(741) STANSKY, M. E. and DASSOW, J. A., *Ind. Eng. Chem., Anal. Ed.*, 1942; **14**, 1; 13
(742) Half-Yearly Report of the Inspectors of Factories, 1835, June 10; p. 48
(743) *Parliamentary Papers*, 1841; **9**; 25
(744) *Annual Report of the Chief Inspector of Factories*, 1941; p. 6
(745) SOMMER, W., *Industry Illustrated*, 1944; **12**, 11; 22
(746) FITZGERALD, A. S., *Electronics*, 1935; **8**, 10; 368
(747) *Electronics*, 1944; **17**, 7; 125
(748) KAUFMANN, M. *The Protective Gear Handbook*, 1945
(749) *Electronics*, 1943; **16**, 8; 130
(750) *Electronics*, 1942; **15**, 2
(751) *Electronics*, 1934; **7**, 10; 316
(752) Department of Scientific and Industrial Research. *Methods for the Detection of Toxic Gases in Industry* (12 Leaflets; H.M.S.O.)
(753) HALDANE, J. S. and GRAHAM, J. J., *Methods of Air Analysis*, 1935
(754) HANSON, V. F., *Electronics*, 1941; **14**, 1; 40
(755) HANSON, V. F., *U.S.P. 2286985*
(756) SILVERMAN, S., *Ind. Eng. Chem., Anal. Ed.*, 1943; **15**, 9; 592
(757) SILVERMAN, S., *Electronics*, 1944; **17**, 9; 148
(758) LAMBERT, P. and LECONITZ, J., *Comp. Rend.*, 1932; **194**; 77
(759) LOWED-BILLROTH, H., *Z. Phys. Chemie*, 1932; B19; 76
(760) MECKE, R., *Z. Astrophys.*, 1933; **6**; 144
(761) CHILDS, W. H. J., *Proc. Roy. Soc. Lond.*, 1936; A153; 555
(762) NORRIS, W. V. and UNGER, H. J., *Phys. Rev.*, 1933; **43**; 467
(763) GLOCKER, G., *Proc. Nat. Acad. Science*, 1925; **11**; 74
(764) KREMULA, W. and MRAZEK, ST., *Comp. Rend.*, 1932; **195**; 1004
(765) DUNCAN, A. B. F. and HOWE, J. P., *J. Chem. Phys.*, 1934; **2**; 851
(766) KREMENEVSKY, N., *Z. Physik*, 1931; **71**; 792
(767) *Electronics*, 1930; **1**; 5
(768) *Ind. Eng. Chem., Ind. Ed.*, 1945; **37**, 4; 78
(769) *Electronics*, 1944; **17**, 9; 148
(770) BEHRENS, F. B., *Oil & Gas J.*, 1940; March 28
(771) LESTER, D. and ORDUNG, PH. F., *J. Ind. Hygiene & Toxicology*, 1944; **26**, 6; 197
(772) *Ind. Heating*, 1943; **10**, 4; 565

(773) Beatty, R. L., Berger, L. B. and Schrenck, H. H.. Bureau of Mines, Dept. of the Interior, Washington
(774) Bycichin and Laska, *Chem. Listy* (*C.S.R.*), 1936; **30**; 149
(775) *Ind. Eng. Chem., Ind. Ed.*, 1945; **37**, 7; 71
(776) Cole, P. A. and Armstrong, D. W., *J.O.S.A.*, 1941; **31**, 12; 740
(777) Cole, P. A., *J.O.S.A.*, 1942; **32**, 5; 304
(778) Zhitkova, A. S., *Some Methods for the Detection and Estimation of Poisonous Gases and Vapours in the Air*, 1931
(779) Nordländer, B. W., *Ind. Eng. Chem.*, 1927; **19**; 518
(780) Lester, D., *J. Ind. Hygiene & Toxicology*, 1944; **26**, 2; 61
(781) Perepelitzka, V. K., *Bull. Makeevski Sci. Instr., Safety in Mines*, 1939; **5**; 4
(782) Perepelitzka, V. K., *Bull. Makeevski Sci. Instr., Safety in Mines*, 1939; **7**; 7
(783) Perepelitzka, V. K., *Bull. Makeevski Sci. Instr., Safety in Mines*. 1940; **11**; 7
(784) Martienssen, H., *Z. Techn. Phys.*, 1924; p. 519
(785) Safety in Mines Research Board, *Paper No. 19*
(786) Preventive Engineering Series of the Air Hygiene Foundation of America, Inc., Pittsburgh, Penn., *Bull. 2*; Part 3
(787) Schrenck, H. H., Pierce and Yaut, Bureau of Mines, *Report of Investigation 3287*; Oct. 1935
(788) Preventive Engineering Series of the Air Hygiene Foundation of America, Inc., Pittsburgh, Penn., *Bull. 2*; Part 1
(789) Davies, W., *Brit. Colliery Owners Res. Ass.* (*B.C.O.R.A.*), Quart. Bull., 1945; **5**; 10
(790) Davies, W., *Phil. Mag.*, 1934; **17**, vii; 233
(791) Davies, W., *Phil. Mag.*, 1935; **19**, vii; 309
(792) Davies, W., *Phil. Mag.*, 1936; **21**, vii; 513
(793) Davies, W., *Fuel*, 1943; **22**; 72
(794) Hansen, C. A., Jr., *G.E. Rev.*, 1940; **43**, 4; 166
(795) Roberts, S. and Minors, G., *J. Soc. Chem. Ind.*, 1934; **53**, 24; 529
(796) Müller, F., *Physikalische Methoden der Anal. Chemie* (W. Böttger, Editor), 1939. English Translation, 1943; 3 vols. *Die Photelektrischen Methoden der Analyse*, vol. 3, p. 322 (500 references)
(797) *Electrical Times*, 1944; Nov. 9, and Nov. 30
(798) *Electrical News and Engineering*, 1934; **43**; 27
(799) *G.E. Rev.*, 1936; **39**, 6; 309
(800) *Electronics*, 1931; **3**, 10; 156
(801) *Electronics*, 1933; **6**, 4; 103
(802) Maine Technology Experimental Station, *Bull. 28*
(803) *Electronics*, 1934; **7**, 12
(804) *Electronics*, 1934; **7**, 1
(805) Sukhikh, V. A., *Trans. All-Union Conference on Analytical Chemistry*, 1943; **2**; 258 (in Russian)
(806) *Industrial Chemist*, 1945; **21**, 249; 557
(807) Geffcken, H., Richter, H. and Winckelmann, L., *Die Lichtempfindliche Zelle als Technisches Steuerorgan*, 1935
(808) Kluge, W. and Briebacher, H., *V.D.I.*, 1934; **78**; 935
(809) Barnett, C. E., *J. Phys. Chem.*, 1942; **46**; 69
(810) *Electronics*, 1945; **18**, 6; 180
(811) *E.T.Z.*, 1936; **57**, 6; 155
(812) Plank, R., *V.D.I.*, 1940; **84**, 10; 165
(813) *Electronics*, 1945; **18**, 2; 416
(814) Carruthers, Chr., *Ind. Eng. Chem., Anal. Ed.*, 1942; **14**, 10; 826
(815) Isaacs, M. L., *Ind. Eng. Chem., Anal. Ed.*, 1942; **14**, 12; 948
(816) Diller, I. M., De Gray, R. J. and Wilson, J. W., Jr., *Ind. Eng. Chem., Anal. Ed.*, 1942; **14**, 8; 607
(817) *Oil & Gas J.*, 1945; June 16; 120
(818) Hochgesang, F. P. and Schlesman, C. H., *Electronics*, 1944; **17**, 9; 116

(*819*) Ives, H. E. and Kingsbury, E. F., *J.O.S.A.*, 1931; **21,** 5; 541
(*820*) van den Akker, J. A., *J.O.S.A.*, 1937; **27,** 12; 401
(*821*) Davenport, T. B., *J. Sci. Instr.*, 1944; **21,** 5; 84
(*822*) Davenport, T. B., *J. Sci.*, 1944; **21,** 10; 188
(*823*) Spengler, O. and Hirschmüller, H., *Z. Wirtsch. Zuckerind.*, 1940; **90;** 426
(*824*) Spengler, O. and Hirschmüller, H., *Int. Sugar J.*, 1941; **43;** 283
(*825*) Evans, R. M. and Silberstein, E. P., *J. Soc. Mot. Pict. Eng.*, 1939; **30,** 3
(*826*) Morton, G. A. and Heilbron, I. M., *Biochemical J.*, 1928; **22;** 987
(*827*) Morton, G. A. and Heilbron, I. M., *Nature*, 1928; **122,** 3062; 10
(*828*) Morgareidge, K., *Ind. Eng. Chem., Anal. Ed.*, 1942; **14,** 9; 700
(*829*) Zscheile, F. P. and Henry, R. L., *Ind. Eng. Chem., Anal. Ed.*, 1942; **14,** 5; 422
(*830*) McFarlan, R. L., Reddie, J. W., Merrill, E. C., *Ind. Eng. Chem., Anal. Ed.*, 1937; **9,** 7; 324
(*831*) *Ind. Eng. Chem., Ind. Ed.*, 1945; **37,** 6; 81
(*832*) Morgan, R. H., *Am. J. Roentgenology and Radium Therapy*, 1942; **48,** 2; 88
(*833*) Liebhafsky, H. A. and Winslow, E. H., *G.E. Rev.*, 1945; **48,** 4; 36
(*834*) Baier, J. G., *Ind. Eng. Chem., Anal. Ed.*, 1943; **15,** 2; 144
(*835*) Baier, J. G., *Electronics*, 1944; **17,** 7; 226
(*836*) Wilson, J. L. and Mendenhall, E. E., *Ind. Eng. Chem., Anal. Ed.*, 1944; **16,** 4; 251
(*837*) Klotz, I. M., *Ind. Eng. Chem., Anal. Ed.*, 1943; **15,** 4; 277
(*838*) Müller, R. H. and Partridge, H. M., *Ind. Eng. Chem., Anal. Ed.*, 1928; **20;** 423
(*839*) Hartridge, H. and Harris, D. T., *J. Sci. Instr.*, 1929; **6,** 1; 74
(*840*) *Z.f. Elektrochemie*, 1934; **40,** 1; 46
(*841*) Lee, J. A., *Trans. Electrochem. Soc.*, 1931; **59;** 229
(*842*) *Chem. & Met. Eng.*, 1945, March
(*843*) *Revue générale Electrique*, 1934; **35,** 1; 125
(*844*) *Electronics*, 1934; **7,** 4; 126
(*845*) Finley, R., *Electronics*, 1937; **10,** 11; 39
(*846*) Gutmann, F., *Textile J. Australia*, 1945; **20;** 45
(*847*) Lothian, G. F., *Trans. Faraday Soc.*, 1937; **33;** 1239
(*848*) Moyle, C. L. and Bass, S. L., *U.S.P., 2151984*
(*849*) Larsen, B. M. and Shenk, W. E., *J. Appl. Phys.*, 1940; **11;** 555
(*850*) Larsen, B. M. and Shenk, W. E., *U.S.P. 2054382*
(*851*) *Electrical Times*, 1944; Dec. 7; p. 666
(*852*) Vedder, E. H. and Evans, M. S., *Electrical Engineering* (*A.I.E.E.*), 1935; **54,** 6; 645
(*853*) *Ind. Heating*, 1943; **10,** 5; 664
(*854*) Roess, L. C. and Dacus, E. N., *Rev. Sci. Instr.*, 1945; **16,** 7; 164
(*855*) Zabel, R. M. and Hancox, R. R., *Rev. Sci. Instr.*, 1934; **5,** 1; 28
(*856*) *Electronics*, 1944; **17,** 11; 236
(*857*) King, W. R., *G.E. Rev.*, 1936; **39;** 526
(*858*) *Electronics*, 1931; **3,** 11
(*859*) Hubing, G. F., *J.O.S.A.*, 1936; **26,** 6; 260
(*860*) Powers, R. A., *Electronics*, 1937; **10,** 4; 12
(*861*) Nat. Bureau Stand., *Publication No. 56;* 1925
(*862*) Mathematical Tables (Nat. Bur. Stand.) MT-17; part 1
(*863*) *Intern. Crit. Tables*, 1928; vol. 5; pp. 238-242; Table 2
(*864*) Lowan, A. N. and Blanch, G., *J.O.S.A.*, 1940; **30,** 2; 70
(*865*) Caldin, E. F., *Proc. Phys. Soc. Lond.*, 1945; **57,** v, 323; 440
(*866*) Ives, H. E., *J.O.S.A.*, 1926; **12,** 1; 75
(*867*) Geiss, W., *Licht*, 1943; **12;** 33
(*868*) Work, H. K., *Trans. Am. Inst. Mining & Met. Eng.*, 1941; 145
(*869*) Goller, G. N., *America's Soc. for Metals*, 1943, Reprint 28
(*870*) General Electric, *Electron Tube Experiment Book*
(*871*) *Foundry Trade J.*, 1939; **61,** 1208; 251

(872) *Gmelin's Handbuch der Anorg. Chemie* (*System 59*), *Eisen, Teil A*, 1934-1939; pp. 648
(873) Price, D. J. and Lowerly, H., *Iron & Steel Inst. J.*, 1944; **149;** 523
(874) *Edgar Allen News*, July 1944
(875) Mecke, R. and Kempter, H., *Z. Techn. Phys.*, 1940; **21;** 85
(876) Waring, Ch. E. and Robison, G., *Rev. Sci. Instr.*, 1943; **14,** 5; 143
(877) Zeluff, V., *Scient. American*, 1945; **4;** 210
(878) Brown, R. V., *Electronics*, 1943; **16,** 7; 113
(879) Roof, J. G., *Electronics*, 1943; **16,** 10; 168
(880) Weiller, P. G. and Blatz, I. H., *Electronics*, 1944; **17,** 7; 138
(881) Meserve, W. E., *Rev. Sci. Instr.*, 1931; **2,** 2; 47
(882) *Electronics*, 1937; **10,** 4
(883) Maron, W., *Electronics*, 1945; **18,** 10; 216
(884) Adams, W. G. and Day, R. E., *Proc. Roy. Soc. Lond.*, 1876; **25;** 113
(885) *Electrical Review*, 1943; Dec. 10; p. 791
(886) *Electronics*, 1943; **16,** 6; 212
(887) *Electronics*, 1945; **18,** 2; 148
(888) *Electronics*, 1943; **16,** 5; 116
(889) Bisang, L., *V.D.I.*, 1937; **81;** 805
(890) Steiner, K. and Ravensbeck, F., *Oil Burner Service Manual*, 1942.
(891) *Electronics*, 1944; **17,** 9; 152
(892) Atkinson, L., *Electronic Engineering*, 1945; **17,** 208; 553
(893) Wynn-Williams, C. E., *Proc. Roy. Soc. Lond.*, 1931; A-132; 295
(894) Wynn-Williams, C. E., *Proc. Roy. Soc. Lond.*, 1932; A-136; 312
(895) Mäder, M., *A.E.G.-Mitteilungen*, 1936; Heft 7; 266
(896) Lord, H. W. and Livingston, O. W., *Electronics*, 1933; **6,** 9; 257
(897) Lord, H. W. and Livingston, O. W., *Electronics*, 1934; **7,** 1; 7
(898) Potter, J. T., *Electronics*, 1944; **17,** 6; 110
(899) Potter, J. T., *Electronics*, 1945; **18,** 5; 348
(900) Giatarrana, J., *Rev. Sci. Instr.*, 1937; **8,** 10; 390
(901) Reich, H. J., *Rev. Sci. Instr.*, 1938; **9,** 7; 222
(902) Lifschutz, H. and Lawson, J. L., *Rev. Sci. Instr.*, 1938; **9,** 3; 83
(903) Coven, A. W., *Rev. Sci. Instr.*, 1938; **9,** 7; 230
(904) Neher, H. V. and Harper, W. W., *Phys. Rev.*, 1936; **49;** 490
(905) Wellman, B. and Roeder, K., *Electronics*, 1942; **15,** 10; 74
(906) Shepherd, W. G. and Haxby, R. O., *Rev. Sci. Instr.*, 1936; **7,** 11; 425
(907) Gingrich, N. S., Evans, R. D. and Edgerton, H. E., *Rev. Sci. Instr.*, 1936; **7,** 12; 450
(908) Evans, R. D. and Alder, R. L., *Rev. Sci. Instr.*, 1939; **10,** 11; 332
(909) Lane, T. B., *J. Sci. Instr.*, 1936; **13,** 10; 364
(910) Rymer, T. B., *J. Sci. Instr.*, 1939; **16,** 3; 84
(911) *Electronics*, 1944; **17,** 2; 204
(912) *A.E.G.-Mitteilungen*, 1936; Heft 11; p. 387
(913) Downie, E. G., *G.E. Rev.*, 1944; **47,** 11; 50
(914) *Rev. Sci. Instr.*, 1936; **7,** 2; 43
(915) *Electronics*, 1943; **16,** 3
(916) *Electronics*, 1943; **16,** 4; 84
(917) *Electronics*, 1943; **16,** 12; 94
(918) *Electronics*, 1944; **17,** 6; 127
(919) *Electronics*, 1944; **17,** 7; 93
(920) *Electronic Engineering*, 1943; **15,** 178; 290
(921) *Electronic Engineering*, 1944; **16,** 195; 509
(922) *Electronic Engineering*, 1944; **17,** 196; 28
(923) *Electronic Engineering*, 1944; **17,** 200; 214
(924) Bainbridge Bell, L. H., *Electronic Engineering*, 1945; **17,** 208; 546
(925) *Electronics*, 1945; **18,** 8; 136
(926) *B.S.S. 530/1937* (also revised edition)
(927) *A.S.A.* (Section Radio) Z-32.5-1944
(928) *A.S.A.* (Section Electronic Devices) Z-32.10-1944
(929) Schmidek, A. J., *Arch. f. Elektrotech.*, 1942; **36,** 3; 181

(*930*) *E.T.Z.*, 1936; **57;** 141
(*931*) Dudley, B., *Electronics*, 1938; **11,** 5; 18
(*932*) Beale, F. S., *Electronics*, 1939; **12**
(*933*) *Electronics*, 1941; **14,** 1; 29
(*934*) *Electronics*, 1931; **2,** 1; 467
(*935*) Clothier, W. K., *J. Sci. Instr.*, 1939; **16,** 9; 285
(*936*) *Electronics*, 1945; **18,** 5; 365
(*937*) Shrader, R. E. and Wood, E. J., *Electronics*, 1944; **17,** 9; 98
(*938*) Kegamaster, H. L., *Electronics*, 1933; **6,** 1
(*939*) Gillings, D. W., *Electronic Engineering*, 1945; **17,** 204; 372
(*940*) Serfass, E. J., *Ind. Eng. Chem., Anal. Ed.*, 1941; **13,** 4; 262
(*941*) McDowell, E. B., *Electrical World*, 1943; pp. 2071, 2270
(*942*) Cockrell, W. D., *G.E. Rev.*, 1943; **46,** 9; 489
(*943*) *Electronics*, 1933; **6,** 4; 102
(*944*) *Electronics*, 1934; **7,** 9; 285
(*945*) *G.E. Rev.*, 1945; **48,** 5; 16
(*946*) *Electronics*, 1945; **18,** 1; 164
(*947*) Clark, D. B., *American Cinematographer*, April 1943
(*948*) Penther, C. J. and Weiske, C., *Electronics*, 1943; **16,** 9; 114
(*949*) Nunan, T. J., *Electronics*, 1939; **12,** 2; 12
(*950*) Sookne, A. M. and Rutherford, H. A., *J. of Res., Nat. Bur. Stand.*, July 1943; RP 1546
(*951*) McNickle, R. C., *Electronics*, 1944; **17,** 9; 110
(*952*) Powers, R. A., *Electronics*, 1939; **12,** 9; 54
(*953*) Walsh, C., *Electronics*, 1942; **15,** 10; 56
(*954*) *Ind. Heating*, 1943; **10,** 9; 1298
(*955*) Johannsen, K., *E.T.Z.*, 1936; **57,** 6; 150
(*956*) *Electronics*, 1931; **3,** 11; 196
(*957*) *Electronics*, 1931; **3,** 8
(*958*) *Electronics*, 1934; **7,** 1
(*959*) *Electronics*, 1945; **18,** 5; 150
(*960*) *Sci. American*, 1945; July 173
(*961*) Müller, R. H., Garman, R. L. and Droz, M. E., *Experimental Electronics*, 1945
(*962*) Fies, J., *Electrical World*, 1933; **102;** 396
(*963*) *Electronics*, 1936; **9,** 10; 40
(*964*) McComb, R. D., *Electronics*, 1943; **16,** 12; 172
(*965*) *Machine Design*, 1945; **7,** 7; 106
(*966*) Walker, D. S., *Electronics*, 1945; **18,** 7; 100
(*967*) Cockrell, W. D., *Industrial Electronic Control*, 1944
(*968*) Aronoff, S. and Young, D. A., *Electr. J.*, 1929; June 255
(*969*) *U.S.P. 1864627*
(*970*) *U.S.P. 1878658*
(*971*) Lenahan, B. E., *Electronics*, 1943; **16,** 7; 116
(*972*) Proctor, R. R., *Instruments*, 1942; June
(*973*) Proctor, R. R., *Electronics*, 1942; **15,** 10; 110
(*974*) Church, L., *Electronics*, 1935; **8,** 9; 293
(*975*) Hall, A. W., *Electronics*, 1943; **16,** 12; 124
(*976*) *Electronics*, 1943; **16,** 4; 144
(*977*) *Electronics*, 1931; **2,** 3; 556
(*978*) Cockrell, W. D., *Electronics*, 1943; **16,** 10; 94
(*979*) *Electronics*, 1940; **13,** 10
(*980*) *Electronics*, 1939; **12,** 9; 44
(*981*) Chute, G. M., *Steel*, 1944; **114,** 5; 126
(*982*) *Electronic Engineering*, 1944; **17,** 196; 30
(*983*) Antes, L. L., *Electronics*, 1944; **17,** 6; 114
(*984*) *Electronics*, 1944; **17,** 1; 302
(*985*) *Electronics*, 1944; **17,** 3; 168
(*986*) Weber, H. C., *Electronics*, 1933; **6,** 4; 103
(*987*) *Engineering*, 1945; **160,** 4152; 106

(*988*) *RCA Application Note* No. 82
(*989*) RICHARDSON, E. G., *Colliery Guardian*, 1934; **149;** 1144
(*990*) *Electronics*, 1933; **6,** 7
(*991*) *Electronics*, 1933; **6,** 10
(*992*) *Electronics*, 1943; **16,** 1; 116
(*993*) FIRESTONE, F. A. and VINCENT, H. B., *Automobile Eng.*, 1933; **23,** 5; 173
(*994*) POWERS, R. A., *Electronics*, 1935; **8,** 9; 276
(*995*) POWERS, R. A., *Electronics*, 1936; **9,** 6; 22
(*996*) POWERS, R. A., *Electronics*, 1939; **12,** 4; 12
(*997*) LORD, H. W. and LIVINGSTON, O. W., *Electronics*, 1933; **6,** 4; 96
(*998*) Brit. Res. Assoc., Torridon, Leeds; *Publication 105*; Dec. 1928
(*999*) SCHMID, R. C., *E.T.Z.*, 1934; **55;** 385
(*1000*) SAXL, I. I., *Rev. Sci. Instr.*, 1936; **7,** 11; 429
(*1001*) POWERS, R. A., *Electronics*, 1941; **14,** 7; 17
(*1002*) POWERS, R. A., *Electronics*, 1941; **14,** 8; 37
(*1003*) *Electronics*, 1939; **12,** 9; 54
(*1004*) *Electronics*, 1944; **17,** 5; 148
(*1005*) *Machinery*, 1945; **51,** 6; 188, 196
(*1006*) RESCORLA, A. R., FRY, E. M. and CARNAHAN, F. L., *Ind. Eng. Chem., Anal. Ed.*, 1936; **8,** 4; 242
(*1007*) STORY, B. W. and KALICHEVSKY, V. A., *Ind. Eng. Chem., Anal. Ed.*, 1933; **5,** 4; 214
(*1008*) MOSS, K. NEVILLE, *Gases, Dust and Heat in Mines*, 1927
(*1009*) BEADLE, D. G., *J. Sci. Instr.*, 1939; **16,** 8; 262
(*1010*) KALISCHER, P. R., *Trans. Electrochem. Soc.*, 1944; **85;** 163
(*1011*) *Electronics*, 1944; **17,** 2; 308
(*1012*) DILIBERTI, E. and KALLAS, D. H., *Modern Plastics*, 1945; **22,** 8; 150
(*1013*) *Power*, 1945; July 68 (434)
(*1014*) LAMB, A. H., *Electr. Eng.*, 1935; **54,** 11; 1186
(*1015*) *Electronics*, 1943; **16,** 2; 112
(*1016*) PODOLSKI, L., *Electronics*, 1933; **6,** 7; 180
(*1017*) CARLSON, R. W., *Electronics*, 1938; **11,** 10; 28
(*1018*) BERRY, T. M., *G.E. Rev.*, 1940; **43,** 3; 137
(*1019*) WEY, R. J., *Electronic Engineering*, 1944; **16,** 191; 334
(*1020*) SNYDER, W. B., *Electrical World*, 1932; **99,** 2; 327
(*1021*) HIGGINS, B. G. *Mechanical Handling*, 1945; **32,** 5; 238
(*1022*) *Electronics*, 1931; **3,** 10; 156
(*1023*) *Electronics*, 1933; **6,** 6; 162
(*1024*) HEYMANN, N., *Electronics*, 1933; **6,** 6; 163
(*1025*) *G.E. Rev.*, 1936; **39,** 2; 117
(*1026*) *Electronics*, 1945; **18,** 7; 152
(*1027*) CEAGLSKE, N. H. and KESSLINGER, S. A., *Ind. Eng. Chem., Anal. Ed.*, 1944; **16,** 6; 393
(*1028*) HALLER, C. E., *Electronics*, 1944; **17,** 7; 126
(*1029*) *Electronics*, 1945; **18,** 3; 379
(*1030*) *Electronics*, 1933; **6,** 10
(*1031*) *Electronics*, 1933; **6,** 7
(*1032*) *Electronics*, 1942; **15,** 3; 72
(*1033*) *Electronic Engineering*, 1944; **17,** 200; 195
(*1034*) CLARK, H. L., *G.E. Rev.*, 1942; **45,** 7; 383
(*1035*) ROBINSON, D., *Electronic Engineering*, 1945; **17,** 207; 493
(*1036*) FAGAN, CHR. P., *J. Sci. Instr.*, 1942; **19,** 12; 184
(*1037*) OSTER, G., *J. Appl. Physics*, 1945; **16,** 3; 121
(*1038*) ARKADIEV, V., *Nature*, 1944; **154,** 3900; 157
(*1039*) *Chem. & Met. Eng.*, 1945; **52,** 3; 102
(*1040*) BEHAR, M. F., *Electronics*, 1942; **15,** 12; 72
(*1041*) *Electronics*, 1942; **15,** 12; 84
(*1042*) ZENOR, H. M., *Phys. Rev.*, 1936; **49,** ii, 5; 421
(*1043*) STILES, W. S. and SMITH, T., *Proc. Phys. Soc. Lond.* 1944; **56,** 316; 251
(*1044*) PALMER, H. L., *Electrical Contracting*, 1944; **43,** 5; 112

(*1045*) *Modern Plastics* 1945; **23,** 3; 107
(*1046*) *Scientific and Industrial Reports* (*U.S.A.*). S. Benzer, PB 28644
(*1047*) GANNETT, D. K., *Bell Lab. Rec.*, 1939-1940; **18,** 12; 378
(*1048*) *Electronics*, 1942; **15,** 10; 60
(*1049*) PRINGSHEIM, P., *Electronics*, 1945; **18,** 12; 340
(*1050*) *Electronic Engineering*, 1946; **18,** 215; 27
(*1051*) WOO, SHO-CHOW; LIU, TA-KONG; CHU, T. C. and CHIH, WU, " Near ultra-violet bands of acetylene ", *J. Chem. Phys.*, 1938; **6,** 5; 240
(*1052*) GERMERSHAUSEN, K. J. and EDGERTON, H. E., " A cold-cathode arc-discharge tube ", *Electr. Eng.*, 1936; **55,** 7; 790
(*1053*) VEDDER, E. H. and EVANS, M. S., " Photo-electric control of resistor-type metal heaters " (Discussion), *Electr. Eng.*, 1936; **55,** 2; 189
(*1054*) EDGAR, R. F., " A new photo-electric hysteresigraph ", *Electrical Eng.*, 1937; **56,** 7; 805
(*1055*) FAIRBROTHER, F. and TUCK, J. L., " The photo-electric measurement of the absorption of sodium resonance radiation", *Trans. Faraday Soc.*, 1936; **32;** 624
(*1056*) "Various papers on smoke particles", *Trans. Faraday Soc.*, 1936; **32;** pp. 1055
(*1057*) GREEN, H. L., " Size frequency of particles in mineral dust ", *Trans. Faraday Soc.*, 1936; **32;** 1091
(*1058*) HILL, A. S. G., " Measurement of the optical densities of smoke stains on filter papers ", *Trans. Faraday Soc.*, 1936; **32;** 1125
(*1059*) BOSWORTH, R. C. L., " The photosensitisation of films of potassium by means of hydrogen ", *Trans. Faraday Soc.*, 1936; **32;** 1369
(*1060*) FRANK, L., " Migration of cesium on tungsten oxide ", *Trans. Faraday Soc.*, 1936; **32;** 1403
(*1061*) BOSWORTH, R. C. L., " The photo-electric Schottky-effect in films of sodium and potassium on tungsten ", *Trans. Faraday Soc.*, 1937; **33;** 590
(*1062*) LOTHIAN, G. F., " A photo-electric method of measuring pH values with indicator solution ", *Trans. Faraday Soc.*, 1937; **33;** 1239
(*1063*) NOYES, W. A. Jr., " The near ultra-violet absorption spectrum of acetone vapour ", *Trans. Faraday Soc.*, 1937; **33;** 1495
(*1064*) WEISS, J., " Photosensitising action and the fluorescence of uranium salts ", *Trans. Faraday Soc.*, 1938; **34;** 451
(*1065*) GOODEVE, C. F. and KITCHENER, J. A., " Photosensitisation by titanium dioxide ", *Trans. Faraday Soc.*, 1938; **34;** 570
(*1066*) GOODEVE, J. W., " The absorption spectra of methyl methacrylate and its polymer ", *Trans. Faraday Soc.*, 1938; **34;** 1239
(*1067*) MADDOCK, A. J., " Absolute intensities in the spectrum of a low-pressure quartz mercury vapour discharge burner ", *Proc. Phys. Soc. Lond.*, 1936; **48,** 264; 57
(*1068*) BARNARD, G. P., " The dependence of sensitivity of the selenium-sulphur rectifier photo-electric cell on the obliquity of the incident light, and a method of compensation therefor ", *Proc. Phys. Soc. Lond.*, 1936; **48,** 264; 153
(*1069*) WRIGHT, W. D. and NELSON, J. H., " The relation between the apparent intensity of a beam of light and the angle at which the beam strikes the retina ", *Proc. Phys. Soc. Lond.*, 1936; **48,** 266; 401
(*1070*) HULL, R. A., " Transmission of light through a pile of parallel plates ", *Proc. Phys. Soc. Lond.*, 1936; **48,** 267; 574
(*1071*) CAMPBELL, N. R., NOBLE, H. R. and STOODLEY, L. G., "Time lag in photo-electric cells ", *Proc. Phys. Soc. Lond.*, 1936; **48,** 267; 589
(*1072*) PRESTON, J. S. and CUCKOW, F. W., " A photo-electric spectrophotometer of high accuracy ", *Proc. Phys. Soc. Lond.*, 1936; **48,** 269; 869
(*1073*) PRESTON, J. S. and CUCKOW, F. W., " A photo-electric spectrophotometer of high accuracy ", *Proc. Phys. Soc. Lond.*, 1937; **49,** 271; 189
(*1074*) CAMPBELL, N. R. and RIVLIN, R. S., " The effect of hydrogen on the time-lag of argon-filled photo-electric cells ", *Proc. Phys. Soc. Lond.*, 1937; **49,** 270; 12

(*1075*) Griffiths, J. H. E., " A circuit for counting impulses at high speeds of counting ", *Proc. Phys. Soc. Lond.*, 1937; **49,** 271; 85

(*1076*) Lovell, A. C. B., " The electrical conductivity of thin films of the alkali metals spontaneously deposited on glass surfaces ", *Proc. Phys. Soc. Lond.*, 1937; **49,** 271; 89

(*1077*) Treloar, R. L. G., " Secondary electron emission from complex surfaces ", *Proc. Phys. Soc. Lond.*, 1937; **49,** 273; 392

(*1078*) Powell, R. W., " The thermal and electrical conductivity of a sample of Acheson graphite from 0° C. to 800° C.", *Proc. Phys. Soc. Lond.*, 1937; **49,** 273; 419

(*1079*) Mott, N. F., " Note on the theory of photoconductivity ", *Proc. Phys. Soc. Lond.*, 1938; **50,** 278; 196

(*1080*) Lythgoe, R. J., " The structure of the retina and the role of its visual purple ", *Proc. Phys. Soc. Lond.*, 1938; **50,** 279; 321

(*1081*) Alfvén, H. " A simple scale-of-two counter ", *Proc. Phys. Soc. Lond.*, 1938; **50,** 279; 358

(*1082*) Preston, J. S., " The relative luminosity of radiation at wavelengths 5,780 and 5,461 AU. for the average photometric observer ", *Proc. Phys. Soc. Lond.*, 1938; **50,** 279; 398

(*1083*) Gaydon, A. G., " Colour sensations produced by ultra-violet light ", *Proc. Phys. Soc. Lond.*, 1938; **50,** 281; 714

(*1084*) Atkinson, J. R., Campbell, N. R., Palmer, E. H. and Winch, G. T., " The accuracy of rectifier photo-electric cells ", *Proc. Phys. Soc. Lond.*, 1938; **50,** 282; 934

(*1085*) Barnard, G. P., " The spectral sensitivity of selenium rectifier photo-electric cells ", *Proc. Phys. Soc. Lond.*, 1938; **50,** 284; 22

(*1086*) Bor, J., Hobson, A. and Wood, C., " The application of a new photo-electric method in the determination of the optical constants of some pure metals ", *Proc. Phys. Soc. Lond.*, 1938; **50,** 288; 932

(*1087*) Uffelmann, F. L., " An accurate hard-valve (decimal) counter chronograph ", *Proc. Phys. Soc. Lond.*, 1938; **50,** 288; 1028

(*1088*) Duncan, D. R., " The colour of pigment mixtures ", *Proc. Phys. Soc. Lond.*, 1940; **52,** 291; 390

(*1089*) Wright, W. D., " The sensitivity of the eye to small colour differences ", *Proc. Phys. Soc. Lond.*, 1941; **53,** 296; 93

(*1090*) Perry, J. W., " Colour, its measurement, discrimination, and specification ", *Proc. Phys. Soc. Lond.*, 1941; **53,** 297; 272

(*1091*) McGregor-Morris, J. T. and Stainsby, A. G., " A rotating differential photo-electric photometer for precision work ", *Proc. Phys. Soc. Lond.*, 1941; **53,** 299; 584

(*1092*) McGregor-Morris, J. T. and Stainsby, A. G., (same as 1091; discussion), *Proc. Phys. Soc. Lond.*, 1942; **54,** 301; 66

(*1093*) Holmes, J. G., " The nature and measurement of whiteness ", *Proc. Phys. Soc. Lond.*, 1942; **54,** 302; 81

(*1094*) Harrison, V. G. W., " The measurement of near-whites in the paper industry ", *Proc. Phys. Soc. Lond.*, 1942; **54,** 302; 86

(*1095*) Heys-Hallett, C. G., " The whiteness of cinema screens ", *Proc. Phys. Soc. Lond.*, 1942; **54,** 302; 98

(*1096*) Eddington, Sir A., " The theoretical values of physical constants ", *Proc. Phys. Soc. Lond.*, 1942; **54,** 306; 491

(*1097*) Knipe, G. F. G. and Reid, J. B., " A photo-electric tricolorimeter ", *Proc. Phys. Soc. Lond.*, 1943; **55,** 308; 81

(*1098*) Sommer, A., " Photo-electric alloys of alkali metals ", *Proc. Phys. Soc. Lond.*, 1943; **55**, 308; 145

(*1099*) Johnson, B. K., " Recent optical materials and their possible applications " *Proc. Phys. Soc. Lond.*, 1943; **55,** 310; 291

(*1100*) Wearmouth, W. G., " Plastics and the optical industry ", *Proc. Phys. Soc. Lond..*, 1943; **55,** 310; 301

(*1101*) Strange, J. W., " The chemical and physical properties of luminescent materials ", *Proc. Phys. Soc. Lond.*, 1943; **55,** 311; 364

(*1102*) Fawcett, G. S., " Sixty years of colorimetry ", *Proc. Phys. Soc. Lond.*, 1944; **56,** 313; 8
(*1103*) Harding, H. G. W., " A yellow glass filter for colour temperature measurements ", *Proc Phys. Soc. Lond.*, 1944; **56,** 313; 21
(*1104*) Harding, H. G. W., " Colours of total radiators on the C.I.E. trichromatic system for the temperature range 1,500-10-9,000° K.), *Proc. Phys. Soc. Lond.*, 1944; **56,** 317; 305
(*1105*) Stiles, W. S. " Current problems of visual research ", *Proc. Phys. Soc. Lond.*, 1944; **56,** 317; 329
(*1106*) Preston, J. S. and Smith, G. W. G., " The interval resistance of the selenium rectifier photocell, with special reference to the sputtered metal film ", *Proc. Phys. Soc. Lond.*, 1945; **57,** 319; 1
(*1107*) Cashman, R. J. and Jamison, N. C., " Photo-electric work function of barium ", *Phys. Rev.*, 1936; **49,** ii, 2; 195
(*1108*) Cashman, R. J. and Jamison, N. C., " Photo-electric work function of barium ", *Phys. Rev.*, 1936; **49,** ii, 11; 877
(*1109*) Jamison, N. C. and Cashman, R. J., " Photo-electric work function of calcium ", *Phys. Rev.*, 1936; **49,** ii, 2; 201
(*1110*) Hill, A. G. and DuBridge, L. A., " The energy distribution of photo-electrons from sodium ", *Phys. Rev.*, 1936; **49,** ii, 11; 877
(*1111*) Rentschler, H. C. and Henry, D. E., " Photo-electric emission from alkali deposits on other metals ", *Phys. Rev.*, 1936; **49,** ii, 11; 877
(*1112*) Mann, M. M., Jr. and DuBridge, L. A., " Absolute yields of magnesium, beryllium, and sodium ", *Phys. Rev.*, 1936; **50,** ii, 4; 398
(*1113*) Jamison, N. C. and Cashman, R. J., " Note on the analysis of photo-electric data ", *Phys. Rev.*, 1936; **50,** ii, 6; 568
(*1114*) Mann, M. M., Jr., and DuBridge, L. A., " Absolute yields of magnesium, beryllium, and sodium ", *Phys. Rev.*, 1937; **51,** ii, 2; 120
(*1115*) Weber, A. H. and Bazzoni, C. B., " The effect of current through bismuth ", *Phys. Rev.* 1937; **51,** ii, 5; 378
(*1116*) Skelett, A. M., "Time lag in gasfilled cells", *Phys. Rev.*, 1937; **51,** ii, 11; 1026
(*1117*) Houston, W. V., " The surface photo-electric effect ", *Phys. Rev.*, 1937; **52,** ii, 10; 1047
(*1118*) King, W. R., " The photo-electric pyrometer ", *Gen. Electric Rev.*, 1936; **39,** 11; 526
(*1119*) Watrons, W. W. and Marshall, D. E., " Common misapplications of gaseous tubes ", *Electronics,* 1942; **15,** 1; 42
(*1120*) Smith, C. C., " A densitometer ", *Electronics*, 1942; **15,** 12; 79
(*1121*) Dushman, S. and Malpica, J. T. Mireles, " Measuring the creep of metal ", *Electronics*, 1942; **15,** 11; 86
(*1122*) Thompson, H. W. and Whiffen, D. H., " Sources of infra-red radiation ", *Trans. Faraday Soc.*, 1945; **41;** 180
(*1123*) Torkington, P. and Thompson, H. W., " Solvents for use in the infra-red ," *Trans. Faraday Soc.*, 1945; **41;** 184
(*1124*) Herington, E. F. G., " The refractive indices of some binary hydrocarbon mixtures ", *Trans. Faraday Soc.*, 1944; **40;** 481
(*1125*) Hirshberg, Y. and Haskelberg, L., " The fluorescence of phenylated anthracenes ", *Trans. Faraday Soc.*, 1943; **39;** 45
(*1126*) Tomkins, F. C., " A photo-electric turbidimeter for use in solution kinetics ", *Trans. Faraday Soc.*, 1942; **38;** 128
(*1127*) Sambursky, S. and Wolfsohn, G., " On the fluorescence and absorption spectra of anthracene and phenanthrene in solutions ", *Trans. Faraday Soc.*, 1940; **36;** 427
(*1128*) Marsh, A. E. L., " A new type of flow meter for slow rates of flow (1 to 0·25 cc./min.) ", *Trans. Faraday Soc.*, 1940; **36;** 626
(*1129*) " A general discussion on luminescence ", *Trans. Faraday Soc.*, 1939; **35;** 2
(*1130*) Cashman, R. J. and Bassoe, E., " Spectral sensitivity of strontium and magnesium ", *Phys. Rev.*, 1938; **53,** ii, 12; 919
(*1131*) Condon, E. U., " Note on the external photo-electric effect of semi-conductors ", *Phys. Rev.*, 1938; **54,** ii, 12; 1089

(*1132*) Cashman, R. J. and Bassoe, E., " Surface and volume emission from barium ", *Phys. Rev.*, 1939; **55,** ii, 1; 63

(*1133*) Goss, W. H. and Henderson, J. E., " A new method for the measurement of workfunctions ", *Phys. Rev.*, 1939; **56,** ii, 8; 857

(*1134*) Cashman, R. J., " External photo-electric effect in semi-conductors ", *Phys. Rev.*, 1940; **57,** ii, 11; 1090

(*1135*) Maurer, R. J., " The photo-electric and optical properties of sodium and barium ", *Phys. Rev.*, 1940; **57,** ii, 9; 653

(*1136*) DuBridge, L. A., " New theories of the photo-electric effect ", *Actualitées Scientifiques et industrielles*, 1936; 268

(*1137*) Weber, A. H. and Eisele, L. J., " Photo-electric properties of thin bismuth films ", *Phys. Rev.*, 1941; **59,** ii, 5; 473 (also cf. vols. 53 and 57)

(*1138*) Tykociner, J. T. and Bloom, L. R., " Photo-electric sensitisation of metal surfaces in group II by optical dissociation of water vapour ", *Phys. Rev.*, 1941; **59,** ii, 1; 115

(*1139*) Jupink, H., " Photo-electric properties of bismuth ", *Phys. Rev.*, 1941; **60,** ii, 12; 884

(*1140*) Weber, A. H. and Eisele, L. J., " Photo-electric threshold of thin bismuth films ", *Phys. Rev.*, 1941; **60,** ii, 8; 570

(*1141*) Weber, A. H. and O'Brien, D. F., " Photo-electric emission of thin bismuth films ", *Phys. Rev.*, 1941; **60,** ii, 8; 574

(*1142*) Weisskopf, V. F. and Apker, L. W., " On the theory of the photo-effect in semi-conductors ", *Phys. Rev.*, 1941; **60,** ii, 2; 170

(*1143*) Rogers, F. T., Jr., " Photometry with photo-electric cells ", *Phys. Rev.*, 1942; **61,** ii, 6; 394

(*1144*) Weber, A. H. and Friedrich, L. M., " Photoconductance of evaporated bismuth films ", *Phys. Rev.*, 1943; **63,** ii, 6; 217

(*1145*) Goldman, J. E. and Lawson, A. W., " The photoconductivity of lead chromate ", *Phys. Rev.*, 1943; **64,** ii, 1; 11

(*1146*) Weber, A. H., " Threshold and intensity from bismuth film ", *Phys. Rev.*, 1938; **53,** ii, 11; 895

(*1147*) Ferguson, J. N., Jr., " Photoconductivity of sodium chloride in the far ultra-violet ", *Phys. Rev.*, 1944; **66,** ii, 8; 220

(*1148*) Rentschler, H. C. and Henry, D. E., " Photo-electric work function and the action of oxygen, nitrogen, and hydrogen ", *Phys. Rev.*, 1943; **63,** ii, 6; 217

(*1149*) Boettner, E. A. and Brewington, G. P., " The application of multiplier phototubes to quantitative spectro-chemical analysis ", *Phys. Rev.*, 1943; **64,** ii, 2; 45

(*1150*) Gulliksen, F. H. and Stoddard, R. N., " Industrial electronic control applications ", *Electrical Engineering*, 1935; **54,** 1; 40. (Discussion): *Electr. Engineering*, 1935; **54,** 7; 752

(*1151*) Chambers, D. E., " Applications of electron tubes in industry ", *Electr. Eng.*, 1935; **54,** 1; 82 (Discussion): *Electr. Eng.*, 1935; **54,** 7; 754

(*1152*) Metcalf, G. F., " Operating characteristics in photo-electric tubes ", *Proc. I.R.E.*, 1929; **11;** 2064

(*1153*) Jouaust, R., " Photo-electric cells ", *Soc. Franc. Elec. Bull.*, 1932; **2,** 10; 1024

(*1154*) Sewig, R., *Z. f. Instrumentenkunde*, 1930; **50,** 7; 426

(*1155*) Vedder, E. H. and Evans, M. S., " Photo-electric control of resistance type metal heaters ", *Electr. Eng.*, 1935; **54,** 6; 645. (Discussion): ref. (1053)

(*1156*) Nord, G. L., " The effect of ultra-violet on the breakdown voltage ", *Electr. Eng.*, 1935; **54,** 9; 955

(*1157*) Stout, M. B., " Analysis of rectifier filter circuits ", *Electr. Eng.*, 1935; **54,** 9; 977

(*1158*) Pike, O. W. and Ulrey, D., " Ratings of industrial electronic tubes ", *Electr. Eng.*, 1934; **53,** 12; 1577. (Discussion): *Electr. Eng.*, 1935; **54,** 7; 754

(*1159*) EMMS, S. A. G. and ROGERSON, D. C., " The electrical control of the swing span of Kincardine-on-Forth Bridge ", *G.E.C. Journal*, 1936; **7,** 4; 235
(*1160*) WINCH, G. T. and MACHIN, C. F., " The design of precision commercial photo-electric photometers ", *G.E.C. Journal*, 1935; **6,** 4; 205
(*1161*) TRELOAR, L. R. G., " Secondary electron emission from complex surfaces ", *G.E.C. Journal*, 1937; **8,** 4; 254
(*1162*) BOWTELL, J. N. and MILES, E. E., " Phosphorescence and its applications ", *G.E.C. Journal*, 1941; **11,** 4; 256
(*1163*) STRONG, J., " On a method of decreasing the reflexions from non-metallic substances ", *J.O.S.A.*, 1936; **26,** 1; 73
(*1164*) SMITH, A. E. and FOWLER, R. D., " Low voltage source of ultra-violet continuum ", *J.O.S.A.*, 1936; **26,** 2; 79
(*1165*) INGERSOLL, L. R., WINANS, J. G. and KRAUSE, E. H., " Polarizing characteris-, tics of Polaroid plates for wavelengths 4,000 to 20,000 AU.", *J.O.S.A.* 1936; **26,** 6; 233
(*1166*) TUTTLE, C., "Recording physical densitometer", *J.O.S.A.*, 1936; **26,** 7; 282
(*1167*) ESTEY, R. S., "Selection of colour temperature altering filters", *J.O.S.A.*, 1936; **26,** 7; 293
(*1168*) WEAVER, K. S., " Calculation of filters for colour temperature conversion ", *J.O.S.A.*, 1936; **26,** 9; 339
(*1169*) PFUND, A. H., " Electric Welsbach Lamp ", *J.O.S.A.*, 1936; **26,** 12; 439
(*1170*) GILBERT, R. W., " D.C. amplifier for photocell application ", *Electronics*, 1938; **11,** 1; 44
(*1171*) " Photo-electric counters in printing and book-binding plant ", *Electronics*, 1938; **11,** 1; 60
(*1172*) " A photo-electric flour tester ", *Electronics*, 1938; **11,** 2; 47
(*1173*) " Highspeed counting by radio control ", *Electronics*, 1938; **11,** 3; 38
(*1174*) " Phototube drawer opener used to safeguard dental patients from infections ", *Electronics*, 1938; **11,** 3; 40
(*1175*) " Phototube colour analyzer used in chemical research ", *Electronics*, 1938; **11,** 3; 40
(*1176*) " Phototube limit on conveyor ", *Electronics*, 1938; **11,** 3; 48
(*1177*) " Automatic type-setting machine (Semagraph) operating a linotype machine from telegraph signals ", *Electronics*, 1938; **11,** 8; 33
(*1178*) " Temperature monitoring equipment maintains temperature (1,000° F.) constant within 10° F.", *Electronics*, 1938; **11,** 8; 33
(*1179*) " Electronics helps make beer ", *Electronics*, 1938; **11,** 9; 13
(*1180*) DEETER, E. L., " Colour matching in the paper industry ", *Electronics*, 1938; **11,** 9; 18
(*1181*) PICKERING, W. H., " A circuit for the rapid extinction of the arc in a thyratron ", *R.S.I.*, 1938; **9,** 6
(*1182*) " High frequency ammeter employs phototube indicator (3 to 6 amp. at 5 to 42 Mc/s.) ", *Electronics*, 1938; **11,** 9; 44
(*1183*) BALL, A., " Phototube saves coating metals (electroplating) ", *Electronics*, 1938; **11,** 11; 48
(*1184*) " Phototube scans steel for pin-hole flaws at speeds up to 900 ft./min.", *Electronics*, 1938; **11,** 12; 42
(*1185*) CONSIDINE, D. M., "Control of material feed rate", *Chem. & Met. Eng.*, 1945; **52,** 5; 112
(*1186*) DOGNON, A., " The colorimetry of turbid media ", *Revue d'Optique*, 1940; **19;** 205
(*1187*) BIRD, L. F., " An automatic high-pressure mercury arc lamp control circuit ", *J. Soc. Mot. Pict. Eng.*, 1945; **45,** 1; 38
(*1188*) BIRD, L. F., " Metal pouring controlled by photo-tube ", *Scient. American*, 1945; **173,** 3; 16
(*1189*) ALEXANDER, E. H., " Photo-electric width gage ", *Electronics*, 1942; **15,** 1; 66

(*1190*) " Industrial tube characteristics ", *Electronics*, 1942; **15,** 6; 52
(*1991*) " Tubes at work," *Electronics*, 1942; **15,** 6; 70
(*1192*) MacDonald, " Intrusion detector system ", *Electronics*, 1942; **15,** 2; 38
(*1193*) " Electronics at the Chemical Exhibition ", *Electronics*, 1942; **15,** 1; 56
(*1194*) Wright, W. L., " Phototubes in multicolour printing ", *G.E. Rev.*, 1941; **44,** 11
(*1195*) " Photo-electric scanner ", *Electronics*, 1942; **15,** 3; 70
(*1196*) " Phototube-controlled revolving door ", *Electronics*, 1942; **15,** 3; 72
(*1197*) " Photo-electric intrusion detector ", *Electronics*, 1942; **15,** 3; 73
(*1198*) Boss, L. F., " Universal electronic relay ", *Electronics*, 1942; **15,** 5; 68
(*1199*) Towne, R. D. and Considine, D. M., " Continuous balance potentiometer pyrometer ", *Electronics*, 1942; **15,** 8; 92
(*1200*) Smith, C. C., " A photo-electric densitometer ", *Electronics*, 1942; **15,** 12; 79
(*1201*) " A thorium detector ", *Electronics*, 1942; **15,** 12; 82
(*1202*) " R-F heating aids tin-can makers ", *Electronics*, 1942; **15,** 12; 86
(*1203*) " Integrator for irregular plane surfaces ", *Electronics*, 1940; **13,** 2; 36
(*1204*) Sheard, Ch. " Photo-electric spectrophotometer " *Electronics*, 1940; **13,** 5; 44
(*1205*) Berry, T. M., " Photo-electric time interval meter ", *G.E. Rev.*, 1940; **43,** 3
(*1206*) Roberts, W. van B., " Photo-electric exposure meter for photographic enlarging ", *R.S.I.*, 1940; **11,** 5
(*1207*) Roulleau, J., " Influence de la température sur l'effet photoélectrique de contact métal-oxyde cuivreux ", *Compt. rend.*, 1936; **202;** 749
(*1208*) Dauvillier, A., " Sur un photomagnétron et son application à la mesure des éclairements crépusculaires ", *Compt. rend.*, 1936; **202;** 738
(*1209*) Boutry, G.-A., " La loi de Talbot en photométrie photoélectrique ", *Compt. rend.*, 1936; **202;** 1580
(*1210*) Jonescu, Th. V., " Sur la structure du photon ", *Compt. rend.*, 1936; **203;** 864
(*1211*) Placinteanu, J. J., " Sur la nature électronique de la lumière ", *Compt. rend.*, 1936; **203;** 1343
(*1212*) Boutry, G.-A., " Un nouveau type de cellule photoémissive ", *Compt. rend.* 1937; **204;** 120
(*1213*) Hoang thi Nga, " Effets photovoltaïques des diamines de la naphthalène ", *Compt. rend.*, 1937; **204;** 429
(*1214*) Hoang thi Nga, " Effets photovoltaïques des diamines de la naphthalène ", *Compt. rend.*, 1937; **204;** 763
(*1215*) Roulleau, J., " Influence de l'intensité lumineuse sur la sensibilité des compteurs photoélectriques ", *Compt. rend.*, 1937; **204;** 1191
(*1216*) Grandmontagne, R., " Etude photoélectrique de la couleur du ciel nocturne ", *Compt.* rend., 1937; **204;** 337
(*1217*) Roure, R., Quevron, L. and Gense, R., " Comparateur photoélectrique (thickness gauge) ", *Compt. rend.*, 1937; **205;** 131
(*1218*) Grivet, P. " Modulation de la lumière en haute frequence; son application à la mesure des temps très courts ", *Compt. rend.*, 1938; **206;** 339
(*1219*) Grivet, P. " Un phénomène nouveau dans la fonctionnement de la cellule photoélectrique en haute frequence ", *Compt. rend.*, 1938; **206;** 1798
(*1220*) Audubert, R. and Mattler, J., " Influence des vapeurs sur la courbe de sensibilité spectrale des compteurs photoélectriques ", *Compt. rend.*, 1938; **206;** 1005
(*1221*) Boutry, G.-A. and Gillod, J., " Propriétés d'un nouveau type de cellule photoémissive ", *Compt. rend.*, 1938; **206;** 1807
(*1222*) Liandrat, G. " Sur deux examples différents de non-additivité des effets photoélectriques de flux lumineux simultanés ", *Compt. rend.*, 1938; **207;** 1396
(*1223*) Uyterhoeven, W. and Verburg, C., " Température des électrons dans une décharge à colonne positive en courant alternatif (50 c.p.s.) ", *Compt. rend.*, 1938; **207;** 1386

(*1224*) VOYATZAKIS, E., " Sur l'éffet photoélectrique et la photoconductibilité des sulfures phosphorescents et des fluorines ", *Compt. rend.*, 1939; **209;** 31
(*1225*) DESTRIAU, G. " Luminescence dans les champs électriques et phénomènes électroniques dans les semi-conducteurs ", *Compt. rend.*, 1939; **209;** 36
(*1226*) SADDY, J. " Sensibilisation de sulfure de zinc phosphorescence à l'action des rayons rouges ", *Compt. rend.*, 1939; **209;** 93
(*1227*) TERRIEN, J., " Emploi de cellules photoélectriques au sélénium par la photo: metrie de précision ", *Compt. rend.*, 1939; **209;** 300
(*1228*) FROGER, CHR., " Procédé de détection de chlorure de chlorovinylarsine (lewisite) ", *Compt. rend.*, 1939; **209;** 351
(*1229*) DAUVILLIER, A. and VASSY, E., " Etude de photocompteurs dans l'ultraviolet ", *Compt. rend.*, 1939; **209;** 394
(*1230*) KARPEN, V., " Rôle des électrons dans la production de la force électromotrice au contact métal-électrolyte ", *Compt. rend.*, 1939; **209;** 474
(*1231*) JONESCU, TH., " Sur le rayon de l'électron et le calcul de la constante photoélectrique des métaux ", *Compt. rend.*, 1940; **210;** 170
(*1232*) SERVIGNE, M., " Sur la photoluminescence des scheelites ", *Compt. rend.*, 1940; **210;** 440
(*1233*) ASHMORE, R. L., " A new type of photocell ' watchdog ' ", *Electronic Engineering*, 1936; **9,** 100; 325
(*1234*) " The Philips photo-electric cell ", *Electronic Eng.*, 1936; **9;** 96; 90
(*1235*) " An electric balancer for rotating parts ", *Electronics*, 1945; **18,** 11; 364
(*1236*) WINDRED, G., " Photo-electric effects ", *Electronic Eng.*, 1937; **10,** 110 217
(*1237*) WINDRED, G., " Photo-electric effects ", *Electronic Eng.*, 1937; **10,** 111; 283
(*1238*) " Multiplier photocells ", *Electronic Eng.*, 1937; **10,** 117; 662
(*1239*) " Barrier layer photo-electric cells ", *Electronic Eng.*, 1938; **11,** 125; 399
(*1240*) " The photocell in industry ", *Electronic Eng.*, 1938; **11,** 125; 411
(*1241*) " The photo-electric cell in practical use ", *Electronic Eng.*, 1938; **11,** 130; 721
(*1242*) " Transparency, colour, and gloss comparisons with the photocell ", *Electronic Eng.*, 1939; **12,** 141; 626
(*1243*) " A ' pea ' photo-electric cell ", *Electronic Eng.*, 1943; **15,** 183; 504
(*1244*) WALKER, R. C., " Photo-electric cells ", *G.E.C. Journal*, 1936; **7,** 4; 249
(*1245*) VESZI, G. A., " Some measurements on selenium photocells ", *Electronic Eng.*, 1943; **15,** 183; 505
(*1246*) WEY, R. J., " Smoke density measurement using photocells ", *Electronic Eng.*, 1943; **15,** 183; 507
(*1247*) LANCE, T. M. C., " The spectral response of photo-electric cells ", *Electronic Eng.*, 1943; **15,** 183; 501
(*1248*) SAMSON, K. A. R., " A photo-electric voltage control gear ", *Electronic Eng.*, 1943; **15,** 183; 516
(*1249*) *Electronics*, 1938; **11,** 3; 46
(*1250*) " Pressure sensing unit ", *Electronics*, 1945; **18,** 12; 252
(*1251*) *Electronics*, 1945; **18,** 12; 180
(*1252*) GOODEVE, C. F., LYTHGOE, R. J. and SCHNEIDER, E. E., *Proc. Roy. Soc. Lond.*, 1941; **130,** B, 861; 380
(*1253*) GOODEVE, C. F., *Proc. Roy. Soc. Lond.*, 1936; **155,** A, 886; 664
(*1254*) KATZMANN, J., *Electronics*, 1938; **11,** 6; 54
(*1255*) *Am. Standards Assoc.* (*ASA*), *Bull.* Z 1.1-1941; Z 1.2-1942; Z 1.3-1942
(*1256*) BESSO, D. and BROWN, H., *The Science Forum*, 1945, March
(*1257*) WINCH, G. T. and MACHIN, C. F., *GEC Journal*, 1935; **6,** 4; 205
(*1258*) *Westinghouse Bulletin* TD 83
(*1259*) BRENTANO, J. C. M., *Nature*, 1921; **108,** 2721; 532
(*1260*) BRENTANO, J. C. M. and INGLEBY, P., *J. Sci. Instr.*, 1939; **16,** 3; 81
(*1261*) DUBRIDGE, L. A. and BROWN, H., *R.S.I.*, 1933; **4,** 10; 532
(*1262*) AGNEW, W. B. R., *Electronics*, 1945; **18,** 12; 160
(*1263*) KING, E. J., *The Lancet*, 1942; **1;** 511

(*1264*) Sommer, W., *Electronic Eng*., 1945; **17;** 777
(*1265*) Dircksen, A. R., *Electr. Eng*. (*J.A.I.E.E.*), 1944; **63,** 7; 247
(*1266*) Malatesta, S., *L'Elettrotecnica*, 1938; **25,** 6; 188
(*1267*) Ferri and Madesini, *Giornale di Medicina Militare*, 1936; Jan., p. 36
(*1268*) Sartori, M., *The War Gases*, 1939 (English edition), Translated by L. W. Marrison
(*1269*) *U.S. Patent 2122824*
(*1270*) *B.P. 485386*
(*1271*) *B.P. 492759*
(*1272*) *B.P. 540243*
(*1273*) *U.S. Patent 2207309*, p. 3, col. 2, lines 38 to 62
(*1274*) *B.P. 558300*
(*1275*) *B.P. 567934*
(*1276*) *Modern Plastics*, 1946; **23,** 5; 116
(*1277*) Brous, S. L., *Modern Plastics*, 1945; **23,** 4; 107
(*1278*) Berry, T. M., *Electr. Eng*., 1944; **63,** 4; 195
(*1279*) Harris, L. D., *Electronics*, 1946; **18,** 1; 150
(*1280*) *Electronics*, 1936; **9,** 11; 16
(*1281*) *U.S. Patent 2141789*
(*1282*) *U.S. Patent 2193953*
(*1283*) *U.S. Patent 2181494*
(*1284*) *U.S. Patent 2198233*
(*1285*) *U.S. Patent 20823* (re-issue)
(*1286*) *U.S. Patent 2064517*
(*1287*) Livingston, O. W. and Lord, H. W., *Electronics*, 1934; **7,** 1; 7
(*1288*) Smith, J. F. D., *J. Franklin Inst*., 1940; **229;** 775
(*1289*) Wells, W. F., *J. Franklin Inst*., 1944; **238,** 3; 185
(*1290*) DeJuhasz, K. J., *J. Franklin Inst*., 1940; **229;** 53
(*1291*) *U.S. Patent 2193590*
(*1292*) Luckiesh, M., Taylor, A. H. and Kerr, G. P., *J. Franklin Inst*., 1944; **238,** 1; 1
(*1293*) Luckiesh, M , Taylor, A H. and Kerr, G. P., *J. Franklin Inst*., 1939; **228;** 425
(*1294*) Zeluff, V.. *Scient. American*, 1945; **4;** 212
(*1295*) Becquerel, E., *Ann. chim. phys*., 1848; **22;** 244
(*1296*) Becquerel, E., *Ann. chim. phys*., 1859; **55;** 5
(*1297*) Becquerel, E., *Ann. chim. phys*., 1859; **57;** 40
(*1298*) St. John, A. and Isenburger, H. R., *Industrial Radiology*, 1943, (1,300 references)
(*1299*) Isenburger, H. R., *Bibliography on Industrial Radiology* (suppl. to the above)
(*1300*) Sargrove, J. A., " Counting with barrier layer photocells ", *Electronic Eng*., 1940; **13,** 143; 14
(*1301*) Sargrove, J. A., " Barrier layer photocells in differential circuits ", *Electronic Eng*., 1940; **13,** 147; 210
(*1302*) " Manufacture of barrier layer photocells ", *Electronic Eng*., 1940; **13,** 149; 312
(*1303*) Sargrove, J. A., " Colour matching in Industry ", *Electronic Eng*., 1940; **13,** 149; 318
(*1304*) " Electronic counting circuits ", *Electronic Eng*., 1940; **13;** 148; 261
(*1305*) Levy, L. and West, D. W., " Phosphorescent phosphors ", *Electronic Eng*., 1940; **13,** 146; 173
(*1306*) " The Photo-Augetron and its applications ", *Electronic Eng*., 1940; **13,** 144; 75
(*1307*) " Theoretical and practical aspects of photocells ", *Electronic Eng*., 1940; **13,** 146; 149
(*1308*) Forster, E. W., " Photo-electric control of paper registration ", *Electronic Eng*., 1940; **13,** 150; 353
(*1309*) " Ionization time of thyratrons ", *Electronic Eng*., 1940; **13,** 146; 160
(*1310*) Jupe, J. J., " Safety devices ", *Electronic Eng*., 1941; **14,** 163; 393
(*1311*) Jupe, J. J., " Control devices ", *Electronic Eng*., 1941; **14,** 164; 444

(*1312*) JUPE, J. J., " Measurement ", *Electronic Eng.*, 1941; **14,** 165; 492
(*1313*) WINDRED, G., " Photoconductivity ", *Electronic Eng.*, 1941; **14,** 160; 249
(*1314*) GALL, D. C., " Photocell and thyratron ", *Electronic Eng.*, 1942; **14,** 170; 727
(*1315*) " Light control ", *Electronic Eng.*, 1941; **14,** 165; 500
(*1316*) VESZI, G. A., " Selenium photocells ", *Electronic Eng.*, 1941; **14,** 164; 436
(*1317*) WINDRED, G., " Photo-electricity ", *Electronic Eng.*, 1941; **14,** 162; 345
(*1318*) WINDRED, G., " Photovoltaic effects ", *Electronic Eng.*, 1941; **14,** 161; 298
(*1319*) PRINGSHEIM, P. and SALTMARSH, O. D., " Fluorescent emission of the Hg-line 2,537 AU. at pressures between 10^{-3} and 10^{-1} mm.", *Proc. Roy. Soc. Lond.*, 1936; **154,** A, 881; 90
(*1320*) BONE, W. A. and GARDNER, J. B., " Comparative studies of the slow combustion of methane, etc.", *Proc. Roy. Soc. Lond.*, 1936; **154,** A, 882; 297
(*1321*) ROUGHTON, F. J. W. and MILLIKAN, G. A., " Photo-electric methods of measuring the velocity of rapid reactions: I. General principles and controls ", *Proc Roy Soc. Lond.*, 1936; **155,** A, 885; 258
(*1322*) ROUGHTON, F. J. W. and MILLIKAN, G. A., " Photo-electric methods of measuring the velocity of rapid reactions: II. A simple apparatus for rapid pH and other changes requiring 200 cc. or more of each reagent ", *Proc. Roy. Soc. Lond.*, 1936; **155,** A, 885; 269
(*1323*) ROUGHTON, F. J. W. and MILLIKAN, G. A., " Photo-electric methods of measuring the velocity of rapid reactions: III. A portable micro-apparatus applicable to an extended range of reactions ", *Proc. Roy. Soc. Lond.*, 1936; 155, A, 885; 277
(*1324*) " Industrial tube characteristics ", *Electronics*, 1942; **15,** 6; 52
(*1325*) DARTNALL, H. J. A., GOODEVE, C. F. and LYTHGOE, R. J., " The quantitative analysis of the photochemical bleaching of Visual Purple solutions in monochromatic light ", *Proc. Roy. Soc. Lond.*, 1936; **156,** A, 887; 158
(*1326*) LOVELL, A. C. B., " The electric conductivity of thin metal films: I. Rubidium on Pyrex ", *Proc. Roy. Soc. Lond.*, 1937; **157,** A, 891; 311
(*1327*) LOVELL, A. C. B., " The electric conductivity of thin metal films: II. Cesium and Potassium on Pyrex ", *Proc. Roy. Soc. Lond.*, 1937; **158,** A, 895; 718
(*1328*) RICHARDSON, L. F., " The behaviour of an Osglim lamp: I.", *Proc. Roy. Soc. Lond.*, 1937; **162,** A, 910; 293
(*1329*) RICHARDSON, L. F., " The behaviour of an Osglim lamp: II.", *Proc. Roy. Soc. Lond.*, 1937; **162,** A, 910; 316
(*1330*) MAKINSON, R. E. B., " Metallic reflexion and the surface photo-electric effect ", *Proc. Roy. Soc. Lond.*, 1937; **162,** A, 910; 367
(*1331*) RICHARDSON, L. F. " The behaviour of an Osglim lamp: III.", *Proc. Roy. Soc. Lond.*, 1937; **163,** A, 914; 380
(*1332*) DARTNALL, H. J. A., GOODEVE, C. F. and LYTHGOE, R. J., " The effect of temperature on the photochemical bleaching of Visual Purple solutions ", *Proc. Roy. Soc. Lond.*, 1938; **164,** A, 917; 216
(*1333*) KANE, G. P., " The two-stage auto-ignition of hydro-carbons and ' knock ' ", *Proc. Roy. Soc. Lond.*, 1938; **167,** A, 928; 62
(*1334*) GARNER, W. E. and HAM, A. J., " The combustion of methane ", *Proc. Roy. Soc. Lond.*, 1939; **170,** A, 940; 80
(*1335*) RANDALL, J. T., " The fluorescence of compounds containing manganese ", *Proc. Roy. Soc. Lond.*, 1939; **170,** A, 941; 272
(*1336*) MATT, N. F., " Note on copper—copper oxide photocells ", *Proc. Roy. Soc. Lond.*, 1939; **171,** A, 946; 281
(*1337*) HOPPER, V. D. and LABY, T. H., " The electronic charge ", *Proc. Roy. Soc. Lond.*, 1941; **178,** A, 974; 243

(*1338*) Uyterhoeven, W. and Verburg, C., " Température des électrons dans une décharge en colonne positive dans un mélange (Ne—Na) ", *Compt. rend.*, 1936; **202**; 1498

(*1339*) Georgeson, E. H. M., " The free streaming of gases in sloping galleries ", *Proc. Roy. Soc. Lond.*, 1942; **180**, A, 983; 484

(*1340*) Gaydon, A. G., " Flame spectra in the photographic infra-red ", *Proc. Roy. Soc. Lond.*, 1942; **181**, A, 985; 197

(*1341*) Gaydon, A. G., " Continuous spectra in flames; the rôle of atomic oxygen in combustion ", *Proc. Roy. Soc. Lond.*, 1944; **183**, A, 992; 111

(*1342*) Poole, H. H. and Atkins, W. R. G., " The standardization of photo-electric cells for the measurement of visible light ", *Trans. Roy. Soc.*, 1936; **235**, A; 1

(*1343*) McGregor-Morris, J. T. and Billington, R. M., " The selenium rectifier photocell. Its characteristic and response to intermittent illumination ", *J.I.E.E.*, 1936; **79**, 475; 435. (Discussion: p. 448)

(*1344*) Preston, J. S., ' The selenium rectifier photocell. Its manufacture, properties, and use in photometry ", *J.I.E.E.*, 1936; **79**, 465; 424. (Discussion: p. 448)

(*1345*) Zworykin, V. K., " Electron-optical systems and their application ", *J.I.E.E.*, 1936; **79**, 475; 1

(*1346*) Paterson, C. C., " Uniformity in photocells ", *J.I.E.E.*, 1936; **79**, 475; 659

(*1347*) James, E. G., Polgreen, G. R. and Warren, G. W., " Instruments incorporating thermionic valves, and their characteristics ", *J.I.E.E.*, 1939; **85**, 512; 242

(*1348*) Williams, A. L. and Thompson, L. E., " Photo-electric properties of metal rectifiers ", *J.I.E.E.*, 1941; **88**; 360

(*1349*) Perucca, E. and Deaglio, R., " Effetto fotoelettrico dello ' Sperrschicht ' ed effetto fotoelettrico Hallwachs ", *Accad. Torino*, 1937; **72**; 500

(*1350*) Drigo, A., " Principali charatteristiche del funzionamento della cellula fotoelettrica a strato di sbarramento al ferro-selenio ", *Energia Elettrica*, 1937; **14**, 10; 822

(*1351*) Barlotta, S., " Un problema riguardante la fotometria fotoelettrica ", *Elettrotecnica*, 1937; **24**, 22; 711

(*1352*) Perucca, E., " Nuove proprietà elettriche di pellicole metalliche sottili ", *Nuovo Cimento*, 1937; **14**, 10; 506

(*1353*) Petralia, S., " Sudi una riduzone dell' effetto fotoelettrico nelle cellule comuni ", *Nuovo Cimento*, 1937; **14**, 9; 411

(*1354*) Malatesta, S., " Il telescopio elettronico ", *Elettrotecnica*, 1938; **25**, 6; 188

(*1355*) Drigo, A., " La valvola termoionica nella misura di debolissima corrente elettrica di intensità costante ", *Energia Elettrica*, 1938; **15**, 4; 253

(*1356*) Mazza, L. " Determinazione quantitative diretta di alcuni elementi negli spetri di fiamma per via fotoelettrica ", *Atti del X Congresso Internazionale di Chimica in Roma*, 1938

(*1357*) Todesco, G., " L'emissione fotoelettrica e le sue applicazione ", *Elettrotecnica*, 1938; **25**, 9; 300

(*1358*) Lovera, G., " Le comuni lampadine al neon come contatori di raggi gamma ", *Nuovo Cimento*, 1938; **15**, 3; 145

(*1359*) Perucca, E., " Ricerche sulle pellicole metalliche sottili—Conduzione elettrica ", *Nuovo Cimento*, 1938; **15**, 6; 365

(*1360*) Majorana, Q., " Azione della luce periodica su sottili lamine d'oro " *Acc. Lincei*, 1938; **28**, 5-6

(*1361*) Majorana, Q., " Ulteriori ricerche sull'azione della luce su sottili lamine metalliche ", *Acc. Lincei*, 1938; **28**, 5-6; 132

(*1362*) Majorana, Q., " Teoria termica della fotoresistenza metallica ", *Acc. Lincei*, 1938; **28**, 7-8; 177

(*1363*) Drigo, A., " Contatori di fotoni e lastra fotografica nella rivelazione di deboli intensità luminose ", *Ist. Veneto*, 1938; **97**, 1; 1

(*1364*) Clerici, C., " La Visione ", *Energia Elettrica*, 1939; Y, 16, iii; 232

(*1365*) SCHUPFER, F., " Un nuovo interferometro per lo studio del potere risolutivo della retina ", *Ric. Scient.*, 1939; **10,** 9; 852
(*1366*) LAPIERRE, C. W. and MANSFIELD, A. P., " Photo-electric weft-straightener control ", *Electrical Engineering*, 1938; **57,** 9; 513
(*1367*) FITZGERALD, A. S., " The Petoscope: A new principle in photo-electric applications ", *J. Franklin Inst.*, 1936; **222,** 1329; 289
(*1368*) TUTTLE, C., " Devices for the photo-electric control of exposure in photographic printing ", *J. Franklin Inst.*, 1937; **224,** 1343; 615
(*1369*) TUTTLE, C. M., " Photo-electric photometry ", *J. Franklin Inst.*, 1937; **224,** 1341; 315
(*1370*) STRELZOFF, J. A., " Mercury vapour grid controlled tubes; their electric control by a phase-shifting network ", *J. Franklin Inst.*, 1937; **224,** 1339; 55
(*1371*) STRELZOFF, J. A., " Mercury vapour grid controlled tubes; their electric control by a phase-shifting network ", *J. Franklin Inst.*, 1937; **224,** 1340; 191
(*1372*) BEESE, N. C., MARDEN, J. W. and MEISTER, G., " Measurement of light from a tellurium vapour arc ", *J. Franklin Inst.*, 1938; **225,** 1345; 45
(*1373*) MULDER, P. J., " Growth and decay of phosphorescence of calcium sulphide by a photo-electric method ", *J. Franklin Inst.*, 1938; **225,** 1349; 527
(*1374*) HARRISON, G. R., " Spectroscopy in Industry ", *J. Franklin Inst.*, 1938; 226, 1351; 1
(*1375*) SHEWHART, W. A., " Application of statistical methods to manufacturing problems ", *J. Franklin Inst.*, 1938; **226,** 1352; 163
(*1376*) MACKEOWN, S. S. and WOUK, V., " Generation of electric charges by moving rubber-tyred vehicles ", *Electrical Engineer*, 1943; **62,** 5, 207
(*1377*) BERRY, T. M., " Polarized light servo-system ", *Electrical Engineering*, 1944; **63,** 4; 195
(*1378*) POTTER, E. V., " Electronic devices aid metallurgical research ", *Electrical Engineering*, 1944; **63,** 5; 175
(*1379*) KUEHNI, H. P. and PETERSON, H. A., " A new differential analyzer ", *Electrical Engineering*, 1944; **63,** 5; 221
(*1380*) LINDSAY, M. H. A., " Electronic protective systems ", *Electrical Engineering*, 1944; **63,** 10; 367
(*1381*) PLUMB, H. T., " Fluorescence aids mining ", *Electrical Engineering*, 1944; **63,** 7; 243
(*1382*) " Bibliography of relay literature, 1940-43 ", *Electrical Engineering*, 1944; **63,** 10; 705
(*1383*) KULIN, S. A., " Fluorescent inspection of tungsten ", *Electronics*, 1943; **16,** 7; 95
(*1384*) BROWN, R. V., " Electronics applied to heat transfer test ", *Electronics*, 1943; **16,** 7; 113
(*1385*) " Trouble shooting in electronic equipment ", *Electronics*, 1943; **16,** 7; 134
(*1386*) " Electronic time interval measuring instrument (10^{-4} sec.)", *Electronics*, 1943; **16,** 8; 152
(*1387*) STAIR, R. and SMITH, W. O., " Light sources for photo-electric radiometry ", *Electronics*, 1943; **16,** 8; 174
(*1388*) BOUMA, P. J., " Physiologisch-optische Grundlagen für die Probleme der Luftschutzverdunklung ", *Physica*, 1941; **8,** 4; 398
(*1389*) BOUMA, P. J., " Der Zusammenhang zwischen den Begriffen Leuchtdichte, Stilb, Helligkeit, Dunkelleuchtdichte, usw. ", *Physica*, 1941; **8,** 4; 413
(*1390*) BREUNING, H., " Secondary electron emission from metals with a low work function ", *Physica*, 1941; **8,** 10; 1161
(*1391*) GISOLF, J. H., DE GROOT, W. and KRÖGER, F. A., " The absorption spectra of zinc sulphide and Willemite ", *Physica*, 1941; **8,** 7; 805
(*1392*) DE GROOT, W., " The decay of the luminescence of zinc sulphide phosphors excited by X-rays ", *Physica*, 1941; **8,** 7; 789
(*1393*) KRÖGER, F. A. and BAKKER, J., " Luminescence of cerium compounds ", *Physica*, 1941; **8,** 7; 628

(*1394*) STRUTT, M. J. O. and VAN DER ZIEL, A., " Verringerung und Beseitigung der spontanen Schwankungen bei der Verstärkung kleinster Photoströme ", *Physica*, 1941; **8,** 6; 576
(*1395*) STRUTT, M. J. O. and VAN DER ZIEL, A., " Welche Grössen kennzeichnen die Verwendbarkeit einer Elektronenröhre zur Verstärkung kleinster Signale? ", *Physica* 1941; **8,** 4; 424
(also cf. reference *1561*)
(*1396*) ENGBERT, W., (Discussion of the above paper), *Physica*, 1941; **8,** 8; 903
(*1397*) BOUMA, P. J., " Mathematical relationship between the colour vision systems of trichromats and dichromats ", *Physica*, 1942; **9,** 8; 773
(*1398*) BOUMA, P. J., " Die Wahrnehmungsschwelle punktförmiger farbiger Lichter ", *Physica*, 1942; **9,** 8; 890
(*1399*) RÜTGERS, G. A. W., " Der Helligkeitseindruck punktförmiger farbiger Lichtflecke ", *Physica*, 1942; **9,** 8; 875
(*1400*) HIRSCH, A. and KAUTSKY, K., *Z. anorg. allgem. Chemie*, 1935; **222;** 126
(*1401*) FRANCK, J. and PRINGSHEIM, P., *J. Chem. Phys.*, 1943; **11;** 21
(*1402*) POLLACK, M., PRINGSHEIM, P. and TERWOOD, D., *J. Chem. Phys.*, 1944; **12;** 295
(*1403*) SEITZ, F., *J. Chem. Phys.*, 1938; **6;** 150
(*1404*) *U.S. Pat. 2227117*
(*1405*) *U.S. Pat. 2233483*
(*1406*) *U.S. Pat. 2234696*
(*1407*) *U.S. Pat. 2246906*
(*1408*) JUPE, J. H., *Electronics*, 1939; **12,** 4; 44
(*1409*) *U.S. Pat. 2221944*
(*1410*) *U.S. Pat. 2244362*
(*1411*) *U.S. Pat. 2239362*
(*1412*) *U.S. Pat. 2259372*
(*1413*) *B.P. 469949*
(*1414*) BROWN, W. F., *Electronics*, 1946; **19,** 2; 168
(*1415*) GOODMAN, D., *Electronics*, 1946; **19,** 2; 146
(*1416*) REDEMSKE, R. F., *Electronics*, 1946; **19,** 2; 128
(*1417*) *Electronics*, 1946; **19,** 2; cover
(*1418*) *U.S. Pat. 2261644*
(*1419*) SOMMER, W., *Electronics*, 1946; **19,** 1; 356
(*1420*) DODDS, E. M., *Automobile Engineer*, 1935; **25,** 3; 323
(*1421*) DODDS, E. M., *Engineering*, 1935; **140,** Aug. 23; 183
(*1422*) DODDS, E. M., *Soc. Automob. Eng. J.*, 1936, Dec.
(*1423*) DODDS, E. M., *J. Inst. Autom. Eng.*, 1937; **6,** 2; 41
(*1424*) CAMPBELL, D. A., *Instruments*, 1945; **18,** 12; 868
(*1425*) *Instruments*, 1945; **18,** 12; 926
(*1426*) *Instruments*, 1946; **19,** 1; 38
(*1427*) *Instruments*, 1946; **19,** 1; 54
(*1428*) *U.S. Pat. 2360663*
(*1429*) KALISCHER, P. R., *Instruments*, 1945; **18,** 12; 894
(*1430*) *Electronics*, 1946; **19,** 3; 105
(*1431*) PARSEGIAN, V. L., *Electronics*, 1946; **19,** 3; 105
(*1432*) *U.S. Pat. 2348296*
(*1433*) *U.S. Pat. 2395781*
(*1434*) COCKRELL, W. D., *Electrical World*, 1943; p. 1886
(*1435*) JOFFÉ, A. J., *Bull. Acad. Sci. de l'URSS*, 1945; **9;** 259
(*1436*) SHOENBERG, D., *Nature*, 1946; **157,** 3990; 525
(*1437*) KAY, H. D., *Nature*, 1946; **157,** 3990; 511
(*1438*) *Electronics*, 1943; **16,** 9; 94
(*1439*) SKELETT, A. M., *J. Appl. Phys.*, 1938; **9,** 10; 631
(*1440*) JOHNSON, R. P., *J. Appl. Phys.*, 1938; **9,** 8; 508
(*1441*) MCFARLAN, R. L., *J. Appl. Phys.*, 1938; **9,** 9; 573
(*1442*) MORSE, PH. M., BODEN, R. H. and SCHECTER, H., *J. Appl. Phys.*, 1938; **9,** 1; 16
(*1443*) *Prov. B.P. Spec. 11915/46*

(*1444*) Quick, A. L. and Hall, H. D., *Electronics*, 1945; **18,** 12; 147
(*1445*) Skinner, D. G., *B.C.O.R.A.*, 1944; **2,** 6; 9
(*1446*) Porter, T. C., *Proc. Roy. Soc. Lond.*, 1902; **70;** 313
(*1447*) Sommer, W., *J. Telev. Soc.*, 1945; **4,** 7; 150
(*1448*) Schanz, F., *Arch. f. Ophthalmologie*, 1913; **86;** 549
(*1449*) Graham, W. P., *J.O.S.A.*, 1922; **4,** 8; 605
(*1450*) *U.S. Pat. 2122860*
(*1451*) *B.P. 460012*
(*1452*) Skinner, D. G., *B.C.O.R.A.*, 1945; **7,** 9; 22
(*1453*) Eppig, H. J., *C.I.O.S.*, Items No. 3 and 17; File XXXII-1. (H.M.S.O.)
(*1454*) *C.I.O.S.*, Item No. 9; File XIII-5. (H.M.S.O.)
(*1455*) Hardy, G. H., *Illum. Eng.*, 1941; **36,** 3; 295
(*1456*) Graham, J. I. and Stanley, H. A., *B.C.O.R.A.*, 1945; **8;** 6
(*1457*) Williams, G. A., *Electronic Eng.*, 1946; **18,** 221; 208
(*1458*) Bromilow, J. G., *Trans. Inst. Min. Eng., Lond.*, 1945; **104;** 267
(*1459*) Bromilow, J. G., *Colliery Guardian*, 1945; **170;** 195
(*1460*) Hund, A., *High Frequency Measurements*, 1933 (p. 351)
(*1461*) Melloy, E., Say, M. G., Walker, R. C. and Windred, G., *Electrical Engineer* (A Reference Book), 1945
(*1462*) Hunt, C. L., *C.I.O.S.*, Items No. 1 and 9; File XXXII-95. (H.M.S.O.)
(*1463*) *Electrical Times*, 1944; June 1st; 639
(*1464*) Sommer, W., *J. Sci. Instr.*, 1946; **23,** 7; 150
(*1465*) Robins, J. and Varden, L. E., *Electronics*, 1946; **19,** 6; 110
(*1466*) Lafferty, R. E., *Electronics*, 1946; **19,** 5; 158
(*1467*) Cashman, R. J., *J.O.S.A.*, 1946; **36,** 6; 347
(*1468*) Coleman, E. F., *J.O.S.A.*, 1946; **36,** 6; 347
(*1469*) Oxley, C. L., *J.O.S A* , 1946; **36,** 6; 347
(*1470*) Czerny, M., *Z. Phys.*, 1929; **53,** 1; 6
(*1471*) *Electronics*, 1946; **19,** 4; 252
(*1472*) *Electronics*, 1943; **16,** 1; 127
(*1473*) Benedict, M., *R.S.I.*, 1937; **8,** 7; 253
(*1474*) Hardy, A. C., *J.O.S.A.*, 1943; **33,** 2; 71
(*1475*) Chance, J. C. R., *J. Sci. Instr.*, 1946; **23,** 3; 50
(*1467*) MacAdam, D. L., *J.O.S.A.*, 1945; **35,** 10; 670
(*1477*) Harrison, T. R., *J.O.S.A.*, 1945; **35,** 11; 706
(*1478*) Pfund, A. H., *J.O.S.A.*, 1946; **36,** 2; 95
(*1479*) v. Ardenne, M., *Cathode Ray Tubes*, 1939 (English edit.)
(*1480*) Gibson, K. S., *Instruments*, 1936; **9;** 309, 335
(*1481*) Hunter, R. S., *J.O.S.A.*, 1938; **28,** 2; 51
(*1482*) Barnes, B. T., *J.O.S.A.*, 1941; **31,** 8; 463
(*1483*) Hunter, R. S., *J.O.S.A.*, 1938; **28,** 3; 179
(*1484*) Hunter, R. S., *J.O.S.A.*, 1941; **31,** 8; 463
(*1485*) Perry, J. W., *J. Sci. Instr.*, 1938; **15,** 5; 270
(*1486*) Taylor, A. H., *Illum. Eng.*, 1941; **36,** 9; 927
(*1487*) Hall, J. A., *J. Sci. Instr.*, 1946; **23,** 3; 59
(*1488*) Chance, B., *Electronics*, 1940; **13,** 2; 24
(*1489*) Chance, B., *Electronics*, 1940; **13,** 10; 82
(*1490*) Moon, P., *J. Franklin Inst.*, 1940; **230,** 5; 583
(*1491*) Moon, P., *Illum. Eng.*, 1941; **36,** 3; 313
(*1492*) Marx, E., *Phys. Rev.*, 1946; **69,** 9 and 10; 523
(*1493*) Harding, H. G. W., *Proc. Phys. Soc. Lond.*, 1945; **57,** 321; 222
(*1494*) Priest, I. G., *Scient. Pap. Nat. Bur. Stand.*, 1922; **18;** 221
(*1495*) Was, D. A., *Physica*, 1939; **6,** 4; 382
(*1496*) Milatz, J. M. W. and Woudenberg, J. P. M., *Physica*, 1940; **7,** 8; 697
(*1497*) Forsythe, W. E., Easley, M. A. and Hinman, D. D., *J. Appl. Phys.*, 1938; **9,** 3; 209
(*1498*) Smith, S. P., *Electrical Engineering Laboratory Manual,* 1936; p. 30
(*1499*) Wright, R. R., *Electronic Laboratory Manual*, 1945; p. 46
(*1500*) Henderson, Y. and Haggard, H. W., *Noxious Gases and the Principles of Respiration Influencing their Action*, 1943

(1501) REIMERT, L. J., " Properties of metals in a finely divided state ", *J.O.S.A.*, 1946; **36,** 5; 278
(1502) PAUL, F. W., " Experiments on the use of infra-red sensitive phosphors in the photography of the spectrum ", (15,300 AU.), *J.O.S.A.*, 1946; **36,** 3; 175
(1503) LUCKIESH, M. and TAYLOR, A. H., " Transmittance and reflectance of germicidal (2,537 AU.) energy ", *J.O.S.A.*, 1946; **36,** 4; 227
(1504) ELLICKSON, R T " Effect of wavelength distribution on the brightness of phosphors ", *J.O.S.A.*, 1946; **36,** 5; 261
(1505) ELLICKSON, R T, " Light sum of phosphors under thermal and infra-red stimulation ", *J.O.S.A.*, 1946; **36,** 5; 264
(1506) KARRER, E. and ORR, R.S., " Photo-electric refractometer ", *J.O.S.A.*, 1946; **36,** 1; 42
(1507) POWELL, W. M., Jr., " Photo-electric spectrophotometry in the vacuum (Schumann region) ", *Phys Rev.*, 1934; **45;** 154
(1508) LITTLE, E. P., " Photo-electric spectrophotometer for the Schumann region ", *J.O.S.A.*, 1946; **36,** 3; 168
(1509) WARD, R., " Preparation and properties of infra-red sensitive SrSe and S_2Se phosphors ", *J.O.S.A.*, 1946; **36,** 6; 347
(1510) MILLER, N. F., and BARNETT, C. E., " Infra-red sensitive phosphors from CdS and Zn ", *J.O.S.A.*, 1946; **36,** 6; 347
(1511) FONDA, G. R., " Preparation and characteristics of ZnS phosphors sensitive to infra-red ", *J.O.S.A.*, 1946; **36,** 6; 347
(1512) ADAMS, E. Q., " Some suggestions for the nomenclature of radiation ", *J.O.S.A.*, 1946; **36,** 6; 358
(1513) BLOUT, E. R., LAND, E. H., AMON, W. F., Jr., THOMAS, A., SHEPHERD, R. G., Jr., " Near infra-red transmitting filters ", *J.O.S.A.*, 1946; **36,** 6; 360
(1514) SHENK, J. H., HODGE, E. S., MORRIS, R. J., PICKETT, E. E., BRODE, W. R., " Filters for the visible and near infra-red regions ", *J.O.S.A.*, 1946; **36,** 6; 360
(1515) PATCHETT, G. N., " Theory of the non-linear bridge circuit as applied to voltage stabilizers ", *J.I.E.E.*, 1946; **93**, III, 21; 16
(1506) GALLUP, W. D. and HOEFER, J. A., " Determination of vitamin A in liver ", *Ind. Eng. Chem. Anal. Ed.*, 1946; **18,** 5; 288
(1517) HILL, U. T., " Colorimetric determination of fatty acids and esters ", *Ind. Eng. Chem., Anal. Ed.*, 1946; **18,** 5; 317
(1518) HARVEY, R. B., " Electronic make and break for relay operation ", *Ind. Eng. Chem., Anal. Ed.*, 1946; **18,** 5; 331
(1519) RIDER, B. F. and MELLOW, M. G., " Colorimetric determination of nitrates ", *Ind. Eng. Chem., Anal. Ed.*, 1946; **18,** 2; 96
(1520) LYKKEN, L., TRESEDER, R. S. and Zahn, V., " Colorimetric determination of phenols " *Ind. Eng. Chem., Anal. Ed.*, 1946; **18,** 2; 103
(1521) THOMPSON, C. R., et al., " Chemical determination of vitamin A in dried whole eggs ", *Ind. Eng. Chem., Anal. Ed.*, 1946; **18,** 2; 113
(1522) BAIER, J. G., Jr., and MILLINGTON, P. E., " A versatile electronic relay ", *Ind. Eng. Chem., Anal. Ed.*, 1946; **18,** 2; 152
(1523) BERRY, J. W., CHAPPELL, D. G. and BARNES, R. B., " Improved method of flame photometry ", *Ind. Eng. Chem., Anal. Ed.*, 1946; **18,** 1; 19
(1524) BARNES, R. B. et al., " Flame photometry ", *Ind. Eng. Chem., Anal. Ed.*, 1945; **17,** 10; 605
(1525) BRICKER, L. G., WEINBERG, S. and PROCTOR, K. L., " Colorimetric analysis of corrosion-resistant steels ", *Ind. Eng. Chem., Anal. Ed.*, 1945; **17**, 10; 661
(1526) " Photo-electric colorimetry ", *G.E. Rev.*, 1946; **49,** 6; 56
(1527) " Photo-electric testing method for photoflash lamps ", *G.E. Rev.*, 1946; **49,** 6; 56
(1528) WROBEL, H. T. and CHAMBERLAIN, H. H., " Photometric equipment for blocking-layer light-sensitive cells ", *G.E. Rev.*, 1946; **49,** 4; 25

(*1529*) KALLMAN, H. E., "High impedance cable", *Proc. I.R.E.*, 1946; **34,** 6; 348

(*1530*) SPILSBURY, R. S. J., FEETON, A. and PRESTON, J. S., "A photo-electric sun compass for tanks", *J. Sci. Instr.*, 1946; **23,** 6; 128

(*1531*) MAGGS, F. A. P., "A simple electronic relay for switching loads of several kW", *J. Sci. Instr.*, 1946; **23,** 4; 85

(*1532*) HAZEN, H. L. and BROWN, G. S., "The cinema integraph", *J. Franklin Inst.*, 1940; **230;** 19, 183

(*1533*) ROSS, H. M., "A device to assist in resetting an electromagnetic counter to zero", *J. Sci. Instr.*, 1946; **23,** 1; 17

(*1534*) MOONEY, R. L., "Exact theoretical treatment of reflexion-reducing coatings", *J.O.S.A.*, 1945; **35,** 9; 574

(*1535*) NASTOLL, G. A. and BRYAN, F. R., "Application of multiplier phototubes to the spectrochemical analysis of Mg-alloys", *J.O.S.A.*, 1945; **35,** 10; 646

(*1536*) SAUNDERSON, J. L., CALDECOURT, V. D. and PETERSON, E. W., "Photo-electric instrument for direct spectrochemical analysis", *J.O.S.A.*, 1945; **35,** 11; 681

(*1537*) HULBURT, E. O., "Optics of distilled and natural water", *J.O.S.A.*, 1945; **35,** 11; 698

(*1538*) HARRISON, T. R., "Industrial use of radiation pyrometers under non-black body conditions", *J.O.S.A.*, 1945; **35,** 11; 708

(*1539*) THOMPSON, H. W. and TORKINGTON, P. "The infra-red spectra of polymers and related monomers: I", *Proc. Roy. Soc. Lond.*, 1945; **184,** A, 996; 3

(*1540*) THOMPSON, H. W. and TORKINGTON, P. (as above, II), *Proc. Roy. Soc. Lond.*, 1945; **184,** A, 996; 21

(*1541*) RANDALL, J. T. and WILKINS, M. H. F., "The phosphorescence of various solids", *Proc. Roy. Soc. Lond.*, 1945; **184,** A, 999; 347

(*1542*) RANDALL, J. T. and WILKINS, M. H. F., "Phosphorescence and electron traps: I), *Proc. Roy. Soc. Lond.*, 1945; **184,** A, 999; 365

(*1543*) RANDALL, J. T. and WILKINS, M. H. F. (as above, II), *Proc. Roy. Soc. Lond.*, 1945; **184,** A, 999; 390

(*1544*) BARNES, B. T., "Direct reading photo-electric colorimeter," *R.S.I.* 1945; **16,** 12; 337

(*1545*) PAKSWER, S. and KIRK, J., "Colour temperature testing in projector lamp production", *R.S.I.*, 1946; **17,** 4; 157

(*1546*) REGENER, V. H., "Decade counting units", *R.S.I.*, 1946; **17,** 5; 185

(*1547*) GRAY, T. S., "The photo-electric integraph", *J. Franklin Inst.*, 1931; **212;** 77

(*1548*) BRUINING, H. and DE BOER, J. H., "Secondary electron emission: I", *Physica*, 1938; **5,** 1; 17

(*1549*) Committee on colorimetry, "I. Historical background", *J.O.S.A.*, 1943; **33,** 10; 534

(*1550*) Committee on colorimetry, "II. Concept of colour", *J.O.S.A.*, 1943; **33,** 10; 544

(*1551*) Committee on colorimetry, "VII. Quantitative data and methods for colorimetry", *J.O.S.A.*, 1944; **34,** 11; 663
(also cf. references
(*254*) "Physical concepts: radiant energy and its measurement"
(*321*) "The psychophysics of colour"
(*517*) "Colorimeters and colour standards")

(*1552*) BRUINING, H. and DE BOER, J. H., "Secondary electron emission: II", *Physica*, 1938; **5,** 10; 901

(*1553*) BOCK, R. O., "Values of the optical constants for beryllium, magnesium, and zinc", *Phys. Rev.*, 1945; **68,** 1-2; 43

(*1554*) GRANIT, R., "The electrophysiological analysis of the fundamental problem of colour reception", *Proc. Phys. Soc. Lond.*, 1945; **57,** 324; 447

(*1555*) Preston, J. S. and Smith, G. W. G., " The internal resistance of the selenium rectifier photocell with special reference to the sputtered metal film ", *Proc. Phys. Soc. Lond.*, 1945; **57,** 319; 1

(*1556*) Debye, P. P., " Photo-electric instrument for light scattering measurements and a differential refractometer for determining particle size and molecular weights ", *J. Appl. Phys.*, 1946; **17,** 5; 392

(*1557*) Koller, L. R., " Production and decomposition of ozone by low pressure Hg-vapour lamps, and a photo-electric method of measuring the ozone ", *J. Appl. Phys.*, 1945; **16,** 12; 816

(*1558*) Seitz, F., " Basic principles of semi-conductors ", *J. Appl. Phys.*, 1945: **16,** 10; 553

(*1559*) Maurer, R. J., " Electrical properties of semi-conductors ", *J. Appl. Phys.*, 1945; **16,** 10; 563

(*1560*) Bruining, H., " Secondary electron emission: III ", *Physica,* 1938; **5,** 10; 913

(*1561*) Engbert, W., Strutt, M. J. O. and van der Ziel, A., " Welche Grössen kennzeichnen die Verwendbarkeit einer Elektronenröhre zur Verstärkung kleinster Signale? ", *Physica,* 1942; **9,** 2; 248
(also cf. reference (*1395*))

(*1562*) Bruining, H. and de Boer, J. H., " Secondary electron emission: IV ", *Physica,* 1939; **6,** 8; 823

(*1563*) Bruining, H. and de Boer, J. H., " Secondary electron emission: V ", *Physica,* 1939; **6,** 8; 834

(*1564*) de Boer, J. H. and Bruining, H., " Secondary electron emission: VI ", *Physica,* 1939; **6,** 9; 941

(*1565*) Coster, D., Hof, S., Rathenau, G. and Simons, C. F. E., " The absorption of Au and Ag in the ultra-violet region ", *Physica,* 1938; **5,** 7; 643

(*1566*) Gisolf, J. H. and Kröger, F. A., " On the proportionality of the luminescence of ZnS phosphors to the irradiation at low intensities ", *Physica,* 1939; **6,** 9; 1101

(*1567*) Pringsheim, P. and Vogel, H., " Fluoreszenz von Schwermetallkomplexen in wässeriger Lösung ", *Physica,* 1940; **7,** 3; 225

(*1568*) Kröger, F. A., " Luminescence and absorption of ZnS, CdS, and their solid solutions ", *Physica,* 1940; **7,** 1; 1

(*1569*) Kröger, F. A., " Luminescence and absorption of solid solutions in the ternary system ZnS-CdS-MnS ", *Physica,* 1940; **7,** 1; 92

(*1570*) Giltay, J., " A counter arrangement with constant resolving time ", *Physica,* 1943; **10,** 9; 725

(*1571*) Franzen, P., Wondenberg, J. P. M. and Gorter, C. J., " Absorption of light in a solution of samarium nitrate ", (maximum extinction coefficient at 7,450 AU.)", *Physica,* 1943; **10,** 5; 365

(*1572*) Wells, W. F., " Bactericidal irradiation of air ", *J. Franklin Inst.*, 1940; **229,** 3; 347

(*1573*) Walker, E. A., "An instrument for measuring short intervals of time ", *J. Franklin Inst.*, 1941; **231,** 4; 373

(*1574*) " Photometry. Arrangement of a C-R tube and a mask in measuring the spectrum image of lamps ", *G.E.C. Journal,* 1946; **14,** 1; 40

(*1575*) Bonroff, P., " Phosphorescence ", *Compt. rend.*, 1944; **218,** 6; 970

(*1576*) " Paint reflexion tests with mercury and incandescent lighting ", *Electrical Engineering,* 1940; **59,** 2; 62

(*1577*) Chubb, L. W., " Polarized light ", *Electrical Engineering,* 1939; **58,** 11; 45

(*1578*) Terrien, J., " Photoélectricité ", *Compt. rend.*, 1944; **218,** 1; 43

(*1579*) Delattre, M., " Sur la marche en parallèle de plusieurs cellules photoélectriques au sélénium dites à couche d'arrêt ", *Compt. rend.*, 1944; **218,** 1; 112

(*1580*) Bouroff, P., " Sur l'accroissement de la luminescence par l'emploi de plusieurs corps luminogènes ", *Compt. rend.*, 1944; **218,** 2; 317

(*1581*) Audubert, R. and Racz, Ch., " Chimio luminescence ultraviolette par l'oxidation du carbone (above 1,000° C.) ", *Compt. rend.*, 1944; **218,** 5; 753

(*1582*) DESTRIAU, G., " Action des champs électriques sur les scintillations " *Compt. rend.*, 1944; **218,** 5; 791
(*1583*) BOUROFF, P., " Confirmations expérimentales de l'augmentation de l'intensité lumineuse d'un produit phosphorescent par l'adjonction successive de plusieurs activateurs ", *Compt. rend.*, 1944; **218,** 6; 971
(*1584*) CHALONGE, D. and KOWGANOFF, V., " Opacité de la photosphère solaire et spectre de l'ion negatif hydrogène ", *Compt. rend.*, 1945; **221,** 7; 91
(*1585*) BARTÉLÉMY, R., " Contribution à la théorie de l'iconoscope ", *Compt. rend.*, 1945; **221,** 8; 245
(*1586*) BLANC-LAPIERRE, A., " Sur l'effet de scintillation ", *Compt. rend.*, 1945; **221,** 10; 375
(*1587*) BERTRAND, D., " Sur le phénomène de l'optimum de concentration des solutions fluorescentes ", *Compt.* rend., 1945; **220,** 4; 525
(*1588*) KRUITHOF, A. A. and BOUMA, P. J., " Hue estimation of surface colours by the colours of the surroundings ", *Physica*, 1942; **9,** 10; 957
(*1589*) KISTEMAKER, J., " On the volumes of mercury menisci and the surface tension of mercury deduced from them ", *Physica*, 1945; **11,** 4; 270
(*1590*) KISTEMAKER, J., " The capillary depression of mercury and high precision manometry ", *Physica*, 1945; **11,** 4; 277
(*1591*) BLOEMBERGEN, N., " Note on the internal secondary emission and the influence of surface states ", *Physica*, 1945; **11,** 4; 343
(*1592*) BRUINING, H., *Sekundärelektronenemission Fester Körper*, 1942, Berlin
(*1593*) MILATZ, J. M. W. and BLOEMBERGEN, N., " The development of a photoelectric alternating current amplifier with a.c. galvanometer; accuracy equal to that of an ideal d.c. amplifier. Not sensitive to external disturbances ", *Physica*, 1946; **11,** 6; 449
(*1594*) VAN DER VELDEN, H. V., " Over het aantal lichtquanta dat nodig is voor een lichtprikkel bij het menselijk oog ", *Physica*, 1944; **11,** 3; 179
(*1595*) HIBBEN, S. G., " How illuminants are born; data on efficiencies ", *J. Franklin Inst.*, 1945; **239,** 5; 391
(*1596*) MOON, P., and SPENCER, D. E., " International names in colorimetry ", *J.O.S.A.*, 1946; **36,** 7; 427
(*1597*) ADAMS, E. Q., " Some suggestions for the nomenclature of radiation ", *J.O.S.A.*, 1946; **36,** 7; 429
(*1598*) RICHTER, W., ELLIOT, W. H., " An instrument for the determination of contact making and breaking time ", *Electrical Engineering Trans.*, 1943; **62,** 1; 14
(Discussion): p. 459
(*1599*) POTTER, E. V., " Electronic devices and metallurgical research ", *Electrical Engineering*, 1944; **63,** 5; 175
(*1600*) FLUKE, J. M. and PORTER, N. E., *Electronics*, 1946; **19,** 3; 92
(*1601*) *G.E.C. Journal*, 1946; **142;** 38
(*1602*) PACKARD, CH. A., *Relay Engineering*, 1946
(*1603*) WEISZ, P. B., *Electronics*, 1946; **19,** 7; 106
(*1604*) *Electronics*, 1946; **19,** 7; 198
(*1605*) *Electronics*, 1946; **19,** 7; 152
(*1606*) HEINS, H., *Electronics*, 1946; **19,** 7; 96
(*1607*) FILON, L. N. G., *A Manual of Photo-elasticity for Engineers*, 1936
(*1608*) HILLIARD, R. C., *Electronics*, 1946; **19,** 3; 180
(*1609*) American Standards Association Z-37.8—1943
(*1610*) RINIA, H. and LEBLANS, L., *Philips Techn. Rev.*, 1939; **4,** 2; 42
(*1611*) DUCLAUX, J. and BRICOUT, V., *Compt. rend.*, 1944; **219,** 8; 199
(*1612*) V. HIPPEL, A., SCHULMAN, J. H. and RITTNER, E. S., *J. Appl. Phys.*, 1946; **17,** 4; 215
(*1613*) *Veröffentlichungen aus dem Gebiete der Nachrichtentechnik*, 1939; **1,** Folge; 127
(*1614*) MARKEY, CH. J., *Electronics*, 1945; **18,** 3; 125
(*1615*) MONK, G. S., *Light, Principles and Experiments*, 1937
(*1616*) BUKLER, N., *Klin. Wchschr*, 1929, No. 17
(*1617*) BEAUMONT, W., *Infra-red Irradiation*, 1939

(*1618*) Hausser, K. W. and Vahle, *Strahlentherapie*, 1921; **13;** 41
(*1619*) Hausser, K. W. and Vahle, *Strahlentherapie*, 1928; **28;** 24
(*1620*) Wells, W. F., *J. Franklin Inst.*, 1940; **229,** 3; 347
(*1621*) de Ment, J., *Fluorochemistry*, 1945
(*1622*) Luckiesh, M., *Artificial Sunlight*, 1930
(*1623*) Maxwell, L. R. and Hendricks, S. B., *J. Appl. Phys.*, 1938; **9,** 4; 237
(*1624*) *J. Appl. Phys.*, 1938; **9,** 1; 35
(*1625*) Kenty, C., *J. Appl. Phys.*, 1938; **9,** 1; 53
(*1626*) Weinberger, A., *Physical Methods of Organic Chemistry*, 2 vols., 1946
(*1627*) Pearson, H., *Mod. Plastics*, 1945; **23,** 12; 123
(*1628*) Spencer, D. E., *J. Franklin Inst.*, 1943; **236,** 3; 293
(*1629*) Moon, P. and Spencer, D. E., *J. Franklin Inst.*, 1946; **241,** 3; 195
(*1630*) Hecht, S., *Science in Progress*, 4th series; 1945; p. 75
(*1631*) Möglich, F., Rompe, R. and Timoféeff-Ressowsky, N. W., *Die Naturwissenschaften*, 1942; **30;** 408
(*1632*) Einstein, A., *Ann. d. Phys.*, 1906; **20;** 199
(*1633*) Urbach, F., Pearlman, D. and Hemmendinger, H., *J.O.S.A.*, 1946; **36,** 7; 372
(*1634*) O'Brian, Brian, *J.O.S.A.*, 1946; **36,** 7; 369
(*1635*) Fonda, G. R., *J.O.S.A.*, 1946; **36,** 7; 382
(*1636*) Breskin, Ch. A., *Scient. Amer.*, 1946; **9;** 114
(*1637*) Rockwood, G. H., *Electrical Engineering* (*Trans.*), 1941; **60,** 9; 901 (Discussion): 1390
(*1638*) Blout, E. R., Amon, W. F., Jr., Shepherd, R. G., Jr., Thomas, A., West, C. D. and Land, E. H., *J.O.S.A.*, 1946; **36,** 8; 460
(*1639*) Greenlee, L. E., *Electronics*, 1946; **19,** 9; 93
(*1640*) Morton, G. A. and Flory, L. E., *Electronics*, 1946; **19,** 9; 112
(*1641*) Krizek, V. and Vand, V., *Electronic Engineering*, 1946; **18,** 224; 316
(*1642*) Baumann, H., *Teknisk Tidskrift*, 1945; **75,** 32; 893
(*1643*) Baumann, H., *The Engineer's Digest*, 1946; **7,** 5; 144
(*1644*) Lee, E. and Parker, R. C., *Nature*, 1946; **158,** 4015; 518
(*1645*) Preston, J. S., *J. Sci. Instr.*, 1946; **23,** 9; 211
(*1646*) Dept. Sci. and Ind. Res., *Fuel Research, Techn. Paper No. 53*
(*1647*) Jensen, A. T., *Kgl. Danske Videnskabernes Selskab* (*Matematisk-Fysiske Meddelelser*, Bind XX, No. 8), 1943
(*1648*) *U.S. Pat. 2389649*
(*1649*) *Electronics*, 1946; **19,** 11; 210
(*1650*) Barnett, G. F. and Free, A. L., *Electronics*, 1946; **19,** 12; 116
(*1651*) Sommer, W., *Electronic Engineering*, 1946; **18,** 226; 361
(*1652*) Smith, H. M., *Electronics*, 1946; **19,** 11; 180
(*1653*) Sweet, M. H., *Electronics*, 1946; **19,** 11; 105
(*1654*) West, S. S., *Electronic Engineering*, 1947; **19,** 227; 3
(*1655*) Comstock, E. E., "*QST*", 1946; **30,** 11; 56 (Abstracted in: *Electronic Engineering*, 1947; **19,** 227; 30)
(*1656*) Cockrell, W. D., *Trans. Am. I.E.E.*, 1946; **65,** 8; 617
(*1657*) Leverenz, H. W., *RCA Rev.*, 1946; **7,** 2; 199
(*1658*) *Scientific and Industrial Reports* (U.S.A.), PB 1996
(*1659*) *Scientific and Industrial Reports* (U.S.A.), PB 3536
(*1660*) *Scientific and Industrial Reports* (U.S.A.), PB 7923
(*1661*) Dobson, G. M. B., *Proc. Phys. Soc. Lond.*, 1931; **43;** 324
(*1662*) Samuel, J. M., *Eng. and Min. J.*, 1942; **143,** 6; 58
(*1663*) *J. Chem. Phys.*, 1941; **9,** 11; 786
(*1664*) Stillman, J. W., *Proc. Am. Soc. Test. Mat.*, 1944; **44;** 740
(*1665*) *B.P. 562817*
(*1666*) *Power Plant Eng.*, 1946; **50,** 9; 92 (and later)
(*1667*) MacGeorge, W. D., *Electr. World*, 1946; **126,** 75, 8; 3
(*1668*) Morgan, J. M., *Electronics*, 1946; **19,** 10; 92
(*1669*) Iannone, F. and Baller, H., *Electronics*, 1946; **19,** 10; 106
(*1670*) Laing, K. M., *Electronics*, 1946; **19,** 10; 174
(*1671*) *Electronics*, 1946; **19,** 10; 190

(*1672*) Johns, T. F., *BIOS*, Final Report 2, Item No. 9
(*1673*) Weidert, F., *Scientific and Industrial Reports* (U.S.A.), PB 37277
(*1674*) Morton, G. A., and Flory, L. E., *RCA Rev.*, 1946; **7,** 3; 385
(*1675*) Grossdoff, I. E., *RCA Rev.*, 1946; **7,** 3; 428
(*1676*) Kramer, A. W., *Elementary Engineering Electronics*, 1945
(*1677*) Kerris and Weidmann, *Scient. and Ind. Rep.* (U.S.A.), PB 37278
(*1678*) Johns, T. F., *J. Telev. Soc.*, 1946; **4,** 11; 280
(*1679*) Gall, D. C., *J.I.E.E.*, 1942; **89,** II; 434
(*1680*) Ryder, J. D., *Electronics*, 1936; **9,** 4; 31
(*1681*) Lewis, W. B., *Electrical Counting*, 1942
(*1682*) Finlay, R., *Electronics*, 1936; **9,** 7; 12
(*1683*) Wey, J. R., *Engineer*, 1942; **173;** 283, 300, 320, 342
(*1684*) Glover, A. M. and Moore, A. R., *J. Soc. Mot. Pict. Eng.*, 1946; **46,** 5; 379
(*1685*) Phyfe, J. D., *J. Soc. Mot. Pict. Eng.*, 1946; **46,** 5; 405
(*1686*) Redemske, R. F., *J. Soc. Mot. Pict. Eng.*, 1946; **46,** 5; 409
(*1687*) Daily, C. R., *J. Soc. Mot. Pict. Eng.*, 1946; **46,** 5; 343
(*1688*) Raitière, L., *La Technique Cinématographique*, 1946; **17,** 15; 275
(*1689*) Setter, J. A., *Electronics*, 1941; **14,** 11; 72
(*1690*) Glover, A. M. and James, R. B.. *Electronics*, 1940; **13,** 8; 26
(*1691*) McCarthy, R. H., Townsend, J. R. and Mertz, P., *FIAT Final Report* 294
(*1692*) Vedder, E. H., *Trans. A.S.M.E.*, 1944; **66,** 5; 261
(*1693*) *Automobile Engineer*, 1936; **26,** 11; 479
(*1694*) Schulman, D., *Electronics*, 1945; **18,** 2; 177
(*1695*) Fitzgerald, A. S., *Electrical World*, 1937; **107,** 5; 1592
(*1696*) Krulikowsky, S. J., *Scientific and Industrial Reports* (U.S.A.), PB 40430
(*1697*) Klotz, I. M. and Dole, M., *Electronics*, 1947; **20,** 2; 140
(*1698*) *Electronics*, 1947; **20,** 2; 142
(*1699*) Gould, C. D., *Electronics*, 1947; **20,** 3; 106
(*1700*) Wild, J. J., *Electronics*, 1947; **20,** 3; 120

LIST OF PATENTS

The patent literature of the last decade has been scrupulously searched for any matter of importance to the industrial application of photosensitors. Despite the author's desire to restrict the list of patents to as few as reasonably possible, the number of patents quoted is above 550. Not included are photo-electric pick-ups, military applications as, for instance, steering, signalling, locating, measuring (speed of projectiles), calculating machines, aids to the statistical evaluation, manufacture of photosensitors, exposure-meters, etc., although it is obvious that many of the principles laid down in these specifications will readily find industrial applications.

At the end of each section a list is appended of the relevant British and American Patent Specifications, the subject of which is covered by that particular section. Although it was not possible to give brief specifications, not even in the style of the " Abridgments ", the author has tried to give as much information as possible in the title of the specification. For this reason official titles have not always been followed exactly.

For further information the reader is advised to consult the original patent specifications. A continued search in patents, published as they are granted, will be made easy if it is remembered that the classes, in which nearly all industrial applications of photosensitors are grouped, will be found as follows:

British Patent Specifications: Group 40 (III),
U.S.A. Patent Specifications: Class 250, Sub-class 41.5.

In both countries weekly periodicals publish a classified list of the patents granted during such a period. These periodicals are in

Great Britain: *The Official Journal of Patents*,
U.S.A.: *Official Gazette of the United States Patent Office*.

During the war, and at present, neither the *Official Journal* nor the *Abridgments* have been published by the Patent Office, London. The only guides available are handwritten lists which can be consulted at the Library of the Patent Office, London. The code-letters relating to applications of photosensitors are: in Group 40, A-5; O-1; O-3; O-5.

The German patents on the application of photosensitors can be found under Klasse 21g, Gruppe 4/06 for dates from and including 1st January, 1933. Patents, issued prior to this date, are classified in Klasse 21g4 and the headings of Klasse 21 do not inlude " Photozellen " in particular.

In the *Verzeichnis der vom Reichspatentamt im Jahre —— erteilten Patente* the annual list of classified patents is published. A weekly Periodical, the *Patentblatt und Auszüge aus den Patentschriften* is also issued and contains the weekly list of patents pending and granted as well as a series of illustrated *Abkürzungen*, i.e., abridgments.

Patents in the *Verzeichnis der vom Reichspatentamt im Jahre —— erteilten Patente* which are quoted in the abridgments list show their number in the *Abkürzungen* by quoting a figure after the letter " A " (which stands for *Abkürzungen*), thus:

Patent No. 671910; A 637

French patents on the subject of photosensitors are classed in Classe XII, groupes 2 and 6 (mostly in groupe 2).

The abridged specifications can be looked up in the weekly periodical *Bulletin Officiel de la propriété industrielle*, (2e partie: brevets d'invention). A complete survey of the subject matter is published as *Tables des brevets et certificats d'addition imprimés* (Part: *Table des brevets par ordre de matières*).

British Patents

(*1701*) 421256 Photocell with a " spongy-velvety " surface
(*1702*) 423386 Controlling apparatus by light. If damaged the device is put in a state of least activity
(*1703*) 423395 Oil burner control
(*1704*) 424802 Control of torch cutters by replicas
(*1705*) 425602 Detecting the presence of foreign bodies on the bottom of transparent vessels, e.g. bottles
(*1706*) 426126 Photo-e.m.f. cell of single or split electrode type
(*1707*) 426205 Photo-e.m.f. cell of the copper-cuprous oxide or tungsten oxide-on-tungsten type
(*1708*) 426389 Secondary emission cell
(*1709*) 426404 Photolytic cell; copper cuprous oxide in a fatty acid
(*1710*) 427758 same as 423386
(*1711*) 428919, (*1712*) 429725, (*1713*) 429726 Light-sensitive electron valve having a photo-electric and a thermionic cathode
(*1714*) 430073 same as 426404
(*1715*) 431746 Various modifications of photo-e.m.f. cells
(*1716*) 435643 Apparatus (photo-e.m.f. cell) for converting light variations into corresponding electric variations
(*1717*) 439774 Photo-e.m.f. cell of the Pt-on-Cd-on-Se type
(*1718*) 439942 Photo-e.m.f. cell of the Se-on-Fe type
(*1719*) 440227 Alignment of lens, light source, and cell by means of a movable reflector
(*1720*) 443886 Device for maintaining a substantially uniform thickness of thread in a machine for forming threads from filaments drawn from cocoons
(*1721*) 450287 High speed photo-electric relay
(*1722*) 458032 Two-cell circuit for the reduction of fatigue effects in photo-e.m.f. cells
(*1723*) 444811 Copying by scanning (engraving)
(*1724*) 460012 Photo-e.m.f. cell of the (Cs or Rb)-on-(Sb or Bi) type
(*1725*) 460155 Photo-electric device for controlling a bell, turning a gas cock, operating a locking device, etc.

(*1726*) 460452 Photometric apparatus
(*1727*) 460861 Photo-electric control of electric lamp-making machines
(*1728*) 460997 Remote indication and transmission of meter readings
(*1729*) 461100 Controlling apparatus for cigarette-making machine
(*1730*) 461651 Automatic weighing mechanism
(*1731*) 461720 Photo-electrically controlled blinds
(*1732*) 462237 Photo-electric apparatus for making biological tests, for instance, testing eggs
(*1733*) 462733 Photo-electric gas and firedamp detector
(*1734*) 462778 Control of indicating apparatus (telemetering)
(*1735*) 463330 Control of indicating apparatus (telemetering)
(*1736*) 464001 Photo-electric photometer for measuring the colour density of liquids
(*1737*) 464268 Sensitivity of Se-layer increased by admixing $CaWO_4$ or $HgCl_2$.
(*1738*) 465529 Photo-electric control of liquid-level indicators
(*1739*) 468448 Photo-electric apparatus for examining postal envelopes, etc.
(*1740*) 468692 Photo-electric control of sorting apparatus (conveyors)
(*1741*) 468815 Sorting beans, etc., by light-sensitive apparatus
(*1742*) 469146 Controlling electric forging operations by radiant heat
(*1743*) 469458 Photo-electric apparatus for examining milk bottles, etc.
(*1744*) 469467 Photometric apparatus
(*1745*) 469949 Photo-electric apparatus for inspecting liquids in containers (bottles)
(*1746*) 469999 Photometric apparatus
(*1747*) 470134 Photometer
(*1748*) 470454 Photometer
(*1749*) 470546 Controlling metal-working apparatus by radiant heat.
(*1750*) 470638 Photo-electric apparatus for examining and sorting documents
(*1751*) 472116 Photo-electric apparatus for measuring electrical values
(*1752*) 472146 Radiation pyrometer; automatic temperature control system
(*1753*) 472147 Photometer
(*1754*) 472322 Photo-electric control for projectile fuses
(*1755*) 472688 Photo-electric control of engine ignition system
(*1756*) 472963 Escalators controlled by light-cells
(*1757*) 473044 Controlling apparatus by radiant heat
(*1758*) 473594 Photo-electric control of indicating apparatus
(*1759*) 474421 Photo-electric apparatus for indicating, measuring, and recording light variations (smoke densometer)
(*1760*) 474454 Photo-electric control of clocks
(*1761*) 474992 Photo-electric control of copying and like machines
(*1762*) 476299 Viewing objects by infra-red rays
(*1763*) 477365 Radiation pyrometer
(*1764*) 477679 Photo-electric control of fuel supply for burners
(*1765*) 477775 Viewing objects by use of infra-red rays
(*1766*) 477827 Photo-electric gas and firedamp detector
(*1767*) 477988 Photo-electric control of welding apparatus
(*1768*) 478948 Photo-electric apparatus for examining and sorting documents
(*1769*) 479622 Photometric apparatus.
(*1770*) 479825 Preparation of a thallium-thallous sulphide photo-e.m.f. cell
(*1771*) 480042 Photo-electric apparatus for measuring objects
(*1772*) 480708 Photo-electric apparatus for transmitting indications of measuring instruments
(*1773*) 480730 Photo-electric control of fuel supply to burners
(*1774*) 480922 Photo-electric control of spraying apparatus
(*1775*) 482322 Photo-electric burglar alarm system
(*1776*) 482494 Photo-electric control of paper-pulp feeding apparatus
(*1777*) 482498 Photo-electric control of sheet delivering apparatus
(*1778*) 482578 Photo-electric control of paper folding mechanism
(*1779*) 482741 Photo-electric control of grinding and like machines
(*1780*) 482876 Viewing objects by use of infra-red rays

(*1781*) 483033 Photo-electric apparatus for testing lenses and mirrors
(*1782*) 483171 Photo-electric photographic printing meter
(*1783*) 483312 Radiation pyrometer
(*1784*) 484144 Photo-electric apparatus for testing steam
(*1785*) 484277 Photo-electric control of dividing-engines for marking graduations
(*1786*) 484281 Photo-electric control of Röntgen-ray apparatus
(*1787*) 484310 Photo-electric multiplier
(*1788*) 485064 Photo-electric photometer
(*1788*) 485172 Photo-electric apparatus for measuring electrical values
(*1790*) 485386 Photo-electric apparatus for testing hardness of water for use in water softening plant
(*1791*) 485505 Photo-electric colorimeter
(*1792*) 486598 Photo-electric control of lifts
(*1793*) 488366 Photo-electric apparatus for testing levels of contents and sorting containers
(*1794*) 488726 Photo-electric control of printing-machines
(*1795*) 488773 Photo-electric control of copying-machines
(*1796*) 488792 Photo-electric control of window-blinds
(*1797*) 489038 Photo-electric recording apparatus
(*1798*) 490305 Photo-electric control of web-feeding mechanism
(*1799*) 490759 Baffle tube
(*1800*) 491613 Photo-electric photometer
(*1801*) 491714 Photo-electric control of fuel supply for burners
(*1802*) 491856 Photo-electric photometer
(*1803*) 492035 Sorting apparatus
(*1804*) 492782 Control of indicators of weighing apparatus
(*1805*) 493644 Control of film-feeding mechanism
(*1806*) 494154 Photo-electric counting apparatus
(*1807*) 495762 Control of drilling machine
(*1808*) 495818 Control of drilling and reaming machine
(*1809*) 495946 Control of wrapping machine
(*1810*) 496965 Control of machine tools by records representing the co-ordinates
(*1811*) 497087 Control of grinding and like machines
(*1812*) 497105 Control of sheet stacking and folding machines
(*1813*) 497106 Control of knitting machines and looms
(*1814*) 497275 Photo-electric apparatus for testing the turbidity of liquids
(*1815*) 497491 Apparatus for indicating or recording the density of solid particles, e.g., smoke
(*1816*) 497874 Control of knitting machines and looms
(*1817*) 497942 Control of web-feeding mechanisms
(*1818*) 498427 Control of photograhic printing apparatus
(*1819*) 498486 Apparatus for controlling the filling and emptying of hoppers
(*1820*) 499230 Apparatus for light analysis
(*1821*) 499753 Apparatus for testing woven fabrics and controlling feed mechanism
(*1822*) 499791 Apparatus for measuring the brightness of zinc coatings and like surfaces
(*1823*) 500104 Control of copying machines
(*1824*) 500168 Apparatus for comparing liquid levels
(*1825*) 500496 Control of web-feeding mechanisms
(*1826*) 501012 Apparatus for testing the turbidity of liquids
(*1827*) 501029 Control of sheet feeding mechanism
(*1828*) 501111 Apparatus for centring lamp bulbs
(*1829*) 501712 Apparatus for centring lamp bulbs
(*1830*) 502261 Control of weighing machines
(*1831*) 502326 Control of broaching machines
(*1832*) 502881 Apparatus for indicating voltage variations
(*1833*) 502898 Control of sheet feeding mechanism
(*1834*) 502971 Apparatus for detecting suspended matter in fluids
(*1835*) 503142 Control of cigarette-packing machine
(*1836*) 504185 Control of water supply system

(*1837*) 504203 Photo-electric photometer
(*1838*) 504683 Photo-electric sorting apparatus
(*1839*) 504719 Examining printed records
(*1840*) 504818 Control of sheet delivering apparatus
(*1841*) 504836 Measuring apparatus; hot-wire high frequency detector
(*1842*) 506055 Apparatus for detecting gases
(*1843*) 506219 Photometric apparatus
(*1844*) 506596 Photo-electric radiation thermometer
(*1845*) 507089 Control of printing machines
(*1846*) 507185 Apparatus for determining the level or height of substances
(*1847*) 507235 Control of copying apparatus
(*1848*) 507536 Control of screw-feeds
(*1849*) 508786 Control apparatus (sorting sheets by gauging the thickness)
(*1850*) 508802 Photo-electric colorimeter
(*1851*) 509061 Apparatus for testing liquids
(*1852*) 509776 Improvements in photographic film printing apparatus
(*1853*) 509928 Guard device for presses and like machines
(*1854*) 510670 Transparent plastic electrostatic shields
(*1855*) 510756 Control of high frequency oscillator
(*1856*) 510982 Protection of electrical plant and apparatus from lightning flashes
(*1857*) 511083 Determination of smoke density
(*1858*) 511163 Quantitative spectrum analysis
(*1859*) 511200 Illumination control
(*1860*) 511280 System for automatically controlling variable magnitudes
(*1861*) 511313 Control system
(*1862*) 512969 Method of photographic development to a predetermined value of contrast
(*1863*) 512977 Control of knitting or weaving machines
(*1864*) 513629 Control of internal combustion engine ignition system
(*1865*) 513654 Photo-electric gravitymeters
(*1866*) 513764 Photo-electrically controlled packing-machines
(*1867*) 513851 Photo-electrically controlled feed of projection arc carbons
(*1868*) 514153 Flow meter
(*1869*) 514653 Detection of suspended matter in fluids
(*1870*) 514728 Control of electric forging and apparatus therefore
(*1871*) 515314 Control of container coating machine
(*1872*) 515340 Automobile headlight-tester
(*1873*) 516817 Limit switch for precision grinding machines
(*1874*) 517033 Distant control system
(*1875*) 517229 Inspection of transparent vessels
(*1876*) 517245 Indicating or recording device for magnetic field balances
(*1877*) 517462 Means for indicating, recording, or registering the content of a substance present in a liquid
(*1878*) 517526 Infra-red radiating tubes
(*1879*) 518071 Distant control system
(*1880*) 518200 Improvements in potentiometer circuits for controlling bias voltages for push-pull photocell circuits
(*1881*) 518542 Registering and holding devices for multi-colour printing
(*1882*) 519030 Feed control of chocolate grinders and refiners
(*1883*) 519068 Timing apparatus for clocks and watches
(*1884*) 519229 Recording of variations in the chemical composition of a substance
(*1885*) 519417 Device for measuring mechanical forces
(*1886*) 519579 Photo-electric measuring apparatus
(*1887*) 520485 Apparatus for counting and delivering predetermined numbers of articles
(*1888*) 521158 Improvements in light-sensitive cells
(*1889*) 521621 Detection of the presence of smoke or suspended matter in air or fluid streams
(*1890*) 522028 Method and apparatus for measuring the colour of light

(*1891*)	522402	An instrument for use in measuring the intensity of ultra-violet radiation
(*1892*)	522965	Photo-electric relay
(*1893*)	523050	Photo-electric testing generator for image reproducing systems
(*1894*)	523381	Treatment of water
(*1895*)	523935	Means for separating, counting, and delivering various objects
(*1896*)	524303	Door controlling apparatus
(*1897*)	524922	Improvements in the manufacture of tube
(*1898*)	525344	Improvements in photo-electric cells
(*1899*)	526442	Control of sheet folding, interleaving, and like machines
(*1900*)	526926	Apparatus for measuring webs of fabric
(*1901*)	528543	Means responsive to breakage or tension of threads in warping or other textile machines
(*1902*)	528701	Photo-electric photometers
(*1903*)	528841	Apparatus for automatically regulating the load in electric circuits
(*1904*)	528849	Photo-electric control of machines by means of printed cards
(*1905*)	528967	Method of, and apparatus for, colour comparison
(*1906*)	529051	Control of sheet-feeding mechanism for printing machines
(*1907*)	529877	Control of water supply system
(*1908*)	529907	Apparatus for timing photographic exposure (reproduction enlarger)
(*1909*)	530257	Method and apparatus for testing flour
(*1910*)	530314	Control mechanism for printing presses
(*1911*)	530431	Control of photographic printing apparatus
(*1912*)	530456	Protective (motor) control system
(*1913*)	530724	Method of comparing the surface finish of an object
(*1914*)	531418	Control of ion-exchange plants (pH-determination)
(*1915*)	531426	Testing of water
(*1916*)	532416	Apparatus for assorting record cards, sheets, etc.
(*1917*)	532611	Control of photographic printing apparatus
(*1918*)	532797	Control of automatic paper feeding machine
(*1919*)	533591	Apparatus for measuring electrical power (high frequency ammeter)
(*1920*)	533924	Control of weaving machinery
(*1921*)	534116	Control of gas producers (control of coal feed)
(*1922*)	534200	Apparatus for temperature control
(*1923*)	534380	Method and apparatus for preparing and handling rubber material
(*1924*)	534468	Transformation of the frequency of radiant energy (infra-red to luminous)
(*1925*)	534649	Protective supervision of (petrol) filling stations
(*1926*)	534710	Control of signal oscillator
(*1927*)	534873	Follow-up mechanism
(*1928*)	537406	Apparatus for indicating the registration of a web in a multi-unit web conditioning apparatus, such as a multi-unit web printing press
(*1929*)	537611	Apparatus for measuring relative movements or deflections of associated or interconnected parts
(*1930*)	537662	Photo-electric engine indicator
(*1931*)	537784	An amplifier for d.c. and a.c. of low frequency (cf. *2043*)
(*1932*)	538278	Gauging or testing the form or shape of manufactured articles
(*1933*)	538696	Calculating device for use in photographic printing processes
(*1934*)	539664	Control device for the charging valves of gas producers
(*1935*)	539670	Integrating measuring instrument for small electric currents
(*1936*)	539995	Control of weaving machinery
(*1937*)	540068	Means for exploring local intensities in high frequency electromagnetic fields
(*1938*)	540948	Follow-up mechanism
(*1939*)	541729	Stop motion or signalling device for knitting machines
(*1940*)	543316	Web registering mechanism
(*1941*)	543469	Machine for use in examining or assorting metallic or other plates or sheets, particularly tin plates

(*1942*) 543802 Means for modulating a light beam
(*1943*) 544084 Register control system
(*1944*) 544537 Fault protection system for electric switch gear
(*1945*) 544583 Control of the heat treating of articles in high frequency fields
(*1946*) 544601 Register control system
(*1947*) 544830 Register control system
(*1948*) 545010 Controlled machine tools
(*1949*) 545140 Indicating device (steel strip control)
(*1950*) 545451 Control of the manufacture of bonded paper insulation
(*1951*) 545469 Control of the manufacture of light-sensitive photographic material
(*1952*) 546489 Control of the manufacture of seamless containers
(*1953*) 547748 Protective device for looms
(*1954*) 547767 Contour follower
(*1955*) 548031 Control of machines through which paper and the like sheets are passed
(*1956*) 549242 Control of flow meter
(*1957*) 550310 Remote control system
(*1958*) 550359 Apparatus for manufacturing commutators for small electric machines
(*1959*) 550675 Apparatus for testing photographic shutters
(*1960*) 551228 Method of improving selective electrical circuits
(*1961*) 551986 Register control
(*1962*) 551995 Control of manufacturing methods of elastic diaphragms
(*1963*) 552046 Device for locating a source of radiation
(*1964*) 552081 Means for protection against fire and burglary
(*1965*) 552287 Measuring or indicating device
(*1966*) 552398 Apparatus for determining the total specific surface or the particle size distribution of powdered articles
(*1967*) 553491 Device for signalling the position of a movable mark
(*1968*) 553593 Photo-electric polarograph
(*1969*) 553925 Apparatus for the grading or sorting of irregularly shaped articles, such as containers, bottles, jars, and the like
(*1970*) 554030 Multipoint recorder-controller embodying an electrical amplifier
(*1971*) 554658 Apparatus for testing gases
(*1972*) 554985 Detection or determination of the quantity of suspended solid matter in gas streams
(*1973*) 555103 Means for determining the position of an object
(*1974*) 555432 Apparatus for ascertaining the wear on grinding discs in grinding machines
(*1975*) 555792 Control of the slides of precision machine tools
(*1976*) 555798 Apparatus for feeding thread from a beam or the like to a textile machine
(*1977*) 555928 Refractometer for controlling chemical reactions
(*1978*) 556179 Balanced automatic control apparatus
(*1979*) 556568 Photocell hum demodulator
(*1980*) 557019 Apparatus for supplying web material
(*1981*) 557126 Time switch
(*1982*) 558187 Means for remote indication of movement
(*1983*) 558731 Amplifier circuits
(*1984*) 558848 Apparatus for determining with precision the position of an object carrying a graduation
(*1985*) 559181 Windows in the envelopes of vacuum valves
(*1986*) 560327 Control of apparatus for twisting together two or more pieces of dough
(*1987*) 560998 Illumination control
(*1988*) 561171 Control of mechanical (contour) copying machines
(*1989*) 561631 Self-balancing recorders and the like
(*1990*) 562450 Apparatus for measuring lengths and correcting skew and bow in woven material
(*1991*) 562751 Apparatus for feeding and severing strip material

(*1992*) 562792 Testing hermetically sealed envelopes
(*1993*) 563091 Apparatus for improving the durability of glass containers
(*1994*) 563424 Apparatus for transmitting the indications of measuring instruments
(*1995*) 563774 Photo-electric photometer
(*1996*) 563893 Apparatus for measuring the operating speed of a (metal) extrusion press
(*1997*) 564620 Control of electric hand driers
(*1998*) 565215 Measuring of temperature
(*1999*) 565881 Apparatus for comparing the dimensions of objects
(*2000*) 566278 Means for the indication of infra-red radiation
(*2001*) 566589 Apparatus for variable speed couplings of the electromagnetic type
(*2002*) 567475 Means for optically scanning reflecting surfaces
(*2003*) 567491 Photo-electric generation of sound waves
(*2004*) 568039 Control of milling and the like machine tools
(*2005*) 568137 Control of turbo-generator installations
(*2006*) 568622 Signalling system
(*2007*) 569025 Instrument adapted for remote control
(*2008*) 570102 Apparatus for the gravitational control of photo-electric cells
(*2009*) 570184 Measuring instrument
(*2010*) 570601 Control circuit with twin-cell
(*2011*) 570684 Controlling and measuring the changes in fluid pressure
(*2012*) 571775 Apparatus for measuring or comparing the dimensions or forms of objects
(*2013*) 572108 Control system for the reproduction of pattern contours
(*2014*) 572177 Control of electrical billet heating machines
(*2015*) 572625 Control of web winding
(*2016*) 572659 Control of web splicing
(*2017*) 573796 Control of electric stop motions for textile machines
(*2018*) 576425 Method of and means for measuring the density of a small area of a photographic negative or other semi-transparency
(*2019*) 576803 Improvements in the manufacture of metal sheets, continuous electrolytic tinning same, pin-hole detection, etc.
(*2020*) 577395 Apparatus for recording polar reflexion curves
(*2021*) 578098 Accurate and positive control of the amount of coating liquid applied to a web
(*2022*) 578101 Elapsed time-indicating device
(*2023*) 578204 Method and apparatus for controlling machines operating periodically on a continuously moving piece of material
(*2024*) 578730 Electrical systems for determining the direction of movable objects
(*2025*) 579115 Apparatus for timing impulses
(*2026*) 579833 Spectrophotometer
(*2027*) 581964 Improvements relating to magnetic means for the hardness testing of metals on the basis that a relationship exists between the hardness of the metal and its residual magnetism
(*2028*) 582096 Lens centring device
(*2029*) 582367 Method and apparatus for measuring unidirectional flux as flowing in large busbars or cables
(*2030*) 582511 Photometer
(*2031*) 582673 Photometer
(*2032*) 582891 Automatic follow-up mechanism
(*2033*) 583086 Automatic regulation of the shutters of roof light windows mounted on the south facing slope of a roof
(*2034*) 583170 Selenium cell and lacquer
(*2035*) 583520 Improvements in mechanical copying machines
(*2036*) 583531 Thallium sulphide cell
(*2037*) 583537 Light modulating device
(*2038*) 583851 Burner control
(*2039*) 583904 Automatic follow-up mechanism

(*2040*) 584170 }
(*2041*) 584506 } Apparatus for use in quantitative spectrographic analysis
(*2042*) 584507 Apparatus for automatic recording devices to record simultaneously three variables by placing fiduciary marks on a graph being recorded by the device
(*2043*) 585419 Direct current amplifier using a galvanometer circuit (cf. *1931*)
(*2044*) 585698 Electric switching system
(*2045*) 586142 Apparatus for measuring or indicating the rate of flow of liquids
(*2046*) 586575 Weft straightening method and apparatus
(*2047*) 586590 Automatic follow-up mechanism
(*2048*) 586612 Detection of pin-holes in metal strip
(*2049*) 586935 Apparatus for detecting the presence of foreign bodies in transparent vessels
(*2050*) 586936 ditto
(*2051*) 586937 ditto
(*2052*) 586938 ditto
(*2053*) 586939 ditto
(*2054*) 587055 Photo-electric indicating or control device using a galvanometer as the indicating instrument

United States of America Patents

(*2055*) 2028153 Radiation detector
(*2056*) 2030250 Light target for illumination meters
(*2057*) 2031952 Electro-optical system for modulating light
(*2058*) 2033016 Photo-electric controllers
(*2059*) 2034586 Triple photocell
(*2060*) 2034334 Photosensitor
(*2061*) 2035906 Photo-electric circuit and system
(*2062*) 2035907 Photo-electric circuit and system
(*2063*) 2036286 Light control device
(*2064*) 2037190 Admission counter
(*2065*) 2037191 Admission counter
(*2066*) 2037925 Apparatus for measuring radiation
(*2067*) 2040632 Copper-oxide photo-e.m.f. cell
(*2068*) 2041079 Photorelay using polarization effect
(*2069*) 2041953 Selenium-on-iron photo-e.m.f. cell with graphite anode and carbon-selenide electron barrier plane
(*2070*) 2043671 Lighting control
(*2071*) 2044146 Selective control system
(*2072*) 2044164 Automatic feeder control
(*2073*) 2047665 Counting apparatus
(*2074*) 2048269 Power photorelay
(*2075*) 2048740 Unidirectional control system
(*2076*) 2049283 Limit switch
(*2077*) 2049355 Relay
(*2078*) 2049376 Counter
(*2079*) 2049647 Cold cathode valve relay
(*2080*) 2049669 Regulating apparatus using modulating light
(*2081*) 2050737 Light translating apparatus
(*2082*) 2052916 Photo-touch sensitive apparatus
(*2083*) 2054836 Light responsive device
(*2084*) 2057384 Photorelay
(*2085*) 2058011 Relay circuit
(*2086*) 2058941 Converter for light rays
(*2087*) 2059786 Potentiometric indicator
(*2088*) 2060977 Converter for light rays
(*2089*) 2065048 Unidirectional counting device
(*2090*) 2065365 Measuring system

(*2091*) 2065421 Measuring and regulating system
(*2092*) 2065723 Photocurrent amplifier
(*2093*) 2065758 Photo-electric circuit
(*2094*) 2066934 Regulating system
(*2095*) 2067613 Control device
(*2096*) 2075094 Signalling system with polarized light
(*2097*) 2075120 Photo-electric relay
(*2098*) 2077451 Method and apparatus for controlling the actuation of recorders
(*2099*) 2078645 Photo-electric discharge apparatus
(*2100*) 2080613 Photometer
(*2101*) 2080926 Light sensitive device
(*2102*) 2082036 Translating apparatus
(*2103*) 2082627 Feedback amplifying circuit for light sensitive devices
(*2104*) 2082941 Unidirectional counter
(*2105*) 2086964 Photometer
(*2106*) 2088198 Photo-electric system
(*2107*) 2088416 Photo-electric relay
(*2108*) 2089830 Lightsensitive apparatus
(*2109*) 2094379 Control for electric vacuum discharge apparatus
(*2110*) 2095124 Translating circuit
(*2111*) 2096323 Temperature measuring apparatus
(*2112*) 2096427 Regulating system
(*2113*) 2096863 Emissive type photocell
(*2114*) 2096916 Photorelay using a selenium resistor
(*2115*) 2098217 Grid-controlled photo-electric cell
(*2116*) 2099764 Control system
(*2117*) 2100460 Method for controlling the current output of grid controlled glow discharge tubes
(*2118*) 2100755 Photometer
(*2119*) 2100765 Photosensitive discharge valve
(*2120*) 2102145 Automatic regulator
(*2121*) 2103498 Grid controlled photocell
(*2122*) 2106204 Washbox discharge control
(*2123*) 2111013 Resistance welding current control
(*2124*) 2113947 Automatic meter control
(*2125*) 2121211 Automatic line tracker
(*2126*) 2122941 Photocell housing
(*2127*) 2123470 Control device
(*2128*) 2123639 Amplifying system
(*2129*) 2124031 Light and electrical impulse conversion apparatus
(*2130*) 2124600 Electrical amplifying device
(*2131*) 2125073 Light sensitive system
(*2132*) 2125273 Polarizing and output circuit for photosensitive devices
(*2133*) 2130296 Speed indicator for motor vehicles
(*2134*) 2131028 Photo-electric control system
(*2135*) 2132254 Follow-up mechanism (steering of a craft)
(*2136*) 2137278 Amplifier system
(*2137*) 2139489 Frequency responsive (light modulated) relay
(*2138*) 2140355 Control apparatus
(*2139*) 2140368 Radio receiver
(*2140*) 2140373 Light sensitive system
(*2141*) 2140387 Photorelay
(*2142*) 2140942 Photorelay
(*2143*) 2142154 Photo-electrically controlled balance
(*2144*) 2142378 Velocity detector
(*2145*) 2142602 Speed limit indicator
(*2146*) 2143093 Wave generator
(*2147*) 2145021 Electromagnetic device
(*2148*) 2145591 Indicating and control system
(*2149*) 2147422 Automatic control system

(*2150*) 2148023 Photo-electric amplifier
(*2151*) 2148482 Electric device and method of operating same
(*2152*) 2151474 Light valve control
(*2153*) Re-21806 ex 1941 Light valve control (follow-up mechanism)
(*2154*) 2154480 Photorelay
(*2155*) 2155224 Illumination switch
(*2156*) 2156886 Electric discharge apparatus
(*2157*) 2159181 Electric control system
(*2158*) 2160037 Photorelay
(*2159*) 2160383 Multi-electrode light sensitive device
(*2160*) 2162508 Circuit with grid glow tubes
(*2161*) 2164114 Speed control
(*2162*) 2165048 Electric discharge apparatus
(*2163*) 2169405 Photo-electric system
(*2164*) 2170157 Electronic switching device
(*2165*) 2171362 Photo-electric system to control spacing of travelling articles
(*2166*) 2173164 Signalling apparatus
(*2167*) 2179954 Photo-electric amplifier
(*2168*) 2182987 Housing for photocell
(*2169*) 2185104 Temperature control apparatus
(*2170*) 2185361 Fire detector
(*2171*) 2186218 Control of welding apparatus
(*2172*) 2189122 Method and apparatus for sensing radiant energy
(*2173*) 2192735 Control circuit
(*2174*) 2193789 Scanner (photocell pick-up)
(*2175*) 2196830 Multilayer selenium cell
(*2176*) 2197205 Pressure responsive control means
(*2177*) 2197514 Photo-electric attachment for scales
(*2178*) 2199071 Temperature control
(*2179*) 2199394 Light control system
(*2180*) 2203761 Baffle for light sensitive apparatus
(*2181*) 2203882 Amplifier system
(*2182*) 2205207 Multiplier cell
(*2183*) 2205254 Photo-electric regulator
(*2184*) 2205777 Indicating controller
(*2185*) 2206713 Photo-electric multiplier cell
(*2186*) 2207097 Cell housing maintained dry
(*2187*) 2208386 Controlled UV spark
(*2188*) 2213534 Light absorptiometer
(*2189*) 2215906 Electric valve control system
(*2190*) 2216472 Measuring and control apparatus
(*2191*) 2222429 Photo-electric system for sorting machines
(*2192*) 2222788 Photo-e.m.f. cell moulded in Lucite housing (transparent plastic = Perspex). Body shaped to form lens or lenses
(*2193*) 2226716 Selenium-on-iron photo-e.m.f. cell
(*2194*) 2227095 Multi-electrode cell
(*2195*) 2227147 Burglar alarm system
(*2196*) 2227562 Push-pull photo-electric circuit
(*2197*) 2228560 Compensating circuit for photo-electric amplifier
(*2198*) 2228780 System of light control for selenium cells
(*2199*) 2229451 Photo-electric apparatus for inspecting material (strip steel; paper web)
(*2200*) 2231621 Photocell system (amplification of d.c. impulses by a.c.)
(*2201*) 2234011 Photo-electric relay
(*2202*) 2234697 Optical scanning
(*2203*) 2236255 Control unit
(*2204*) 2237579 Relay system
(*2205*) 2237665 Control apparatus
(*2206*) 2237950 D.C. amplifier

(*2207*) 2240800 Remote control system
(*2208*) 2241743 Electro-optical instrument
(*2209*) Re-21806 ex 1939 Light valve control
(*2210*) 2242638 Light control methods
(*2211*) 2243456 Follow-up mechanism
(*2212*) 2243591 Converter
(*2213*) 2243600 Method and apparatus for generating harmonics
(*2214*) 2245124 Measuring apparatus (insensitive to voltage fluctuations)
(*2215*) 2246884 Potentiometer
(*2216*) 2248611 Control apparatus for electric vapour discharge devices
(*2217*) 2251306 Light sensitive circuit means
(*2218*) 2252457 Relay
(*2219*) 2254022 Electrical wave generator
(*2220*) 2256595 Photo-electric system using movable light conductors as controlling elements
(*2221*) Re-21907 Device controlling the intensity of a light source
(*2222*) 2258369 Speed indicator
(*2223*) 2258436 Photocell for the translation of images
(*2224*) 2259287 Photo-electric control
(*2225*) 2259323 Amplifier
(*2226*) 2262537 Insulation for photo-electric apparatus for operation under ambient temperature conditions varying within a range greater than normal temperature changes
(*2227*) 2262790 Temperature control for liquid fuel burners
(*2228*) 2263228 Speed-responsive device
(*2229*) 2264256 Damped photo-electric indicating controller
(*2230*) 2265149 Device for operating a switch at any selected altitude
(*2231*) 2265784 Method of producing electrical oscillations
(*2232*) 2269340 Burglar alarm
(*2233*) 2276506 Measuring, controlling, and recording apparatus
(*2234*) 2277502 Follow-up mechanism (line tracker)
(*2235*) 2280948 Photo-electric inspection scheme
(*2236*) 2280978 Negative transconductance device
(*2237*) 2282198 Differential analyzer
(*2238*) 2287322 Apparatus for testing colour
(*2239*) 2293521 Electro-optical system
(*2240*) 2294375 Photocell circuit
(*2241*) 2294376 Photocell hum demodulator
(*2242*) 2294377 Photocell hum demodulator
(*2243*) 2295536 Light sensitive circuit
(*2244*) 2295894 System for controlling lighting circuits
(*2245*) 2295960 Measuring and control apparatus
(*2246*) 2296269 Photo-electric electronic tube
(*2247*) 2309329 Photo-electric apparatus
(*2248*) 2316772 Photo-electrically controlled gas discharge tube
(*2249*) 2319406 Temperature control instrument
(*2250*) 2320977 Photo-electric cell and circuit
(*2251*) 2322022 Photo-electric control device
(*2252*) 2323966 Amplifier
(*2253*) 2329423 D.C. amplifier system
(*2254*) 2331475 Photo-electric control device
(*2255*) 2336376 Photo-electric control device
(*2256*) 2336673 Photo-electric control device
(*2257*) 2337535 Limit switch warning indicator
(*2258*) 2339204 Web alignment detector
(*2259*) 2345501 High-gain multistage high-vacuum valve amplifier
(*2260*) 2352240 Cold cathode tube relay
(*2261*) 2354954 Motion controlling device (maintaining oscillatory motion)
(*2262*) 2374916 Apparatus for the reversal of colour photographic negatives

(*2263*)	2375130	Cold cathode tube relay
(*2264*)	2375456	Safety circuit
(*2265*)	2376234	Weighing apparatus
(*2266*)	2376235	Light sensitive apparatus for process control
(*2267*)	2377589	Automatic aiming control
(*2268*)	2385725	Control system
(*2269*)	2386320	Integrating exposure meter
(*2270*)	2387952	Timing system for sorting apparatus
(*2271*)	2392895	Grid controlled cell
(*2272*)	2397933	Follow-up mechanism (line tracker)
(*2273*)	2398904	Measuring device
(*2274*)	2401396	Control
(*2275*)	2401712	Device for determining electrically the position of an element or object
(*2276*)	2402405	Inspection device
(*2277*)	2403387	Radiant energy responsive directional control
(*2278*)	2404131	Amplifier
(*2279*)	2406299	Machine tool with photo-electric positioning of the work table
(*2280*)	2407580	Long period pendulum
(*2281*)	2408313	Counter for counting rapidly moving closely spaced-apart metal sheet
(*2282*)	2408589	Apparatus for producing electrical oscillations
(*2283*)	2410104	Light directing device
(*2284*)	2410115	Image intensifier
(*2285*)	2410732	Secondary emission cell controlled by a magnetic r-f field
(*2286*)	2411078	Circuit with tetrode
(*2287*)	2411092	Turbidimeter
(*2288*)	2411531	Electro-optical control system
(*2289*)	2412424	Control device for camera diaphragms
(*2290*)	2412822	Photo-electrical device
(*2291*)	2413076	System detecting the direction of movement
(*2292*)	2413208	Refractometer for chemical reactions
(*2293*)	2413486	Detecting irregularities of filamentary materials
(*2294*)	2413660	Flickering beam spectrophotometer
(*2295*)	2413870	Scanner
(*2296*)	2414636	Apparatus for photo-electrically controlling the current in a work circuit
(*2297*)	2415167	Inspection circuit
(*2298*)	2415168	Timer
(*2299*)	2415174	Sizing mechanism
(*2300*)	2415175	Ganging of flexible tubular casings
(*2301*)	2415176	Scanner
(*2302*)	2415177	Apparatus for photo-electric camming
(*2303*)	2415178	ditto
(*2304*)	2415179	ditto
(*2305*)	2416215	Translation system for photo-e.m.f. cells
(*2306*)	2419459	Detecting apparatus
(*2307*)	2418845	Flame control

German Patents

(*2308*)	629609	Lichtempfindliche Schalteinrichtung mit in einem Vakuumgefäss angeordneten, durch Strahlungsdruck bewegtem Flügelrad
(*2309*)	636028	Relaisschaltung zur Auslösung von Schaltvorgängen mittels Photozelle
(*2310*)	638722	Wechselstrom gespeiste lichtelektrische Schalteinrichtung, bei der eine Photozelle das Gitter einer Verstärker Röhre steuert
(*2311*)	461721	Lichtelektrische frequenzabhängige Wechselstrom Schalteinrichtung insbesondere zum Öffnen von Türen

(*2312*) 642328 Auslösen von Schaltvorgängen
(*2313*) 643007 Einrichtung zur intermittierenden Speisung von Verbrauchern, insbesondere zum Betrieb von Blinkzeichen aus einem Wechselstromnetz unter Anwendung der optisch-elektrischen Rückkopplung mit Hilfe einer Photozelle
(*2314*) 645537 Auf kurzzeitige Spannungsänderungen, von Photozellen herrührend, ansprechende Relaisschaltung
(*2315*) 645636 Mit Wechselstrom betriebenes Lichtrelais mit einer lichtelektrisch wirksamen, als Gleichrichter dienenden, Glimmlampe
(*2316*) 654847 Bei verschiedenen Belichtungsstärken unterschiedliche Schaltmittel steuernde photoelektrische Relaisanordnung
(*2317*) 660324 Relaisanordnung mit von einer Elektronenröhre gesteuertem Kontaktrelais und mit hochohmigem, insbesondere eine Photozelle enthaltendem, Gitter Steuerkreis
(*2318*) 661495 Anordnung zur Steuerung von einem Relais über Elektronenröhren, deren Steuerströme in der Grössenordnung der Gitterströme liegen, insbesondere durch Photozellen
(*2319*) 663866 Elektrisch oder magnetisch gesteuertes, aus einem durchsichtigen flüssigen Medium bestehenden, Lichtventil
(*2320*) 663931 Anzeige bewegter Objekte
(*2321*) 668829 Vorrichtung zur Prüfung der Betriebsfähigkeit einer Photozellen Anordnung
(*2322*) 671910 Verfahren zur Verwendung der photochemischen Reaktion eines durch Elektrolyse einer Flüssigkeit erzeugten lichtempfindlichen Gasgemisches zur Herstellung eines Lichtrelais, und Ausführungsformen derartiger Lichtrelais
(*2323*) 673269 Thyratron Kontrolle vermittels Photozellen
(*2324*) 674230 Vorrichtung zur Intensitätssteuerung von Lichtstrahlen einer konstanten Lichtquelle
(*2325*) 674365 Vorrichtung zur piezo-elektrischen Helligkeitssteuerung eines Lichtbündels
(*2326*) 675739 Lichtelektrische Steuereinrichtung
(*2327*) 676195 Kontrolle von Relais
(*2328*) 676350 Dämpfung von Lichtsteuergeräten
(*2329*) 676382 Auf Verdunklung ansprechendes Relais
(*2330*) 676471 Lichtrelais
(*2331*) 678813 Elektromagnetisches Lichtsteuergerät
(*2332*) 680129 Einrichtung zur Regelung und Änderung der Lichtstrahlensteuerung
(*2333*) 682469 Piezo-elektrische Lichtsteuervorrichtung
(*2334*) 689294 Vorrichtung zur Lichtsteuerung mit Hilfe eines doppelbrechenden Körpers
(*2335*) 701966 Verfahren und Vorrichtung zum Umwandeln von Helligkeitsänderungen in mechanische Wirkungen
(*2336*) 707825 Photoelektrische Steuervorrichtung
(*2337*) 708858 Elektrisches Relais mit in einem Gasentladungsgefäss angeordneter, durch die Gasentladung thermisch deformierbarer, Elektrode
(*2338*) 713399 Lichtelektrisches Sekundärelektronen Relais
(*2339*) 718361 Lichtelektrische Einrichtung
(*2340*) 724141 Kathodenstrahlschalter zur Verteilung einer Modulation auf mehrere Kanäle
(*2341*) 724852 Photomechanische Steuereinrichtung, bei der ein Lichtzeiger, der kleine Ausschläge, vorzugsweise Drehungen, einer spiegelnden Fläche anzeigt, seine Intensität in Abhängigkeit vom Ausschlag ändert
(*2342*) 725216 Einrichtung zur photoelektrischen Auslösung eines Instrumentes
(*2343*) 726225 Lichtelektrisches Relais mit Gas- oder Dampffüllung
(*2344*) 727450 Einrichtung zur Erfassung der Änderung der spektralen Zusammensetzung eines Steuerlichtes

(*2345*) 728331 Lichtgerät zum Auslösen von Schaltvorgängen
(*2346*) 734517 Glimmrelais mit kalten Elektroden

French Patents

(*2347*) 796087 Dispositif pour la réglage de la mise en circuit des cellules photo-électriques
(*2348*) 797862 Procédé et appareil pour assurer la visibilité malgré le brouillard et les nuages naturels ou artificiels
(*2349*) 798240 Dispositif de contrôle photo-électrique
(*2350*) 798279 Photo-valve
(*2351*) 802492 Perfectionnements aux cellules photo-sensibles
(*2352*) 803789 Dispositif photo-électrique de mesure et de réglage, plus speciale-ment pour appareils de tirage
(*2353*) 804264 Système électro-optique
(*2354*) 806544 Dispositif pour examiner des objets au moyen de rayons infrarouges émis par ces objets
(*2355*) 806997 Perfectionnements aux procédés permettant de rendre visibles les rayons invisible à l'oeil nu, telsque les infrarouges
(*2356*) 807618 Procédé et appareil de perception visuelle d'objets en lumière infrarouge
(*2357*) 809247 Cellule photo-électrique
(*2358*) 811387 Perfectionnements aux systèmes d'alimentation des cellules photo-électriques
(*2359*) 826674 Cellule photo-électrique à multiplication d'électrons secondaires
(*2360*) 828052 Cellule photo-électrique à système amplificateur secondaire
(*2361*) 839858 Tubes photo-électriques
(*2362*) 839919 Cellule photo-électrique à couche d'arrêt pour rayons Röntgen ou autres rayons de courte longueur d'onde
(*2363*) 840478 Titrographe
(*2364*) 841111 Procédé et dispositifs pour transformer les variations d'éclaire-ment en actions méchaniques
(*2365*) 841765 Amplificateur à électrons secondaires
(*2366*) 843392 Modulateur électronique de lumière
(*2367*) 844963 Dispositif servant à limiter les rayons lumineux tombant sur une cellule photo-sensible et destiné en particulier aux pose-mètres photo-électriques
(*2368*) 845225 Cellule photo-électrique avec amplification par électrons second-aires
(*2369*) 846104 Montage push-pull pour cellules photo-électriques
(*2370*) 846544 Densimètre photo-électrique
(*2371*) 847511 Système optique à source de lumière linéaire
(*2372*) 50133/811387 (Certificat d'addition). Perfectionnements aux systèmesd' aliment-ation des cellules photo-électriques
(*2373*) 850392 Dispositif pour éloigner des cellules photo-électriques la lumière indésirable
(*2374*) 852053 Perfectionnements aux filtres pour sources lumineuses
(*2375*) 50213/811387 (Certificat d'addition). Perfectionnements aux systèmes d'aliment-ation des cellules photo-électriques
(*2376*) 853821 Dispositif photo-électrique utilisable à bord d'un véhicule tel qu'un aéronef pour contrôler la route, pour mésurer la dérive, la vitesse réelle et l'altitude et pour déceler et signaler des ob-stacles
(*2377*) 853970 Cellules photo-électriques
(*2378*) 854757 Montage comportant une cellule photo-électrique suivie d'un amplificateur
(*2379*) 863859 Dispositif pour diriger de la lumière de luminescence dans la direction de la source de la lumière excitatrice

(*2380*) 864167 Détecteur optique à cellule photo-électrique et appareils en comportant application
(*2381*) 864360 Cellule photo-électrique
(*2382*) 864467 Dispositif photo-électrique pour appareils de prize de vues
(*2383*) 864990 Appareil de surveillance utilisant la réflexion lumineuse
(*2384*) 869158 Appareil pour mise en route et interruption périodique d'une opération sous l'influence de la lumière
(*2385*) 870559 Réflecteur constitué par une partie ellipsoïdale de sommet et une partie paraboloïdale de bord
(*2386*) 872460 Lumière phosphorescente entretenue électriquement et dispositifs d'utilization
(*2387*) 879930 Procédé et dispositifs pour la surveillance et la protection optique applicables surtout aux éspaces fermés

ADDITIONAL REFERENCES

(*2388*) CASHMAN, R. J., *Proc. Nat. Electronics Conference*, 1947; **2;** 171
(*2389*) GRANIT, RAGNAR, *Sensory Mechanisms of the Retina*, 1947
(*2390*) WILLMER, E. N., *Retinal Structure and Colour and Colour Vision*, 1946
(*2391*) HOLMES, F. H., " A Review of the Literature on Diffusion in Solutions and the Estimation of Particle Size from Diffusion Measurements ", *Brit. Cotton Ind. Res. Assoc.*, 1945
(*2392*) Scientific and Industrial Reports (U.S.A.); German infra-red equipment, PB-1531; PB-1587; PB-1612; PB-1623; PB-2336; PB-19746
Electronics, 1944; **17,** 1; 156
Electronics, 1946; **19,** 6; 95, 224
(*2393*) SAGER, I., " Multiple thyratron circuits ", *Electronics*, 1946; **19,** 12; 158
(*2394*) " High speed counter for 10^6 impulses/sec.", *Electronics*, 1946; **19,** 11; 190
(*2395*) KRAEHENBUEHL, J. O. and CHANON, H. J., " The technology of brightness production by near u-v radiation ", *Trans. Illum. Eng. Soc.*, 1941; **36,** 2; 151
(*2396*) MARDEN, J. W. and BEESE, N. C., " U-v excitation of fluorescent compounds ", *Trans. Illum. Eng. Soc.*, 1941; **36,** 2; 235
(*2397*) NOGL, E. B., " Radiation from high pressure Hg-arcs ", *Trans. Illum. Eng. Soc.*, 1941; **36,** 2; 243
(*2398*) FOUND, C. G. and HENELLY, E. F., " Relation between electric and spectroscopic characteristics in low-pressure discharge lamps ", *Trans. Illum. Eng. Soc.*, 1941; **36,** 3; 400
(*2399*) HAYS, R. F. " Characteristics of low-voltage fluorescent lamps at high frequencies ", *Trans. Illum. Eng. Soc.*, 1941; **36,** 5; 570
(*2400*) MARDEN, J. W. and MEISTER, G., " High and low voltage fluorescent lamps ", *Trans. Illum. Eng. Soc.*, 1941; **36,** 10; 1286
(*2401*) PETRAGLIA, F. A., *Electronic Engineering Master Index*, 2 vols., Vol. 2, sections 113; 114; 115; 116; 117; 118; 119; 120
(*2402*) BEESE, N. C., " Fluorescence of phosphors in rare gases ", *J.O.S.A.*, 1946; **36,** 9; 493
(*2403*) ELLICKSON, R. T., " Light storage in infra-red sensitive phosphors ", *J.O.S.A.* 1946; **36,** 9; 501
(*2404*) KING, P. and LOCKHART, L. B., " Experimental and theoretical results in two-layer low reflecting coatings for glass ", *J.O.S.A.*, 1946; **36,** 9; 513
(*2405*) PERFECT, D. S. and WITHERS, R. M. J., " A photographic method of indicating small displacements and of timing a moving body," *J. Sci. Instr.*, 1946; **23,** 9; 204
(*2406*) LINDSAY, M. H. A., " Electronic protective systems ", *Electrical Engineering*, 1944; **63,** 10; 367
(*2407*) SOMMER, A., *Photo-electric Cells*, 1946
(*2408*) PINEGIN, E. I., *Nature*, 1944; **154;** 770
(*2409*) PINEGIN, E. I., *Nature*, 1945; **155;** 20

(*2410*) PAKSWER, S., *J. Appl. Phys.*, 1947; **18,** 2; 203
(*2411*) RANDALL, J. T., " Luminescence and its application ", *G.E.C. Journal*, 1937; **8,** 2; 103
(*2412*) RENTSCHLER, H. C., NAGY, R. and MOUROMSEFF, G., *J. Bact.*, 1941; **41;** 745
(*2413*) SHARP, D. G., *J. Bact.*, 1939; **37;** 447
(*2414*) WELLS, W. F., *Science*, 1940; **91;** 172
(*2415*) MELLON, M. G., *Colorimetry for Chemists*, 1945
(*2416*) CHUBB, A. A., *Electronic Engineering*, 1947; **19,** 232; 173
(*2417*) CHUBB, A. A., *Electronic Engineering*, 1947; **19,** 233; 211
(*2418*) DEJARDIN, G., *Rev. gén. élec.*, 1933; **34;** 629
(*2419*) FEDDOV, N. T., FEDDOVA, V. I., PLAKHOV, A. G. and SELETZKAYA, L. O., *J. Phys. Akad. Sci. U.S.S.R.*, 1940; **3;** 5
(*2420*) GRIFFIN, D. R., HUBBARD, R. and WALD, G., *J.O.S.A.*, 1947; **37,** 7; 546
(*2421*) GOODEVE, C. F., *Nature*, 1934; **134,** 3385; 416
(*2422*) GAYDON, A. G. and MINKOFF, G. J., *Nature*, 1946; **158,** 4022; 788
(*2423*) SINSHEIMER, R. L. and LOOFBOUROW, J. .R, *Nature*, 1947; **160,** 4072; 674
(*2424*) PAKSWER, S., *Electronic Industries*, 1947; **6,** 9
(*2425*) TUCKER, M. J. and COLLINS, G., *Electronic Engineering*, 1947; **19,** 238; 398
(*2426*) MORELAND, H. D., *Electronic Industries*, 1945; **4,** 1; 96
(*2427*) DEGELMAN, J., *Electronics*, 1948; **21,** 1; 134
(*2428*) HEWLETT, C. W., *G.E. Rev.*, 1947; **50,** 4; 22
(*2429*) MOSS, T. S. and CHASMAR, R. P., *Nature*, 1948; **161,** 4085; 244
(*2430*) FELLGETT, P. B., *J.O.S.A.*, 1949; **39,** 11; 970
(*2431*) BOYD, R. L. F., *Nature*, 1948; **161,** 4085; 227
(*2432*) BIOS Final Report, 867; Items No. 1, 7 and 9; p. 45
(*2433*) BIOS Final Report No. 530; Item No. 9
(*2434*) FIAT Final Report No. 575; p. 49
(*2435*) MOSS, T. S., *Nature*, 1948; **161,** 4098; 766
(*2436*) *Dept. Sci. Ind. Res.*, " The Fundamental Research Problems of Telecommunication, 1948 (H.M.S.O.)
(*2437*) SCOTT, B. A., *Nature*, 1948; **161,** 4088; 358
(*2438*) " German Infra-red Driving and Fire Control Equipment ", *BIOS Misc. Rep.*, 66
(*2439*) STANWORTH, J. E., *Nature*, 1948; **161,** 4100; 856
(*2440*) KOHN, H. and v. FRAGSTEIN, K., *Phys. Z.*, 1932; **33;** 929
(*2441*) LAPIERRE, C. W. and MANSFIELD, A. P., " Photo-electric weft-straightener control ", *Electrical Engineering* (*Trans.*), 1938; **57,** 12; 513
(*2442*) SCHWARZ, E. R., *J.O.S.A.*, 1937; **27,** 1; 44
(*2443*) ENGSTRÖM, R. W., *R.S.I.*, 1947; **18,** 8; 587
(*2444*) *Electronics*, 1948; **21,** 4; 198
(*2445*) SOMMER, A., *Electronic Engineering*, 1945; **17,** 207; 526
(*2446*) CURRAN, S. C. and BAKER, W. R., *R.S.I.*, 1948; **19,** 2; 116
(*2447*) FARNSWORTH, P. T. J., *J. Franklin Inst.*, 1934; **218;** 411
(*2448*) ZWORYKIN, V. K. J., *J.I.E.E.*, 1936; **79;** 1
(*2449*) KLUGE, W., *Z. Phys.*, 1935; **93;** 789
(*2450*) SCHAFFERNICHT, W., *Z. Techn. Phys.*, 1936; **17;** 597
(*2451*) SUMMER, W., *Brit. J. Phys. Med.*, 1948; **11,** 2; 53
(*2452*) PRATT, T. H., *J. Sci. Instr.*, 1947; **24,** 12; 312
(*2453*) CRABTREE, J. I., EATON, G. T. and MUEHLER, L. E., " The quantitative determination of hypo in photographic prints with silver nitrate ", *J. Franklin Inst.*, 1943; **235,** 4; 351
(*2454*) GLOVER, A. M., *Proc. I.R.E.*, 1941; **29,** 8; 413
(*2455*) *American Exporter*, 1945; July; 166
(*2456*) BARDEEN, J., *J. Appl. Phys.*, 1940; **11;** 88
(*2457*) DARBY, H. H., JOHNSON, E. R. F. and BARNES, G. W., *Papers from the Tortuga Laboratory*, vol. 31; No. 8
(*2458*) DARBY, H. H. JOHNSON E. R. F. and BARNES, G. W., *Publ. Carnegie Inst.*, Washington, 1937; No. 475, Oct. 15; 191
(*2459*) *Electrical World*, 1948; Aug. 14; 105
(*2460*) *Power*, 1948; July; 172

(*2461*) SHAW, J. F., *Brit. Chem. Abstr.*, 1932; B; 403
(*2462*) *Electronics*, 1946; **19,** 3; 116
(*2463*) MCCOMB, R. D., *Electronics*, 1943; **16,** 12; 172
(*2464*) *Electrical Times*, 1945; June 1st; 795
(*2465*) *Electronics*, 1946; **19,** 4; 123
(*2466*) HOUGHTON, J. L., *J. Sci. Instr.*, 1949; **26,** 6; 178
(*2467*) FURTH, R. and PRINGLE, R. W., *Phil. Mag.*, 1944; **35,** 249; 643
(*2468*) FURTH, R. and PRINGLE, R. W., *Electronics*, 1945; **18,** 4; 254
(*2469*) ROBERTS, W. O., *Electronics*, 1946; **19,** 6; 100
(*2470*) *Scientific American*, 1945; April; 212
(*2471*) VAN SUCHELEN, H., WARMHOLTZ, N. and WIGGERINK, G. L., *Phil. Techn. Rev.*, 1949; **11,** 3; 91
(*2472*) MORTON, G. A., *J. Soc. Mot. Pict. Eng.*, 1936; **27;** 321
(*2473*) GIBSON, A. F., MOSS, T. S., *Proc. Phys. Soc. Lond.*, 1950; A-63, 362; 176
(*2474*) KRENZIEN, O., *Z. Phys.*, 1949; 126, 7-9; 666
(*2475*) FRANK, K. and RAITHEL, K., *Z. Phys.*, 1949; 126; 377
(*2476*) FRERICHS, R. and SIEGERT, A. J. F., *Phys. Rev.*, 1948; 74, Dec. 15; 1875
(*2477*) BRENTANO, J. C. M. and DAVIS, D. H., *Phys. Rev.*, 1948; 74, Sept. 15; 711
(*2478*) TERRIEN, J. and MOREAU, H., *Revue d'Optique*, 1948; 27, **5;** 295
(*2479*) WATTS, B. N. *Proc. Phys. Soc. Lond.*, 1949; A-62, **7;** 456
(*2480*) MOSS, T. S., *Proc. Phys. Soc. Lond.*, 1949; A-62, **352;** 264
(*2481*) MILNER, C. J. and WATTS, B. N., *Nature*, 1949; **163;** 322
(*2482*) WLÉRICK, G., *Rev. Sci. Paris*, 1948; **86;** 464
(*2483*) SAYAMA, Y., *J.O.S.A.*, 1949; **39,** 2; 162
(*2484*) SAYAMA, Y., *J. Phys. Soc. Japan*, 1947; **2,** 5; 103
(*2485*) BAYLISS, N. S. and RIVIÈRE, J. C., *Nature*, 1949; **163;** 765
(*2486*) LALLEMAND, A., *Vide*, 1949; **4,** 5; 618
(*2487*) SCHAETTI, N., *Helv. Phys. Acta.*, 1950; **23,** 1-2; 108
(*2488*) PRATT, T. H., *Electronic Engineering*, 1948; **20,** 247; 274
(*2489*) COSTER, D., HOF, S., RATHENAU, G., SIMONS, C. F. E., *Physica*, 1938; **5,** 7; 643
(*2490*) MILATZ, J. M. W. and BLOEMBERGEN, N., *Physica*, 1946; **11,** 6; 449
(*2491*) SARGROVE, J. A., *J. Brit. I.R.E.*, 1947; **7,** 3; 86
(*2492*) VEITH, W., *C.R. Acad. Sci. Paris*, 1950; **230;** 947
(*2493*) GENZEL, L. and MÜSER, H., *Z. Phys.*, 1950; **127,** 3; 194
(*2949*) OKADA, T. and UNO, R., *J. Phys. Soc., Japan*, 1949; **4;** 351, (abstr. in *Sci. Abstr.*, 1950; **53,** A, 632; 5838)
(*2495*) PICK, H., *Ann. Phys. Lpz.*, 1948; ser. 6, 3; 255
(*2496*) FASSBENDER, J., *Ann. Phys. Lpz.*, 1949; ser. 6, 5; 33
(*2497*) ARNIKAR, H. J., *Curr. Sci.*, 1950; **19,** 2; 47
(*2498*) LEO, W. and HÜBNER, W., *Z. angew. Phys.*, 1950; II, 11; 454
(*2499*) GÖRLICH, P., *Z. Naturforsch.*, 150; 5a, Oct.; 563
(*2500*) DEL PIANTO, E. and QUERCIA, I. F., *Ricerca Sci.*, 1950; **20,** 11; 1658
(*2501*) HÜBNER, W., *Elektrotechnik, Berlin*, 1950; **4,** 11; 378
(*2502*) BACON, R. C. and POLLARD, J. R., *Electronic Engng.*, 1950; **22,** 5; 173
(*2503*) FRIMER, A. I. and SINITSKAYA, I. G., *Dokl. Akad. Nauk, U.S.S.R.*, 1949; **66,** 1; 49, (abstr. in *Sci. Abstr.*, 1949; **52,** A, 623; 6204)
(*2504*) KOLOMIETS, B. T., *Elektrichestvo*, 1949; **3;** 57, (abstr. in *Sci. Abstr.*, 1949; **52,** A, 623; 6209)
(*2505*) SIMPSON, O., *Proc. Phys. Soc. Lond.*, 1948; **61,** 11; 486
(*2506*) SUTHERLAND, G. B. B. M. and LEE, E., *Rep. Phys. Soc. Progr. Phys.*, 1946-47; **11;** 144
(*2507*) CARLISLE, S. S. and ALDERTON, G., *Nature*, Lond., 1949; **163;** 529
(*2508*) KOLOMIETS, B. T., *J. Techn. Phys. U.S.S.R.*, 1948; **18,** 11; 1456, (abstr. in *Sci. Abstr.*, 1949; **52,** A, 617; 1912)
(*2509*) WEISS, K., *Z. Naturforsch.*, 1947; 2a; 650
(*2510*) FRANK, K. and RAITHEL, K., *Z. Phys.*, 1949; **126;** 377
(*2511*) BARBER, C. R. and PYATT, C., *Nature*, Lond., 1950; **165;** 691
(*2512*) SCHWARZ, E., *Proc. Phys. Soc. Lond.*, 1950; **63,** B, 8; 624

(*2513*) ZIEMECKI, S., *Bull. Int. Acad. Polonaise Sci. Lett.*, 1949; **5-6,** A, 3; 141, (abstr. in *Sci. Abstr.*, 1950; **53,** A, 633; 6417)
(*2514*) VARTANYAN, A. T., *Dokl. Akad. Nauk, U.S.S.R.*, 1950; **71,** 4; 641, (abstr. in *Sci. Abstr.*, 1950; **53,** A, 634; 7249)
(*2515*) SHIVE, J. N., *Phys. Rev.*, 1949; **76;** 575
(*2516*) ROTHLEIN, B. J. and STAHL, F. A., *Sylv. Techn.*, 1950; **3,** 4; 8, (abstr. in *Sci. Abstr.*, 1950; **53,** A, 636; 8741
(*2517*) KÖNIG, H., *Rev. Opt* (*Théor. Instrum.*), 1950; **29,** 8-9; 439
(*2518*) STÖCKMANN, F., *Z. Phys.*, 1950; **128,** 2; 185
(*2519*) SCHWETZOFF, V. and ROBIN, S., *C.R. Acad. Sci., Paris*, 1950; **230;** 1759
(*2520*) KOLOMIETS, B. T., *J. Techn. Phys., U.S.S.R.*, 1949; **19,** 1; 126, (abstr. in *Sci. Abstr.*, 1950; **53,** A, 626; 967)
(*2521*) BERGSTRAND, E., *Nature*, 1950; **165,** 4193; 405
(*2522*) SCHAETTI, N., *Z. Angewandte Math. Phys.*, 1951; **2,** May 15; 123
(*2523*) DIEMER, G. and JONKER, J. L. H., *Philips Res. Rep.*, 1950; **5;** 161
(*2524*) DRIGO, A., *Nuovo Cim.*, 1950; **7,** 5; 267
(*2525*) JONKER, J. L. H., *Philips Res. Rep.*, 1952; **7;** 1
(*2526*) COPELAND, P. L., *Phys. Rev.*, 1934; **46;** 167
(*2527*) *Electronics*, 1950; **23,** 7; 166
(*2528*) VOLMER, M. and RIGGERT, K., *Z. Phys. Chem*., 1922; **120;** 502
(*2529*) SUZUKI, M. and VOLMER, M., *Naturwiss*, 1935; **23;** 197
(*2530*) NORMAND, C. W. B. and KAY, R. H., *J. Sci. Instr.*, 1952; **29,** 2; 33
(*2531*) *Electronics*, 1951; **24,** 1; 126
(*2532*) SCHWETZOFF, V. and ROBIN, S., *C.R. Acad. Sci., Paris*, 1952; **234;** 316
(*2533*) SCHAETTI, N. and BAUMGARTNER, W., *Vide*, 1951; **6,** July-Sept.; 1041
(*2534*) SCHWETZOFF, V. and ROBIN, S., *C.R. Acad. Sci., Paris*, 1951; **233;** 475
(*2535*) SCHWETZOFF, V. and ROBIN, S., *C.R. Acad. Sci., Paris*, 1951; **233;** 518
(*2536*) VEITH, W., *J. Phys. Radium*, 1950; **11;** 507
(*2537*) SCHAETTI, N. and BAUMGARTNER, W., *Helv. Phys. Acta*, 1950; **23,** 5; 524
(*2538*) WOLF, I., *Ann. Phys., Leipz.*, 1950; **8,** 1-2; 30
(*2539*) BIRKS, T. B., *Proc. Phys. Soc. Lond.*, 1951; **64,** A; 874
(*2540*) BENEDETTI, S. and RICHINGS, H. J., *R.S.I.*, 1952; **23,** 1; 37
(*2541*) OWEN, R. B., *J. Sci. Instr.*, 1951; **28;** 221
(*2542*) COLTMAN, J. W. and MARSHAL, F. H., *Nucleonics*, 1947; **1,** 3; 58
(*2543*) ALBRECHT, H. O. and MANDEVILLE, C. E., *Phys. Rev.*, 1951; **81;** 163
(*2544*) *R.S.I.*, 1949; **20,** 6; 394
(*2545*) CURRAN, S. C. and CRAGGS, J. D., *Counting Tubes*, 1949
(*2546*) MICHELSSEN, F., *Optik*, 1951; **8,** 1-2; 75
(*2547*) SMALLER, B., MAY, J. and FREEDMAN, M., *Phys. Rev.*, 1951; **79,** 6; 940
(*2548*) KOSKI, W. S., *Phys. Rev.*, 1951; **82;** 230
(*2549*) BELCHER, E. H., *Nature*, 1951; **167;** 314
(*2550*) SMITH, J. W. and BLACKMORE, L., *Nature*, 1950; **165,** 4200; 688
(*2551*) PRINGLE, R. W., *Atomics*, 1950; **1,** 7; 49
(*2552*) NELSON, R. C., *J. Chem. Phys.*, 1951; **19,** 6; 798
(*2553*) ROBINSON, L. B. and ARNOLD, J. R., *R.S.I.*, 1949; **20;** 549
(*2554*) SHERR, R., *R.S.I.*, 1947; **18,** 10; 767
(*2555*) DRAPER, J. E., *R.S.I.*, 1951; **22,** 7; 543
(*2556*) TER-POGOSSIAN, M. and BITTNER, W., III, *R.S.I.*, 1951; **22,** 8; 646
(*2557*) BITTNER, W., III and TER-POGOSSIAN, M., *R.S.I.*, 1951; **22,** 8; 638
(*2558*) HOYT, R. C., *R.S.I.*, 1949; **20,** 3; 178
(*2559*) ANGER, H. O., *R.S.I.*, 1951; **22,** 12; 912
(*2560*) SCHARDT, A. W. and BERNSTEIN, W., *R.S.I.*, 1951; **22,** 12; 1020
(*2561*) MAYNEORD, W. N. and BELCHER, E. H., *Nature*, 1950; **165;** 930
(*2562*) BELCHER, E. H., *Nature*, 1950; **166;** 826
(*2563*) BELCHER, E. H. and EVANS, H. D., *J. Sci. Instr.*, 1951; **28;** 71
(*2564*) VEALL, N., *Brit. Med. Bull.*, vol 8, Nos. 2-3
(*2565*) STONE, R. P., *R.S.I.*, 1949; **20,** 12; 935
(*2566*) ELMORE, W. C., *R.S.I.*, 1949; **20,** 12; 965
(*2567*) SCHAETTI, N., BAUMGARTNER, W. and FLURY, C., *Helv. Phys. Acta*, 1951; **24,** 6; 609

(*2568*) SCHAETTI, N. and BAUMGARTNER, W., *Helv. Phys. Acta*, 1951; **24,** 6; 614
(*2569*) DUCHESNE, M., *C.R. Acad. Sci. Paris*, 1948; **227;** 1155
(*2570*) MÜSER, H., *Z. Phys.*, 1951; **129,** 5; 504
(*2571*) BRAITHWAITE, J. G. N., *Proc. Phys. Soc., Lond.*, 1951; **64,** B, 3; 274
(*2572*) CRONEMEYER, D. C. and GILLEO, M. A., *Phys. Rev.*, 1951; **82;** 975
(*2573*) JACOBS, J. E., *Electr. Engrg., N.Y.*, 1951; **70,** 8; 667
(*2574*) FRERICHS, R. and JACOBS, J. E., *Gen. Electr. Res.*, 1951; Aug.; 42
(*2575*) BLACKBAND, W. T., *Nature*, 1951; **168;** 704
(*2576*) CORSON, D. R. and WILSON, R. R., *R.S.I.*, 1948; **19,** 4; 207
(*2577*) BAY, Z., *Nature*, 1938; **141;** 284
(*2578*) BAY, Z., *Nature*, 1938; **141;** 1011
(*2579*) BAY, Z., *R.S.I.*, 1941; **12;** 127
(*2580*) ALLEN, J. S., *Phys. Rev.*, 1939; **55;** 966
(*2581*) ALLEN, J. S., *R.S.I.*, 1941; **12;** 484
(*2582*) ALLEN, J. S., *Phys. Rev.*, 1942; **61;** 692
(*2583*) MAKIEJ, B., *J. Sci. Instr.*, 1951; **28,** 6; 188
(*2584*) HOADLEY, H. O., *R.S.I.*, 1949; **20,** 1; 188
(*2585*) WIGHT, K. C., *J. Sci. Instr.*, 1951; **28,** 9; 276
(*2586*) HÜBNER, W., *Elektrotechnik, Berlin*, 1950; **4,** 11; 378
(*2587*) LEO, W. and HÜBNER, W., *Z. angew. Phys.*, 1950; **2,** 11; 454
(*2588*) FRANKENHAEUSER, B. and MACDONALD, D. K. C., *J. Sci. Instr.*, 1949; **26,** 5; 145
(*2589*) STAFFORD, F., *J. Sci. Instr.*, 1949; **26,** 5; 158
(*2590*) PLYMALE, W. S. and HANSON, D. F., *Electronics*, 1950; **23,** 2; 102
(*2591*) BEARDEN, J. A. and WATTS, H. M., *Phys. Rev.*, 1951; **81,** 1; 73
(*2592*) PLYMALE, W. S., Jr., *R.S.I.*, 1947; **18,** 8; 535
(*2593*) PALLETZ, H., *Electronics*, 1951; **24,** 1; 180
(*2594*) PALLETZ, H., *Electronics*, 1951; **24,** 3; 326
(*2595*) *Electronics*, 1951; **24,** 5; 218
(*2596*) LALLEMAND, A. and DUCHESNE, M., *C.R. Acad. Sci., Paris*, 1951; **233;** 305
(*2597*) HOGAN, A. W., *J. Soc. Mot. Pict. Telev. Engrs.*, 1951; **56,** 6; 635
(*2598*) AMDURSKY, M. E., REED, W. O. and PAKSWER, S., *J.O.S.A.*, 1951; **41,** 5; 361
(*2599*) HOLIDAY, E. R. and WILD, W., *J. Sci. Instr.*, 1951; **28,** 9; 282
(*2600*) DIGHTON, D. T. R. and HERZ, R. H., *J. Sci. Instr.*, 1949; **26,** 12; 404
(*2601*) SUMMER, W., *Food*, 1952; **21,** 1; 16
(*2602*) ALDER, K. F., *J. Sci. Instr.*, 1948; **25,** 9; 300
(*2603*) *Electronics*, 1950; **23,** 1; 123
(*2604*) BRUCK, G., HIGGINS, J. and WARD, J., *Electronics*, 1950; **23,** 5; 74
(*2605*) LAUNER, H. F., *R.S.I.*, 1949; **20,** 2; 103
(*2606*) CARSEN, D. R. and WILSON, R. R., *R.S.I.*, 1948; **19,** 4; 207
(*2607*) CHUTE, G. M., *Electronics*, 1951; **24,** 5; 92
(*2608*) *Electronics*, 1951; **24,** 5; 118
(*2609*) *Electronics*, 1951; **24,** 11; 200
(*2610*) WITTENBERG, H. H., *Electronics*, 1950; **23,** 1; 91
(*2611*) FINK, D. G., *Electronics*, 1950; **23,** 4; 102
(*2612*) CARRINGTON, T. and DAVIDSON, N., *J. Chem. Phys.*, 1951; **19,** 10; 1313
(*2613*) EISLER, J. D., NEWTON, G. R. and ADCOCK, W.A ., *R.S.I.*, 1952; **23,** 1; 17
(*2614*) STONE, D. E., KANE, L. J., CORRIGAN, T. E., WAINWRIGHT, H. W. and SEIBERT, C. B., *U.S. Bur. Mines, Re. Invest.*, 4782 (1951)
(*2615*) RIGHINI, G. *Atti Fond.* " Giorgio Ronchi " 1951; **6,** 2; 8
(*2616*) GIBSON, A. F., *J. Sci. Instr.*, 1951; **28,** 5; 153
(*2617*) ROBERTS, M. H., *J. Sci. Instr.*, 1948; **25,** 10; 337
(*2618*) UNDERWOOD, N. and DOERMANN, A. H., *R.S.I.*, 1947; **18,** 9; 665
(*2619*) *Electronics*, 1950; **23,** 9; 176
(*2620*) ATKINS, C. and LYTTON, F. A., *J. Sci. Instr.*, 1951; **28,** 12; 386
(*2621*) SUMMER, W., *J. Sci. Instr.*, 1952; **29,** 3; 100
(*2622*) *Steel*, 1951; **129,** 27 Aug.; 90
(*2623*) *B.C.U.R.A.*, 1952; **16,** 3; 112
(*2624*) SCHALLER, A., *Arch. techn. Messen*, 1952; **193,** 2 (Z 634-7); 43

(*2625*) DAVIES, C. N. and AYLWARD, M., *Brit. J. Appl. Phys.*, 1951; **2,** 12; 352
(*2626*) TEAL, G. K., FISHER, J. R. and TREPTOW, A. W., *J. Appl. Phys.*, 1946; **17;** 879
(*2627*) HINDLEY, H. R. and LEATON, E. J., *J. Sci. Instr.*, 1949; **26,** 12; 396
(*2628*) HUMPHREY, J. H., *J. Sci. Instr.*, 1948; **25,** 9; 314
(*2629*) FURTH, R. and OLIPHANT, W. D., *J. Sci. Instr.*, 1948; **25,** 9; 289
(*2630*) GLASSER, L. G., *Science*, 1951; **114;** 360
(*2631*) GÖRLICH, P., *Optik*, 1951; **8,** 11; 512
(*2632*) MIKA, J., *Acta Tech. Hungarica*, 1951; **2,** 1; 189
(*2633*) DEL PIANTO, E. and QUERCIA, I. F., *Riv. Sci.*, 1950; **20,** 11; 1658
(*2634*) LANGE, P. W. and Stenius, A. S., *R.S.I.*, 1951; **22,** 12; 865
(*2635*) CHANCE, B., *R.S.I.*, 1951; **22,** 8; 619
(*6236*) RAMSEY, J. A., Falloon, S. W. H. W. and MACHIN, K. E., *R.S.I.*, 1951; **22,** 3; 75
(*2637*) BAIR, J. K. and MAIENSCHEIN, F. C., *R.S.I.*, 1951; **22;** 343
(*2638*) JOHANNSEN, S. A. E., *Nature*, 1950; **166;** 795
(*2639*) ROSENBLUM, P. and DE BRETTVILLE, A., *R.S.I.*, 1949; **20,** 4; 321
(*2640*) HERWIG, L. O., *R.S.I.*, 1951; **22,** 9; 668
(*2641*) *Electronics*, 1950; **23,** 1; 152
(*2642*) ODEBLAD, E., *R.S.I.*, 1951; **22,** 11; 847
(*2643*) *Electronics*, 1952; **25,** 1; 92
(*2644*) KELLY, J. M., *Bell Syst. Techn. J.*, 1932; **11,** 3
(*2645*) SMITH, B. O. and CARLISLE, S. S., *J. Iron and Steel Inst.*, 1952; **171,** 7; 273
(*2646*) *D.S.I.R.*, *Fuel Res.*, Tech. Paper No. 53; 1946
(*2647*) *Electronics*, 1946; **19,** 12; 116
(*2648*) KELLY, J. M., *Bell Lab. Rec.*, 1933; **7,** 2; (Oct.)

INDEX